C000260188

RARE
CLASSICAL RECORD
PRICE GUIDE
2004

Edited by
Barry Browne

Email : classical.guide@btinternet.com

RARE CLASSICAL RECORD
PRICE GUIDE 2004
Copyright © 2003 Sylverwood Publishing.

All Rights Reserved

No part of this book may be reproduced in any form,
by photocopying or by any electronic or mechanical means,
Including information storage or retrieval systems,
without permission in writing from both the copyright
owner and the publisher of this book.

ISBN 0-954512-0-3

First Published May 2003
Sylverwood Publishing

First Reprint June 2003

Printed in Great Britain by Copytech UK Ltd.
For the publishers Sylverwood Publishing

RARE
CLASSICAL RECORD
PRICE GUIDE
2004

Contents

Introduction to the first edition............................ 7

How to use this guide 8

Grading 8

Decca LXT Mono LP's... 9

Decca SXL 2000 series Stereophonic LP's 113

Decca SXL 6000 series Stereophonic LP's 143

Decca SET Stereophonic LP's............................ 215

Columbia 33CX series Monophonic LP's 233

Columbia SAX series Stereophonic LP's........... 325

HMV ALP series Monophonic LP's 361

HMV ASD 3-digit series Stereophonic LP's...... 457

HMV ASD 4-digit series Stereophonic LP's...... 495

HMV Angel SAN series Stereophonic LP's....... 589

Introduction to the first edition

Classical records have been sought by collectors since recorded music began. Unlike popular music, which passes through phases of being 'in', classical music has stood the test of time and only the quality of performance and recording changes. With the introduction of 'microgroove' (33rpm) records, the quality of the recordings entered a new era.

Many of the records listed in this book were such performances and the quality of the recordings have a warmth and character that is hard to achieve today. This may be that the microphones, amplifiers, tape recorders and record lathes were often constructed using valve technology, or maybe just the economy of the time allowed far more elaborate recording sessions than are economically feasible nowadays.

The rapid growth in trade conducted on the various international internet auctions has only recently begun to highlight the high prices paid by collectors to obtain good copies of these sought after records, although many specialist dealers have been trading in them for many years. For many collectors and dealers, information regarding classical records and their values, is very hard to obtain. With this is mind, we have set out to bring a concise price guide of the most popularly collected records into one book, while also providing information on each record to assist the completist collector.

The Classical Record Price Guide lists every British made classical record released by Decca, HMV and Columbia in the LXT, SXL, SET, ALP, ASD, SAN and SAX series. There are many other valuable classical records not listed in this edition of the Classical Record Price Guide, but which are also sought after by dealers and collectors alike. These include the Mercury stereo records (SR or AMS series). RCA 'Living Stereo' (SB or LSC Series), Deutsche Grammophon mono and stereo records (DG, SLPM, LPM, etc., particularly the original German pressed records), plus occasional recordings from Parlophone, Phillips, CBS, Supraphon and other smaller record labels. To have included complete listings of all of these classical records in this guide would have produced a work of many volumes, but we hope to include further listings in future editions.

How to use this guide

The price guide lists the Catalogue Number and Value of the first pressing in bold type, followed by subsequent pressings and their values in normal type, where applicable. The next lines lists the composer, the title or description of the repertoire, soloist, orchestra and conductor. Finally, a cross reference is given to each recordings stereo or mono counterpart in all cases where different numbering sequences have been used, thus;

ASD 278	G/c : **£60**	S/c : £15	P.Stamp : £6
MENDELSSOHN / TCHAIKOVSKY		Violin Concertos	Ferras
Philharmonia Orchestra	Silvestri		
Mono Issue : ALP1543			

It is important to realise, that any record is only worth the price that another is willing to pay for it. Indeed, there will be records listed in this guide that will achieve many times their listed value, while others may attract no interest whatsoever. That being said, the prices listed in this guide are a good indication of the desirability of the recording and have been repeatedly tested against actual prices realised from a number of different sources.

Grading

Prices quoted in this guide are for mint condition, British pressed LP records, with sleeves (or boxes) in perfect condition with original inner sleeves and any original paperwork (libretto, etc.) included. Any visible or audible ticks or noise will significantly detract from the prices in this guide (as will torn or damaged sleeves),

---

IMPORTANT NOTE

While every effort has been taken to ensure the accuracy of the information contained in this guide, the publishers cannot be held responsible for any errors or omissions, nor can they be held responsible or liable for any loss or damage to any person acting of the information in this guide.

Decca LXT Mono LP's

The Decca LXT series was first launched in 1950 and were produced until 1969, after which, all new releases were Stereo only.

The earliest labels, up to LXT 5118, are Orange with Gold lettering for all logos and text. These are identified as **Gold** in this section of the guide.

The second label is identical to the first, other than the print being in Silver lettering instead of gold. This label was used on all mono LXT records from LXT 5119 onwards and on re-pressed copies of the earlier records. These are listed as **Silver** in this section of the guide.

The catalogue contains many impressive performances by musicians who were at their peak before the introduction of stereophonic recordings.

LXT 2501 Gold : **£10** Silver : £4
BACH   Brandenburg Concerto No.4 in G, No.6 in Bb
Stuttgart Chamber Orchestra Munchinger
No Stereo

LXT 2502 Gold : **£10** Silver : £6
STRAVINSKY Petrouchka Suisse Romande Orchestra Ansermet
No Stereo

LXT 2503-5 Gold : **£10** Silver : £6
BACH   Art of Fugue BWV1080
Beromunster Radio Orchestra Scherchen
No Stereo

LXT 2506 Gold : **£14** Silver : £8
BEETHOVEN Piano Concerto (Emperor) Curzon
London Philharmonic Orchestra Szell
No Stereo

LXT 2507 Gold : **£25** Silver : £10
Various   Operatic Recital Tebaldi
No Stereo

LXT 2508 Gold : **£10** Silver : £5
RIMSKY-KORSAKOV Scheherezade
Paris Conservatoire Orchestra Ansermet
No Stereo

LXT 2509 Gold : **£30** Silver : £10
TCHAIKOVSKY Violin Concerto Ricci
New Symphony Orchestra Sargent
No Stereo

LXT 2510 Gold : **£10** Silver : £4
BIZET   Carmen Suite, L'Arlesienne Suite
London Philharmonic Orchestra Collins, Van Beinum
No Stereo

LXT 2511 Gold : **£15** Silver : £10
TCHAIKOVSKY Symphony No.4
Paris Conservatoire Orchestra Kleiber
No Stereo

LXT 2512   Gold : **£8**   Silver : £5
BERLIOZ   Faust Excerpts, Romeo and Juliet Excerpts
Paris Conservatoire Orchestra   Munch
No Stereo

LXT 2513   Gold : **£50**   Silver : £30
BEETHOVEN   Symphony No.5 Paris Conservatoire Orchestra Schuricht
No Stereo

LXT 2514   Gold : **£15**   Silver : £10
Various   Recital   Conley   New Symphony Orchestra   Kisch
No Stereo

LXT 2515   Gold : **£8**   Silver : £6
MOZART   Quartet in Gmin.   Griller Quartet   Gilbert
No Stereo

LXT 2516   Gold : **£10**   Silver : £5
BLOCH   Sacred Service   Bond
London Philharmonic Orchestra   Bloch
No Stereo

LXT 2517   Gold : **£15**   Silver : £12
BRAHMS   Symphony No.4   London Symphony Orchestra   Krips
No Stereo

LXT 2518   Gold : **£8**   Silver : £6
BORODIN / FALLA   Polovtsian Dances, El Amour Brujo
Collings London Philharmonic Orchestra   Van Beinum
No Stereo

LXT 2519   Gold : **£25**   Silver : £15
DVORAK   Piano Quintet   Quintetto Chigiano
No Stereo

LXT 2520   Gold : **£16**   Silver : £8
FRANCK   Piano Quintet   Quintetto Chigiano
No Stereo

LXT 2521   Gold : **£8**   Silver : £6
ALBENIZ / FALLA   Music from Spain, Iberia
Paris Conservatoire Orchestra   Jorda
No Stereo

LXT 2522-3   (==== Not Issued ====)

LXT 2524   Gold : **£20**   Silver : £10
DEBUSSY   Images   Suisse Romande Orchestra   Ansermet
No Stereo

LXT 2525   Gold : **£6**   Silver : £3
ELGAR   Wand of Youth Suite,Cockaigne
London Philharmonic Orchestra   Van Beinum
No Stereo

LXT 2526   (==== Not Issued ====)

LXT 2527   Gold : **£20**   Silver : £10
WAGNER   Prelude Liebestod from Tristan
London Philharmonic Orchestra   Krauss
No Stereo

LXT 2528   Gold : **£12**   Silver : £5
Various   Recital   Micheau
No Stereo

LXT 2529   Gold : **£10**   Silver : £6
BARTOK   Concerto for Orchestra
Concertgebauw Orchestra of Amsterdam   Van Beinum
No Stereo

LXT 2530   Gold : **£16**   Silver : £12
DVORAK / MOZART   Quartet 6, Adagio & Fugue   Griller Quartet
No Stereo

LXT 2531   Gold : **£8**   Silver : £6
TCHAIKOVSKY   Romeo Juliet, Francesca da Rimini
London Philharmonic Orchestra   Van Beinum
No Stereo

LXT 2532   Gold : **£16**   Silver : £10
BEETHOVEN   Piano Sonata No.12 & 21   Backhaus
No Stereo

LXT 2533   Gold : **£10**   Silver : £6
SCHUBERT   Quintet in A, Op.114   Vienna Octet
No Stereo

LXT 2534   Gold : **£8**   Silver : £6
MOZART / HANDEL   Symphony 35, Water Music
Concertgebauw Orchestra of Amsterdam   Van Beinum
No Stereo

LXT 2535   Gold : **£30**   Silver : £10
BEETHOVEN / CHOPIN   Piano Sonata No.30, Sonata No.2 Backhaus
No Stereo

LXT 2536-8   Gold : **£10**   Silver : £6
MOZART   Entfuhrung aus dem Serail (Abduction from the Harem)
Lipp   Vienna Philharmonic Orchestra   Krips
No Stereo

LXT 2539   Gold : **£20**   Silver : £10
SCHUBERT   Schubert Leider   Schlusnus
No Stereo

LXT 2540   Gold : **£6**   Silver : £3
BACH   Brandenburg Concerto No.1 in F, No.5 in D
Stuttgart Chamber Orchestra Munchinger
No Stereo

LXT 2541   (═══ Not Issued ═══)

LXT 2542   Gold : **£12**   Silver : £6
MOZART   Divertiment No.17   Vienna Octet
No Stereo

LXT 2543   Gold : **£25**   Silver : £10
SCHUBERT / FAURE   Gerard Souzay Racital   Souzay
No Stereo

LXT 2544   Gold : **£10**   Silver : £6
TCHAIKOVSKY   Symphony No.6   Paris Conservatoire Orchestra   Munch
No Stereo

LXT 2545   Gold : **£12**   Silver : £6
TCHAIKOVSKY   Symphony No.5
London Philharmonic Orchestra   Celibadache
No Stereo

LXT 2546 Gold : **£15** Silver : £7
BEETHOVEN Symphony No.3
Concertgebauw Orchestra of Amsterdam Kleiber
No Stereo

LXT 2547 Gold : **£10** Silver : £6
BEETHOVEN Symphony No.7
Concertgebauw Orchestra of Amsterdam Kleiber
No Stereo

LXT 2548 Gold : **£8** Silver : £4
STRAUSS Also Spracht Zarathustra
Vienna Philharmonic Orchestra Krauss
No Stereo

LXT 2549 Gold : **£15** Silver : £7
STRAUSS Don Juan, Till Eulenspiegel
Vienna Philharmonic Orchestra Krauss
No Stereo

LXT 2550-1 Gold : **£20** Silver : £10
STRAUSS Die Fledermaus Gueden
Vienna Philharmonic Orchestra Krauss
No Stereo

LXT 2552 (═══ Not Issued ═══)

LXT 2553 Gold : **£15** Silver : £7
BEETHOVEN Piano.Concerto No.3 Backhaus
Vienna Philharmonic Orchestra Bohm
No Stereo

LXT 2554 Gold : **£10** Silver : £5
Various Operatic Excerpts Schoeffler
Vienna Philharmonic Orchestra Bohm
No Stereo

LXT 2555 Gold : **£30** Silver : £20
ROSSINI Boutique Fantastique
London Symphony Orchestra Ansermet
No Stereo

LXT 2556   Gold : **£15**   Silver : £7
SCHUMANN / BRAHMS   Frauenliebe und Leben, 4 Serious songs Ferrier
No Stereo

LXT 2557   Gold : **£25**   Silver : £10
Various   Operatic Recital by Suzanne Danco   Danco
Suisse Romande Orchestra   Erede
No Stereo

LXT 2558   Gold : **£14**   Silver : £8
MOZART   Symphony No.25, Symphony No.36
London Philharmonic Orchestra, Vienna   Bohm
No Stereo

LXT 2559   Gold : **£20**   Silver : £12
TCHAIKOVSKY   Piano Concerto   Curzon
New Symphony Orchestra   Szell
No Stereo

LXT 2560-1   Gold : **£15**   Silver : £6
WAGNER   Die Meistersinger von Nurnburg Act II
Schoeffler   Vienna Philharmonic Orchestra   Knappertsbusch
No Stereo

LXT 2562   Gold : **£10**   Silver : £6
MOZART   Symphony No.29, Symphony No.36
Suisse Romande Orchestra, Vienna Philharmonic   Maag / Bohm
No Stereo

LXT 2563   Gold : **£20**   Silver : £15
STRAVINSKY   Le Sacre du Printemps
Suisse Romande Orchestra   Ansermet
No Stereo

LXT 2564   Gold : **£6**   Silver : £4
BEETHOVEN   Symphony No.4 in BbMaj.
London Philharmonic Orchestra   Solti
No Stereo

LXT 2565   Gold : **£12**   Silver : £8
RAVEL   Piano Concerto in Gmin., Left Hand Only   Henriot,
Blanchard   Paris CO,   Suisse Romande   Munch, Ansermet
No Stereo

15

LXT 2566   Gold : **£50**   Silver : £30
BRAHMS   Violin Concerto   Renardy
Concertgebauw Orchestra of Amsterdam   Munch
No Stereo

LXT 2567   Gold : **£20**   Silver : £10
Various   Operatic Recital   Welitsch
Vienna State Opera Orchestra   Moralt
No Stereo

LXT 2568   Gold : **£20**   Silver : £10
Various   Leider and Arias   Souzay
No Stereo

LXT 2569   (==== Not Issued ====)

LXT 2570   Gold : **£20**   Silver : £10
LOEWE   Ballads of Loewe   Strienz
No Stereo

LXT 2571   Gold : **£6**   Silver : £3
RESPIGHI / PERGOLETTI   Ancient Airs & Dances
Stuttgart Chamber Orchestra   Munchinger
No Stereo

LXT 2572   Gold : **£15**   Silver : £8
LISZT   Music of Liszt   Kempff
No Stereo

LXT 2573   Gold : **£25**   Silver : £16
BEETHOVEN   String Quartet Op.132   Griller Quartet
No Stereo

LXT 2574   Gold : **£80**   Silver : £40
BARTOK   Concert for Violin Rostal
London Symphony Orchestra   Sargent
No Stereo

LXT 2575   Gold : **£15**   Silver : £10
SIBELIUS   String Quartet Op.56   Griller Quartet
No Stereo

LXT 2576   Gold : **£4**   Silver : £2
STRAUSS   Die Fledermaus (Highlights) Gueden
Vienna Philharmonic Orchestra   Krauss
No Stereo

LXT 2577   Gold : **£20**   Silver : £15
SCHUBERT   Piano Sonata in Bb   Kempff
No Stereo

LXT 2578   Gold : **£5**   Silver : £2
BACH / FRANCK Bach and Franck Recital   Demessieux
No Stereo

LXT 2579-80   Gold : **£10**   Silver : £6
RACHMANINOV 24 Preludes   Lympany
No Stereo

LXT 2581   Gold : **£15**   Silver : £10
BEETHOVEN   Piano Sonata No.2, Sonata in Ab   Guilda
No Stereo

LXT 2582-4   Gold : **£30**   Silver : £20
OFFENBACH   Tales of Hoffman   Rounseville
Royal Philharmonic Orchestra   Beecham
No Stereo

LXT 2585   Gold : **£12**   Silver : £8
SCHUBERT   Symphony No.6 London Symphony Orchestra Krips
No Stereo

LXT 2586   Gold : **£65**   Silver : £50
BRAHMS   Symphony No.2 in Dmaj.
London Philharmonic Orchestra   Furtwangler
No Stereo

LXT 2587   Gold : **£10**   Silver : £7
BEETHOVEN   Symphony No.6
London Philharmonic Orchestra   Kleiber
No Stereo

LXT 2588   Gold : **£35**   Silver : £15
PAGANINI   24 Caprices   Ricci
No Stereo

LXT 2589   Gold : **£8**   Silver : £3
SUPPE   Suppe Overtures
London Philharmonic Orchestra   Solti
No Stereo

LXT 2590   Gold : **£30**   Silver : £18
OFFENBACH   Offenbach Overtures
London Philharmonic Orchestra   Martinon
No Stereo

LXT 2591   Gold : **£20**   Silver : £15
SCHUMANN / VERDI   String Quartet Op.41/2, Quartet   Italian Quartet
No Stereo

LXT 2592   Gold : **£20**   Silver : £8
Various   Opera and Leider   Dermota
Vienna Philharmonic Orchestra   Bohm
No Stereo

LXT 2593   Gold : **£12**   Silver : £5
LEHAR   Count of Luxemburg   Glawitsch
Tonhalle Orchestra   Reinshagen
No Stereo

LXT 2594   Gold : **£12**   Silver : £8
BEETHOVEN   Variations & Fugue in EbMaj. Sonata No.26   Guilda
No Stereo

LXT 2595   Gold : **£20**   Silver : £10
RACHMANINOV Piano Concerto No.2   Katchen
New Symphony Orchestra   Fistoulari
No Stereo

LXT 2596   Gold : **£50**   Silver : £30
BACH / BRUCH Partita No.2 in Dmin., Concerto No.1 in Gmin.
Campoli   New Symphony Orchestra   Kisch
No Stereo

LXT 2597-9   Gold : **£15**   Silver : £6
WEBER   Der Freischutz   Poell
Vienna Philharmonic Orchestra   Ackermann
No Stereo

LXT 2600   Gold : **£40**   Silver : £25
VIVALDI   Four Seasons   Barchet
Stuttgart Chamber Orchestra   Munchinger
No Stereo

LXT 2601   Gold : **£12**   Silver : £6
DVORAK   Quartet No.3   Boskovsky Quartet
No Stereo

LXT 2602   Gold : **£14**   Silver : £10
SCHUMANN   Symphony No.1
Suisse Romande Orchestra   Ansermet
No Stereo

LXT 2603   Gold : **£30**   Silver : £10
BEETHOVEN   Piano Sonata No.5, 6, 25   Backhaus
No Stereo

LXT 2604   Gold : **£14**   Silver : £8
BACH J.C / SCHUBERT   Symphony No.1 in Eb Op.18, Symphony No.3
in D   Cincinatti Symphony Orchestra   Johnson
No Stereo

LXT 2605   Gold : **£20**   Silver : £10
BERLIOZ   Nuits D'ete   Danco
Cincinatti Symphony Orchestra   Johnson
No Stereo

LXT 2606   Gold : **£20**   Silver : £15
ADAM   Overture from Si J'etais Roi (If I were King)
London Philharmonic Orchestra   Martinon
No Stereo

LXT 2607   Gold : **£12**   Silver : £5
LEHAR   The Merry Widow   Lichtegg
Tonhalle Orchestra   Reinshagen
No Stereo

LXT 2608   Gold : **£15**   Silver : £10
DVORAK   Symphony No.5   New Symphony Orchestra   Jorda
No Stereo

LXT 2609   Gold : **£ 5**   Silver : £2
SULLIVAN   Sullivan Overtures   D'oyly Carte   Godfrey
No Stereo

LXT 2610   Gold : **£ 8**   Silver : £4
IPPOLITOU / TCHAIKOVSKY   Caucasian Sketches, Sleeping
Princess   Paris Conservatoire Orchestra   Desormiere
No Stereo

LXT 2611   Gold : **£ 10**   Silver : £6
TCHAIKOVSKY   Nutcracker Paris Conservatoire Orchestra   Fistoulari
No Stereo

LXT 2612-3   Gold : **£ 10**   Silver : £5
STRAUSS   Zigeunerbaron (Gipsy Baron)Poell
Vienna Philharmonic Orchestra   Krauss
No Stereo

LXT 2614   Gold : **£ 15**   Silver : £10
MOZART   Symphony No.38, Symphony No.34
Suisse Romande Orchestra   Ansermet, Maag
No Stereo

LXT 2615-7   Gold : **£ 30**   Silver : £15
BIZET   Carmen   Juyol
Opera Comique Chorus & Orchestra   Wolff
No Stereo

LXT 2618-20   Gold : **£ 12**   Silver : £8
MASSENET   Manon   Micheau
Opera Comique Chorus & Orchestra   Wolff
No Stereo

LXT 2621   Gold : **£ 20**   Silver : £12
FALLA   Three Cornered Hat London Symphony Orchestra Jorda
No Stereo

LXT 2622-3   Gold : **£ 20**   Silver : £10
PUCCINI   La Boheme   Tebaldi
St. Cecilia Academy, Rome   Erede
No Stereo

LXT 2624 Gold : **£15** Silver : £10
BEETHOVEN Piano Sonata No.29Guilda
No Stereo

LXT 2625 Gold : **£15** Silver : £10
Various French Overtures
Paris Opera Comique Orchestra Wolff
No Stereo

LXT 2626 Gold : **£18** Silver : £10
BLOCH Piano Quintet Quintetto Chigiano
No Stereo

LXT 2627 Gold : **£8** Silver :
BEETHOVEN Piano Concerto No.1 Guilda
Vienna Philharmonic Orchestra Bohm
No Stereo

LXT 2628 Gold : **£16** Silver : £10
KREUTZER Grand Septet Op.62 Vienna Octet
No Stereo

LXT 2629 Gold : **£15** Silver : £10
BEETHOVEN Piano Concerto No.4 Backhaus
Vienna Philharmonic Orchestra Krauss
No Stereo

LXT 2630 Gold : **£15** Silver : £6
ALFVEN / GRIEG Midsummer Vigil Op.19, Sigurd Jorsalfar Op.56
Cincinatti Symphony Orchestra Johnson
No Stereo

LXT 2631 Gold : **£15** Silver : £8
STRAVINSKY / MARTIN La Baiser de la Fee, Petit Symphony Suisse
Romande Orchestra Ansermet
No Stereo

LXT 2632 Gold : **£25** Silver : £15
DEBUSSY La Mer
Suisse Romande Orchestra Ansermet
No Stereo

LXT 2633   Gold : **£15**   Silver : £6
WEBER   Overtures
Vienna Philharmonic Orchestra   Bohm
No Stereo

LXT 2634   Gold : **£6**   Silver : £3
STRAUSS   Music of Johann Strauss
Vienna Philharmonic Orchestra   Krauss
No Stereo

LXT 2635   Gold : **£6**   Silver : £4
MOZART   Arias from Entfuhrung aus demSerial   Lipp
Vienna Philharmonic Orchestra   Krips
No Stereo

LXT 2636   Gold : **£120**   Silver : £80
SCHUMANN   Etudes Symphoniques Op.13   Mewton-Wood
No Stereo

LXT 2637   Gold : **£20**   Silver : £10
DEBUSSY / RAVEL   Nocturnes, Rhapsody Espagnole
Suisse Romande Orchestra   Ansermet
No Stereo

LXT 2638-40   Gold : **£20**   Silver : £10
PUCCINI   Madame Butterfly   Tebaldi
St. Cecilia Academy, Rome   Erede
No Stereo

LXT 2641   Gold : **£10**   Silver : £6
DVORAK   Symphony No.4
Concertgebauw Orchestra of Amsterdam   Szell
No Stereo

LXT 2642   Gold : **£10**   Silver : £6
BERLIOZ   Symphony Fantastique
Concertgebauw Orchestra of Amsterdam   Van Beinum
No Stereo

LXT 2643   Gold : **£8**   Silver : £4
STRAUSS   Sinfonia Domestica
Vienna Philharmonic Orchestra   Krauss
No Stereo

LXT 2644   Gold : **£ 15**   Silver : £5
Various   Operatic Recital   Lechleitner
No Stereo

LXT 2645   Gold : **£ 6**   Silver : £3
STRAUSS   New Year Concert
Vienna Philharmonic Orchestra   Krauss
No Stereo

LXT 2646-7   Gold : **£ 15**   Silver : £6
WAGNER   Die Meistersinger von Nurnberg Act I
Schoeffler   Vienna Philharmonic Orchestra   Knappertsbusch
No Stereo

LXT 2648-50   Gold : **£ 20**
WAGNER   Die Meistersinger von Nurnberg Act III
Schoeffler   Vienna Philharmonic Orchestra   Knappertsbusch

LXT 2651-6   Gold : **£ 60**   Silver :
WAGNER   Parsifal   London
Beyruth Festival Orchestra & Chorus   Knappertsbusch
No Stereo

LXT 2657   Gold : **£ 16**   Silver : £6
GRIEG   Concerto in A Min. for Piano & Orchestra
Curzon   London Symphony Orchestra   Fistoulari
No Stereo

LXT 2658   Gold : **£ 10**   Silver : £2
Various   Music of Switzerland   Frey, Manoliu
No Stereo

LXT 2659-64   Gold : **£ 70**   Silver : £35
WAGNER   Die Meistersinger von Nurnberg   Schoeffler
Vienna Philharmonic Orchestra   Knappertsbusch
No Stereo

LXT 2665   Gold : **£ 12**   Silver : £8
RANGSTROM   Symphony No.1   Stockholm Concert Assembly Mann
No Stereo

LXT 2666   Gold : **£ 14**   Silver : £10
MOZART   Piano Sonatas No. 3, 5, 15 & 16   Blanchard
No Stereo

LXT 2667   Gold : **£ 18**   Silver : £12
PROKOFIEV   Symphony No.6
Suisse Romande Orchestra   Ansermet
No Stereo

LXT 2668   Gold : **£ 8**   Silver : £4
BACH / BEETHOVEN   Fugue in Gmin., Amin., Ricercare, Great Fugue
Stuttgart Chamber Orchestra   Munchinger
No Stereo

LXT 2669   Gold : **£ 6**   Silver : £4
HAYDN / WAGNER   Symphony No.45, Siegfried Iydll
Stuttgart Chamber Orchestra   Munchinger
No Stereo

LXT 2670   Gold : **£ 20**   Silver : £10
LISZT / SCHUMANN   Music of Liszt and Schumann   Kempff
No Stereo

LXT 2671   Gold : **£ 25**   Silver : £15
MOZART   Serenade No.9   Suisse Romande Orchestra Maag
No Stereo

LXT 2672   Gold : **£ 8**   Silver : £2
Various   Operatic Excerpts   Edelmann, Patzak
Vienna Philharmonic Orchestra   Moralt, Bohm
No Stereo

LXT 2673   Gold : **£ 40**   Silver : £30
BACH   Suite No.4 in Eb for solo Cello   Mainardi
No Stereo

LXT 2674   Gold : **£ 30**   Silver : £10
BEETHOVEN   Violin Concerto   Campoli
London Symphony Orchestra   Krips
No Stereo

LXT 2675 Gold : **£8** Silver : £4
BRAHMS Symphony No.1
Concertgebauw Orchestra of Amsterdam Van Beinum
No Stereo

LXT 2676 Gold : **£12** Silver : £10
BRAHMS Symphony No.3
Concertgebauw Orchestra of Amsterdam Szell
No Stereo

LXT 2677 Gold : **£10** Silver : £6
BERLIOZ / RAVEL Overtures, Bolero
Paris Conservatoire Orchestra Munch
No Stereo

LXT 2678 Gold : **£125** Silver : £55
SEMENOFF / RODRIGO Violin Sonata in E, Concerto d'ete for Violin &
Orchestra Ferras Paris Conservatoire Orchestra Enesco
No Stereo

LXT 2679 Gold : **£20** Silver : £10
BEETHOVEN / SCHUBERT String Quartet No.9, Quartettsatz
Italian Quartet
No Stereo

LXT 2680 Gold : **£16** Silver : £8
BOCCHERINI / HAYDN String Quartet Op.6/1, Quartet No. 68
Italian Quartet
No Stereo

LXT 2681-2 Gold : **£40** Silver : £15
TCHAIKOVSKY Swan Lake Campoli
London Symphony Orchestra Fistoulari
No Stereo

LXT 2683 Gold : **£14** Silver : £8
HAYDN Symphony No.100, Symphony No.104
London Philharmonic Orchestra Van Beinum
No Stereo

LXT 2684   Gold : **£16**   Silver : £10
MOZART   Famous Overtures of Mozart
London Symphony Orchestra   Kripps
No Stereo

LXT 2685   Gold : **£15**   Silver : £10
MOZART   Mozart Arias   Reining
No Stereo

LXT 2686   Gold : **£8**   Silver : £4
HAYDN / MOZART   Symphony No.94, Symphony No.33
Concertgebauw Orchestra of Amsterdam   Van Beinum
No Stereo

LXT 2687   Gold : **£8**   Silver : £4
BRAHMS   Piano Quintet   Quintetto Chigiano
No Stereo

LXT 2688   Gold : **£14**   Silver : £10
Various   Recital   Prandelli St. Cecilia Academy, Rome Erede
No Stereo

LXT 2689   Gold : **£10**   Silver : £6
MOZART   Symphony No.31, Symphony No.39
London Symphony Orchestra   Krips
No Stereo

LXT 2690   Gold : **£2**   Silver : £2
Spoken Word   Shakespear Henry VIII   Thorndike
No Stereo

LXT 2691   Gold : **£25**   Silver : £15
PROKOFIEV   Piano Sonata No.2 & 5   Cornman
No Stereo

LXT 2692   Gold : **£10**   Silver : £6
FRANCK   Symphony in Dmin.   Joyce
Paris Conservatoire Orchestra   Munch
No Stereo

LXT 2693   Gold : **£6**   Silver : £3
VAUGHAN WILLIAMS   London Symphony
London Philharmonic Orchestra   Boult
No Stereo

LXT 2694   Gold : **£8**   Silver : £5
SIBELIUS   Symphony No.1 London Symphony Orchestra   Collins
No Stereo

LXT 2695   Gold : **£10**   Silver : £10
Test Record
No Stereo

LXT 2696   Gold : **£6**   Silver : £4
TCHAIKOVSKY   1812 Overture, Hamlet
London Philharmonic Orchestra   Boult
No Stereo

LXT 2697   Gold : **£8**   Silver : £5
NIELSEN   Symphony No.3   Danish State Radio Orchestra Tuxen
No Stereo

LXT 2698   Gold : **£12**   Silver : £6
MOZART   Clarinet Quintet   Italian Quartet
No Stereo

LXT 2699   Gold : **£6**   Silver : £4
ELGAR / VAUGHAN WILLIAMS   English music for Strings
New Symphony Orchestra   Collins
No Stereo

LXT 2700   Gold : **£16**   Silver : £10
SCHUBERT   Quartet Op.29   Vegh Quartet
No Stereo

LXT 2701   Gold : **£10**   Silver : £6
RACHMANINOV Piano Concerto No 3   Lympany
New Symphony Orchestra   Collins
No Stereo

LXT 2702   Gold : **£ 15**   Silver : £6
BURKHARD / MULLER   Toccatta Op.86, Sinfonia Op.40
Zurich College Orchestra   Sacher
No Stereo

LXT 2703   Gold : **£ 40**   Silver : £30
BECK   Viola Concerto   Kagi
Suisse Romande Orchestra   Meylan
No Stereo

LXT 2704-8   Gold : **£ 20**   Silver : £15
Various   Gregorian Chant   St. Pierre de Solesme Abbey Choir
No Stereo

LXT 2709   Gold : **£ 16**   Silver : £10
SCHUBERT   String Quartet in A Maj.   Vegh Quartet
No Stereo

LXT 2710   Gold : **£ 25**   Silver : £15
BRAHMS   Quartet No.2 & 3   Vegh Quartet
No Stereo

LXT 2711-4   Gold : **£ 32**   Silver : £20
DEBUSSY   Pelleas et Melisande   Danco
Suisse Romande Orchestra   Ansermet
No Stereo

LXT 2715   Gold : **£ 30**   Silver : £20
BEETHOVEN   Piano Sonata No.23, 28   Backhaus
No Stereo

LXT 2716   Gold : **£ 25**   Silver : £18
FALLA   Three Cornered Hat   Suisse Romande Orchestra   Ansermet
No Stereo

LXT 2717   Gold : **£ 8**   Silver : £6
BEETHOVEN   Piano Trio No.7   Trio di Trieste
No Stereo

LXT 2718   Gold : **£ 10**   Silver : £6
MAHLER   Symphony No.4   Richie
Concertgebauw Orchestra of Amsterdam   Van Beinum
No Stereo

LXT 2719   Gold : **£6**   Silver : £3
SCHUBERT   Symphony No.9
Concertgebauw Orchestra of Amsterdam   Krips
No Stereo

LXT 2720   Gold : **£10**   Silver : £6
POULENC / SCARLATTI   Les Biches, Good Humoured Ladies   Paris
Conservatoire Orchestra   Desormiere
No Stereo

LXT 2721-2   Gold : **£60**   Silver : £20
MAHLER   Das Lied von der Erde   Ferrier
Vienna Philharmonic Orchestra   Walter
No Stereo

LXT 2723   Gold : **£15**   Silver : £10
BRAHMS   Piano Concerto No.2   Backhaus
Vienna Philharmonic Orchestra   Schuricht
No Stereo

LXT 2724   Gold : **£50**   Silver : £25
BEETHOVEN   Symphony No.2
Vienna Philharmonic Orchestra   Schuricht
No Stereo

LXT 2725-6   Gold : **£40**   Silver : £15
BEETHOVEN   Symphony No.9   Gueden
Vienna Philharmonic Orchestra   Kleiber
No Stereo

LXT 2727   Gold : **£50**   Silver : £20
DVORAK   Cello Concerto   Nelsova
London Symphony Orchestra Krips
No Stereo

LXT 2728   Gold : **£8**   Silver : £4
MOZART   String Quartets No.8 & No.17   Griller Quartet
No Stereo

LXT 2729   Gold : **£15**   Silver : £6
STRAUSS   Heldenleben
Vienna Philharmonic Orchestra   Krauss
No Stereo

LXT 2730-2   Gold : **£20**   Silver : £10
PUCCINI   Tosca   Tebaldi
St. Cecilia Academy, Rome   Erede
No Stereo

LXT 2733   Gold : **£20**   Silver : £15
ROSSINI   Overtures
Concertgebauw Orchestra of Amsterdam   Bohm
No Stereo

LXT 2734   Gold : **£20**   Silver : £10
SCHUMANN   Songs   Souzay
No Stereo

LXT 2735-7   Gold : **£20**   Silver : £10
VERDI   Aida   Tebaldi
St. Cecilia Academy, Rome   Erede
No Stereo

LXT 2738-40   Gold : **£30**   Silver : £15
DELIBES   Lakme   Robin
Opera Comique Chorus & Orchestra   Sebastien
No Stereo

LXT 2741   Gold : **£20**   Silver : £10
BEETHOVEN   Prometheus
London Philharmonic Orchestra   Van Beinum
No Stereo

LXT 2742   (==== Not Issued ====)

LXT 2743   Gold : **£10**   Silver : £6
CHABRIER / DEBUSSY   French Choral   Micheau
Paris Conservatoire Orchestra   Fournet
No Stereo

LXT 2744   Gold : **£6**   Silver : £3
SIBELIUS   Symphony No.5, Karelia Suite 2 & 3+F269
Danish State Radio Orchestra   Tuxen, Jenson
No Stereo

LXT 2745   Gold : **£50**   Silver : £20
SCHUMANN   Symphony No.2
Paris Conservatoire Orchestra   Schuricht
No Stereo

LXT 2746   Gold : **£6**   Silver : £3
MASSENET   Cid, Meyerbeer, Patineurs
London Symphony Orchestra   Irving
No Stereo

LXT 2747   Gold : **£30**   Silver : £10
BEETHOVEN   Piano Sonata No.3 & 17   Backhaus
No Stereo

LXT 2748   Gold : **£8**   Silver : £5
NIELSEN   Symphony No.1 Danish State Radio Orchestra Jensen
No Stereo

LXT 2749   Gold : **£20**   Silver : £15
SCHOSTOKOVITCH   Piano Quintet   Quintetto Chigiano
No Stereo

LXT 2750   Gold : **£30**   Silver : £10
BEETHOVEN   Violin Concerto   Ricci
London Philharmonic Orchestra   Boult
No Stereo

LXT 2751   Gold : **£50**   Silver : £30
HANDEL   Six Violin Sonatas   Campoli
No Stereo

LXT 2752   Gold : **£120**   Silver : £65
BEETHOVEN   Violin Sonatas   Rostal
No Stereo

LXT 2753   Gold : **£8**   Silver : £6
HAYDN / MOZART   Symphony No.49, Divertimento No.2
London Mozart Players   Blech
No Stereo

LXT 2754   (==== Not Issued ====)

LXT 2755   Gold : **£6**   Silver : £3
STRAUSS   New Years Concert No.2
Vienna Philharmonic Orchestra   Krauss
No Stereo

LXT 2756   Gold : **£15**   Silver : £8
STRAUSS R.   Strauss from Bourgoise Gentilhomme
Vienna Philharmonic Orchestra   Krauss
No Stereo

LXT 2757   Gold : **£8**   Silver : £2
BACH   A Bach Recital   Ferrier
London Philharmonic Orchestra   Boult
No Stereo

LXT 2758   Gold : **£6**   Silver : £4
TCHAIKOVSKY   Symphony No.5
Hamburg Radio Symphony Orchestra   Schmitt-Issersdedt
No Stereo

LXT 2759   Gold : **£5**   Silver : £2
HANDEL   Organ Concerto   Demessieux
No Stereo

LXT 2760   Gold : **£30**   Silver : £15
Various   Espana   Suisse Romande Orchestra   Ansermet
No Stereo

LXT 2761   Gold : **£25**   Silver : £15
TCHAIKOVSKY   Capriccio Italian,Variations
Paris Conservatoire Orchestra   Schuricht
No Stereo

LXT 2762-3   Gold : **£14**   Silver : £10
TCHAIKOVSKY   Sleeping Princess
Paris Conservatoire Orchestra   Fistoulari
No Stereo

LXT 2764   Gold : **£15**   Silver : £10
PROKOFIEV   Symphony No.5   Ase
Danish State Radio Orchestra   Tuxen
No Stereo

LXT 2765   Gold : **£ 80**   Silver : £30
VIVALDI / BOCCERINI   Concerto for Cello & Strings   Fournier
Stuttgart Chamber Orchestra   Munchinger
No Stereo

LXT 2766   Gold : **£ 80**   Silver : £30
Various   Cello Recital   Fournier
No Stereo

LXT 2767   Gold : **£ 10**   Silver : £6
KHACHATURIAN   Piano Concerto   Lympany
London Philharmonic Orchestra   Fistoulari
No Stereo

LXT 2768   Gold : **£ 15**   Silver :
MENDELSOHNN   Symphony No.3
London Symphony Orchestra   Scherchen
No Stereo

LXT 2769   Gold : **£ 18**   Silver : £12
RIMSKY-KORSAKOV   Coq d'or, Capriccio Espagnole
Suisse Romande Orchestra   Ansermet
No Stereo

LXT 2770   Gold : **£ 8**   Silver : £6
SCHUBERT / MENDELSSOHN   Rosamunde, Midsummer Nights
Dream   Concertgebauw Orchestra of Amsterdam   Van Beinum
No Stereo

LXT 2771   Gold : **£ 8**   Silver : £5
BARTOK / KODALY   Dance Suite, Galanta Dances
London Philharmonic Orchestra   Solti
No Stereo

LXT 2772   Gold : **£ 8**   Silver : £3
MOZART   Piano Quartet No.1 & 2   Amadeus Quartet   Curzon
No Stereo

LXT 2773   Gold : **£ 5**   Silver : £2
LISZT / WIDOR   Organ Fantasia, Symphony Gothique   Demessieux
No Stereo

LXT 2774 Gold : **£ 8** Silver : £6
Various French Songs Jansen
No Stereo

LXT 2775 Gold : **£ 25** Silver : £15
RAVEL Daphnis et Chloe Suisse Romande Orchestra Ansermet
No Stereo

LXT 2776 Gold : **£ 10** Silver : £8
SIBELIUS En Saga, Tapiola
Concertgebauw Orchestra of Amsterdam Van Bienum
No Stereo

LXT 2777 Gold : **£ 30** Silver : £10
BEETHOVEN Piano Sonata No.29 in BbMaj. Backhaus
No Stereo

LXT 2778 Gold : **£ 6** Silver : £3
BRAHMS Variations on a Theme of Haydn, St. Anthoni Vars.
Concertgebauw Orchestra of Amsterdam Van Beinum
No Stereo

LXT 2779 Gold : **£ 12** Silver : £8
SCHUBERT Symphony No.4
Concertgebauw Orchestra of Amsterdam Van Beinum
No Stereo

LXT 2780 Gold : **£ 30** Silver : £10
BEETHOVEN Piano Sonata No.13, 19,14 & 20 Backhaus
No Stereo

LXT 2781 Gold : **£ 25** Silver : £15
SCHUBERT Impromptus No. 5, 6, 7 & 8 Curzon
No Stereo

LXT 2782 Gold : **£ 12** Silver : £10
SPOHR Nonet in F, Op.31 Vienna Octet
No Stereo

LXT 2783-5 (==== Not Issued ====)

LXT 2786   Gold : **£8**   Silver : £6
ELGAR   Coronation of Queen Elizabeth 1953
London Symphony Orchestra   Sargent
No Stereo

LXT 2787   Gold : **£8**   Silver : £4
VAUGHAN WILLIAMS   Symphony No.3, Pastoral   Ritchie
London Philharmonic Orchestra   Boult
No Stereo

LXT 2788   Gold : **£6**   Silver : £4
DELIUS   Song of Summer, Brigg Fair etc
London Symphony Orchestra Collins
No Stereo

LXT 2789   Gold : **£6**   Silver : £2
BIZET   Pechers de Pearls (excerpts)   De Luca
No Stereo

LXT 2790   Gold : **£10**   Silver : £6
BRITTEN   Frank Bridge Variations   Boyd Neel Orchestra
No Stereo

LXT 2791   Gold : **£10**   Silver : £5
LAMBERT / WALTON   Horoscope, Façade Suite
London Symphony Orchestra   Irving
No Stereo

LXT 2792   Gold : **£8**   Silver : £4
HANDEL   Water Music, Royal Fireworks
Concertgebauw Orchestra of Amsterdam   Van Beinum
No Stereo

LXT 2793   Gold : **£4**   Silver : £2
WALTON   English Marches
London Symphony Orchestra   Sargent
No Stereo

LXT 2794   Gold : **£6**   Silver : £4
RUBBRA / VAUGHAN WILLIAMS   St. Dominicus Mass, Mass in Gmin.
Fleet Street Choir
No Stereo

LXT 2795-6 Gold : **£12** Silver : £4
Various Early English Keyboard Music Goble, Dart
No Stereo

LXT 2797 Gold : **£15** Silver : £6
Various Recital Vyvyan
No Stereo

LXT 2798 Gold : **£15** Silver : £8
Various Aldeburgh Festival Pears
Aldeburgh Festival Orchestra Holst
No Stereo

LXT 2799-800 Gold : **£40** Silver : £30
SCHUBERT Wintereisse Schmitt-Issersdedt Walter
No Stereo

LXT 2801 Gold : **£60** Silver : £45
LALO Symphonie Espagnole Campoli
London Philharmonic Orchestra Van Beinum
No Stereo

LXT 2802 Gold : **£85** Silver : £45
MOZART Sonata No.34 in A maj. Grinke
No Stereo

LXT 2803 Gold : **£15** Silver : £8
NIELSON / BOZZA / IBERT Quintet for Wind instrument,
Variations Copenhagen Wind Quartet
No Stereo

LXT 2804 Gold : **£20** Silver : £10
BEETHOVEN 33 variations on a waltz by Diabelli Katchen
No Stereo

LXT 2805 Gold : **£15** Silver : £6
Various Spanish & Portugese Keyboard Music Blumenthal
No Stereo

LXT 2806 Gold : **£20** Silver : £15
SCHUMANN Piano Concerto Kempff
No Stereo

LXT 2807   Gold : **£14**   Silver : £6
DVORAK   Symphony No.2
Hamburg Radio Symphony Orchestra   Schmitt-Issersdedt
No Stereo

LXT 2808   Gold : **£35**   Silver : £15
PAGANINI   Recital   Ricci
No Stereo

LXT 2809   Gold : **£30**   Silver : £10
BEETHOVEN   Piano Sonata No.4 & 7   Backhaus
No Stereo

LXT 2810   Gold : **£80**   Silver : £30
DEBUSSY / FAURE   Violin Sonata, Violin Sonata No.2   Ferras
No Stereo

LXT 2811   Gold : **£20**   Silver : £15
BEETHOVEN / HAYDN   String Quartet No.6, Quartet No.81
Italian Quartet
No Stereo

LXT 2812   Gold : **£25**   Silver : £12
BARTOK / ROREM   Mikrokosmos, Sonata No.2   Katchen
No Stereo

LXT 2813   Gold : **£50**   Silver : £35
SIBELIUS   Violin Concerto   Damen
London Philharmonic Orchestra   Van Beinum
No Stereo

LXT 2814   Gold : **£15**   Silver : £10
BRAHMS / DVORAK   Hungarian, Slavonic Dances
Hamburg Radio Symphony Orchestra   Schmitt-Issersdedt
No Stereo

LXT 2815   Gold : **£8**   Silver : £5
SIBELIUS   Symphony No.2   London Symphony Orchestra   Collins
No Stereo

LXT 2816   Gold : **£ 25**   Silver : £15
RAVEL   Concerto in Dmaj. For the left hand piano & Orchestra
Blanchard   Suisse Romande Orchestra   Ansermet
No Stereo

LXT 2817   Gold : **£ 15**   Silver : £10
DEBUSSY / RAVEL   Suite Bergamasque, Gaspard de la Nuit   Guilda
No Stereo

LXT 2818   Gold : **£ 60**   Silver : £30
STRAUSS / PROKOFIEV   Violin Sonatas   Ricci   Bussotti
No Stereo

LXT 2819   Gold : **£ 10**   Silver : £7
MOZART / HAYDN   Symphony No.40, Symphony No.92
London Symphony Orchestra   Krips
No Stereo

LXT 2820   Gold : **£ 14**   Silver : **£ 8**
BACH   Works of Bach   Kempff
No Stereo

LXT 2821   Gold : **£ 15**   Silver : £10
RAVEL   Tombeau de Couperin, Valses Nobles
Suisse Romande Orchestra   Ansermet
No Stereo

LXT 2822   Gold : **£ 40**   Silver : £15
WAGNER   Tannhauser Ov, Venusberg Music
Vienna Philharmonic Orchestra   Knappertsbusch
No Stereo

LXT 2823   Gold : **£ 15**   Silver : **£ 8**
DUPARC   Songs of Duparc   Souzay
No Stereo

LXT 2824   Gold : **£ 50**   Silver : £20
BEETHOVEN   Symphony No.1 & 8
Vienna Philharmonic Orchestra   Schuricht
No Stereo

LXT 2825   Gold : **£15**   Silver : £6
BRAHMS   Concerto No.1 for Piano & Orchestra   Curzon
Concertgebauw Orchestra of Amsterdam   Van Beinum
No Stereo

LXT 2826   Gold : **£12**   Silver : £8
BACH / MOZART   Recital   Guilda
No Stereo

LXT 2827   Gold : **£80**   Silver : £30
CHAUSSON / RAVEL / HONEGGER Poeme, Tzuqabe   Ferras
Belgium National Orchestra Sebastien
No Stereo

LXT 2828   Gold : **£20**   Silver : £15
RAVEL   L'Heure Espagnole   Danco
Suisse Romande Orchestra   Ansermet
No Stereo

LXT 2829-30   Gold : **£12**   Silver : £8
BRUCKNER / FRANCK   Symphony No.7, Psyche
Concertgebauw Orchestra of Amsterdam   Van Beinum
No Stereo

LXT 2831   Gold : **£8**   Silver : £5
SIBELIUS   Four Ledgends   Danish State Radio Orchestra   Jensen
No Stereo

LXT 2832   Gold : **£15**   Silver : £8
HAYDN   Symphony No.100, Symphony No.84
Danish State Radio Orchestra   Woldike
No Stereo

LXT 2833   Gold : **£25**   Silver : £15
Various   Russian Music Paris Conservatoire Orchestra Ansermet
No Stereo

LXT 2834   Gold : **£20**   Silver : £15
SCHUBERT   Piano Sonata No.16   Kempff
No Stereo

LXT 2835   Gold : **£25**   Silver : £10
Various   Canzone Scordate   Souzay
No Stereo

LXT 2836   Gold : **£25**   Silver : £15
PROKOFIEV   Piano Sonata No.3, 4 & 8   Cornman
No Stereo

LXT 2837   Gold : **£10**   Silver : £6
CHOPIN   Etudes Op 28   Gulda
No Stereo

LXT 2838   Gold : **£20**   Silver : £10
LISZT / MENDELSOHNN   Piano Recital   Katchen
No Stereo

LXT 2839   Gold : **£20**   Silver : £10
BEETHOVEN   Piano Concerto No.5   Backhaus
Vienna Philharmonic Orchestra   Krauss
No Stereo

LXT 2840   Gold : **£25**   Silver : £15
MOZART   Symphony No.28, Symphony No.29
Suisse Romande Orchestra   Maag
No Stereo

LXT 2841   Gold : **£14**   Silver : £8
BOCCHERINI   Quintets in A & D   Quintetto Chigiano
No Stereo

LXT 2842   Gold : **£20**   Silver : £15
STRAUSS   Don Quixote   Fournier
Vienna Philharmonic Orchestra   Krauss
No Stereo

LXT 2843   Gold : **£10**   Silver : £6
BRAHMS   Symphony No.3   Vienna Philharmonic Orchestra   Bohm
No Stereo

LXT 2844   Gold : **£8**   Silver : £4
ADAM   Giselle   Paris Opera Orchestra   Blareau
No Stereo

LXT 2845-6   Gold : **£35**   Silver : £24
LEONCAVALLO I Pagliacci   Monaco
St. Cecilia Academy, Rome   Erede
No Stereo

LXT 2847   Gold : **£14**   Silver : £8
HAYDN   Symphony No.96, Symphony No.97
Concertgebauw Orchestra of Amsterdam   Van Beinum
No Stereo

LXT 2848   Gold : **£6**   Silver : £4
STRAUSS   Graduation Ball New Symphony Orchestra Fistoulari
No Stereo

LXT 2849   Gold : **£15**   Silver : £10
HONEGGER   Petite Suite, Danse de la Chevre   Nicolet
No Stereo

LXT 2850   Gold : **£10**   Silver : £4
BRAHMS   Alto Rhapsody, 4 Songs   Ferrier
London Philharmonic Orchestra   Krauss
No Stereo

LXT 2851   Gold : **£12**   Silver : £6
BEETHOVEN   Symphony No.5
Concertgebauw Orchestra of Amsterdam   Kleiber
No Stereo

LXT 2852   Gold : **£12**   Silver : £8
MOZART   String Quartets No.2 & No.23   Italian Quartet
No Stereo

LXT 2853   Gold : **£12**   Silver : £8
MOZART   String Quartet No.19   Italian Quartet
No Stereo

LXT 2854   Gold : **£14**   Silver : £8
SCHUBERT   String Quartet No.8   Italian Quartet
No Stereo

LXT 2855   Gold : **£14**   Silver : £8
SCHUBERT   String Quartet No.2   Italian Quartet
No Stereo

LXT 2856 Gold : **£20**   Silver : £10
BEETHOVEN   String Quartet No.7   Italian Quartet
No Stereo

LXT 2857 Gold : **£80**   Silver : £60
SCHUBERT / SCHUMANN   Sonata Amn,Fan   Gendron
No Stereo

LXT 2858 Gold : **£10**   Silver : £8
BRAHMS   Quintet in Bmn for Clarinet Vienna Octet Boskowsky
No Stereo

LXT 2859 Gold : **£30**   Silver :
BRAHMS   Symphony No.2
Vienna Philharmonic Orchestra   Schuricht
No Stereo

LXT 2860 Gold : **£10**   Silver : £6
CHABRIER   Suite Pastoral
Paris Conservatoire Orchestra   Lindenberg
No Stereo

LXT 2861 Gold : **£15**   Silver : £10
MOZART   Piano Concerto No.9 & 15   Kempff
No Stereo

LXT 2862 Gold : **£14**   Silver : £10
DOHNANYI / RACHMANINOV   Nursery Variations, Paganini
Rhapsodies   Katchen   London Philharmonic Orchestra Boult
No Stereo

LXT 2863-4 Gold : **£30**   Silver : £10
STRAUSS   Salome   Patzak Vienna Philharmonic Orchestra Krauss
No Stereo

LXT 2865 Gold : **£20**   Silver : £8
STRAUSS   4 Letzte Lieder   Della Casa
Vienna Philharmonic Orchestra   Bohm
No Stereo

LXT 2866   Gold : **£50**   Silver : £20
BRAHMS   Piano Concerto No.1   Backhaus
Vienna Philharmonic Orchestra   Bohm
No Stereo

LXT 2867   Gold : **£16**   Silver : £10
MOZART   Piano Concerto No.23 & 24   Curzon
London Symphony Orchestra   Krips
No Stereo

LXT 2868   Gold : **£10**   Silver : £6
CHOPIN / IBERT Les Sylphides, Divertimento
Paris Conservatoire Orchestra   Desormiere
No Stereo

LXT 2869   Gold : **£20**   Silver : £10
FRANCK / SCHUMANN   Prelude Chorus & Fugue, Symphonic Studies
Katchen
No Stereo

LXT 2870   Gold : **£12**   Silver : £8
MENDELSOHNN Octet Op.20   Vienna Octet
No Stereo

LXT 2871   Gold : **£4**   Silver : £2
HOLST   The Planets   London Symphony Orchestra   Sargent
No Stereo

LXT 2872   Gold : **£10**   Silver : £8
BEETHOVEN   Symphony No.6
Concertgebauw Orchestra of Amsterdam   Kleiber
No Stereo

LXT 2873   Gold : **£20**   Silver : £10
DIEPENBROCK / PIJPER   Marsyas, Symphony No.3
Concertgebauw Orchestra of Amsterdam   Van Beinum
No Stereo

LXT 2874   Gold : **£8**   Silver : £4
BEETHOVEN   Symphony No.4
Concertgebauw Orchestra of Amsterdam   Krips
No Stereo

LXT 2875   Gold : **£20**   Silver : £10
SCHUMANN   Schumann Songs   Souzay
No Stereo

LXT 2876   Gold : **£20**   Silver : £10
KODALY   Quartet No.1   Vegh Quartet
No Stereo

LXT 2877   Gold : **£20**   Silver : £10
LISZT   Music of Liszt   Katin
No Stereo

LXT 2878   Gold : **£15**   Silver : £8
KODALY   Psalms, Peacock London Philharmonic Orchestra Solti
No Stereo

LXT 2879   Gold : **£10**   Silver : £4
Various   Italian Songs   Poggi
No Stereo

LXT 2880-4   Gold : **£85**   Silver : £35
WAGNER   Lohengrin   Windgassen
Beyruth Festival Orchestra & Chorus Keilberth
No Stereo

LXT 2885   Gold : **£15**   Silver : £10
ROSENBERG   Symphony No.3 Stockholm Radio Orchestra Mann
No Stereo

LXT 2886   Gold : **£8**   Silver : £4
BRITTEN   Peter Grimes exc. Young Persons Guide
Concertgebauw Orchestra of Amsterdam   Van Beinum
No Stereo

LXT 2887   Gold : **£10**   Silver : £6
SCHUMANN   Symphony No.4 London Symphony Orchestra Krips
No Stereo

LXT 2888   Gold : **£20**   Silver : £14
TCHAIKOVSKY Symphony No.6 Paris Conservatoire Orchestra Kleiber
No Stereo

LXT 2889   Gold : **£ 50**   Silver : £15
ALBENIZ / TURINA   Iberia, Danzas Fantasticas
Paris Conservatoire Orchestra   Argenta
No Stereo

LXT 2890-2   Gold : **£ 14**   Silver : £10
GOUNOD   Romeo et Juliette   Micheau
French National Opera Chorus & Orchestra   Erede
No Stereo

LXT 2893   Gold : **£ 15**   Silver : £5
GLUCK   Orfeo   Ferrier
Glyndebourne Festival Chorus   Stiedry
No Stereo

LXT 2894   Gold : **£ 25**   Silver : £12
BARTOK / PROKOVIEF   Piano Concerto No.3   Katchen
No Stereo

LXT 2895   Gold : **£ 80**   Silver : £25
SCHUMANN / TCHAIKOVSKY   Concerto, Rococo Theme
Gendron   Ansermet
No Stereo

LXT 2896   Gold : **£ 10**   Silver : £6
MUSSORGSKY / RAVEL   Pictures at an Exhibition, La Valse
Suisse Romande Orchestra   Ansermet
No Stereo

LXT 2897   Gold : **£ 12**   Silver : £6
MILHAUD / FAURE   Song Recital - Poems Juifs, Chansons D'eve
Kolassi
No Stereo

LXT 2898   Gold : **£ 15**   Silver : £8
GOUNOD   Mireille excerpts   Gabriel
Paris Conservatoire Orchestra   Blareau
No Stereo

LXT 2899   Gold : **£ 6**   Silver : £4
DELIUS   Music of Delius   London Symphony Orchestra   Collins
No Stereo

45

LXT 2900   Gold : **£18**   Silver : £12
GRANADOS   Goyescas Book 1   Magaloff
No Stereo

LXT 2901   Gold : **£20**   Silver : £10
BRAHMS   Trio Op.8   Trio di Trieste
No Stereo

LXT 2902   Gold : **£30**   Silver : £10
BEETHOVEN   Piano Sonata Nos.1, 26 & 27   Backhaus
No Stereo

LXT 2903   Gold : **£30**   Silver : £10
BEETHOVEN   Piano Sonata Nos.8, 9 & 15   Backhaus
No Stereo

LXT 2904   Gold : **£20**   Silver : £8
BRUCH / MENDELSSOHN Violin Concertos   Campoli
New Symphony Orchestra   Van Beinum
No Stereo

LXT 2905   Gold : **£80**   Silver : £30
FRANCK   Symphony in D
Vienna Philharmonic Orchestra   Furtwangler
No Stereo

LXT 2906   Gold : **£25**   Silver : £16
LALO / SAINT-SAINS   Cello Concerto   Nelsova
London Philharmonic Orchestra   Boult
No Stereo

LXT 2907-8   Gold : **£18**   Silver : £12
VAUGHAN WILLIAMS   Symphony No.1, Sea Sym, Wasps   Baillie
London Philharmonic Orchestra   Boult
No Stereo

LXT 2909   Gold : **£8**   Silver : £6
VAUGHAN WILLIAMS   Symphony No.4
London Philharmonic Orchestra   Boult
No Stereo

LXT 2910   Gold : **£6**   Silver : £3
VAUGHAN WILLIAMS   Symphony No.5
London Philharmonic Orchestra   Boult
No Stereo

LXT 2911   Gold : **£6**   Silver : £3
VAUGHAN WILLIAMS   Symphony No.6
London Philharmonic Orchestra   Boult
No Stereo

LXT 2912   Gold : **£6**   Silver : £3
VAUGHAN WILLIAMS   Sinfonia Antartica
London Philharmonic Orchestra   Boult
No Stereo

LXT 2913   Gold : **£15**   Silver : £8
STRAUSS   3rd New Year Concert
Vienna Philharmonic Orchestra   Krauss
No Stereo

LXT 2914   Gold : **£15**   Silver : £10
BRAHMS   Ballades, Piano Pieces   Kempff
No Stereo

LXT 2915   Gold : **£5**   Silver : £2
BACH   Bach Organ Works   Demessieux
No Stereo

LXT 2916   Gold : **£12**   Silver : £8
STRAVINSKY   Symphony of Psalms, Firebird
London Philharmonic Orchestra   Ansermet
No Stereo

LXT 2917   Gold : **£8**   Silver : £4
STRAUSS   Aus Italien   Vienna Philharmonic Orchestra   Krauss
No Stereo

LXT 2918   Gold : **£8**   Silver : £6
SCARLATTI   Harpsichord Sonatas   Malcolm
No Stereo

LXT 2919   Gold : **£10**   Silver : £4
BYRD   Mass for 4 Voices, Mass for 5 Voices   Fleet Street Choir
No Stereo

LXT 2920   Gold : **£30**   Silver : £10
BEETHOVEN   Piano Sonata Nos.2 & 11   Backhaus
No Stereo

LXT 2921-4   Gold : **£8**   Silver : £4
HANDEL   Messiah   Vyvyan
London Philharmonic Orchestra   Boult
No Stereo

LXT 2925   Gold : **£15**   Silver : £10
CHOPIN Piano Concerto No.1   Guilda
London Philharmonic Orchestra   Boult
No Stereo

LXT 2926   Gold : **£15**   Silver : £5
BACH   Cantata No.51 & 202   Danco
Stuttgart Chamber Orchestra Munchinger
No Stereo

LXT 2927   Gold : **£25**   Silver : £15
DEBUSSY   Jeux Enfants, 6 Epigraphes
Suisse Romande Orchestra   Ansermet
No Stereo

LXT 2928-9   Gold : **£15**   Silver : £5
MASCAGNI   Cavalleria Rusticana   Del Monaco   Ghione
No Stereo

LXT 2930   Gold : **£65**   Silver : £35
SARASATE   Dances Espanolas   Ricci
No Stereo

LXT 2931   Gold : **£30**   Silver : £10
BEETHOVEN / SCHUMANN   Piano Sonata Nos.10, 22 & 24,
Fantasiestuck   Backhaus
No Stereo

LXT 2932   Gold : **£20**   Silver : £10
LISZT / MENDELSOHNN   Music of Liszt & Mendelsohnn
Katin   London Philharmonic Orchestra   Martinon
No Stereo

LXT 2933   Gold : **£20**   Silver : £15
SCHUMANN   Kinderscenen, Fantasia   Curzon
No Stereo

LXT 2934   Gold : **£8**   Silver : £5
NIELSON   3 Motets   Danish Radio Madrigal Choir   Woldike
No Stereo

LXT 2935   Gold : **£15**   Silver : £10
BRAHMS   Fantasias, Piano Pieces   Kempff
No Stereo

LXT 2936   (==== Not Issued ====)

LXT 2937   Gold : **£6**   Silver : £3
VAUGHAN WILLIAMS   Job   London Philharmonic Orchestra Boult
No Stereo

LXT 2938   Gold : **£16**   Silver : £10
BEETHOVEN   Piano Sonata Nos.3, 19 & 20   Guilda
No Stereo

LXT 2939   Gold : **£30**   Silver : £10
BEETHOVEN   Piano Sonata Nos.31 & 32   Backhaus
No Stereo

LXT 2940   Gold : **£8**   Silver : £6
ELGAR   Falstaff   London Symphony Orchestra   Collins
No Stereo

LXT 2941   Gold : **£6**   Silver : £2
BRITTEN   Seranade for Tenor, Les Illuminations Pears
New Symphony Orchestra   Goossens
No Stereo

LXT 2942   Gold : **£35**   Silver : £15
BEETHOVEN   Violin Sonata No.7 & 10   Ricci
No Stereo

LXT 2943   Gold : **£15**   Silver : £8
Various   Recorder Recital   Dolmetsch
No Stereo

LXT 2944   Gold : **£40**   Silver : £30
MOZART   Violin Sonata No.21, 26 & 33   Langbein
No Stereo

LXT 2945   Gold : **£8**   Silver : £4
Various   Choral Music of the 13th Century   Polifonico Quartet
No Stereo

LXT 2946   Gold : **£4**   Silver : £3
MOZART   Symphony No.25, Symphony No.38
London Symphony Orchestra   Solti
No Stereo

LXT 2947   Gold : **£40**   Silver : £25
Various   Spanish Dance   Spagnolo
No Stereo

LXT 2948   Gold : **£20**   Silver : £15
BEETHOVEN   Concerto No.4 for Piano & Orchestra   Curzon
Vienna Philharmonic Orchestra   Knappertsbusch
No Stereo

LXT 2949   Gold : **£80**   Silver : £30
BRAHMS   Violin Concerto   Ferras
Vienna Philharmonic Orchestra   Schuricht
No Stereo

LXT 2950   Gold : **£30**   Silver : £10
BEETHOVEN   Piano Sonata Nos.31 & 32   Backhaus
No Stereo

LXT 2951   Gold : **£65**   Silver : £40
BACH   Sonata No.1 in Gmin., Partita No.1 in Bmin. for solo
Violin   Telmanyi
No Stereo

LXT 2952 Gold : **£65** Silver : £40
BACH Sonata No.2 in Amin., Partita No.2 in Dmin.for
solo Violin Telmanyi
No Stereo

LXT 2953 Gold : **£65** Silver : £40
BACH Sonata No.3 in C, Partita No.3 in E for solo Violin
Telmanyi
No Stereo

LXT 2954-7 Gold : **£80** Silver : £30
STRAUSS Der Rosenkavalier Gueden
Vienna Philharmonic Orchestra Kleiber
No Stereo

LXT 2958 Gold : **£16** Silver : £10
BEETHOVEN Piano Sonata No1 & 2 Guilda
No Stereo

LXT 2959 Gold : **£50** Silver : £25
WEBER Six sonatas for Violin & Piano Ricci
No Stereo

LXT 2960 Gold : **£8** Silver : £5
SIBELIUS Symphony No.3, Symphony No.7
London Symphony Orchestra Collins
No Stereo

LXT 2961 Gold : **£30** Silver : £10
MENDELSSOHN Overtures Vienna Philharmonic Orchestra Schuricht
No Stereo

LXT 2962 Gold : **£8** Silver : £5
SIBELIUS Symphony No.4, Poljolas Daughter
London Symphony Orchestra Collins
No Stereo

LXT 2963 Gold : **£30** Silver : £15
FUARE / FRANCAIX Ballade, Nocturnes, Concertino Long
London Philharmonic Orchestra Martinon
No Stereo

LXT 2964   Gold : **£ 12**   Silver : £4
Various   Opera Excerpts   Del Monaco
St. Cecilia Academy, Rome   Ghione
No Stereo

LXT 2965   Gold : **£ 6**   Silver : £3
STRAUSS   Johann Strauss   Vienna Philharmonic Orchestra Krauss
No Stereo

LXT 2966   Gold : **£ 25**   Silver : £15
Various   Russian Music   Suisse Romande Orchestra   Ansermet
No Stereo

LXT 2967   Gold : **£ 50**   Silver : £15
BRUCKNER   Symphony No.3
Vienna Philharmonic Orchestra   Knappertsbusch
No Stereo

LXT 2968   Gold : **£ 30**   Silver : £25
BOCCHERINI / HAYDN   Cello Concerto in Bbmaj, Concerto in Dmaj
Fournier   Stuttgart Chamber Orchestra   Munchinger
No Stereo

LXT 2969   Gold : **£ 18**   Silver : £6
Various   Piano Recital   Raucea
No Stereo

LXT 2970   Gold : **£ 100**   Silver : £50
TCHAIKOVSKY   Concerto in Dmaj. For Violin and Orchestra
Elman   London Philharmonic Orchestra   Boult
No Stereo

LXT 2971   Gold : **£ 20**   Silver : £10
LISZT   Music of Liszt   Katin
No Stereo

LXT 2972   Gold : **£ 8**   Silver : £4
HANDEL   Water Music, Royal Fireworks
Concertgebauw Orchestra of Amsterdam   Van Beinum
No Stereo

LXT 2973   Gold : **£8**   Silver : £3
MAHLER   Symphony No.1
Vienna Philharmonic Orchestra   Kubelik
No Stereo

LXT 2974   Gold : **£6**   Silver : £2
Various   Guitar Recital   Yepes
No Stereo

LXT 2975   Gold : **£20**   Silver : £16
TAVARES / PADEREWSKI Concerto in Brazilian forms for Piano &
Orchestra   Blumenthal   London Symphony Orchestra   Fistoulari
No Stereo

LXT 2976   Gold : **£8**   Silver : £6
SABARICH   The Trumpet Vol.II (LX3132 is Vol.I)   Menardi
No Stereo

LXT 2977   Gold : **£6**   Silver : £2
WALTON   Façade   Pears
English Opera Group Ensemble   Collins
No Stereo

LXT 2978   Gold : **£75**   Silver : £40
BERKELEY   Violin Sonatina, Variation for Solo Violin   Grinke
No Stereo

LXT 2979   Gold : **£8**   Silver : £5
NIELSEN   Flute Concerto   Danish State Radio Orchestra Jensen
No Stereo

LXT 2980   Gold : **£8**   Silver : £5
NIELSEN   Symphony No.5, Maskarade Overture
Danish State Radio Orchestra   Jensen
No Stereo

LXT 2981   Gold : **£10**   Silver : £6
BRITTEN   Sinfonia da Requiem
Danish State Radio Orchestra   Britten
No Stereo

LXT 2982   Gold : **£25**   Silver : £15
GLAZUNOV / RIMSKY-KORSAKOV   Stenka Razin, Antar
Suisse Romande Orchestra   Ansermet
No Stereo

LXT 2983   Gold : **£15**   Silver : £10
SCHUBERT   Octet Op.166   Vienna Octet
No Stereo

LXT 2984   Gold : **£10**   Silver : £8
HAYDN   Symphony No.100, Symphony No.102
London Philharmonic Orchestra   Solti
No Stereo

LXT 2985   Gold : **£40**   Silver : £10
SCHUMANN   Symphony No.3, Ov Scherzo Finale Op 52
Paris Conservatoire Orchestra   Schuricht
No Stereo

LXT 2986-7   (==== Not Issued ====)

LXT 2988   Gold : **£10**   Silver : £4
HANDEL   Water Music   Boyd Neel Orchestra
No Stereo

LXT 2989   Gold : **£2**   Silver : £1
HANDEL   Messiah (Highlights)   Vyvyan
London Philharmonic Orchestra   Boult
No Stereo

LXT 2990   Gold : **£8**   Silver : £2
MOZART   Concerto in A for Clarinet, BbMaj. For Bassoon
De Peyer   London Symphony Orchestra   Collins
No Stereo

LXT 2991   Gold : **£6**   Silver : £3
STRAUSS   Johann & Josef Vienna Philharmonic Krauss
No Stereo

LXT 2992-4   Gold : **£25**   Silver : £15
VERDI   La Traviata   Tebaldi
St. Cecilia Academy, Rome   Pradelli
No Stereo

LXT 2995-7 Gold : **£25** Silver : £15
PUCCINI Manon Lescaut Tebaldi
St. Cecilia Academy, Rome Pradelli
No Stereo

LXT 2998 Gold : **£20** Silver : £15
SCHUBERT Symphony No.5, Symphony No.8
Vienna Philharmonic Orchestra Bohm
No Stereo

LXT 2999 Gold : **£30** Silver : £10
DVORAK Cello Concerto Fournier
Vienna Philharmonic Orchestra Kubelik
No Stereo

LXT 5000-2 Gold : **£10** Silver : £6
MENDELSSOHN Elijah Proctor
London Philharmonic Orchestra Krips
No Stereo

LXT 5003 Gold : **£20** Silver : £10
DUKAS / RACHMANINOV La Peri, Isle of the Dead
Paris Conservatoire Orchestra Ansermet
No Stereo

LXT 5004 Gold : **£8** Silver : £3
DUKAS / HONNEGER / RAVEL Sorcerer's Apprentice, Bolero, Etc.
Paris Conservatoire Orchestra Ansermet
No Stereo

LXT 5005 Gold : **£14** Silver : £5
AUBER Overtures Paris Conservatoire Orchestra Wolf
No Stereo

LXT 5006-8 Gold : **£30** Silver : £8
VERDI Rigoletto Del Monaco
St. Cecilia Academy, Rome Erede
No Stereo

LXT 5009-11 Gold : **£30** Silver : £8
VERDI Otello Tebaldi
St. Cecilia Academy, Rome Erede
No Stereo

LXT 5012 Gold : **£20** Silver : £10
KREISLER Homage to Kreisler Campoli
No Stereo

LXT 5013 Gold : **£10** Silver : £6
MOZART / STRAUSS Concerto No.14, Burleske Guilda
London Symphony Orchestra Collins
No Stereo

LXT 5014 Gold : **£15** Silver : £8
ELGAR Violin Concerto Campoli
London Philharmonic Orchestra Boult
No Stereo

LXT 5015 Gold : **£4** Silver : £2
Various English Music London Philharmonic Orchestra Boult
No Stereo

LXT 5016 Gold : **£30** Silver : £10
DIABELLI Variations Backhaus
No Stereo

LXT 5017 Gold : **£10** Silver : £4
STRAUSS Recital Arabella Capriccio Ari Schoeffler
Vienna Philharmonic Orchestra Hollreiser
No Stereo

LXT 5018 Gold : **£5** Silver : £2
DELIBES Lakme Excerpts Robin
Opera Comique Chorus & Orchestra Sebastien
No Stereo

LXT 5019 Gold : **£15** Silver : £3
RAVEL L'Enfants et Les Sortilege Danco
Suisse Romande Orchestra Ansermet
Stereo Issue : SXL2212

LXT 5020 Gold : **£8** Silver : £4
HANDEL 6 Concerto Grossi Boyd Neel Orchestra
No Stereo

LXT 5021   Gold : **£ 5**   Silver : £3
GOUNOD   Romeo & Juliet (Highlights)   Micheau
French National Opera Chorus & Orchestra   Erede
No Stereo

LXT 5022   Gold : **£ 12**   Silver : £8
BORODIN   Symphony No.2 & 3, Igor Overture
Suisse Romande Orchestra   Ansermet
No Stereo

LXT 5023   Gold : **£ 20**   Silver : £10
SCHUBERT   Leider   Souzay
No Stereo

LXT 5024   Gold : **£ 20**   Silver : £6
DEBUSSY   Le Martyre de Saint Sebastien   Danco
Suisse Romande Orchestra   Ansermet
No Stereo

LXT 5025   Gold : **£ 10**   Silver : £6
LISZT   Piano Concerto No.1 & 2   Kempff
London Symphony Orchestra   Fistoulari
No Stereo

LXT 5026   Gold : **£ 35**   Silver :
WAGNER   Tristan, Gotterdammerung
Paris Conservatoire Orchestra   Schuricht
No Stereo

LXT 5027   Gold : **£ 20**   Silver : £10
BRAHMS   String Quartet No.1, String Quartet No.2   Vegh Quartet
No Stereo

LXT 5028   Gold : **£ 4**   Silver : £2
WALTON   Music of Walton   London Philharmonic Orchestra   Boult
No Stereo

LXT 5029   Gold : **£ 4**   Silver : £2
BACH   Preludes & Fugue   Richter
Stereo Issue : SXL2219

LXT 5030   Gold : **£14**   Silver : £8
BIZET   Symphony No.1, Patrie Overture
Suisse Romande Orchestra   Ansermet
No Stereo

LXT 5031   Gold : **£6**   Silver : £3
RAVEL   Ravel Songs   Danco
Suisse Romande Orchestra   Ansermet
No Stereo

LXT 5032   Gold : **£8**   Silver : £6
MOZART   Quartet for Clarinet & Strings   Vienna Octet
No Stereo

LXT 5033   Gold : **£15**   Silver : £5
Various   Operetta Recital   Gueden   Vienna State Opera
No Stereo

LXT 5034   Gold : **£12**   Silver : £8
BERLIOZ / MASSENET   Faust excerpts, Werther excerpts   Jobin
London Symphony Orchestra   Fistoulari
No Stereo

LXT 5035   Gold : **£12**   Silver : £8
ROUSSEL   The Spiders Banquet Op.17, Petite Suite Op.39
Suisse Romande Orchestra   Ansermet
No Stereo

LXT 5036   Gold : **£3**   Silver : £2
BACH   A Musical Offering
Stuttgart Chamber Orchestra   Munchinger
Stereo Issue : SXL2204

LXT 5037   Gold : **£15**   Silver : £6
CHOPIN   Works By Chopin Magaloff
No Stereo

LXT 5038-9   Gold : **£6**   Silver : £2
BRITTEN   The Turn of the Screw   Pears
English Opera Group   Britten
No Stereo

LXT 5040   Gold : **£8**   Silver : £6
HAYDN   Symphony No.88, Symphony No.101
Vienna Philharmonic Orchestra   Munchinger
No Stereo

LXT 5041-3   Gold : **£16**   Silver : £12
HANDEL   Concerto Grossi   Boyd Neel Orchestra
No Stereo

LXT 5044   Gold : **£80**   Silver : £30
MOZART   Violin Concerto No.3 & 6   Ferras
Stuttgart Chamber Orchestra   Munchinger
No Stereo

LXT 5045-8   Gold : **£35**   Silver : £20
MOUSSORGSKY Khovanchina   Tzveych
Belgrade National Opera   Baranovich
No Stereo

LXT 5049-53   Gold : **£40**   Silver : £30
BORODIN   Prince Igor   Popovich
Belgrade National Opera   Danon
No Stereo

LXT 5054-6   Gold : **£35**   Silver : £20
MOUSSORGSKY Boris Godounov   Changalovich
Belgrade National Opera   Baranovich
No Stereo

LXT 5057   Gold : **£15**   Silver : £10
SLAVENSKI   Sinfonia Orienta
Belgrade National Orchestra   Baranovich
No Stereo

LXT 5058   Gold : **£20**   Silver : £15
LHOTKA / BARANOVICH   Devil, Gingerbread Heart
Zagreed Nat. Orchestra, Belgrade Nat. Orch.   Lhotka, Zdravkovich
No Stereo

LXT 5059   Gold : **£8**   Silver : £5
BARTOK / KODALY   Music for Strings
London Philharmonic Orchestra   Solti
No Stereo

LXT 5060   Gold : **£10**   Silver : £6
BRITTEN   St. Nicholas   Aldeburgh Festival Orchestra   Britten
No Stereo

LXT 5061   Gold : **£50**   Silver : £35
HOLMBOE / NIELSON   String Quartet Op.47, String Quartet Op.5
Musica-Vitalis Quartet
No Stereo

LXT 5062   Gold : **£50**   Silver : £15
BLOCH   Voice in Wilderness, Schelmo   Nelsova
Suisse Romande Orchestra   Ansermet
No Stereo

LXT 5063   Gold : **£10**   Silver : £6
GLUCK / GRETRY   Ballet Suite No.2, Ballet Suite
New Symphony Orchestra   Irving
No Stereo

LXT 5064   (==== Not Issued ====)

LXT 5065-6   Gold : **£30**   Silver : £10
BRUCKNER / WAGNER   Symphony No.4, Siegfried Iydll
Vienna Philharmonic Orchestra   Knappertsbusch
No Stereo

LXT 5067   Gold : **£15**   Silver : £5
PUCCINI / VERDI Puccini & Verdi Arias   Del Monaco
No Stereo

LXT 5068   Gold : **£150**   Silver : £80
BEETHOVEN   Violin Concerto   Elman
London Philharmonic Orchestra   Solti
No Stereo

LXT 5069   Gold : **£20**   Silver : £10
GERSHWIN   Rhapsody in Blue, Piano Concerto in F   Katchen
No Stereo

LXT 5070   Gold : **£10**   Silver : £8
DIABELLI / FURSTENAU   Trio for Flute, Viola & Guitar, Suite for Flute &
Guitar   Birkelund
No Stereo

LXT 5071   Gold : **£25**   Silver : £15
BLOCH   String Quartet 1   Griller Quartet
No Stereo

LXT 5072   Gold : **£25**   Silver : £15
BLOCH   String Quartet 2   Griller Quartet
No Stereo

LXT 5073   Gold : **£25**   Silver : £15
BLOCH   String Quartets 3 & 4   Griller Quartet
No Stereo

LXT 5074   Gold : **£10**   Silver : £6
MOZART   Serenade No.4 K203
New Symphony Orchestra   Maag
No Stereo

LXT 5075   Gold : **£30**   Silver : £15
PAGANINI   Violin Concertos No.1 & 2   Ricci
London Symphony Orchestra   Collins
No Stereo

LXT 5076   Gold : **£12**   Silver : £6
VERDI / PUCINNI Verdi & Pucinni Excerpts   Tebaldi
St. Cecilia Academy, Rome   Erede
No Stereo

LXT 5077   Gold : **£80**   Silver : £30
BRAHMS   Cello Sonatas 1,2   Fournier, Backhaus
No Stereo

LXT 5078   Gold : **£150**   Silver : £80
MOZART   Violin Concerti No.4 & 5   Elman
New Symphony Orchestra   Krips
No Stereo

LXT 5079-80   Gold : **£20**   Silver : £15
DVORAK / TCHAIKOVSKY   Slavonic Dances, Romeo & Juliet
Vienna Philharmonic Orchestra   Kubelik
No Stereo

LXT 5081   Gold : **£20**   Silver : £12
BARTOK / MULLER   Divertemento, Symphonia No.2
Zurich Chamber Orchestra   Stoutz
No Stereo

LXT 5082   Gold : **£4**   Silver : £2
RIMSKY-KORSAKOV   Scheherazade
Suisse Romande Orchestra   Ansermet
Stereo Issue : SXL2086

LXT 5083   Gold : **£8**   Silver : £6
SIBELIUS   Symphony No.5, Night Ride & Sunrise
London Symphony Orchestra   Collins
No Stereo

LXT 5084   Gold : **£8**   Silver : £5
SIBELIUS   Symphony No.6, Pelleas excerpts
London Symphony Orchestra Collins
No Stereo

LXT 5085-7   Gold : **£25**   Silver : 16
MOZART   Magic Flute (Die Zauberflote)   Gueden
Vienna Philharmonic Orchestra   Bohm
Stereo Issue : SXL2215-7

LXT 5088-92   Gold : **£45**   Silver : £15
MOZART   The Marriage Of Figaro   Danco, Siepi
Vienna Philharmonic Orchestra   Kleiber
Stereo Issue : SXL2087-90

LXT 5093   Gold : **£20**   Silver : £10
CHOPIN   Sonata No.2 & 3   Katchen
No Stereo

LXT 5094   Gold : **£8**   Silver : £6
BEETHOVEN   Septet in Eb   Vienna Octet
No Stereo

LXT 5095   Gold : **£8**   Silver : £6
BRITTEN   7 Michelangelo Sonnets, Winter words   Pears Britten
No Stereo

LXT 5096   Gold : **£25**   Silver : £12
Various   Operatic Arias   Siepi
St. Cecilia Academy, Rome   Erede
No Stereo

LXT 5097   Gold : **£20**   Silver : £12
OBOUSSIER / GEISER   Antigone, Symphonia   Cavelti
Suisse Romande Orchestra   Ansermet
No Stereo

LXT 5098   Gold : **£8**   Silver : £6
STRAVINSKY   Oedipus Rex   Haefliger
Suisse Romande Orchestra   Ansermet
No Stereo

LXT 5099   Gold : **£8**   Silver : £3
TCHAIKOVSKY   Suite No.3   Paris Conservatoire Orchestra   Boult
No Stereo

LXT 5100   Gold : **£12**   Silver : £8
MASSENET   Sceans   Paris Conservatoire Orchestra   Wolff
No Stereo

LXT 5101-2   Gold : **£30**   Silver : £20
LISZT   Faust Symphony   Paris Conservatoire Orchestra   Argenta
No Stereo

LXT 5103-6   Gold : **£50**   Silver : £20
MOZART   Don Giovanni   Gueden
Vienna Philharmonic Orchestra   Krips
Stereo Issue : SXL2117-20

LXT 5107-9   Gold : **£50**   Silver : £25
MOZART   Cosi Fan Tutte   Della Casa
Vienna Philharmonic Orchestra   Bohm
No Stereo

LXT 5110   Gold : **£5**   Silver : £2
BACH   Toccata & Fugue   Richter
Stereo Issue : SXL2219

LXT 5111   Gold : **£14**   Silver : £8
MOZART   Symphony No.34 & 38
Vienna Philharmonic Orchestra   Bohm
No Stereo

LXT 5112   Gold : **£10**   Silver : £5
MOZART   Divertment No.15 Vienna Octet
No Stereo

LXT 5113   Gold : **£150**   Silver : £80
GRIEG   Violin Sonatas No.1 & 3   Elman
No Stereo

LXT 5114   Gold : **£10**   Silver : £3
LALO   Namouna Ballet Suites 1 & 2
London Philharmonic Orchestra   Martinon
No Stereo

LXT 5115   Gold : **£8**   Silver : £6
STRAVINSKY   Firebird Suisse Romande Orchestra   Ansermet
Stereo Issue : SXL2017

LXT 5116-7   Gold : **£20**   Silver : £10
DEBUSSY   Preludes   Guilda
No Stereo

LXT 5118   Gold : **£12**   Silver : £6
HONEGGER   Symphony No.3, Song of Joy
Paris Conservatoire Orchestra   Denzler
No Stereo

LXT 5119   Silver: **£80**
Various   Encores   Elman
No Stereo

LXT 5120   Silver: **£16**
SCHUMANN   Noveletten   Blanchard
No Stereo

LXT 5121   Silver: **£10**
MOZART   Serinade No.10 Suisse Romande Orchestra   Ansermet
No Stereo

LXT 5122   Silver: £16
CHOPIN   Nocturnes Vol.I Nos.1 - 10   Katin
No Stereo

LXT 5123   Silver: £15
MOZART   Piano Concerto No.27, Sonata No.11   Backhaus
Vienna Philharmonic Orchestra   Bohm
Stereo Issue : SXL2214

LXT 5124   Silver: £6
MOZART   Symphony No.33 & 40
Vienna Philharmonic Orchestra   Munchinger
No Stereo

LXT 5125   Silver: £20
TCHAIKOVSKY Symphony No.4   Suisse Romande Orchestra   Argenta
Stereo Issue : SXL2015

LXT 5126   Silver: £80
BEETHOVEN   Violin Sonata No.5 & 9   Elman
No Stereo

LXT 5127   Silver: £16
Various   Opera Excerpts   Del Monaco
St. Cecilia Academy, Rome   Erede
No Stereo

LXT 5128-30   Silver: £15
PUCCINI   Turandot   Tebaldi
St. Cecilia Academy, Rome   Erede
Stereo Issue : SXL2078-80

LXT 5131-4   Silver: £20
VERDI   La Forza del Destino   Tebaldi
St. Cecilia Academy, Rome   Pradelli
Stereo Issue : SXL2069-72

LXT 5135   Silver: £8
HAYDN / BACH / MOZART / DITTERS   Music from 18th Century
Danish Radio Chamber Orchestra   Woldike
No Stereo

LXT 5136   Silver: **£14**
VERDI   Operatic Choruses Del Monaco
St. Cecilia Academy, Rome   Erede
No Stereo

LXT 5137   Silver: **£10**
ROSSINI   Rossini Overtures London Symphony Orchestra Gamba
No Stereo

LXT 5138   Silver: **£12**
MOZART   Piano Concerto No.25 & 26   Guilda
No Stereo

LXT 5139   (==== Not Issued ====)

LXT 5142   Silver: **£6**
LISZT   Mephisto Waltz, Etc.
Paris Conservatoire Orchestra   Munchinger
No Stereo

LXT 5143   Silver: **£60**
VAUGHAN WILLIAMS / BENJAMIN   Violin Sonatina, Violin Sonata
Grinke
No Stereo

LXT 5144   Silver: **£25**
HAYDN   Piano Sonatas   Long
No Stereo

LXT 5145   Silver: **£15**
MOZART   Piano Concerto No.13 & 20   Katchen
No Stereo

LXT 5146-8   Silver: **£10**
DONIZETTI   La Favorita   Poggi
Maggio Musicale Florentino   Erede
No Stereo

LXT 5149   Silver: **£15**
ROSSINI   William Tell   London Philharmonic Orchestra Martinon
No Stereo

LXT 5150-2   Silver: **£90**
WAGNER   Flying Dutchman   Uhde
Beyruth Festival Orchestra & Chorus   Keilberth
No Stereo

LXT 5153   Silver: **£8**
Various   Contempory Music for Strings
Stuttgart Chamber Orchestra   Munchinger
No Stereo

LXT 5154   Silver: **£15**
STRAVINSKY   Piano Concerto, Capriccio for Piano & Orch.
Magaloff   Suisse Romande Orchestra   Ansermet
No Stereo

LXT 5155-7   Silver: **£10**
DONIZETTI   L'Elisir d'Amour   Di Stefano
Maggio Musicale Florentino   Pradelli
No Stereo

LXT 5158   Silver: **£10**
FAURE   Requiem   Danco
Suisse Romande Orchestra   Ansermet
Stereo Issue : SXL2211

LXT 5159-1   Silver: **£30**
TCHAIKOVSKY   Eugene Onegin   Vershivich
Belgrade National Opera   Danon
No Stereo

LXT 5162   Silver: **£16**
BERLIOZ   Overtures   Paris Conservatoire Orchestra   Wolff
No Stereo

LXT 5163   Silver: **£6**
BRITTEN   The Little Sweep   Pears   English Opera Group   Britten
No Stereo

LXT 5164   Silver: **£10**
LISZT / TCHAIKOVSKY   Hungarian Fantasia, Piano Concerto No.1
Katchen   London Symphony Orchestra   Gamba
No Stereo

LXT 5165   Silver: **£16**
GRIEG / FALLA   Piano Concerto, Nights in the Garden of Spain
Curzon   London Symphony Orchestra   Fistoulari
No Stereo

LXT 5166   Silver: **£35**
BLISS   Violin Concerto, Theme and Variations   Campoli
No Stereo

LXT 5167   Silver: **£40**
MOZART   Fantasia & Sonata in Cmin, Rondo, Sonata No.10 Amin.
Backhaus
No Stereo

LXT 5168   (==== Not Issued ====)

LXT 5169   Silver: **£10**
STRAVINSKY   Appolon Musagete, Renard
Suisse Romande Orchestra   Ansermet
No Stereo

LXT 5170   Silver: **£6**
BLISS   Colour Symphony, Intro & Allegro
London Symphony Orchestra   Bliss
No Stereo

LXT 5171   Silver: **£6**
Various   Gregorian Chant   St. Pierre de Solesme Abbey Choir
No Stereo

LXT 5172   Silver: **£12**
GOUNOD / SCHUBERT   Recital   Poulteau Wind Ensemble
No Stereo

LXT 5173-6   Silver: **£35**
GLINKA   Ivan Susanin or Life for the Czar   Changalovich
Belgrade National Opera   Danon
No Stereo

LXT 5177   Silver: **£8**
MOZART / SCHUBERT   Divertmento No.11, Five Minuets, German
dances   Stuttgart Chamber Orchestra   Munchinger
No Stereo

LXT 5178   Silver: **£10**
RACHMANINOV   Piano Concerto No.2   Curzon
London Philharmonic Orchestra   Boult
No Stereo

LXT 5179   (==== Not Issued ====)

LXT 5180-4   Silver: **£10**
STRAUSS   Die Frau ohne Schatten   Hopf
Vienna Philharmonic Orchestra   Bohm
No Stereo

LXT 5185   Silver: **£5**
BACH   Concerti in Amin for Organ BWV593   Demessieux
No Stereo

LXT 5186   Silver: **£6**
TCHAIKOVSKY Francesca da Rimini, Capriccio Italien
London Symphony Orchestra   Collins
No Stereo

LXT 5187   Silver: **£8**
BEETHOVEN   Piano Sonata No.23, 32   Katchen
No Stereo

LXT 5188   Silver: **£7**
Various   Demonstration Record Vol.5   Mule
Quatuor de Saxophones
No Stereo

LXT 5189-92   Silver: **£10**
TCHAIKOVSKY Queen of Spades   Belgrade National Opera Baranovich
No Stereo

LXT 5193-7   Silver: **£20**
RIMSKY-KORSAKOV   The Snow Maiden Jankovich
Belgrade National Opera   Baranovich
No Stereo

LXT 5198-9   Silver: **£10**
BACH   Brandenburg Concerto No.1 - 6
Stuttgart Chamber Orchestra   Munchinger
No Stereo

LXT 5200   Silver: **£15**
BOCCHERINI   Quartets and Trios   Carmirelli Quartet
No Stereo

LXT 5201   Silver: **£16**
MENDELSSOHN Piano Concerto No.1 & 2   Katin
London Symphony Orchestra   Collins
No Stereo

LXT 5202   Silver: **£5**
Various   Opera Excerpts   Del Monaco
Stereo Issue : SXL2122

LXT 5203   Silver: **£12**
BACH   Harpsichord Concerto in D, Concerto for 2 Harpsichords
Richter   Ansbach Bach Festival Ensemble
No Stereo

LXT 5204   Silver: **£10**
BEETHOVEN / HAYDN   Trio Op.87, Piano Trio No.1   Trio di Trieste
No Stereo

LXT 5205-10   Silver: **£15**
WAGNER   Gotterdammerung   Flagstad
Norwegian Radio Chorus, Oslo Philharmonic   Fjeldsted
No Stereo

LXT 5211-3   Silver: **£10**
LULLY   Bourgeois Gentilhomme
Paris Collegium Musicum   Douatte
No Stereo

LXT 5214   Silver: **£10**
BRAHMS   Symphony No.4
Vienna Philharmonic Orchestra   Kubelik
Stereo Issue : SXL2206

LXT 5215   Silver:
BEETHOVEN   Symphony No.3
Concertgebauw Orchestra of Amsterdam   Kleiber
No Stereo

LXT 5216   Silver: **£ 12**
SCHUMANN / WOLF   Recital   Souzay
New Symphony Orchestra   Bonneau
No Stereo

LXT 5217   Silver: **£ 5**
DELIBES   Coppelia, Sylvia
Paris Conservatoire Orchestra   Desormiere
No Stereo

LXT 5218   Silver: **£ 5**
Various   Spanish & Portugese Keyboard Music   Blumenthal
No Stereo

LXT 5219   Silver: **£ 35**
MOZART   Piano Sonata No.4, 7 & 12   Spagnolo
No Stereo

LXT 5220   Silver: **£ 5**
Various   Operatic Recital   Tebaldi
Stereo Issue : SXL2043

LXT 5221   Silver: **£ 7**
Various   Demonstration Record Vol.6   Mule
Quatuor de Saxophones
No Stereo

LXT 5222   Silver: **£ 80**
BRUCH   Violin Concerto   Elman
London Philharmonic Orchestra   Boult
No Stereo

LXT 5223-5   Silver: **£ 16**
LEONCAVALLO / MASCAGNI   I Pagliacci, Cavalleria Rusticana
Monaco   St. Cecilia Academy, Rome   Erede
No Stereo

LXT 5231   (==== Not Issued ====)

LXT 5232   Silver: **£ 14**
BEETHOVEN   Symphony No.1, Symphony No.8
Suisse Romande Orchestra   Ansermet
No Stereo

LXT 5233   Silver: **£ 8**
STRAVINSKY   Song of the Nightingale
Suisse Romande Orchestra   Ansermet
Stereo Issue : SXL2188

LXT 5234   Silver: **£ 6**
ROUSSEL   Symphony No.3 & 4
Suisse Romande Orchestra   Ansermet
No Stereo
LXT 5235-7   (═══ Not Issued ═══)

LXT 5238   Silver: **£ 16**
CHOPIN   Nocturnes Vol.II Nos.11 – 20   Katin
No Stereo

LXT 5239   Silver: **£ 35**
STRAUSS   Don Juan, Death & Transfiguration
Paris Conservatoire Orchestra   Knappertsbusch
No Stereo

LXT 5240   Silver: **£ 10**
GLAZUNOV   The Seasons   Paris Conservatoire Orchestra   Wolff
Stereo Issue : SXL2141

LXT 5241   Silver: **£ 5**
TCHAIKOVSKY   Symphony No.5   Paris Conservatoire Orchestra   Solti
No Stereo

LXT 5242   Silver: **£ 12**
MOZART   Operatic Recital   Gueden
No Stereo

LXT 5243   (═══ Not Issued ═══)

LXT 5244   Silver: **£ 10**
BERLIOZ / CHAUSSON   Benvenuto Cellini Ov., Symphony Op,20
Suisse Romande Orchestra   Denzler
No Stereo

LXT 5245   Silver: **£ 5**
TCHAIKOVSKY   Symphony No.2   Paris Conservatoire Orchestra   Solti
No Stereo

LXT 5246   Silver: **£14**
CHARPENTIER   Impressions D'Italie Paris Conservatoire Orchestra Wolff
No Stereo

LXT 5247   Silver: **£8**
Various   Ballad Recital   Thomas
No Stereo

LXT 5248   Silver: **£8**
Various   Scottish Songs   Thomas
No Stereo

LXT 5249   Silver: **£12**
WAGNER   Wesendonck Lieder etc   Flagstad
Vienna Philharmonic Orchestra   Knappertsbusch
No Stereo

LXT 5250   Silver: **£12**
Various   Recital   Borkh
No Stereo

LXT 5251   Silver: **£6**
Various   Gregorian Chant St. Pierre de Solesme Abbey Choir
No Stereo

LXT 5252   Silver: **£50**
KODALY / REGER / BACH   Sonata, Suite No.2 for
unaccompanied Cello   Nelsova
No Stereo

LXT 5253   Silver: **£10**
BEETHOVEN / MOZART Ghost Trio, Trio No.4   Trio di Trieste
No Stereo

LXT 5254   Silver: **£2**
Spoken Word   Poems read by Peggy Ashcroft
No Stereo

LXT 5255-6   Silver: **£20**
BRUCKNER / WAGNER Symphony No.5, Gotterdammerung Excerpts
Vienna Philharmonic Orchestra   Knappertsbusch
No Stereo

LXT 5257   Silver: **£50**
MOZART / SCHUBERT   Symphony 35, Symphony 8
Vienna Philharmonic Orchestra   Schuricht
No Stereo

LXT 5258   Silver: **£25**
Various   Leider Recital   Della Casa
No Stereo

LXT 5259   Silver: **£40**
KHACHATURIAN   Violin Concerto   Ricci
London Symphony Orchestra   Fistoulari
No Stereo

LXT 5260-2   Silver: **£15**
VERDI   Il Trovatore   Tebaldi
Maggio Musicale Florentino   Erede
Stereo Issue : SXL2129-31

LXT 5263   Silver: **£10**
SCHUBERT / SCHUMANN   Recital   Flagstad
No Stereo

LXT 5264   Silver: **£12**
GRIEG   Recital   Flagstad
No Stereo

LXT 5265   Silver: **£10**
Various   Recital   Flagstad
No Stereo

LXT 5266-7   (==== Not Issued ====)

LXT 5268   Silver: **£50**
BEETHOVEN   Works for Cello & Piano   Nelsova
No Stereo

LXT 5269   Silver: **£10**
Various   French Operatic Arias   Souzay
New Symphony Orchestra   Bonneau
No Stereo

LXT 5270   Silver: **£30**
BRAHMS   Violin & Piano Sonatas No.2 & 5   Ricci, Katchen
No Stereo

LXT 5271   Silver: **£25**
FRESCOBALDI / PETRASSI   Quattro Pezzi, Concerto No.1
St. Cecilia Academy, Rome   Previtali
No Stereo

LXT 5272   Silver: **£12**
Various   Songs and Arias   Tebaldi
No Stereo

LXT 5273-6   Silver: **£10**
GLUCK   Alceste   Flagstad
Gerrant Jones Orchestra   Jones
No Stereo

LXT 5277   Silver: **£15**
HANDEL / MOZART   Arias   Della Casa
Vienna Philharmonic Orchestra   Krips
No Stereo

LXT 5278   Silver: **£16**
CASELLA / RESPIGHI   La Giara, Pines of Rome   Luzi
St. Cecilia Academy, Rome   Previtali
No Stereo

LXT 5279   Silver: **£6**
ELGAR   The Wand of Youth
London Philharmonic Orchestra   Van Beinum
No Stereo

LXT 5280   Silver: **£12**
SCHUMANN / WEBER   Piano Concerto Op.54, Konzertstuck Op.79
Gulda   Vienna Philharmonic Orchestra   Andreae
No Stereo

LXT 5281-2   (==== Not Issued ====)

LXT 5283-5   Silver: **£15**
ROSSINI   Barber of Seville   Simionato
Maggio Musicale Florentino   Erede
No Stereo

LXT 5286   (===== Not Issued =====)

LXT 5287   Silver: **£6**
Various   Trumpet Music   Menardi   Paris Sextour
No Stereo

LXT 5288   Silver: **£15**
Various   Orchestral Highlights from the Opera
Maggio Musicale Florentino   Gavannali
No Stereo

LXT 5289   Silver: **£12**
Various   Operatic Recital   Cerquetti
Maggio Musicale Florentino   Gavannali
No Stereo

LXT 5290   Silver: **£8**
DVORAK   Symphony No.2
Vienna Philharmonic Orchestra   Kubelik
No Stereo

LXT 5291   Silver: **£2**
DVORAK   Symphony No.9
Vienna Philharmonic Orchestra   Kubelik
Stereo Issue : SXL2005

LXT 5292   Silver: **£10**
BRAHMS   Symphony No.1
Vienna Philharmonic Orchestra   Krips
No Stereo

LXT 5293   Silver: **£10**
MOZART   Quintet in EbMaj. Trio in EbMaj.   Panhoffer
Vienna Octet
No Stereo

LXT 5294　　Silver: **£ 10**
SPOHR　　Octet　　Vienna Octet
No Stereo

LXT 5295-6　　Silver: **£ 4**
Spoken Word　　Reading from Dickens
No Stereo

LXT 5297　　Silver: **£ 6**
TCHAIKOVSKY　Symphony No.3　London Philharmonic Orchestra　Boult
No Stereo

LXT 5298-00　　(==== Not Issued ====)

LXT 5301　　Silver: **£ 5**
Various　　The Clarinet Vol.6　　　　Delecluse
No Stereo

LXT 5302　　Silver: **£ 30**
PAGANINNI / SAINT-SAINS　　Violin Concerto, Violin Concerto No.3
Campoli　London Symphony Orchestra　　　Gamba
No Stereo

LXT 5303　　Silver: **£ 80**
Various　　Suites　　　Elman
No Stereo

LXT 5304　　Silver: **£ 80**
Various　　Showpieces　　Elman
No Stereo

LXT 5305　　Silver: **£ 8**
BARTOK　　Concert for Orchestra
Suisse Romande Orchestra　　　Ansermet
No Stereo

LXT 5306　　Silver: **£ 15**
TCHAIKOVSKY　Symphony No.6　Suisse Romande Orchestra　Ansermet
No Stereo

LXT 5307　　Silver: **£ 12**
Various　Operatic Recital　Corena　Suisse Romande Orchestra　Walker
No Stereo

LXT 5308   Silver: **£ 5**
BRAHMS   Piano Recital   Backhaus
Stereo Issue : SXL2222

LXT 5309   Silver: **£ 4**
BACH   English Suite 6, French Suite 5   Backhaus
Stereo Issue : SXL2205

LXT 5310   (═══ Not Issued ═══)

LXT 5311   Silver: **£ 10**
RIMSKY-KORSAKOV   Russian Easter Festival
Suisse Romande Orchestra   Ansermet
Stereo Issue : SXL2221

LXT 5312   Silver: **£ 10**
HAYDN   Symphony No.45, Symphony No.55
Aldeburgh Festival Orchestra   Britten
No Stereo

LXT 5313   Silver: **£ 25**
TCHAIKOVSKY   Violin Concerto   Campoli
London Symphony Orchestra   Argenta
Stereo Issue : SXL2029

LXT 5314   Silver: **£ 5**
VAUGHAN WILLIAMS   Symphony No.8 Philharmonia Orchestra Boult
Stereo Issue : SXL2207

LXT 5315   (═══ Not Issued ═══)

LXT 5316   Silver: **£ 10**
BACH / HANDEL   Recital   Flagstad
London Philharmonic Orchestra   Boult
No Stereo

LXT 5317   Silver: **£ 15**
Various   Recital   Zeani
Maggio Musicale Florentino   Gavannali
No Stereo

LXT 5318-20   Silver: **£ 12**
CHOPIN   Mazurkas (complete)   Magaloff
No Stereo

LXT 5321-2   Silver: **£ 15**
HONEGGER / STRAVINSKY   Roi David, Soldiers Tale   Danco
Suisse Romande Orchestra   Ansermet
No Stereo

LXT 5323   Silver: **£ 8**
MOZART   Piano Sonatas   Katchen
No Stereo

LXT 5324   Silver: **£ 15**
Various   Recital Broadcast by Radio Norway 1949   Ferrier
No Stereo

LXT 5325   Silver: **£ 15**
Various   Adventure in Sound
London Symphony Orchestra   Gamba
No Stereo

LXT 5326   Silver: **£ 10**
Various   An Evening at the Chicago Lyric Opera   Tebaldi
Chicargo Lyric Opera   Solti
No Stereo

LXT 5327   Silver: **£ 15**
GRIEG   Norwegen Songs   Flagstad
No Stereo

LXT 5328   (===== Not Issued ====)

LXT 5329   Silver: **£ 8**
WOLF / STRAUSS   Recital of Wolf & Strauss Songs   Flagstad
No Stereo

LXT 5330   Silver: **£ 8**
LISZT   Piano Concerto No.1 & 2   Katchen
London Philharmonic Orchestra   Argenta
Stereo Issue : SXL2097

LXT 5331   Silver: **£10**
BRAHMS / WOLF   Leider Recital   Cavelti
No Stereo

LXT 5332   Silver: **£5**
Various   The Bassoon Vol.1
No Stereo

LXT 5333   Silver: **£15**
Various   Espana !   London Symphony Orchestra   Argenta
Stereo Issue : SXL2020

LXT 5334   Silver: **£10**
MENDELSSOHN / BRUCH   Violin Concerto   Ricci
London Symphony Orchestra   Gamba
Stereo Issue : SXL2006

LXT 5335   (==== Not Issued ====)

LXT 5336-7   Silver: **£8**
BRITTEN   Prince of the Pagodas   Pears
Royal Opera House, Covent Garden   Britten
No Stereo

LXT 5338   Silver: **£40**
GRANADOS   Goyescas   Spanish National Orchestra   Argenta
No Stereo

LXT 5339   Silver: **£10**
BRAHMS   Symphony No.2
Vienna Philharmonic Orchestra   Kubelik
Stereo Issue : SXL2059

LXT 5340   (==== Not Issued ====)

LXT 5341   Silver: **£5**
ROSSINI-RESPIEGHI / DUCAS   La Boutique, L'apprenti Sorcier
Israel Philharmonic Orchestra   Solti
Stereo Issue : SXL2007

LXT 5342-3   Silver: **£15**
DELIBES   Coppelia   Suisse Romande Orchestra   Ansermet
Stereo Issue : SXL2084-5

LXT 5344   Silver: **£12**
MENDELSSOHN   Midsummer Nights Dream
London Symphony Orchestra   Maag
Stereo Issue : SXL2060

LXT 5345   Silver: **£12**
BRAHMS   Recital   Flagstad
No Stereo

LXT 5346   Silver: **£10**
STEREO TEST RECORD   Microgroove Frequency Test Record
No Stereo

LXT 5347   Silver: **£8**
SCHUMANN   Symphony No.1, Symphony No.4
London Symphony Orchestra   Krips
Stereo Issue : SXL2223

LXT 5348   Silver: **£25**
DEBUSSY   Images Pour Orchestre
Suisse Romande Orchestra   Argenta
No Stereo

LXT 5349-50   (==== Not Issued ====)

LXT 5351   Silver: **£10**
DEBUSSY   La Boite a Joujoux, Printemps
Suisse Romande Orchestra   Ansermet
Stereo Issue : SXL2136

LXT 5352   Silver: **£10**
BEETHOVEN   Violin Concerto   Campoli
London Symphony Orchestra   Krips
No Stereo

LXT 5353   Silver: **£8**
BEETHOVEN   Piano.Concerto No.3   Backhaus
Vienna Philharmonic Orchestra   Bohm
No Stereo

LXT 5354 Silver: **£8**
BEETHOVEN Piano.Concerto No.4 Backhaus
Vienna Philharmonic Orchestra Krauss
No Stereo

LXT 5355 Silver: **£8**
BEETHOVEN Piano.Concerto No.5 Backhaus
Vienna Philharmonic Orchestra Krauss
No Stereo

LXT 5356 Silver: **£10**
MOZART Symphony No.39, Symphony No.40
London Symphony Orchestra Krips
No Stereo

LXT 5357 Silver: **£14**
FALLA Three Cornered Hat
Suisse Romande Orchestra Ansermet
No Stereo

LXT 5358 Silver: **£6**
BEETHOVEN Symphony No.5
Concertgebauw Orchestra of Amsterdam Kleiber
No Stereo

LXT 5359 Silver: **£8**
BEETHOVEN Symphony No.6
Concertgebauw Orchestra of Amsterdam Kleiber
No Stereo

LXT 5360 Silver: **£8**
BEETHOVEN Symphony No.7
Concertgebauw Orchestra of Amsterdam Kleiber
No Stereo

LXT 5361 Silver: **£5**
BEETHOVEN / MENDELSSOHN Symphony No.8, Symphony No.4
Vienna Philharmonic Orchestra Bohm, Krips
No Stereo

LXT 5362-3 Silver: **£10**
BEETHOVEN Symphony No.9 Gueden VPO Kleiber
No Stereo

LXT 5364   Silver: **£15**
BRAHMS   Piano Concerto No.1   Backhaus
Vienna Philharmonic Orchestra   Bohm
No Stereo

LXT 5365   Silver: **£12**
BRAHMS   Piano Concerto No.2   Backhaus
Vienna Philharmonic Orchestra   Schuricht
No Stereo

LXT 5366   Silver: **£10**
BRAHMS   Symphony No.1
Concertgebauw Orchestra of Amsterdam   Van Beinum
No Stereo

LXT 5367   Silver: **£10**
BRAHMS   Symphony No.3
Concertgebauw Orchestra of Amsterdam   Szell
No Stereo

LXT 5368   Silver: **£10**
BRAHMS   Symphony No.4   London Symphony Orchestra   Krips
No Stereo

LXT 5369   Silver: **£5**
HAYDN   Symphony No.96, Symphony No.104
Vienna Philharmonic Orchestra   Munchinger
No Stereo

LXT 5370   Silver: **£10**
TCHAIKOVSKY   Symphony No.6
Paris Conservatoire Orchestra   Kleiber
No Stereo

LXT 5371   Silver: **£5**
TCHAIKOVSKY   Nutcracker Suites No.1 & 2
Paris Conservatoire Orchestra   Fistoulari
No Stereo

LXT 5372   Silver: **£4**
STRAUSS   Graduation Ball
New Symphony Orchestra   Fistoulari
No Stereo

LXT 5373   Silver: £20
TCHAIKOVSKY Violin Concerto   Ricci
New Symphony Orchestra   Sargent
No Stereo

LXT 5374   Silver: £3
DOHNANYI / RACHMANINOV   Nursery Variations, Paganini
Rhapsodies   Katchen   London Philharmonic Orchestra   Boult
No Stereo

LXT 5375   Silver: £6
STRAVINSKY   Petrouchka   Suisse Romande Orchestra   Ansermet
No Stereo

LXT 5376   Silver: £8
MOZART   Famous Overtures of Mozart
London Symphony Orchestra   Kripps
No Stereo

LXT 5377   Silver: £20
VIVALDI   Four Seasons   Barchet
Stuttgart Chamber Orchestra   Munchinger
No Stereo

LXT 5378   Silver: £4
ADAM   Giselle (Highlights)   Paris Opera Orchestra   Blareau
No Stereo

LXT 5379   Silver: £6
HANDEL   Water Music, Royal Fireworks
London Symphony Orchestra   Van Beinum
No Stereo

LXT 5380   Silver: £12
PROKOFIEV / BIZET   Classical Symphony, Symphony No.1
Suisse Romande Orchestra   Ansermet
No Stereo

LXT 5381   Silver: £10
SCHUBERT   Symphony No.5, Symphony No.8
Vienna Philharmonic Orchestra   Bohm
No Stereo

LXT 5382   Silver: **£5**
BACH / HANDEL   Arias   Ferrier
London Philharmonic Orchestra   Boult
Stereo Issue : SXL2234

LXT 5383   Silver: **£5**
HANDEL   Arias & Choruses from Messiah   Vyvyan, Proctor
London Philharmonic Orchestra   Boult
No Stereo

LXT 5384   Silver: **£3**
PUCCINI   Madame Butterfly (Highlights)   Tebaldi
St. Cecilia Academy, Rome   Erede
No Stereo

LXT 5385   Silver: **£3**
VERDI   Aida (Highlights)   Tebaldi
St. Cecilia Academy, Rome   Erede
No Stereo

LXT 5386   Silver: **£3**
PUCCINI   Tosca (Highlights) Tebaldi
St. Cecilia Academy, Rome   Erede
No Stereo

LXT 5387   Silver: **£3**
PUCCINI   La Boheme (Highlights)   Tebaldi
St. Cecilia Academy, Rome   Erede
No Stereo

LXT 5388   Silver: **£8**
STRAVINSKY   Rite of Spring   Suisse Romande Orchestra   Ansermet
Stereo Issue : SXL2042

LXT 5389-90   Silver: **£15**
WAGNER   Walkure Act III   Flagstad
Vienna Philharmonic Orchestra   Solti
Stereo Issue : SXL2031-2

LXT 5391   Silver: **£8**
BEETHOVEN   Emperor Concerto   Curzon
Vienna Philharmonic Orchestra   Knappertsbusch
Stereo Issue : SXL2002

LXT 5392   Silver: **£6**
Various   Great Sacred Songs Flagstad
Vienna Philharmonic Orchestra   Boult
Stereo Issue : SXL2049

LXT 5393   (=== Not Issued ===)

LXT 5394   Silver: **£20**
BRAHMS   Brahms Overtures
Vienna Philharmonic Orchestra   Knappertsbusch
No Stereo

LXT 5395   Silver: **£6**
MAHLER   Kindertotenlieder   Flagstad
Vienna Philharmonic Orchestra   Boult
Stereo Issue : SXL2224

LXT 5396   (=== Not Issued ===)

LXT 5397   Silver: **£3**
VERDI   Rigoletto (Highlights)   Del Monaco
St. Cecilia Academy, Rome   Erede
No Stereo

LXT 5398   Silver: **£15**
RIMSKY-KORSAKOV   Christmas Eve, Sadko etc
Suisse Romande Orchestra   Ansermet
Stereo Issue : SXL2113

LXT 5399   Silver: **£3**
VERDI   La Traviata (Highlights)   Tebaldi
St. Cecilia Academy, Rome   Pradelli
No Stereo

LXT 5400-2   Silver: **£15**
PONCHIELLI   La Gioconda   Cerquetti
Maggio Musicale Florentino   Gavazeni
Stereo Issue : SXL2225-7

LXT 5403-6   Silver: **£8**
STRAUSS   Arabella   Vienna Philharmonic Orchestra   Solti
Stereo Issue : SXL2050-3

LXT 5407   Silver: **£2**
Various   Opera Excerpts   Bergonzi
St. Cecilia Academy, Rome   Gavazenni
Stereo Issue : SXL2048

LXT 5408   (==== Not Issued ====)

LXT 5409   Silver: **£4**
TCHAIKOVSKY Swan Lake (Highlights)
London Symphony Orchestra   Fistoulari
No Stereo

LXT 5410   Silver: **£10**
Various   Songs & Arias   Tebaldi
No Stereo

LXT 5411-2   Silver: **£10**
GIORDANO   Andre Chenier   Del Monaco
St. Cecilia Academy, Rome   Gavazzeni
Stereo Issue : SXL2208-10

LXT 5413   Silver: **£20**
SCHUMANN / SCHUBERT   Waldscenen, Moments Musicaux Backhaus
No Stereo

LXT 5414   Silver: **£8**
MOZART   Jupiter & Haffner Symphonies
Israel Philharmonic Orchestra   Krips
Stereo Issue : SXL2220

LXT 5415   Silver: **£10**
Various   French Music   Guilda
No Stereo

LXT 5416   Silver: **£6**
BRITTEN   A Boy was Born, Rejoice the Lamb
English Opera Group   Britten
No Stereo

LXT 5417   Silver: **£10**
BRAHMS   Symphony No.1
Vienna Philharmonic Orchestra   Kubelik
Stereo Issue : SXL2013

LXT 5418   Silver: **£10**
HAYDN   Symphony No.94, Symphony No.99
Vienna Philharmonic Orchestra   Krips
Stereo Issue : SXL2098

LXT 5419   Silver: **£4**
BRAHMS   Symphony No.3
Vienna Philharmonic Orchestra   Kubelik
Stereo Issue : SXL2104

LXT 5420   Silver: **£10**
Various   Vienna Holiday
Vienna Philharmonic Orchestra   Knappertsbusch
Stereo Issue : SXL2016

LXT 5421   Silver: **£10**
Various   Overtures in HiFi
Paris Conservatoire Orchestra   Wolff
Stereo Issue : SXL2008

LXT 5422   Silver: **£10**
CHOPIN / DELIBES   Les Sylphides
Paris Conservatoire Orchestra   Maag
Stereo Issue : SXL2044

LXT 5423   Silver: **£15**
BERLIOZ   Symphonie Fantastique
Paris Conservatoire Orchestra   Argenta
Stereo Issue : SXL2009

LXT 5424   Silver: **£8**
DEBUSSY / RAVEL   Mer Prelude Apres Midi Rhapsody
Suisse Romande Orchestra   Ansermet
No Stereo

LXT 5425   Silver: **£6**
STRAVINSKY   Petrouchka   Suisse Romande Orchestra   Ansermet
Stereo Issue : SXL2011

LXT 5426   Silver: **£15**
RAVEL / DEBUSSEY   La Mer L'oye Nocturnes
Suisse Romande Orchestra   Ansermet
Stereo Issue : SXL2062

LXT 5427-8 (==== Not Issued ====)

LXT 5429-30 Silver: **£12**
WAGNER Die Walkure Act I Flagstad
Vienna Philharmonic Orchestra Knappertsbusch
Stereo Issue : SXL2074-5

LXT 5431 Silver: **£10**
Various Memories of Vienna
Vienna Philharmonic Orchestra Krips
Stereo Issue : SXL2047

LXT 5432 Silver: **£2**
STRAUSS Johann Strauss Concert
Vienna Philharmonic Orchestra Boskovsky
Stereo Issue : SXL2082

LXT 5433 Silver: **£6**
SCHUBERT Trout Quintet Curzon Vienna Octet
Stereo Issue : SXL2110

LXT 5434 Silver: **£20**
BRAHMS Piano Concerto No.2 Curzon Knappertsbusch
No Stereo

LXT 5435-7 (==== Not Issued ====)

LXT 5438 Silver: **£10**
SCHUMANN Fantasia Op 17, Arabeske Katchen
No Stereo

LXT 5439 Silver: **£20**
SCHUBERT / SCHUMANN Wanderer fantasia, Carnaval Katchen
No Stereo

LXT 5440 (==== Not Issued ====)

LXT 5441 Silver: **£12**
GRIEG Peer Gynt London Symphony Orchestra Fjelstad
Stereo Issue : SXL2012

LXT 5442 (==== Not Issued ====)

LXT 5443   Silver: £15
MOZART   Don Giovanni (Highlights)   Gueden
Vienna Philharmonic Orchestra   Krips
No Stereo

LXT 5444   Silver: £6
SIBELIUS   Song Recital   Flagstad
London Symphony Orchestra   Fjelstad
Stereo Issue : SXL2030

LXT 5445   Silver: £4
CHOPIN   Recital   Kempff
Stereo Issue : SXL2081

LXT 5446   Silver: £30
PROKOFIEV   Violin Concerto No.1 & 2   Ricci
Suisse Romande Orchestra   Ansermet
No Stereo

LXT 5447   Silver: £5
RACHMANINOV / TCHAIKOVSKY Piano Concerto, Concert Fantasia
Katin   London Philharmonic Orchestra   Boult
Stereo Issue : SXL2034

LXT 5448-9   Silver: £4
LEHAR   Merry Widow   Gueden Vienna State Opera Stolz
Stereo Issue : SXL2022-3

LXT 5450   Silver: £3
VERDI   Othello (Highlights)   Tebaldi
St. Cecilia Academy, Rome   Erede

LXT 5451   Silver: £4
CHOPIN   Recital   Kempff
Stereo Issue : SXL2024

LXT 5452   Silver: £4
CHOPIN   Sonata No.2   Kempff
Stereo Issue : SXL2025

LXT 5453   Silver: **£8**
MENDELSSOHN / BRUCH   Violin Concerto, Scottish Fantasia
Campoli   London Symphony Orchestra   Argenta
Stereo Issue : SXL2026

LXT 5454   Silver: **£12**
DEBUSSY   Jeux Enfants   Suisse Romande Orchestra   Ansermet
Stereo Issue : SXL2027

LXT 5455   Silver: **£15**
SCHUBERT   Octet   Vienna Octet
Stereo Issue : SXL2028

LXT 5456   Silver: **£7**
MASSENET / MEYERBEER   Le Cid, Les Patiners
Israel Philharmonic Orchestra   Martinon
Stereo Issue : SXL2021

LXT 5457   Silver: **£25**
HAYDN   Piano Sonatas   Backhaus
No Stereo

LXT 5458   Silver: **£6**
Various   Opera Excerpts   Simionato
St. Cecilia Academy, Rome   Previtali
No Stereo

LXT 5459   Silver: **£2**
MOZART   The Marriage Of Figaro (Highlights)
Vienna Philharmonic Orchestra   Kleiber
Stereo Issue : SXL2035

LXT 5460   Silver: **£30**
Various   Virtuoso Showpieces   Ricci
No Stereo

LXT 5461   Silver: **£4**
BIZET   Carmen   Suisse Romande Orchestra   Ansermet
Stereo Issue : SXL2037

LXT 5462   (==== Not Issued ====)

LXT 5463-5   Silver: £ 6
PUCCINI   Fanciulla Del West   Tebaldi
St. Cecilia Academy, Rome   Capuana
Stereo Issue : SXL2039-41

LXT 5466-7   (==== Not Issued ====)

LXT 5468-70   Silver: £ 8
PUCCINI   Madama Butterfly   Tebaldi
St. Cecilia Academy, Rome   Serafin
Stereo Issue : SXL2054-6

LXT 5471   Silver: £ 15
SCHUBERT   Symphony No.9   London Symphony Orchestra Krips
Stereo Issue : SXL2045

LXT 5472   Silver: £ 5
MOZART / TCHAIKOVSKY   Eine Kleine Nacht Musik, Serenade
For Strings   Israel Philharmonic Orchestra   Solti
Stereo Issue : SXL2046

LXT 5473   (==== Not Issued ====)

LXT 5474-5   Silver: £ 5
SMETANA   Ma Vlast   Vienna Philharmonic Orchestra   Kubelik
Stereo Issue : SXL2064-5

LXT 5476   (==== Not Issued ====)

LXT 5477   Silver: £ 5
MENDELSSOHN / SCHUBERT   Italian Synphony, Symphony No.5
Israel Philharmonic Orchestra   Solti
Stereo Issue : SXL2067

LXT 5478   Silver: £ 12
WAGNER   Great Scenes   London
London Symphony Orchestra   Knappertsbusch
Stereo Issue : SXL2068

LXT 5479   (==== Not Issued ====)

LXT 5480   Silver: **£4**
ROSSINI   Barber of Seville (Highlights)   Simionato
Maggio Musicale Florentino   Erede
No Stereo

LXT 5481   Silver: **£3**
VERDI   La Forza del Destino (Highlights)   Tebaldi
St. Cecilia Academy, Rome   Pradelli
No Stereo

LXT 5482   Silver: **£10**
BEETHOVEN   Piano Concerto 4   Backhaus
Vienna Philharmonic Orchestra   Schmitt-Isserstedt
Stereo Issue : SXL2010

LXT 5483   Silver: **£10**
TCHAIKOVSKY   Symphony No.6 Pathetique
Vienna Philharmonic Orchestra   Martinon
Stereo Issue : SXL2004

LXT 5484   Silver: **£10**
BRAHMS   Variations and Fugue on a theme by Handel   Katchen
No Stereo

LXT 5485   Silver: **£18**
Various   Italy   Di Stephano
Stereo Issue : SXL2083

LXT 5486   (==== Not Issued ====)

LXT 5487-9   Silver: **£12**
BOITO   Mefistofele   Tebaldi
St. Cecilia Academy, Rome   Serafin
Stereo Issue : SXL2094-6

LXT 5490   Silver: **£6**
RACHMANINOV   Piano Concerto No.2   Katchen
London Symphony Orchestra   Solti
Stereo Issue : SXL2076

LXT 5491   (==== Not Issued ====)

LXT 5492   Silver: **£10**
RODRIGO / FALLA   Guitar Conc, Nights in the Garden of Spain
Yepes   National Orchestra of Spain   Argenta
Stereo Issue : SXL2091

LXT 5493-4   Silver: **£20**
TCHAIKOVSKY Nutcracker Suite   Suisse Romande Orchestra Ansermet
Stereo Issue : SXL2092-3

LXT 5495-7   Silver: **£12**
WAGNER   Das Rheingold   Flagstad
Vienna Philharmonic Orchestra   Solti
Stereo Issue : SXL2101-3

LXT 5498   Silver: **£4**
DONIZETTI   L'Elisir d'amore (Highlights)
Florence May Festival Orchestra   Pradelli
No Stereo

LXT 5499   Silver: **£15**
RAVEL / FALLA   Invitation to the dance
Paris Conservatoire Orchestra   Wolff
Stereo Issue : SXL2105

LXT 5500   Silver: **£10**
BEETHOVEN   Piano Concero No.3   Katchen
London Symphony Orchestra   Gamba
Stereo Issue : SXL2106

LXT 5501-2   Silver: **£20**
TCHAIKOVSKY Swan Lake   Suisse Romande Orchestra   Ansermet
Stereo Issue : SXL2107-8

LXT 5503   Silver: **£20**
TCHAIKOVSKY Symphony No.5   Vienna Philharmonic Orchestra Krips
Stereo Issue : SXL2109

LXT 5504   Silver: **£8**
Various Operatic Recital   Di Stefano   Tonhalle Orchestra   Patane
Stereo Issue : SXL2111

LXT 5505   Silver: **£ 12**
WEBER   Overtures   Suisse Romande Orchestra   Ansermet
Stereo Issue : SXL2112

LXT 5506   (==== Not Issued ====)

LXT 5507   Silver: **£ 4**
BEETHOVEN   Symphony No.4   Suisse Romande Orchestra Ansermet
Stereo Issue : SXL2116

LXT 5508   Silver: **£ 5**
BEETHOVEN   Symphony No.7 Vienna Philharmonic Orchestra Solti
Stereo Issue : SXL2121

LXT 5509   Silver: **£ 8**
PUCCINI   Operatic Recital   Zeani
St. Cecilia Academy, Rome   Patane
Stereo Issue : SXL2123

LXT 5510   Silver: **£ 5**
BEETHOVEN   Symphony No.5 Vienna Philharmonic Orchestra Solti
Stereo Issue : SXL2124

LXT 5511   Silver: **£ 3**
MOZART   Cosi fan tutte (Highlights)   Della Casa
Vienna Philharmonic Orchestra   Bohm
Stereo Issue : SXL2058

LXT 5512-3   Silver: **£ 12**
BACH   Brandendurg Concerto, Suite No.2 in D etc.
Stuttgart Chamber Orchestra   Munchinger
No Stereo SXL2125-7

LXT 5514   Silver: **£ 6**
ROSSINI Berganza Sings Rossini   Berganza
London Symphony Orchestra   Gibson
Stereo Issue : SXL2132

LXT 5515   Silver: **£ 8**
ADAM   Giselle   Paris Conservatoire Orchestra   Martinon
Stereo Issue : SXL2128

LXT 5516   Silver: **£ 20**
BACH   Chromatic Fantasia and Fugue in Dmin.Etc.   Katin
No Stereo

LXT 5517   Silver: **£ 10**
BERLIOZ   Music of Berlioz
Paris Conservatoire Orchestra   Martinon
Stereo Issue : SXL2134

LXT 5518   Silver: **£ 12**
MOZART   Symphony No.32, Symphony No.38
London Symphony Orchestra   Maag
Stereo Issue : SXL2135

LXT 5519   Silver: **£ 10**
VIVALDI   Four Seasons   Stuttgart Chamber Orchestra Munchinger
Stereo Issue : SXL2019

LXT 5520   Silver: **£ 2**
LEHAR   Merry Widow (Highlights)   Gueden
Vienna State Opera   Stolz
Stereo Issue : SXL2133

LXT 5521-3   Silver: **£ 5**
BRITTEN   Peter Grimes
Royal Opera House, Covent Garden Orchestra   Britten
Stereo Issue : SXL2150-2

LXT 5524   Silver: **£ 15**
STRAUSS   Also Sprach Zarathustra
Vienna Philharmonic Orchestra   Karajan
Stereo Issue : SXL2154

LXT 5525   Silver: **£ 8**
BEETHOVEN   Symphony No.5   Suisse Romande Orchestra Ansermet
Stereo Issue : SXL2003

LXT 5526   (=== Not Issued ===)

LXT 5527   Silver: **£ 30**
LALO / RAVEL   Symphonie Espagnole, Tzigane   Ricci
Vienna Philharmonic Orchestra   Ansermet
Stereo Issue : SXL2155

LXT 5528   Silver: **£5**
SCHUBERT   Symphony No.2, Symphony No.8
Vienna Philharmonic Orchestra   Munchinger
Stereo Issue : SXL2156

LXT 5529   Silver: **£12**
BEETHOVEN   Septet   Vienna Octet
Stereo Issue : SXL2157

LXT 5530   Silver: **£12**
BEETHOVEN   Quintet in Eflat op16   Vienna Octet
Stereo Issue : SXL2158

LXT 5531   Silver: **£3**
Various   Operatic Arias   Sutherland
Paris Conservatoire Orchestra   Santi
Stereo Issue : SXL2159

LXT 5532-4   Silver: **£20**
TCHAIKOVSKY   Sleeping Beauty   Suisse Romande Orchestra   Ansermet
Stereo Issue : SXL2160-2

LXT 5535   Silver: **£4**
STRAUSS   Vienna Carnival
Vienna Philharmonic Orchestra   Boskovsky
Stereo Issue : SXL2163

LXT 5536   Silver: **£12**
RAVEL   Daphnis & Chloe
London Symphony Orchestra   Monteux
Stereo Issue : SXL2164

LXT 5537   Silver: **£5**
BEETHOVEN   Symphony No.3   Vienna Philharmonic Orchestra   Solti
Stereo Issue : SXL2165

LXT 5538   Silver: **£8**
TCHAIKOVSKY   Symphony No.4
Paris Conservatoire Orchestra   Wolff
Stereo Issue : SXL2166

LXT 5539-41   Silver: **£8**
VERDI   Aida   Bergonzi
Vienna Philharmonic Orchestra   Karajan
Stereo Issue : SXL2167-9

LXT 5542-3   Silver: **£6**
PUCCINI   La Boheme   Tebaldi
St. Cecilia Academy, Rome   Serafin
Stereo Issue : SXL2170-1

LXT 5544   Silver: **£6**
WAGNER   Die Meistersinger von Nurnburg (Highlights)
Schoeffler   Vienna Philharmonic Orchestra   Knappertsbusch
No Stereo

LXT 5545   (=== Not Issued ===)

LXT 5546   Silver: **£10**
BRAHMS   Piano Concerto No.1   Katchen
London Symphony Orchestra   Monteux
Stereo Issue : SXL2172

LXT 5547   Silver: **£2**
GRIEG / FRANCK Piano Concerto, Symphonic Variations
Curzon   London Philharmonic Orchestra   Boult
Stereo Issue : SXL2173

LXT 5548   Silver: **£6**
SUPPE   Overtures   Vienna Philharmonic Orchestra   Solti
Stereo Issue : SXL2174

LXT 5549   Silver: **£2**
PUCCINI   Turandot (Highlights)   Tebaldi
St. Cecilia Academy, Rome   Erede
Stereo Issue : SXL2175

LXT 5550   Silver: **£2**
RACHMANINOV / DOHNANYI   Rhapsody On A Theme Of Paganini
Katchen   London Philharmonic Orchestra   Boult
Stereo Issue : SXL2176

LXT 5551   Silver: **£4**
WOLF-FERRARI   Music of Wolf-Ferrari
Paris Conservatoire Orchestra   Nello-Santi
Stereo Issue : SXL2177

LXT 5552   Silver: **£10**
BEETHOVEN   Piano Concertos 1, 2   Backhaus
Vienna Philharmonic Orchestra   Schmitt-Isserstedt
Stereo Issue : SXL2178

LXT 5553   Silver: **£10**
BEETHOVEN   Piano Concerto 5   Backhaus
Vienna Philharmonic Orchestra   Schmitt-Isserstedt
Stereo Issue : SXL2179

LXT 5554-5   Silver: **£10**
PUCCINI   Tosca   Tebaldi
St. Cecilia Academy, Rome   Pradelli
Stereo Issue : SXL2180-1

LXT 5556   Silver: **£20**
ROSSINI   Overtures   Paris Conservatoire Orchestra   Maag
Stereo Issue : SXL2182

LXT 5557   Silver: **£5**
LISZT   Dante Sonata   Katin
Stereo Issue : SXL2183

LXT 5558   Silver: **£4**
Various   Songs From Norway   Flagstad
London Symphony Orchestra   Fjelstad
Stereo Issue : SXL2145

LXT 5559   Silver: **£10**
WAGNER   Tristan & Isolde excerpts   Nilsson
Vienna Philharmonic Orchestra   Knappertsbusch
Stereo Issue : SXL2184

LXT 5560-1   Silver: **£14**
LEONCAVALLO I Pagliacci   Monaco
St. Cecilia Academy, Rome   Pradelli
Stereo Issue : SXL2185-6

LXT 5562   (═══ Not Issued ═══)

LXT 5563   Silver: **£12**
Various   Recital   Lichtegg
No Stereo

LXT 5564   Silver: **£4**
BRITTEN   Nocturne   London Symphony Orchestra   Britten
Stereo Issue : SXL2189

LXT 5565   Silver: **£6**
MUSSORGSKY   Pictures at an exhibition
Suisse Romande Orchestra   Ansermet
Stereo Issue : SXL2195

LXT 5566   Silver: **£6**
BEETHOVEN   Symphony No.6
Suisse Romande Orchestra   Ansermet
Stereo Issue : SXL2193

LXT 5567   Silver: **£3**
Various   Recital of Lute songs   Bream, Pears
Stereo Issue : SXL2191

LXT 5568   Silver: **£4**
BOITO   Mefistofele Highlights   Tebaldi
St. Cecilia Academy, Rome   Serafin
Stereo Issue : SXL2192

LXT 5569   Silver: **£20**
PAGANINI   24 Caprices   Ricci
Stereo Issue : SXL2194

LXT 5570   Silver: **£15**
MOZART   Serenata Notturna, Notturna 4 Or
London Symphony Orchestra   Maag
Stereo Issue : SXL2196

LXT 5571   Silver: **£25**
BIZET / SARASATE / SAINT SAINS Carmen Fantasie, Zigeunerweisen,
Rondo   Ricci   London Symphony Orchestra   Gamba
Stereo Issue : SXL2197

LXT 5572   Silver: £3
STRAUSS   Philharmonic Ball
Vienna Philharmonic Orchestra   Boskovsky
Stereo Issue : SXL2198

LXT 5573   Silver: 4
Various   The Instruments of the Orchestra
BBC Symphony Orchestra   Sargent
Stereo Issue : SXL2199

LXT 5574   Silver: £6
SCHUBERT   Die Schone Mullerin   Britten, Pears
Stereo Issue : SXL2200

LXT 5575   Silver: £4
PUCCINI   Madame Butterfly highlights Tebaldi
St. Cecilia Academy, Rome   Serafin
Stereo Issue : SXL2202

LXT 5576   Silver: £15
MAHLER   Das Lied von der Erde   Ferrier
Vienna Philharmonic Orchestra   Walter
No Stereo

LXT 5577   Silver: £8
PROKOFIEV   Peter and the Wolf   Henderson
London Symphony Orchestra   Katchen
Stereo Issue : SXL2218

LXT 5578   Silver: £5
HANDEL   Organ Concertos Vol.1   Richter
Stereo Issue : SXL2115

LXT 5579   Silver: £5
HANDEL   Organ Concertos Vol.2   Richter
Stereo Issue : SXL2187

LXT 5580   Silver: £5
HANDEL   Organ Concertos Vol.3   Richter
Stereo Issue : SXL2201

LXT 5581   Silver: **£8**
TCHAIKOVSKY   Swan Lake (Highlights)
Suisse Romande Orchestra   Ansermet
Stereo Issue : SXL2153

LXT 5582-3   (==== Not Issued ====)

LXT 5584   Silver: **£4**
BEETHOVEN   Symphony No.2   Suisse Romande Orchestra   Ansermet
Stereo Issue : SXL2228

LXT 5585   Silver: **£8**
MENDELSSOHN / SCHUBERT   Midsummer Nights Dream
Suisse Romande Orchestra   Ansermet
Stereo Issue : SXL2229

LXT 5586   Silver: **£3**
WAGNER   Highlights Das Rheingold, Die Walkure
Vienna Philharmonic Orchestra   Solti
Stereo Issue : SXL2230

LXT 5587   Silver: **£15**
RAVEL / PROKOFIEV   String Quartets   Carmirelli Quartet
Stereo Issue : SXL2231

LXT 5588   Silver: **£3**
SEARLE   Symphony No.1 London Philharmonic Orchestra   Boult
Stereo Issue : SXL2232

LXT 5589   Silver: **£5**
MOZART / HAYDN   Arias   Vyvyan
Haydn Orchestra   Newstone
Stereo Issue : SXL2233

LXT 5590   Silver: **£4**
BEETHOVEN   Symphony No.7, Fedelio Overture
Suisse Romande Orchestra   Ansermet
Stereo Issue : SXL2235

LXT 5591   Silver: **£6**
BRAHMS   Piano Concerto No.2   Katchen
London Symphony Orchestra   Ferencsik
Stereo Issue : SXL2236

LXT 5592   Silver: £4
STRAVINSKY   Symphony in C   Suisse Romande Orchestra   Ansermet
Stereo Issue : SXL2237

LXT 5593   Silver: £8
MOZART   Horn Concertos   Tuckwell
London Symphony Orchestra   Maag
Stereo Issue : SXL2238

LXT 5594   Silver: £10
Various   All Time Popular Favourites
Vienna Philharmonic Orchestra   Knappertsbusch
Stereo Issue : SXL2239

LXT 5595   Silver: £30
Various   Solo Violin recital   Ricci
Stereo Issue : SXL2240

LXT 5596   Silver: £20
BEETHOVEN   Piano Sonatas 21 Waldstein, 23 app   Backhaus
Stereo Issue : SXL2241

LXT 5597   Silver: £3
VERDI   Aida (Highlights)   Bergonzi
Vienna Philharmonic Orchestra   Karajan
Stereo Issue : SXL2242

LXT 5598   Silver: £10
ALBENIZ   Iberia, Turina   Suisse Romande Orchestra   Ansermet
Stereo Issue : SXL2243

LXT 5599   Silver: £4
BEETHOVEN   Symphony No.3   Suisse Romande Orchestra   Ansermet
Stereo Issue : SXL2244

LXT 5600   Silver: £6
Various   Classical Indian Music
Stereo Issue : SXL2245

LXT 5601   Silver: £16
MENDELSSOHN   Symphony No.3, Fingal's Cave
London Symphony Orchestra   Maag
Stereo Issue : SXL2246

LXT 5602   Silver: **£10**
MOZART   Concert Arias for Bass   Corena Quadri
Royal Opera House, Covent Garden Orchestra   Fernando
Stereo Issue : SXL2247

LXT 5603-7   (==== Not Issued ====)

LXT 5608   Silver: **£2**
PUCCINI   La Boheme (Highlights)   Tebaldi
St. Cecilia Academy, Rome   Serafin
Stereo Issue : SXL2248

LXT 5609   Silver: **£18**
BRAHMS / DVORAK   Hungarian, Slavonic Dances
Vienna Philharmonic Orchestra   Reiner
Stereo Issue : SXL2249

LXT 5610   Silver: **£2**
STRAUSS   Graduation Ball etc
Vienna Philharmonic Orchestra   Boskovsky
Stereo Issue : SXL2250

LXT 5611   Silver: **£8**
Various   Eighteenth Century Arias   Berganza
Royal Opera House, Covent Garden Orchestra   Gibson
Stereo Issue : SXL2251

LXT 5612   Silver: **£10**
BIZET   Jeux D'enfants   Paris Conservatoire Orchestra   Martinon
Stereo Issue : SXL2252

LXT 5613-5   Silver: **£8**
MASCAGNI / LEONCAVELLO   Cavalleria Rusticana, I Pagliacci
Simionato   St. Cecilia Academy, Rome   Serafin
Stereo Issue : SXL2253-5

LXT 5616   Silver: **£2**
Various   Art Of Prima Donna Pt1.   Sutherland
Royal Opera House, Covent Garden Orchestra   Molinari Pradelli
Stereo Issue : SXL2256

LXT 5617   Silver: **£2**
Various   Art Of Prima Donna Pt2.   Sutherland
Royal Opera House, Covent Garden Orchestra   Molinari Pradelli
Stereo Issue : SXL2257

LXT 5618   Silver: **£4**
PUCCINI   Tosca (Highlights)   Tebaldi
St. Cecilia Academy, Rome   Pradelli
Stereo Issue : SXL2258

LXT 5619   Silver: **£4**
BACH   Harpsichord Recital   Malcolm
Stereo Issue : SXL2259

LXT 5620   Silver: **£3**
STRAUSS   Till Eulenspiegel, Death and Transfiguration
Vienna Philharmonic Orchestra   Karajan
Stereo Issue : SXL2261

LXT 5621   Silver: **£6**
BEETHOVEN   Diabelli Variations   Katchen
Stereo Issue : SXL2262

LXT 5622   Silver: **£12**
Various   French Overtures
Suisse Romande Orchestra   Ansermet
Stereo Issue : SXL2263

LXT 5623   Silver: **£4**
STRAUSS   Der Rosenkavalier (Highlights)   Gueden
Vienna Philharmonic Orchestra   Kleiber
No Stereo

LXT 5624   Silver: **£3**
BRITTEN   Spring Symphony
Royal Opera House, Covent Garden Orchestra   Britten
Stereo Issue : SXL2264

LXT 5625   Silver: **£4**
CORELLI / GLUCK   Concerto Grosso 8, Chaconne etc
Stuttgart Chamber Orchestra   Munchinger
Stereo Issue : SXL2265

LXT 5626   Silver: £6
ROSSINI   Rossini Overtures London Symphony Orchestra Gamba
Stereo Issue : SXL2266

LXT 5627   Silver: £2
PUCCINI   Fanciulla del West (Highlights)   Tebaldi
St. Cecilia Academy, Rome   Capuana
Stereo Issue : SXL2267

LXT 5628   Silver: £5
RIMSKY-KORSAKOV / BORODIN Scheherazade, Polvonian Dances
Suisse Romande Orchestra   Ansermet
Stereo Issue : SXL2268

LXT 5629   Silver: £4
TCHAIKOVSKY / STRAUSS   Romeo & Juliet, Don Juan
Vienna Philharmonic Orchestra   Karajan
Stereo Issue : SXL2269

LXT 5630   Silver: £12
MOZART   Eine Kleine Nachmusik
Vienna Philharmonic Orchestra   Munchinger
Stereo Issue : SXL2270

LXT 5631   Silver: £5
Various   Operatic Recitals   Sciutti
Stereo Issue : SXL2271

LXT 5632   Silver: £4
MOZART   Haffner Serenade
Vienna Philharmonic Orchestra   Munchinger
Stereo Issue : SXL2272

LXT 5633   Silver: £12
RAVEL   Daphnis et Chloe
Suisse Romande Orchestra   Ansermet
Stereo Issue : SXL2273

LXT 5634   Silver: £8
BIZET   Symphony in C
Suisse Romande Orchestra   Ansermet
Stereo Issue : SXL2275

LXT 5635-7 (==== Not Issued ====)

LXT 5638 Silver: **£ 5**
MAHLER Symphony No.4
Concertgebouw Orchestra of Amsterdam Solti
Stereo Issue : SXL2276

LXT 5639 Silver: **£ 8**
STRAVINSKY Les Noces Symphony Of Psalms
Suisse Romande Orchestra Ansermet
Stereo Issue : SXL2277

LXT 5640 Silver: **£ 6**
FRANCK Piano Quintet Curzon Vienna Quartet
Stereo Issue : SXL2278

LXT 5641 Silver: **£ 15**
TCHAIKOVSKY / DVORAK Violin Concerto Ricci
London Symphony Orchestra Sargent
Stereo Issue : SXL2279

LXT 5642 Silver: **£ 6**
OFFENBACH / GOUNOD Gaite Parisienne, Faust
Royal Opera House, Covent Garden Orchestra Solti
Stereo Issue : SXL2280

LXT 5643-4 Silver: **£ 6**
MASCAGNI Cavalleria Rusticana Simionato
St. Cecilia Academy, Rome Serafin
Stereo Issue : SXL2281-2

LXT 5645 Silver: **£ 18**
BEETHOVEN Symphony No.9 Gueden
Vienna Philharmonic Orchestra Kleiber
No Stereo

LXT 5646 (==== Not Issued ====)

LXT 5647 Silver: **£ 8**
HAYDN Symphony No.44, Symphony No.48
Vienna Philharmonic Orchestra Munchinger
Stereo Issue : SXL2284

LXT 5648   Silver: **£6**
TCHAIKOVSKY   Scens from Swan Lake
Concertgebouw Orchestra of Amsterdam   Fistoulari
Stereo Issue : SXL2285

LXT 5649   Silver: **£10**
MOZART   Quartet No.20 & 22   Vienna Quartet
Stereo Issue : SXL2286

LXT 5650   Silver: **£8**
DEBUSSY / RAVEL   Symphony, Images, Iberia, Pavane
Suisse Romande Orchestra   Ansermet
Stereo Issue : SXL2287

LXT 5651   Silver: **£4**
STRAUSS   Thousand And One Nights
Vienna Philharmonic Orchestra   Boskovsky
Stereo Issue : SXL2288

LXT 5652   Silver: **£8**
DVORAK   Symphony No.9 Vienna Philharmonic Orchestra Kertesz
Stereo Issue : SXL2289

LXT 5653   Silver: **£4**
MOZART   Divertiment K136   Vienna Octet
Stereo Issue : SXL2290

LXT 5654   Silver: **£8**
FRANCK   Symphony in D   Suisse Romande Orchestra   Ansermet
Stereo Issue : SXL2291

LXT 5655   Silver: **£12**
PROKOFIEV / BORODIN / GLINKA Classical Symphony, etc.
Suisse Romande Orchestra   Ansermet
Stereo Issue : SXL2292

LXT 5656   Silver: **£6**
Various   Encores   Katchen
Stereo Issue : SXL2293

LXT 5657   Silver: **£2**
Various   Christmas with Leontyne Price   Price
Vienna Philharmonic Orchestra   Karajan
Stereo Issue : SXL2294

LXT 5658   Silver: **£4**
Various   Operetta Evergreens   Gueden
Stereo Issue : SXL2295

LXT 5659   Silver: **£15**
FALLA   Three Cornered Hat
Suisse Romande Orchestra   Ansermet
Stereo Issue : SXL2296

LXT 5660   Silver: **£8**
BRAHMS   Clarinet Quintet   Vienna Octet
Stereo Issue : SXL2297

LXT 5661   Silver: **£10**
BRITTEN / DEBUSSY   Cello Sonata in C#, Cello sonata in Dmin
Rostropovich   Britten
Stereo Issue : SXL2298

LXT 5662   Silver: **£15**
Various   Norwegian Hymns   Flagstad
No Stereo

LXT 5663   Silver: **£10**
Various   Art of Slobodskaya 1945-61   Slobodskaya
London Symphony Orchestra   Fistoulari
Stereo Issue : SXL2299

LXT 5664-5   Silver: **£14**
BACH   Orchestral Suites
Stuttgart Chamber Orchestra   Munchinger
Stereo Issue : SXL2300-1

LXT 5666   Silver: **£4**
HANDEL   Water Music, Royal Fireworks
London Symphony Orchestra   Szell
Stereo Issue : SXL2302

LXT 5667　　　Silver: **£5**
FAURE / DEBUSSY　　　Pelleas & Melisande, Petite Suite
Suisse Romande Orchestra　　　　　Ansermet
Stereo Issue : SXL2303

LXT 5668　　　Silver: **£3**
Various　　　On the Wings of Opera　　　Regina Resnik
Royal Opera House, Covent Garden Orchestra　　Downes
Stereo Issue : SXL2304

LXT 5669　　　Silver: **£3**
HOLST　　　The Planets　　Vienna Philharmonic Orchestra　　Karajan
Stereo Issue : SXL2305

LXT 5670　　　(==== Not Issued ====)

LXT 5671-2　　　Silver: **£16**
PROKOFIEV　　　Romeo & Juliet, Cinderella
Suisse Romande Orchestra　　　　　Ansermet
Stereo Issue : SXL2306-7

LXT 5673　　　Silver: **£4**
TCHAIKOVSKY / GRIEG　Nutcracker, Peer Gynt
Vienna Philharmonic Orchestra　　　Karajan
Stereo Issue : SXL2308

LXT 5674　　　Silver: **£2**
BRITTEN　　　Peter Grimes (Highlights)
Royal Opera House, Covent Garden Orchestra　　Britten
Stereo Issue : SXL2309

LXT 5675　　　Silver: **£10**
SCHUMANN　　　Dichterleibe　　　Brendel　　　　Wachter
Stereo Issue : SXL2310

LXT 5676　　　Silver: **£10**
MARTIN　　　Concerto for 7 Wind Instruments
Suisse Romande Orchestra　　　　　Ansermet
Stereo Issue : SXL2311

LXT 5677   Silver: **£ 12**
DEBUSSY / RAVEL   Prelude L'Apres Midi, Favanne
London Symphony Orchestra   Monteux
Stereo Issue : SXL2312

LXT 5678-81   (==== Not Issued ====)

LXT 5682   Silver: **£ 3**
HEROLD-LANCHBERRY   La Fille Mal Gardee
Royal Opera House Covent Garden Orchestra   Lanchberry
Stereo Issue : SXL2313

LXT 5683   Silver: **£ 4**
VERDI   Otello (Highlights)
Vienna Philharmonic Orchestra   Karajan
Stereo Issue : SXL2314

LXT 5684   Silver: **£ 2**
DONIZETTI   Lucia di Lammermoor
St. Cecilia Academy, Rome   Pritchard
Stereo Issue : SXL2315

LXT 5685   Silver: **£ 2**
HANDEL   Messiah (Highlights)
London Symphony Orchestra   Boult
Stereo Issue : SXL2316

LXT 6014   Silver: **£ 12**
BEETHOVEN   Diabelli Variations   Backhaus
No Stereo

LXT 6126   Silver: **£ 8**
Various   Recital   Teyte
No Stereo

LXT 6277-80   Silver: **£ 40**
Various   Vienna Philharmonic Festival
Vienna Philharmonic Orchestra   Knappertsbusch, Kleiber
No Stereo

Decca SXL 2000 series Stereophonic LP's

The Decca SXL 2000 series was first launched in 1958. The earliest labels, used throughout the entire SXL2000 series, are Black with silver lettering. A deep circular groove runs around the label, about 1.5cm in from the edge and the *words 'Original Recording by the Decca co. ltd. London'* are printed around the top of the label. The Decca logo, also in silver, is printed in large letters, with the FFSS circular logo printed above and the words 'Full Frequency Stereophonic Sound' filling a 1cm silver band running full width across the label just below it. These are identified as **WBg** (Wide band grooved) in the guide.

The second label looks very similar to the first, but the inner groove is no longer apparent and The words *'Made in England by the Decca co. ltd. London'* replace the *'Original Recording...'* text printed around the top of the label. This label was used on some later re-pressed SXL2000 records. These are shown as **WB** in the guide.

The third label sees the silver band reduce in size, the circular FFSS logo is removed and the Decca logo is replaced with a silver rectangular box with Decca printed inside. These labels are referred to as **NB** (Narrow Band) throughout the guide.

The earliest of many of the Decca WBg records prior to SXL2111, have a blue and white border on the reverse of the outer sleeve with the words *'Full Frequency Range Recording'* printed in Blue within the white sections and *'Full Frequency Stereophonic Sound'* printed in Blue within the Blue sections. The prices given in this guide for the relevant WBg records have assumed the Blue Border sleeve. In a sleeve without a blue border, the pricing should be reduced by about 15%.

SXL2001   WBg : **£45**   WB : £30   NB : £10
TCHAIKOVSKY   1812 Overture, Cappricio Italien
London Symphony Orchestra   Alwyn
Mono Issue : No LXT

SXL2002   WBg : **£60**   WB : £40   NB : £12
BEETHOVEN   Emperor Concerto Curzon
Vienna Philharmonic Orchestra   Knappertsbusch
Mono Issue : LXT 5391

SXL2003   WBg : **£75**   WB : £50   NB : £15
BEETHOVEN   Symphony No.5 Suisse Romande Orchestra Ansermet
Mono Issue : LXT 5525

SXL2004   WBg : **£80**   WB : £50   NB : £15
TCHAIKOVSKY   Symphony No.6 Pathetique
Vienna Philharmonic Orchestra   Martinon
Mono Issue : LXT 5483

SXL2005   WBg : **£30**   WB : £20   NB : £6
DVORAK   Symphony No.9 New World
Vienna Philharmonic Orchestra   Kubelik
Mono Issue : LXT 5291

SXL2006   WBg : **£80**   WB : £50   NB : £15
MENDELSSOHN / BRUCH   Violin Concerto Ricci
London Symphony Orchestra   Gamba
Mono Issue : LXT 5334

SXL2007   WBg : **£50**   WB : £35   NB : £10
ROSSINI-RESPIEGHI / DUCAS   La Boutique, L'apprenti Sorcier
Israel Philharmonic Orchestra   Solti
Mono Issue : LXT 5341

SXL2008   WBg : **£80**   WB : £50   NB : £15
Various   Overtures in HiFi
Paris Conservatoire Orchestra   Wolff
Mono Issue : LXT 5421

SXL2009   WBg : **£100**   WB : £65   NB : £20
BERLIOZ   Symphonie Fantastique
Paris Conservatoire Orchestra   Argenta
Mono Issue : LXT 5423

SXL2010   WBg : **£125**   WB : £80   NB : £25
BEETHOVEN   Piano Concerto 4   Backhaus
Vienna Philharmonic Orchestra   Schmitt-Isserstedt
Mono Issue : LXT 5482

SXL2011   WBg : **£90**   WB : £60   NB : £18
STRAVINSKY   Petrouchka   Suisse Romande Orchestra   Ansermet
Mono Issue : LXT 5425

SXL2012   WBg : **£125**   WB : £75   NB : £20
GRIEG   Peer Gynt   London Symphony Orchestra   Fjelstad
Mono Issue : LXT 5441

SXL2013   WBg : **£135**   WB : £90   NB : £25
BRAHMS   Symphony No.1
Vienna Philharmonic Orchestra   Kubelik
Mono Issue : LXT 5417

SXL2014   WBg : **£40**   WB : £20   NB : £8
GIORDANO   Andre Chenier (Highlights)   Tebaldi,
Del Monaco   St. Cecilia Academy, Rome   Gavazzeni
Mono Issue : No LXT

SXL2015   WBg : **£200**   WB : £125   NB : £35
TCHAIKOVSKY   Symphony No.4
Suisse Romande Orchestra   Argenta
Mono Issue : LXT 5125

SXL2016   WBg : **£160**   WB : £100   NB : £30
Various   Vienna Holiday
Vienna Philharmonic Orchestra   Knappertsbusch
Mono Issue : LXT 5420

SXL2017   WBg : **£45**   WB : £30   NB : £8
STRAVINSKY   Firebird   Suisse Romande Orchestra   Ansermet
Mono Issue : LXT 5115

SXL2018(==== Not Issued ====)

SXL2019   WBg : **£120**   WB : £75   NB : £25
VIVALDI   Four Seasons
Stuttgart Chamber Orchestra   Munchinger
Mono Issue : LXT 5519

SXL2020   WBg : **£150**   WB : £100   NB : £30
Various   Espana ! London Symphony Orchestra   Argenta
Mono Issue : LXT 5333

SXL2021   WBg : **£85**   WB : £55   NB : £15
MASSENET / MEYERBEER   Le Cid, Les Patiners
Israel Philharmonic Orchestra   Martinon
Mono Issue : LXT 5456

SXL2022-3   WBg : **£60**   WB : £40   NB : £10
LEHAR   Merry Widow Gueden Vienna State Opera   Stolz
Mono Issue : LXT 5448-9

SXL2024   WBg : **£60**   WB : £40   NB : £10
CHOPIN   Recital   Kempff
Mono Issue : LXT 5451

SXL2025   WBg : **£50**   WB : £30   NB : £8
CHOPIN   Sonata No.2   Kempff
Mono Issue : LXT 5452

SXL2026   WBg : **£45**   WB : £25   NB : £8
MENDELSSOHN / BRUCH   Violin Concerto, Scottish Fantasia
Campoli   London Symphony Orchestra   Argenta
Mono Issue : LXT 5453

SXL2027   WBg : **£225**   WB : £150   NB : £40
DEBUSSY   Jeux Enfants Suisse Romande Orchestra Ansermet
Mono Issue : LXT 5454

SXL2028   WBg : **£125**   WB : £80   NB : £25
SCHUBERT   Octet   Vienna Octet
Mono Issue : LXT 5455

SXL2029   WBg : **£250**   WB : £165   NB : £50
TCHAIKOVSKY Violin Concerto   Campoli
London Symphony Orchestra   Argenta
Mono Issue : LXT 5313

SXL2030   WBg : **£140**   WB : £90   NB : £30
SIBELIUS   Song Recital   Flagstad
London Symphony Orchestra   Fjelstad
Mono Issue : LXT 5444

SXL2031-2   WBg : **£125**   WB : £80   NB : £25
WAGNER   Walkure Act III   Flagstad
Vienna Philharmonic Orchestra   Solti
Mono Issue : LXT 5389-90

SXL2033(==== Not Issued ====)

SXL2034   WBg : **£40**   WB : £20   NB : £5
RACHMANINOV / TCHAIKOVSKY Piano Concerto, Concert Fantasia
Katin   London Philharmonic Orchestra   Boult
Mono Issue : LXT 5447

SXL2035   WBg : **£40**   WB : £20   NB : £5
MOZART   The Marriage Of Figaro (Highlights)
Vienna Philharmonic Orchestra   Kleiber
Mono Issue : LXT 5590

SXL2036(==== Not Issued ====)

SXL2037   WBg : **£60**   WB : £35   NB : £10
BIZET   Carmen   Suisse Romande Orchestra   Ansermet
Mono Issue : LXT 5461

SXL2038(==== Not Issued ====)

SXL2039-41   WBg : **£50**   WB : £30   NB : £10
PUCCINI   Fanciulla Del West   Tebaldi
St. Cecilia Academy, Rome   Capuana
Mono Issue : LXT 5463-5

SXL2042   WBg : **£100**   WB : £65   NB : £20
STRAVINSKY   Rite of Spring   Suisse Romande Orchestra   Ansermet
Mono Issue : LXT 5388

SXL2043   WBg : **£40**   WB : £20   NB : £6
Various   Operatic Recital   Tebaldi
Mono Issue : LXT 5220

SXL2044   WBg : **£80**   WB : £50   NB : £15
CHOPIN / DELIBES   Les Sylphides
Paris Conservatoire Orchestra   Maag
Mono Issue : LXT 5422

117

SXL2045   WBg : **£150**   WB : £100   NB : £25
SCHUBERT   Symphony No.9 London Symphony Orchestra   Krips
Mono Issue : LXT 5471

SXL2046   WBg : **£50**   WB : £30   NB : £8
MOZART / TCHAIKOVSKY   Eine Kleine Nacht Musik, Serenade
For Strings   Israel Philharmonic Orchestra   Solti
Mono Issue : LXT 5472

SXL2047   WBg : **£100**   WB : £60   NB : £20
Various   Memories of Vienna
Vienna Philharmonic Orchestra   Krips
Mono Issue : LXT 5431

SXL2048   WBg : **£50**   WB : £30   NB : £8
Various   Opera Excerpts   Bergonzi
St. Cecilia Academy, Rome   Gavazenni
Mono Issue : LXT5407

SXL2049   WBg : **£65**   WB : £40   NB : £10
Various   Great Sacred Songs   Flagstad
Vienna Philharmonic Orchestra   Boult
Mono Issue : LXT 5392

SXL2050-3   WBg : **£80**   WB : £50   NB : £12
STRAUSS   Arabella   Vienna Philharmonic Orchestra   Solti
Mono Issue : LXT 5403-6

SXL2054-6   WBg : **£75**   WB : £45   NB : £12
PUCCINI   Madama Butterfly   Tebaldi
St. Cecilia Academy, Rome   Serafin
Mono Issue : LXT 5468-70

SXL2057   WBg : **£80**   WB : £50   NB : £12
STEREO TEST RECORD   Microgroove Frequency Test Record
Mono Issue : LXT 5346

SXL2058   WBg : **£30**   WB : £12   NB : £3
MOZART   Cosi fan tutte (Highlights)   Della Cass
Vienna Philharmonic Orchestra   Bohm
Mono Issue : LXT 5511

SXL2059   WBg : **£100**   WB : £60   NB : £18
BRAHMS   Symphony No.2
Vienna Philharmonic Orchestra   Kubelik
Mono Issue : LXT 5339

SXL2060   WBg : **£100**   WB : £65   NB : £20
MENDELSSOHN   Midsummer Nights Dream
London Symphony Orchestra   Maag
Mono Issue : LXT 5344

SXL2061(==== Not Issued ====)

SXL2062   WBg : **£175**   WB : £125   NB : £40
RAVEL / DEBUSSEY   La Mer L'oye Nocturnes
Suisse Romande Orchestra   Ansermet
Mono Issue : LXT 5426

SXL2063(==== Not Issued ====)

SXL2064-5   WBg : **£45**   WB : £20   NB : £6
SMETANA   Ma Vlast   Vienna Philharmonic Orchestra   Kubelik
Mono Issue : LXT 5474-5

SXL2066(==== Not Issued ====)

SXL2067   WBg : **£60**   WB : £35   NB : £10
MENDELSSOHN / SCHUBERT   Italian Synphony, Symphony No.5
Israel Philharmonic Orchestra   Solti
Mono Issue : LXT 5477

SXL2068   WBg : **£120**   WB : £70   NB : £20
WAGNER   Great Scenes   London
London Symphony Orchestra   Knappertsbush
Mono Issue : LXT 5478

SXL2069-72   WBg : **£120**   WB : £70   NB : £20
VERDI   La Forza del Destino   Tebaldi
St. Cecilia Academy, Rome   Pradelli
Mono Issue : LXT 5131-4

SXL2073(==== Not Issued ====)

SXL2074-5   WBg : **£100**   WB : £65   NB : £20
WAGNER   Die Walkure Act I   Flagstad
Vienna Philharmonic Orchestra   Knappertsbush
Mono Issue : LXT 5429-30

SXL2076   WBg : **£55**   WB : £30   NB : £10
RACHMANINOV   Piano Concerto No.2   Katchen
London Symphony Orchestra   Solti
Mono Issue : LXT 5490

SXL2077   WBg : **£200**   WB : £140   NB : £45
SIBELIUS   Violin Concerto   Ricci
London Symphony Orchestra   Fjelstad
Mono Issue : No LXT

SXL2078-80   WBg : **£150**   WB : £100   NB : £30
PUCCINI   Turandot   Tebaldi
St. Cecilia Academy, Rome   Erede
Mono Issue : LXT 5128-30

SXL2081   WBg : **£70**   WB : £40   NB : £12
CHOPIN   Recital   Kempff
Mono Issue : LXT 5445

SXL2082   WBg : **£45**   WB : £25   NB : £8
STRAUSS   Johann Strauss Concert
Vienna Philharmonic Orchestra   Boskovsky
Mono Issue : LXT 5432

SXL2083   WBg : **£200**   WB : £140   NB : £45
Various   Italy   Giuseppi Di Stephano
Mono Issue : LXT 5485

SXL2084-5   WBg : **£160**   WB : £100   NB : £35
DELIBES   Coppelia   Suisse Romande Orchestra   Ansermet
Mono Issue : LXT 5342-3

SXL2086   WBg : **£45**   WB : £20   NB : £8
RIMSKY-KORSAKOV   Scheherezade
Paris Conservatoire Orchestra   Ansermet
Mono Issue : No LXT

SXL2087-90   WBg : **£400**   WB : £300   NB : £100
MOZART   Figaro   Danco, Siepi
Vienna Philharmonic Orchestra   Kleiber
Mono Issue : LXT 5088-91

SXL2091   WBg : **£140**   WB : £90   NB : £25
RODRIGO / FALLA   Guitar Concerto, Nights in the Garden of Spain
Yepes   National Orchestra of Spain   Argenta
Mono Issue : LXT 5492

SXL2092-3   WBg : **£160**   WB : £100   NB : £25
TCHAIKOVSKY   Nutcracker Suite
Suisse Romande Orchestra   Ansermet
Mono Issue : LXT 5493-4

SXL2094-6   WBg : **£200**   WB : £125   NB : £35
BOITO   Mefistofele   Tebaldi
St. Cecilia Academy, Rome   Serafin
Mono Issue : LXT 5487-9

SXL2097   WBg : **£100**   WB : £60   NB : £18
LISZT   Piano Concerto No.1 & 2   Katchen
London Philharmonic Orchestra   Argenta
Mono Issue : LXT 5330

SXL2098   WBg : **£100**   WB : £75   NB : £20
HAYDN   Symphony No.94 & 99
Vienna Philharmonic Orchestra   Krips
Mono Issue : LXT 5418

SXL2099   (==== Not Issued ====)

SXL2100   WBg : **£350**   WB : £250   NB : £100
LEIMER   Piano Concerto   Leimer
Vienna Philharmonic Orchestra
Mono Issue : Not Issued

SXL2101-3   WBg : **£90**   WB : £55   NB : £15
WAGNER   Das Rheingold   Flagstad
Vienna Philharmonic Orchestra   Solti
Mono Issue : LXT 5495-7

SXL2104 WBg : **£50** WB : £25 NB : £8
BRAHMS Symphony No.3
Vienna Philharmonic Orchestra Kubelik
Mono Issue : LXT 5419

SXL2105 WBg : **£150** WB : £100 NB : £30
RAVEL / FALLA Invitation to the dance
Paris Conservatoire Orchestra Wolff
Mono Issue : LXT 5499

SXL2106 WBg : **£85** WB : £55 NB : £15
BEETHOVEN Piano Concero No.3 Katchen
London Symphony Orchestra Gamba
Mono Issue : LXT 5500

SXL2107-8 WBg : **£160** WB : £100 NB : £30
TCHAIKOVSKY Swan Lake Suisse Romande Orchestra Ansermet
Mono Issue : LXT 5501-2

SXL2109 WBg : **£175** WB : £120 NB : £40
TCHAIKOVSKY Symphony No.5
Vienna Philharmonic Orchestra Krips
Mono Issue : LXT 5503

SXL2110 WBg : **£60** WB : £30 NB : £10
SCHUBERT Trout Quintet Curzon Vienna Octet
Mono Issue : LXT 5433

SXL2111 WBg : **£75** WB : £35 NB : £12
Various Operatic Recital Di Stefano
Tonhalle Orchestra Patane
Mono Issue : LXT 5504

SXL2112 WBg : **£120** WB : £80 NB : £20
WEBER Overtures Suisse Romande Orchestra Ansermet
Mono Issue : LXT 5505

SXL2113 WBg : **£250** WB : £150 NB : £50
RIMSKY-KORSAKOV Christmas Eve, Sadko etc
Suisse Romande Orchestra Ansermet
Mono Issue : LXT 5398

SXL2114   WBg : **£50**   WB : £30   NB : £10
TCHAIKOVSKY   Piano Concerto No.1   Curzon
Vienna Philharmonic Orchestra   Solti
Mono Issue : No LXT

SXL2115   WBg : **£25**   WB : £10   NB : £2
HANDEL   Organ Concertos   Richter
Mono Issue : LXT 5578

SXL2116   WBg : **£50**   WB : £25   NB : £8
BEETHOVEN   Symphony No.4
Suisse Romande Orchestra   Ansermet
Mono Issue : LXT 5507

SXL2117-20   WBg : **£400**   WB : £275   NB : £100
MOZART   Don Giovanni   Danco
Vienna Philharmonic Orchestra   Krips
Mono Issue : LXT 5103-6

SXL2121   WBg : **£40**   WB : £20   NB : £6
BEETHOVEN   Symphony No.7
Vienna Philharmonic Orchestra   Solti
Mono Issue : LXT 5508

SXL2122   WBg : **£55**   WB : £30   NB : £7
Various   Opera Excerpts   Del Monaco
Mono Issue : LXT 5202

SXL2123   WBg : **£85**   WB : £45   NB : £15
PUCCINI   Recital   Zeani
St. Cecilia Academy, Rome   Patane
Mono Issue : No LXT

SXL2124   WBg : **£85**   WB : £50   NB : £15
BEETHOVEN   Symphony No.5
Vienna Philharmonic Orchestra   Solti
Mono Issue : LXT 5507

SXL2125   WBg : **£40**   WB : £20   NB : £6
BACH   Brandenburg Concertos No.1 & 6
Stuttgart Chamber Orchestra   Munchinger
Mono Issue : No LXT

SXL2126   WBg : **£40**   WB : £20   NB : £6
BACH   Brandenburg Concertos No.2 & 5
Stuttgart Chamber Orchestra   Munchinger
Mono Issue : No LXT

SXL2127   WBg : **£40**   WB : £20   NB : £6
BACH   Brandenburg Concertos No.3 & 4
Stuttgart Chamber Orchestra   Munchinger
Mono Issue : No LXT

SXL2128   WBg : **£85**   WB : £45   NB : £12
ADAM   Giselle   Paris Conservatoire Orchestra   Martinon
Mono Issue : LXT 5515

SXL2129-31   WBg : **£100**   WB : £60   NB : £15
VERDI   Il Trovatore   Tebaldi
Maggio Musicale Florentino   Erede
Mono Issue : LXT 5260-2

SXL2132   WBg : **£85**   WB : £50   NB : £15
ROSSINI   Berganza Sings Rossini   Berganza
London Symphony Orchestra   Gibson
Mono Issue : LXT 5514

SXL2133   WBg : **£15**   WB : £10   NB : £4
LEHAR   Merry Widow (Highlights)   Gueden
Vienna State Opera   Stolz
Mono Issue :

SXL2134   WBg : **£100**   WB : £65   NB : £15
BERLIOZ   Music of Berlioz
Paris Conservatoire Orchestra   Martinon
Mono Issue : LXT 5517

SXL2135   WBg : **£120**   WB : £75   NB : £25
MOZART   Symphony No.32 & 38
London Symphony Orchestra   Maag
Mono Issue : LXT 5518

SXL2136   WBg : **£130**   WB : £85   NB : £25
DEBUSSY   La Boite a Joujoux, Printemps
Suisse Romande Orchestra   Ansermet
Mono Issue : LXT 5351

SXL2137-40 (==== Not Issued ====)

SXL2141   WBg : **£120**   WB : £75   NB : £20
GLAZUNOV   The Seasons   Paris Conservatoire Orchestra   Wolff
Mono Issue : LXT 5240

SXL2142-4 (==== Not Issued ====)

SXL2145   WBg : **£45**   WB : £20   NB : £6
Various   Songs From Norway   Flagstad
London Symphony Orchestra   Fjelstad
Mono Issue : LXT 5558

SXL2146-9 (==== Not Issued ====)

SXL2150-2   WBg : **£50**   WB : £25   NB : £8
BRITTEN   Peter Grimes
Royal Opera House, Covent Garden Orchestra   Britten
Mono Issue : LXT 5521-3

SXL2153   WBg : **£60**   WB : £30   NB : £8
TCHAIKOVSKY   Swan Lake (Highlights)
Suisse Romande Orchestra   Ansermet
Mono Issue : LXT 5581

SXL2154   WBg : **£150**   WB : £100   NB : £30
STRAUSS   Also Sprach Zarathustra
Vienna Philharmonic Orchestra   Karajan
Mono Issue : LXT 5524

SXL2155   WBg : **£400**   WB : £275   NB : £100
LALO / RAVEL   Symphonie Espagnole, Tzigane   Ricci
Vienna Philharmonic Orchestra   Ansermet
Mono Issue : LXT 5527

SXL2156   WBg : **£50**   WB : £25   NB : £8
SCHUBERT   Symphony No.2 & 8
Vienna Philharmonic Orchestra   Munchinger
Mono Issue : LXT 5528

SXL2157   WBg : **£100**   WB : £60   NB : £20
BEETHOVEN   Septet   Vienna Octet
Mono Issue : LXT 5529

SXL2158   WBg : **£120**   WB : £70   NB : £20
BEETHOVEN   Quintet in Eflat op16   Vienna Octet
Mono Issue : LXT 5530

SXL2159   WBg : **£25**   WB : £10   NB : £2
Various   Operatic Arias   Sutherland
Paris Conservatoire Orchestra   Santi
Mono Issue : LXT 5531

SXL2160-2   WBg : **£200**   WB : £135   NB : £45
TCHAIKOVSKY   Sleeping Beauty
Suisse Romande Orchestra   Ansermet
Mono Issue : LXT 5532-4

SXL2163   WBg : **£40**   WB : £20   NB : £6
STRAUSS   Vienna Carnival
Vienna Philharmonic Orchestra   Boskovsky
Mono Issue : LXT 5535

SXL2164   WBg : **£120**   WB : £70   NB : £20
RAVEL   Daphnis & Chloe
London Symphony Orchestra   Monteux
Mono Issue : LXT 5536

SXL2165   WBg : **£45**   WB : £20   NB : £6
BEETHOVEN   Symphony No.3
Vienna Philharmonic Orchestra   Solti
Mono Issue : LXT 5537

SXL2166   WBg : **£80**   WB : £45   NB : £12
TCHAIKOVSKY   Symphony No.4
Paris Conservatoire Orchestra   Wolff
Mono Issue : LXT 5538

SXL2167-9   WBg : **£60**   WB : £35   NB : £10
VERDI   Aida   Vienna Philharmonic Orchestra   Karajan
Mono Issue : LXT 5539-41

SXL2170-1   WBg : **£80**   WB : £45   NB : £12
PUCCINI   La Boheme   Serafin   St. Cecilia Academy, Rome
Mono Issue : LXT 5542-3

SXL2172 WBg : **£100** WB : £55 NB : £15
BRAHMS Piano Concerto No.1 Katchen
London Symphony Orchestra Monteux
Mono Issue : LXT 5546

SXL2173 WBg : **£25** WB : £10 NB : £2
GRIEG / FRANCK Piano Concerto, Symphonic Variations
Curzon London Philharmonic Orchestra Boult
Mono Issue : LXT 5547

SXL2174 WBg : **£75** WB : £40 NB : £10
SUPPE Overtures
Vienna Philharmonic Orchestra Solti
Mono Issue : LXT 5548

SXL2175 WBg : **£20** WB : £10 NB : £2
PUCCINI Turandot Highlights
St. Cecilia Academy, Rome Erede
Mono Issue : LXT 5549

SXL2176 WBg : **£20** WB : £10 NB : £2
RACHMANINOV / DOHNANYI Rhapsody On A Theme Of Paganini
Katchen London Philharmonic Orchestra Boult
Mono Issue : LXT 5550

SXL2177 WBg : **£40** WB : £15 NB : £4
WOLF-FERRARI Music of Wolf-Ferrari
Paris Conservatoire Orchestra Nello-Santi
Mono Issue : LXT 5551

SXL2178 WBg : **£125** WB : £80 NB : £20
BEETHOVEN Piano Concertos 1, 2 Backhaus
Vienna Philharmonic Orchestra Schmitt-Isserstedt
Mono Issue : LXT 5552

SXL2179 WBg : **£125** WB : £80 NB : £20
BEETHOVEN Piano Concerto 5 Backhaus
Vienna Philharmonic Orchestra Schmitt-Isserstedt
Mono Issue : LXT 5553

SXL2180-1   WBg : **£85**   WB : £45   NB : £12
PUCCINI   Tosca   Tebaldi
St. Cecilia Academy, Rome   Pradelli
Mono Issue : LXT 5554-5

SXL2182   WBg : **£250**   WB : £160   NB : £50
ROSSINI   Overtures   Paris Conservatoire Orchestra   Maag
Mono Issue : LXT 5556

SXL2183   WBg : **£40**   WB : £15   NB : £4
LISZT   Dante Sonata   Katin
Mono Issue : LXT 5557 &2877

SXL2184   WBg : **£150**   WB : £100   NB : £30
WAGNER   Tristan & Isolde excerpts   Nilsson
Vienna Philharmonic Orchestra   Knappertsbusch
Mono Issue : LXT 5559

SXL2185-6   WBg : **£175**   WB : £125   NB : £40
LEONCAVALLO   I Pagliacci (Also SXL 2253-5)
Monaco   St. Cecilia Academy, Rome   Pradelli
Mono Issue : LXT 5560-1

SXL2187   WBg : **£15**   WB : £8   NB : £2
HANDEL   Organ Concerto Vol.2   Richter
Mono Issue : LXT 5579

SXL2188   WBg : **£80**   WB : £50   NB : £15
STRAVINSKY   Song of the Nightingale
Suisse Romande Orchestra   Ansermet
Mono Issue : LXT 5233

SXL2189   WBg : **£40**   WB : £20   NB : £5
BRITTEN   Nocturne   London Symphony Orchestra   Britten
Mono Issue : LXT 5564

SXL2190   WBg : **£120**   WB : £70   NB : £20
BEETHOVEN   Piano Concerto 3   Backhaus
Vienna Philharmonic Orchestra   Schmitt-Isserstedt
Mono Issue : No LXT

SXL2191   WBg : **£75**   WB : £35   NB : £8
Various   Recital of Lute songs   Bream, Pears
Mono Issue : LXT 5567

SXL2192   WBg : **£18**   WB : £8   NB : £2
BOITO   Mefistofele (Highlights)   Tebaldi
St. Cecilia Academy, Rome   Serafin
Mono Issue : LXT 5568

SXL2193   WBg : **£80**   WB : £50   NB : £15
BEETHOVEN   Symphony No.6
Suisse Romande Orchestra   Ansermet
Mono Issue : LXT 5566

SXL2194   WBg : **£125**   WB : £75   NB : £25
PAGANINI   24 Caprices   Ricci
Mono Issue : LXT 5571

SXL2195   WBg : **£80**   WB : £45   NB : £12
MUSSORGSKY   Pictures at an exhibition
Suisse Romande Orchestra   Ansermet
Mono Issue : LXT 5565

SXL2196   WBg : **£200**   WB : £125   NB : £40
MOZART   Serenata Notturna, Notturna 4 Or
London Symphony Orchestra   Maag
Mono Issue : LXT 5570

SXL2197   WBg : **£150**   WB : £100   NB : £30
SARASATE / SAINT SAINS   Recital   Ricci
London Symphony Orchestra   Gamba
Mono Issue : LXT 5571

SXL2198   WBg : **£45**   WB : £20   NB : £6
STRAUSS   Philharmonic Ball
Vienna Philharmonic Orchestra   Boskovsky
Mono Issue : LXT 5572

SXL2199   WBg : **£80**   WB : £45   NB : £15
Various   The Instruments of the Orchestra
BBC Symphony Orchestra   Sargent
Mono Issue : LXT 5573

SXL2200   WBg : **£65**   WB : £35   NB : £10
SCHUBERT   Die Schone Mullerin   Britten, Pears
Mono Issue : LXT5574

SXL2201   WBg : **£20**   WB : £10   NB : £2
HANDEL   Organ Concertos Vol.3   Richter
Mono Issue : LXT 5580

SXL2202   WBg : **£15**   WB : £8   NB : £2
PUCCINI   Madame Butterfly (Highlights)
St. Cecilia Academy, Rome   Serafin
Mono Issue : LXT 5575

SXL2203(==== Not Issued ====)

SXL2204   WBg : **£30**   WB : £15   NB : £4
BACH   A Musical Offering
Stuttgart Chamber Orchestra   Munchinger
Mono Issue : LXT 5036

SXL2205   WBg : **£40**   WB : £20   NB : £5
BACH   Recital   Backhaus
Mono Issue : No LXT

SXL2206   WBg : **£140**   WB : £85   NB : £30
BRAHMS   Symphony No.4
Vienna Philharmonic Orchestra   Kubelik
Mono Issue :   LXT5214

SXL2207   WBg : **£60**   WB : £35   NB : £10
VAUGHAN WILLIAMS   Symphony No.8
Philharmonia Orchestra   Boult
Mono Issue : LXT 5314

SXL2208-10   WBg : **£85**   WB : £65   NB : £15
GIORDANO   Andre Chenier   Del Monaco
St. Cecilia Academy, Rome   Gavazzeni
Mono Issue : LXT 5411-2

SXL2211   WBg : **£85**   WB : £50   NB : £12
FAURE   Requiem   Danco
Suisse Romande Orchestra   Ansermet
Mono Issue : LXT 5158

SXL2212   WBg : **£ 250**   WB : £175   NB : £60
RAVEL   L'Enfants et Les Sortilege
Suisse Romande Orchestra   Ansermet
Mono Issue : LXT 5019

SXL2213   WBg : **£ 50**   WB : £25   NB : £5
Various   Italian Opera Recital   Cesare Siepe
Mono Issue : No LXT

SXL2214   WBg : **£ 160**   WB : £85   NB : £20
MOZART   Piano Concerto No.27   Backhaus
Vienna Philharmonic Orchestra   Bohm
Mono Issue : LXT 5123

SXL2215-7   WBg : **£ 250**   WB : £175   NB : £55
MOZART   Magic Flute   Berger
Vienna Philharmonic Orchestra   Bohm
Mono Issue : LXT 5085-7

SXL2218   WBg : **£ 100**   WB : £60   NB : £20
PROKOFIEV   Peter and the Wolf Henderson
London Symphony Orchestra   Katchen
Mono Issue : LXT 5577

SXL2219   WBg : **£ 20**   WB : £8   NB : £2
BACH   Toccata & Fugue   Richter
Mono Issue : LXT 5110

SXL2220   WBg : **£ 85**   WB : £50   NB : £14
MOZART   Jupiter & Haffner Symphonies
Israel Philharmonic Orchestra   Krips
Mono Issue : LXT 5414

SXL2221   WBg : **£ 100**   WB : £60   NB : £15
RIMSKY-KORSAKOV   Russian Easter Festival
Suisse Romande Orchestra   Ansermet
Mono Issue : LXT5311

SXL2222   WBg : **£ 45**   WB : £20   NB : £5
BRAHMS   Piano Recital   Backhaus
Mono Issue : LXT5308

SXL2223 WBg : **£ 75** WB : £40 NB : £10
SCHUMANN Symphonies Nos.1 & 4
London Symphony Orchestra Krips
Mono Issue : LXT 5347

SXL2224 WBg : **£ 65** WB : £35 NB : £10
MAHLER Kindertotenlieder Flagstad
Vienna Philharmonic Orchestra Boult
Mono Issue : LXT 5395

SXL2225-7 WBg : **£ 175** WB : £130 NB : £35
PONCHIELLI La Gioconda Cerquetti
Maggio Musicale Florentino Gavazeni
Mono Issue : LXT 5400-2

SXL2228 WBg : **£ 45** WB : £20 NB : £5
BEETHOVEN Symphony No.2 Suisse Romande Orchestra Ansermet
Mono Issue : LXT 5584

SXL2229 WBg : **£ 80** WB : £50 NB : £15
MENDELSSOHN / SCHUBERT Midsummer Nights Dream
Suisse Romande Orchestra Ansermet
Mono Issue : LXT 5585

SXL2230 WBg : **£ 15** WB : £8 NB : £2
WAGNER Das Rheingold, Die Walkure (Highlights)
Vienna Philharmonic Orchestra Solti
Mono Issue : LXT 5586

SXL2231 WBg : **£ 175** WB : £125 NB : £40
RAVEL / PROKOFIEV String Quartets Carmirelli Quartet
Mono Issue : LXT 5587

SXL2232 WBg : **£ 20** WB : £10 NB : £2
SEARLE Symphony No.1
London Philharmonic Orchestra Boult
Mono Issue : LXT 5588

SXL2233 WBg : **£ 85** WB : £50 NB : £12
MOZART / HAYDN Arias Vyvyan
Haydn Orchestra Newstone
Mono Issue : LXT 5589

SXL2234   WBg : **£40**   WB : £20   NB : £4
BACH / HANDEL   Arias   Ferrier
London Philharmonic Orchestra   Boult
Mono Issue : LXT 5382

SXL2235   WBg : **£35**   WB : £15   NB : £4
BEETHOVEN   Symphony No.7, Fedelio Overture
Suisse Romande Orchestra   Ansermet
Mono Issue : LXT 5590

SXL2236   WBg : **£75**   WB : £45   NB : £12
BRAHMS   Piano Concerto No.2   Katchen
London Symphony Orchestra   Ferencsik
Mono Issue : LXT 5591

SXL2237   WBg : **£20**   WB : £10   NB : £2
STRAVINSKY   Symphony in C
Suisse Romande Orchestra   Ansermet
Mono Issue : LXT 5592

SXL2238   WBg : **£100**   WB : £60   NB : £18
MOZART   Horn Concertos   Tuckwell
London Symphony Orchestra   Maag
Mono Issue : LXT 5593

SXL2239   WBg : **£100**   WB : £60   NB : £18
Various   Popular Favorites
Vienna Philharmonic Orchestra   Knappersbusch
Mono Issue : LXT 5594

SXL2240   WBg : **£60**   WB : £35   NB : £10
Various   Solo Violin recital   Ricci
Mono Issue : LXT 5595

SXL2241   WBg : **£200**   WB : £125   NB : £40
BEETHOVEN   Piano Sonatas 21 Waldstein, 23 app   Backhaus
Mono Issue : LXT 5596

SXL2242   WBg : **£10**   WB : £4   NB : £2
VERDI   Aida excerpts   Vienna Philharmonic Orchestra   Karajan
Mono Issue : LXT 5597

SXL2243 WBg : **£120** WB : £75 NB : £20
ALBENIZ Iberia, Turina
Suisse Romande Orchestra Ansermet
Mono Issue : LXT 5598

SXL2244 WBg : **£40** WB : £20 NB : £6
BEETHOVEN Symphony No.3
Suisse Romande Orchestra Ansermet
Mono Issue : LXT 5599

SXL2245 WBg : **£20** WB : £10 NB : £2
Various Classical Indian Music
Mono Issue : LXT 5600

SXL2246 WBg : **£200** WB : £140 NB : £40
MENDELSSOHN Symphony No.3, Fingal's Cave
London Symphony Orchestra Maag
Mono Issue : LXT 5601

SXL2247 WBg : **£100** WB : £65 NB : £20
MOZART Concert Arias for Bass Corena Quadri
Royal Opera House, Covent Garden Orchestra Fernando
Mono Issue : LXT 5602

SXL2248 WBg : **£10** WB : £4 NB : £2
PUCCINI La Boheme (Highlights) Serafin
St. Cecilia Academy, Rome
Mono Issue : LXT 5608

SXL2249 WBg : **£250** WB : £175 NB : £50
BRAHMS / DVORAK Hungarian, Slavonic Dances
Vienna Philharmonic Orchestra Reiner
Mono Issue : LXT 5609

SXL2250 WBg : **£60** WB : £35 NB : £8
STRAUSS Graduation Ball etc
Vienna Philharmonic Orchestra Boskovsky
Mono Issue : LXT 5610

SXL2251 WBg : **£125** WB : £85 NB : £20
Various Eighteenth Century Arias Berganza
Royal Opera House, Covent Garden Orchestra Gibson
Mono Issue : LXT5611

SXL2252   WBg : **£120**   WB : £75   NB : £25
BIZET   Jeux D'enfants
Paris Conservatoire Orchestra   Martinon
Mono Issue : LXT5612

SXL2253-5   WBg : **£120**   WB : £85   NB : £25
MASCAGNI / LEONCAVELLO   Cavalleria Rusticana, I Pagliacci
Simionato   St. Cecilia Academy, Rome   Serafin
Mono Issue : LXT 5613-5

SXL2256   WBg : **£20**   WB : £10   NB : £2
Various   Art Of Prima Donna Pt1.   Sutherland
Royal Opera House, Covent Garden Orchestra   Molinari
Mono Issue : LXT 5616

SXL2257   WBg : **£20**   WB : £10   NB : £2
Various   Art Of Prima Donna Pt2.   Sutherland
Royal Opera House, Covent Garden Orchestra   Molinari
Mono Issue : LXT 5617

SXL2258   WBg : **£15**   WB : £8   NB : £2
PUCCINI   Tosca (Highlights) Tebaldi   Pradelli
Mono Issue : LXT 5618

SXL2259   WBg : **£45**   WB : £20   NB : £5
BACH   Harpsichord Recital   Malcolm
Mono Issue : LXT 5619

SXL2260   WBg : **£150**   WB : £70   NB : £20
FALLA   El Amor Brujo, Master Peters puppet show
Suisse Romande / Spanish Nat. Orchestra   Ansermet, Argenta
Mono Issue : No LXT

SXL2261   WBg : **£60**   WB : £35   NB : £10
STRAUSS   Till Eulenspiegel, Death and Transformation
Vienna Philharmonic Orchestra   Karajan
Mono Issue : LXT 5620

SXL2262   WBg : **£75**   WB : £45   NB : £12
BEETHOVEN   Diabelli Variations   Katchen
Mono Issue : LXT 5621

SXL2263   WBg : **£120**   WB : £80   NB : £25
Various   French Overtures
Suisse Romande Orchestra   Ansermet
Mono Issue : LXT 5622

SXL2264   WBg : **£15**   WB : £8   NB : £2
BRITTEN   Spring Symphony
Royal Opera House, Covent Garden Orchestra   Britten
Mono Issue : LXT 5624

SXL2265   WBg : **£50**   WB : £30   NB : £10
CORELLI / GLUCK   Concerto Grosso 8, Chaconne etc
Stuttgart Chamber Orchestra   Munchinger
Mono Issue : LXT 5625

SXL2266   WBg : **£85**   WB : £50   NB : £12
ROSSINI Overtures   London Symphony Orchestra   Gamba
Mono Issue : LXT 5626

SXL2267   WBg : **£15**   WB : £8   NB : £2
PUCCINI   Fanciulla del West (Highlights)   Capuana
St. Cecilia Academy, Rome
Mono Issue : LXT 5627

SXL2268   WBg : **£55**   WB : £30   NB : £8
RIMSKY-KORSAKOV / BORODIN   Scheherazade Polovian Dances
Suisse Romande Orchestra   Ansermet
Mono Issue : LXT 5628

SXL2269   WBg : **£60**   WB : £35   NB : £10
TCHAIKOVSKY / STRAUSS   Romeo & Juliet, Don Juan
Vienna Philharmonic Orchestra   Karajan
Mono Issue : LXT 5629

SXL2270   WBg : **£200**   WB : £140   NB : £50
MOZART   Eine Kleine Nachmusik
Vienna Philharmonic Orchestra   Munchinger
Mono Issue : LXT 5630

SXL2271   WBg : **£65**   WB : £35   NB : £7
Various   Operatic Recitals   Sciutti
Mono Issue : LXT 5631

SXL2272 WBg : **£30** WB : £15 NB : £4
MOZART Haffner Serenade
Vienna Philharmonic Orchestra Munchinger
Mono Issue : LXT 5632

SXL2273 WBg : **£200** WB : £125 NB : £40
RAVEL Daphnis & Chloe
Suisse Romande Orchestra Ansermet
Mono Issue : LXT 5633

SXL2274 WBg : **£50** WB : £30 NB : £8
BEETHOVEN Symphony No.9
Suisse Romande Orchestra Ansermet
Mono Issue : No LXT

SXL2275 WBg : **£80** WB : £50 NB : £12
BIZET Symphony in C
Suisse Romande Orchestra Ansermet
Mono Issue : LXT 5634

SXL2276 WBg : **£50** WB : £30 NB : £8
MAHLER Symphony No.4
Concertgebouw Orchestra of Amsterdam Solti
Mono Issue : LXT 5638

SXL2277 WBg : **£80** WB : £50 NB : £12
STRAVINSKY Les Noces Symphony Of Psalms
Suisse Romande Orchestra Ansermet
Mono Issue : LXT 5639

SXL2278 WBg : **£100** WB : £60 NB : £15
FRANCK Piano Quintet Curzon Vienna Quartet
Mono Issue : LXT 5640

SXL2279 WBg : **£125** WB : £80 NB : £20
TCHAIKOVSKY / DVORAK Violin Concerto Ricci
London Symphony Orchestra Sargent
Mono Issue : LXT 5641

SXL2280 WBg : **£75** WB : £45 NB : £10
OFFENBACH / GOUNOD Gaite Parisienne, Faust
Royal Opera House, Covent Garden Orchestra Solti
Mono Issue : LXT 5642

137

SXL2281-2   WBg : **£60**   WB : £40   NB : £12
MASCAGNI   Cavalleria Rusticana   Simionato
St. Cecilia Academy, Rome   Serafin
Mono Issue : LXT 5643-4

SXL2283(==== Not Issued ====)

SXL2284   WBg : **£75**   WB : £50   NB : £10
HAYDN   Symphony No.100, Symphony No.83
Vienna Philharmonic Orchestra   Munchinger
Mono Issue : LXT 5647

SXL2285   WBg : **£85**   WB : £50   NB : £12
TCHAIKOVSKY   Scenes from Swan Lake
Concertgebouw Orchestra of Amsterdam   Fistoulari
Mono Issue : LXT 5648

SXL2286   WBg : **£100**   WB : £65   NB : £18
MOZART   Quartet No.20 & 22   Vienna Quartet
Mono Issue : LXT 5649

SXL2287   WBg : **£80**   WB : £50   NB : £12
DEBUSSY / RAVEL   Symphony, Images, Iberia, Pavane
Suisse Romande Orchestra   Ansermet
Mono Issue : LXT 5650

SXL2288   WBg : **£50**   WB : £30   NB : £10
STRAUSS   Thousand And One Nights
Vienna Philharmonic Orchestra   Boskovsky
Mono Issue : LXT 5651

SXL2289   WBg : **£90**   WB : £60   NB : £15
DVORAK   Symphony No.9
Vienna Philharmonic Orchestra   Kertesz
Mono Issue : LXT 5652

SXL2290   WBg : **£40**   WB : £20   NB : £5
MOZART   Divertiment K136   Vienna Octet
Mono Issue : LXT 5653

SXL2291   WBg : **£80**   WB : £50   NB : £12
FRANCK   Symphony in D
Suisse Romande Orchestra   Ansermet
Mono Issue : LXT 5654

SXL2292   WBg : **£120**   WB : £85   NB : £20
PROKOFIEV / BORODIN / GLINKA Classical Symphony, etc.
Suisse Romande Orchestra   Ansermet
Mono Issue : LXT 5655

SXL2293   WBg : **£60**   WB : £30   NB : £10
Various   Encores   Katchen
Mono Issue : LXT 5656

SXL2294   WBg : **£80**   WB : £45   NB : £12
Various   Christmas with Leontyne Price   Price
Vienna Philharmonic Orchestra   Karajan
Mono Issue : LXT 5657

SXL2295   WBg : **£150**   WB : £100   NB : £25
Various   Operetta Evergreens   Gueden
Mono Issue : LXT 5658

SXL2296   WBg : **£250**   WB : £175   NB : £55
FALLA   Three Cornered Hat
Suisse Romande Orchestra   Ansermet
Mono Issue : LXT5656

SXL2297   WBg : **£80**   WB : £45   NB : £10
BRAHMS   Clarinet Quintet   Vienna Octet
Mono Issue : LXT 5660

SXL2298   WBg : **£150**   WB : £100   NB : £25
BRITTEN / DEBUSSY   Cello Sonata in C#, Cello sonata in Dmin
Rostropovich   Britten
Mono Issue : LXT 5661

SXL2299   WBg : **£100**   WB : £65   NB : £20
Various   Art of Slobodskaya 1945-61   Slobodskaya
London Symphony Orchestra   Fistoulari
Mono Issue : LXT 5663

SXL2300-1   WBg : **£150**   WB : £100   NB : £25
BACH   Orchestral Suites
Stuttgart Chamber Orchestra   Munchinger
Mono Issue : LXT 5664-5

SXL2302   WBg : **£40**   WB : £20   NB : £6
HANDEL   Water Music, Fireworks
London Symphony Orchestra   Szell
Mono Issue : LXT 5666

SXL2303   WBg : **£55**   WB : £30   NB : £8
FAURE / DEBUSSY   Pelleas & Melisande,Petite Suite
Suisse Romande Orchestra   Ansermet
Mono Issue : LXT 5667

SXL2304   WBg : **£120**   WB : £85   NB : £20
Various   On the Wings of Opera   Regina Resnik
Royal Opera House, Covent Garden Orchestra   Downes
Mono Issue : LXT 5668

SXL2305   WBg : **£25**   WB : £10   NB : £2
HOLST   The Planets   Vienna Philharmonic Orchestra   Karajan
Mono Issue : LXT 5669

SXL2306-7   WBg : **£200**   WB : £130   NB : £35
PROKOFIEV   Romeo & Juliet, Cinderella
Suisse Romande Orchestra   Ansermet
Mono Issue : LXT 5671-2

SXL2308   WBg : **£50**   WB : £30   NB : £8
TCHAIKOVSKY / GRIEG   Nutcracker, Peer Gynt
Vienna Philharmonic Orchestra   Karajan
Mono Issue : LXT 5673

SXL2309   WBg : **£8**   WB : £4   NB : £2
BRITTEN   Peter Grimes (Highlights)
Royal Opera House, Covent Garden Orchestra   Britten
Mono Issue : LXT 5674

SXL2310   WBg : **£100**   WB : £65   NB : £15
SCHUMANN   Dichterleibe   Brendel   Wachter
Mono Issue : LXT 5675

SXL2311   WBg : **£120**   WB : £75   NB : £20
MARTIN   Concerto for 7 Wind Instruments
Suisse Romande Orchestra   Ansermet
Mono Issue : LXT 5676

SXL2312   WBg : **£150**   WB : £100   NB : £30
DEBUSSY / RAVEL   Prelude L'Apres Midi, Favanne
London Symphony Orchestra   Monteux
Mono Issue : LXT 5677

SXL2313   WBg : **£60**   WB : £30   NB : £8
HEROLD-LANCHBERRY   La Fille Mal Gardee
Royal Opera House, Covent Garden Orchestra   Lanchberry
Mono Issue : LXT 5682

SXL2314   WBg : **£20**   WB : £10   NB : £2
VERDI   Otello (Highlights)
Vienna Philharmonic Orchestra   Karajan
Mono Issue : LXT 5683

SXL2315   WBg : **£18**   WB : £10   NB : £2
DONIZETTI   Lucia di Lammermoor
St. Cecilia Academy, Rome   Pritchard
Mono Issue : LXT 5684

SXL2316   WBg : **£8**   WB : £4 NB : £2
HANDEL   Messiah (Highlights)
London Symphony Orchestra   Boult
Mono Issue : LXT 5685

Decca SXL 6000 series Stereophonic LP's

The Decca SXL 6000 series was simply a continuation of the
SXL2000 series, but with a new numbering system which is now
paired with its mono counterpart. Thus the Mono version of SXL6239
would be LXT6239. For this reason, no mono equivalents are listed in
this section of the guide.

The earliest labels, up until SXL6368, are the WBg (Wide band
grooved) type described previously. Later pressings may be WB
(Wide Band) or NB (Narrow Band) types.

With the exception of SXL6435 and SXL6447 which only exist as
narrow band labels, all records between SXL6369 and SXL6448 have
the Wide Band without the groove as the first label.

After SXL6449, the first label is the Narrow Band label.

SXL6000 WBg : **£65** WB : £20 NB : £2
KHACHATURIAN Spartacus, Gayaneh
Vienna Philharmonic Orchestra Khachaturian

SXL6001 WBg : **£100** WB : £65 NB : £12
KHACHATURIAN Symphony No.2, The Bell
Vienna Philharmonic Orchestra Khachaturian

SXL6002 WBg : **£50** WB : £20 NB : £5
ADAM Giselle Vienna Philharmonic Orchestra Karajan

SXL6003 WBg : **£50** WB : £25 NB : £5
HONEGGER Christmas Cantata, Symphony for Strings
Suisse Romande Orchestra Ansermet

SXL6004 WBg : **£50** WB : £25 NB : £5
BACH Suite No.2 & No.3
Suisse Romande Orchestra Ansermet

SXL6005 WBg : **£80** WB : £50 NB : £10
Various Spanish & Italian Arias Berganza

SXL6006 WBg : **£20** WB : £10 NB : £2
HOLST Hymn of Jesus
London Philharmonic Orchestra Boult

SXL6007 WBg : **£25** WB : £12 NB : £10
BRITTEN Folk Songs Pears Britten

SXL6008 WBg : **£10** WB : £6 NB : £2
VERDI Rigoletto (Highlights) Sanzogno
St. Cecilia Academy, Rome

SXL6009 WBg : **£12** WB : £8 NB : £3
HANDEL Messiah choruses McCarthy
London Symphony Orchestra Boult

SXL6010 WBg : **£20** WB : £10 NB : £2
HANDEL Messiah London Symphony Orchestra Boult

SXL6011 WBg : **£20** WB : £10 NB : £3
PUCCINI Manon Lescaut (Highlights) Tebaldi
St. Cecilia Academy, Rome Pradelli

SXL6012   WBg : **£ 25**   WB : £10   NB : £3
MASCAGNI / LEONCAVELLO   Cavalleria Rusticana, I Pagliacci
St. Cecilia Academy, Rome   Serafin

SXL6013   WBg : **£ 10**   WB : £5   NB : £3
VERDI   Un Ballo In Maschera (Highlights)
St. Cecilia Academy, Rome   Solti

SXL6014   WBg : **£ 75**   WB : £25   NB : £12
BEETHOVEN   Diabelli Variations   Backhaus

SXL6015-6   WBg : **£ 20**   WB : £8   NB : £3
STRAUSS   Die Fledermaus
Vienna Philharmonic Orchestra   Karajan

SXL6017   WBg : **£ 12**   WB : £6   NB : £3
CILEA   Adriana Lecouvrer (Highlights)
St. Cecilia Academy, Rome

SXL6018   WBg : **£ 85**   WB : £60   NB : £8
SHOSTAKOVICH   Symphony No.5
Suisse Romande Orchestra   Kertesz

SXL6019   (==== Not Issued ====)

SXL6020   WBg : **£ 25**   WB : £10   NB : £5
HAYDN   Symphonies   Suisse Romande Orchestra   Ansermet

SXL6021   WBg : **£ 40**   WB : £10   NB : £5
HAYDN   Symphonies   Suisse Romande Orchestra   Ansermet

SXL6022   WBg : **£ 25**   WB : £10   NB : £5
HAYDN   Symphonies   Suisse Romande Orchestra   Ansermet

SXL6023   WBg : **£ 25**   WB : £10   NB : £8
BRAHMS   Piano Concerto No.1   Curzon
London Symphony Orchestra   Szell

SXL6024   WBg : **£ 40**   WB : £10   NB : £8
SMETANA / DVORAK   Bohemian Rhapsody
Israel Philharmonic Orchestra   Kertesz

SXL6025   WBg : **£30**   WB : £8   NB : £6
BEETHOVEN   Overtures Fidelio,Leonore1-3
Israel Philharmonic Orchestra   Maazel

SXL6026   WBg : **£75**   WB : £30   NB : £10
BARTOK   Divertimento   Moscow Chamber Orchestra   Barshai

SXL6027   WBg : **£85**   WB : £12   NB : £8
SAINT-SAENS   Symphony No.3   Suisse Romande Orchestra   Ansermet

SXL6028   WBg : **£30**   WB : £10   NB : £6
GRIEG / SCHUMANN   Piano Concertos   Katchen
Israel Philharmonic Orchestra   Kertesz

SXL6029   WBg : **£35**   WB : £10   NB : £6
STRAUSS   Great Strauss Waltzes
Vienna Philharmonic Orchestra   Boskovsky

SXL6030   WBg : **£45**   WB : £18   NB : £5
Various   The Best Of Tebaldi   Tebaldi
St. Cecilia Academy, Rome   Various

SXL6031   (==== Not Issued ====)

SXL6032   WBg : **£35**   WB : £25   NB : £8
Various   The Art of Advocacy   Birkett

SXL6033   WBg : **£25**   WB : £8   NB : £4
VERDI   Opera Recital   Nilsson
Royal Opera House, Covent Garden   Quadri

SXL6034   (==== Not Issued ====)

SXL6035   WBg : **£100**   WB : £60   NB : £14
HINDEMITH / BRUCH   Violin Concerto, Scottish Fantasia   Oistrakh
London Symphony Orchestra   Hornstein

SXL6036   WBg : **£100**   WB : £70   NB : £15
BORODIN / SHOSTAKOVITCH   Quartet No.2, Quartet No.8
Borodin Quartet

SXL6037   WBg : **£25**   WB : £14   NB : £4
Various   Songs   Prey

SXL6038   WBg : **£30**   WB : £15   NB : £5
Various   Russian and Italian Opera Arias Ghiaurov
London Symphony Orchestra   Downes

SXL6039   WBg : **£30**   WB : £10   NB : £6
LORTZING Der Waffenschmied Zar Und Zimmermann Gueden
Vienna Volksoper Orchestra   Ronnefeld

SXL6040   WBg : **£25**   WB : £10   NB : £4
STRAUSS   Tales from the Vienna Woods
Vienna Philharmonic Orchestra   Boskovsky

SXL6041   WBg : **£40**   WB : £20   NB : £8
BRAHMS   Sonata in Fmin Op.5   Curzon

SXL6042   WBg : **£35**   WB : £10   NB : £6
WAGNER   Kirsten Flagstad In Memoriam Flagstad
Vienna Philharmonic Orchestra   Knappertsbusch

SXL6043   WBg : **£40**   WB : £20   NB : £8
DVORAK / SCHUBERT Quintet in A, Quartet No.12 Curzon
Vienna Quartet

SXL6044   WBg : **£15**   WB : £8   NB : £3
DVORAK   Symphony No.8
London Symphony Orchestra   Kertesz

SXL6045   WBg : **£55**   WB : £30   NB : £5
MOZART   Teresa Berganza
London Symphony Orchestra   Pritchard

SXL6046   WBg : **£30**   WB : £15   NB : £4
SIBELIUS / STRAUSS Songs Krause

SXL6047-8   (===== Not Issued =====)

SXL6049   WBg : **£20**   WB : £9   NB : £3
MOZART   Wind Music Vol.3 London Wind Soloists Brymer

SXL6050   WBg : **£20**   WB : £9   NB : £3
MOZART   Wind Music Vol.1 London Wind Soloists Brymer

SXL6051 WBg : **£20** WB : £9 NB : £3
MOZART Wind Music Vol.2 London Wind Soloists Brymer

SXL6052 WBg : **£20** WB : £9 NB : £3
MOZART Wind Music Vol.4 London Wind Soloists Brymer

SXL6053 WBg : **£20** WB : £9 NB : £3
MOZART Wind Music Vol.5 London Wind Soloists Brymer

SXL6054 WBg : **£15** WB : £8 NB : £3
MOZART Clarinet Concerto, Flute & Harp Concerto
Vienna Philharmonic Orchestra Munchinger

SXL6055 WBg : **£85** WB : £60 NB : £8
MOZART / HAYDN Divertiment K287, Divertiment in Gmaj
Vienna Octet

SXL6056 WBg : **£80** WB : £50 NB : £8
MOZART Symphony No.33 & No.39
Vienna Philharmonic Orchestra Kertesz

SXL6057 WBg : **£20** WB : £9 NB : £4
RACHMANINOV Piano Concerto No.3 Ashkenazy
London Symphony Orchestra Fistoulari

SXL6058 WBg : **£20** WB : £9 NB : £4
TCHAIKOVSKY Piano Concerto No.1 Ashkenazy
London Symphony Orchestra Maazel

SXL6059 WBg : **£100** WB : £65 NB : £15
BRAHMS Symphony No.1 Suisse Romande Orchestra Ansermet

SXL6060 WBg : **£50** WB : £30 NB : £6
BRAHMS Symphony No.2 Suisse Romande Orchestra Ansermet

SXL6061 WBg : **£80** WB : £50 NB : £10
BRAHMS Symphony No.3 Suisse Romande Orchestra Ansermet

SXL6062 WBg : **£100** WB : £65 NB : £15
BRAHMS Symphony No.4 Suisse Romande Orchestra Ansermet

SXL6063 WBg : **£80** WB : £25 NB : £15
BEETHOVEN Piano Sonatas No.17 & No.28 Backhaus

SXL6064   WBg : **£80**   WB : £25   NB : £15
BEETHOVEN   Piano Sonatas No.12 & No.18   Backhaus

SXL6065   WBg : **£80**   WB : £50   NB : £12
RAVEL   Bolero, La Valse, Dukas, Honegga
Suisse Romande Orchestra   Ansermet

SXL6066   WBg : **£120**   WB : £85   NB : £15
STRAVINSKY   Baiser de la Fee   Suisse Romande Orchestra   Ansermet

SXL6067   WBg : **£40**   WB : £15   NB : £5
MOZART / HAYDN   Symphony No.41 Symphony No.103
Vienna Philharmonic Orchestra   Karajan

SXL6068   WBg : **£25**   WB : £8   NB : £4
VERDI   Great Sceans from Aida   Nilsson
Royal Opera House, Covent Garden   Pritchard

SXL6069   WBg : **£25**   WB : £14   NB : £4
SCHUBERT   Schwanangesang   Prey

SXL6070-2   (==== Not Issued ====)

SXL6073   WBg : **£14**   WB : £8   NB : £2
Various   Joan Sutherland Command Performance Volume 1
Sutherland   London Symphony Orchestra   Bonynge

SXL6074   WBg : **£14**   WB : £8   NB : £2
Various   Joan Sutherland Command Performance Volume 2
Sutherland   London Symphony Orchestra   Bonynge

SXL6075   WBg : **£25**   WB : £8   NB : £4
Various   Italian Arias   Crespin Royal Opera House Downes

SXL6076   WBg : **£25**   WB : £10   NB : £8
LISZT   Sonata in Bmin, Liebestraum 3 etc   Curzon

SXL6077   WBg : **£30**   WB : £8   NB : £4
Various   Birgit Nilsson sings German Opera   Nilsson
Royal Opera House, Covent Garden

SXL6078   WBg : **£20**   WB : £8   NB : £4
Various   After the Opera - Piano Improvisations   Halm

SXL6079 WBg : **£20** WB : £10 NB : £3
VERDI Great sceans from Falstaff Resnik,Sutherland
New Symphony Orchestra of London   Downes

SXL6080 WBg : **£10** WB : £5 NB : £2
HANDEL Alcina (Highlights) Sutherland
London Symphony Orchestra

SXL6081 WBg : **£30** WB : £10 NB : £5
BERLIOZ Nuites d'ete Crespin
Suisse Romande Orchestra Ansermet

SXL6082 WBg : **£40** WB : £8 NB : £4
BEETHOVEN Piano Concerto No.2 & No.4 Katchen
London Symphony Orchestra Gamba

SXL6083 WBg : **£35** WB : £8 NB : £6
Various Operatic Recital Merrill

SXL6084 WBg : **£20** WB : £9 NB : £4
SIBELIUS Symphony No.1, Karelia Suite
Vienna Philharmonic Orchestra Maazel

SXL6085 WBg : **£20** WB : £10 NB : £4
TCHAIKOVSKY Symphony No.5
Vienna Philharmonic Orchestra Maazel

SXL6086 WBg : **£40** WB : £15 NB : £6
SCHUBERT Symphony No.4 & No.5
Vienna Philharmonic Orchestra Munchinger

SXL6087 WBg : **£45** WB : £30 NB : £6
MOZART Clarinet works Vienna Octet

SXL6088 WBg : **£40** WB : £25 NB : £6
MOZART Sinfonia Concertante K364 etc Oistrakh
Moscow Philharmonic Orchestra Kondrashin

SXL6089 WBg : **£60** WB : £40 NB : £7
SCHUBERT Symphony No.9
Vienna Philharmonic Orchestra Kertesz

SXL6090   WBg : **£60**   WB : £45   NB : £7
SCHUBERT   Symphony No.8
Vienna Philharmonic Orchestra   Kertesz

SXL6091   WBg : **£65**   WB : £45   NB : £8
MOZART   Symphony No.36
Vienna Philharmonic Orchestra   Kertesz

SXL6092   WBg : **£30**   WB : £15   NB : £4
SCHUBERT   Death and the Maiden   Vienna Philharmonic Orchestra

SXL6093   WBg : **£50**   WB : £40   NB : £10
HAYDN   Quartets Op 32:3,5;Op 76,2   Janacek Quartet

SXL6094   WBg : **£20**   WB : £8   NB : £3
WAGNER   Ansermet conducts Wagner
Suisse Romande Orchestra   Ansermet

SXL6095   WBg : **£80**   WB : £50   NB : £10
SIBELIUS   Symphony No.4, Tapiola
Suisse Romande Orchestra   Ansermet

SXL6096   WBg : **£40**   WB : £20   NB : £4
BEETHOVEN   Symphony No.1 & No.8
Suisse Romande Orchestra   Ansermet

SXL6097   WBg : **£25**   WB : £10   NB : £6
BEETHOVEN   Piano Sonatas No.1, No.5, 6 & 7   Backhaus

SXL6098   WBg : **£20**   WB : £10   NB : £3
MARTIN   In Terra Pax   Suisse Romande Orchestra   Ansermet

SXL6099   WBg : **£20**   WB : £10   NB : £4
RACHMANINOV Piano Concerto In Cmin., Etudes-Tableaux
Ashkenazy   Moscow Philharmonic Orchestra

SXL6100   WBg : **£80**   WB : £60   NB : £12
SIBELIUS   Symphony No.2
Suisse Romande Orchestra   Ansermet

SXL6101   WBg : **£18**   WB : £8   NB : £6
BACH   Harpsichord Concerto No.1, 2
Stuttgart Chamber Orchestra   Munchinger

SXL6102   WBg : **£35**   WB : £15   NB : £4
PERGOLESI   Concertinos 1-4
Stuttgart Chamber Orchestra   Munchinger

SXL6103   WBg : **£30**   WB : £12   NB : £3
DVORAK   Quartets No.2-6   Janacek Quartet

SXL6104   WBg : **£40**   WB : £20   NB : £5
PERGOLESI   Flute Concerti Nos.1 & 2
Stuttgart Chamber Orchestra   Munchinger

SXL6105   WBg : **£20**   WB : £8   NB : £5
BRAHMS   Complete Piano Works Vol.1   Katchen

SXL6106   WBg : **£15**   WB : £6   NB : £2
Various   Spanish and Latin American Songs   Alva

SXL6107   WBg : **£30**   WB : £15   NB : £4
STRAUSS   Leider   Prey

SXL6108   WBg : **£40**   WB : £10   NB : £8
MOZART   Horn Concertos   Tuckwell
London Symphony Orchestra   Maag

SXL6109   WBg : **£60**   WB : £25   NB : £6
BEETHOVEN   Piano Concerto No.5   Katchen
London Symphony Orchestra   Gamba

SXL6110   WBg : **£15**   WB : £5   NB : £2
BRITTEN   Serenade Opus 31
London Symphony Orchestra   Britten

SXL6111   WBg : **£20**   WB : £10   NB : £4
BARTOK   Miraculous Mandarin Music for String, Percussion
London Symphony Orchestra   Solti

SXL6112   WBg : **£50**   WB : £30   NB : £8
MOZART / BACH / GLUCK   Flute Concerto 2
London Symphony Orchestra   Monteux

SXL6113   WBg : **£20**   WB : £9   NB : £3
MAHLER   Symphony No.1   London Symphony Orchestra   Solti

SXL6114 WBg : **£40** WB : £10 NB : £5
Various Operatic Recital Previdi
Royal Opera House, Covent Garden

SXL6115 WBg : **£24** WB : £10 NB : £4
DVORAK Symphony No.7
London Symphony Orchestra Kertesz

SXL6116 WBg : **£18** WB : £8 NB : £2
HANDEL Arias From Julius Caesar
New Symphony Orchestra London Bonynge

SXL6117 (==== Not Issued ====)

SXL6118 WBg : **£18** WB : £9 NB : £4
BRAHMS Complete Piano Works Vol.2 Katchen

SXL6119 WBg : **£80** WB : £60 NB : £10
MUSSORGSKY / KHOVANCHINA / GLINKA Night on Bare Mountain
Suisse Romande Orchestra Ansermet

SXL6120 WBg : **£100** WB : £75 NB : £8
PROKOFIEV Symphony No.5
Suisse Romande Orchestra Ansermet

SXL6121 WBg : **£70** WB : £45 NB : £7
BARTOK Dance Suite, 2 Portraits, Rumania
Suisse Romande Orchestra Ansermet

SXL6122 WBg : **£20** WB : £8 NB : £6
PUCCINI Tabarro Gardelli Florence Maggio Musicale

SXL6123 WBg : **£20** WB : £10 NB : £3
PUCCINI Suor Angelica Tebaldi

SXL6124 WBg : **£25** WB : £10 NB : £3
PUCCINI Gianni Schicchi Tebaldi
Florence Maggio Musicale Gardelli

SXL6125 WBg : **£45** WB : £30 NB : £6
SIBELIUS Symphony No.2
Vienna Philharmonic Orchestra Maazel

SXL6126   WBg : **£35**   WB : £20   NB : £5
Various   Recital   Teyte

SXL6127   WBg : **£25**   WB : £10   NB : £3
VERDI   La Traviata   Florence Maggio Musicale   Pritchard

SXL6128   WBg : **£12**   WB : £6   NB : £2
BELLINI   La Sonnambula   Sutherland
Florence Maggio Musicale   Bonynge

SXL6129   WBg : **£30**   WB : £12   NB : £6
BRAHMS   Complete Piano Works Vol.3   Katchen

SXL6130   WBg : **£30**   WB : £12   NB : £5
MOZART   Sonata for two pianos   Ashkenazy   Tuckwell

SXL6131   WBg : **£25**   WB : £8   NB : £3
MOZART   Complete Dances & Marches Vol.1
Vienna Mozart Ensemble   Boskovsky

SXL6132   WBg : **£25**   WB : £8   NB : £3
MOZART   Complete Dances & Marches Vol.2
Vienna Mozart Ensemble   Boskovsky

SXL6133   WBg : **£25**   WB : £8   NB : £3
MOZART   Complete Dances & Marches Vol.3
Vienna Mozart Ensemble   Boskovsky

SXL6134   WBg : **£20**   WB : £8   NB : £3
STRAUSS   Don Juan, Tod und Verklarung
Vienna Philharmonic Orchestra   Maazel

SXL6135   WBg : **£30**   WB : £12   NB : £6
SCHUBERT   Sonata in D op.53   Curzon

SXL6136   WBg : **£30**   WB : £10   NB : £4
KODALY   Hary Janos, Dances of Galanta
London Symphony Orchestra   Kertesz

SXL6137   WBg : **£28**   WB : £8   NB : £4
Various   Pas de Deux   London Symphony Orchestra   Bonynge

SXL6138
BRITTEN
Orchestra

WBg : **£50**
Symphony for Cello & Orchestra, Concerto for Cello &
Rostropovich
English Chamber Orchestra Britten

WB : £15   NB : £8

SXL6139
VERDI

WBg : **£10**
Choruses

WB : £4   NB : £2
St. Cecilia Academy, Rome Franci

SXL6140
Various
St. Cecilia Academy, Rome

WBg : **£16**
Opera Excerpts

WB : £5   NB : £2
Del Monaco
Franci

SXL6141
RESPIGHI
Suisse Romande Orchestra

WBg : **£65**
Pines and Fountains of Rome
Ansermet

WB : £25   NB : £8

SXL6142
WAGNER
Vienna Philharmonic Orchestra

WBg : **£18**
Siegfried forge scene,final due
Solti

WB : £8   NB : £3
Nilsson

SXL6143
CHOPIN 4

WBg : **£12**
Ballades & 3 Nouvelles Etudes

WB : £5   NB : £2
Ashkenazy

SXL6144
Various

WBg : **£18**
Love Duets

WB : £10   NB : £3
McCracken, Warfield

SXL6145

(==== Not Issued ====)

SXL6146
STRAUSS
Vienna Philharmonic Orchestra

WBg : **£25**
Der Rosenkavalier Scenes   Crespin
Varviso

WB : £8   NB : £4

SXL6147
Various
London Symphony Orchestra

WBg : **£40**
Russian and French Arias   Ghiaurov
Downes

WB : £15   NB : £4

SXL6148
BEETHOVEN

WBg : **£40**
Quartets

WB : £15   NB : £4
Weller Quartet

SXL6149
Various

WBg : **£40**
Vocal Recital

WB : £20   NB : £8
Horne Royal Opera House Lewis

SXL6150
MOZART

WBg : **£30**
Divertiment etc

WB : £15   NB : £4
Vienna Octet

SXL6151 WBg : **£85** WB : £45 NB : £10
BRAHMS String Quartets Weller Quartet

SXL6152 WBg : **£40** WB : £15 NB : £5
Various Recital Tebaldi

SXL6153 WBg : **£40** WB : £20 NB : £8
PERGOLESI Stabat Mater
Orchestra Rossini Di Napoli Caracciolo

SXL6154 WBg : **£12** WB : £6 NB : £2
BELLINI I Puritani Sutherland
Florence Maggio Musicale Bonynge

SXL6155 WBg : **£10** WB : £5 NB : £2
STRAUSS Die Fledermaus (Highlights) Gueden
Vienna Philharmonic Orchestra Karajan

SXL6156 WBg : **£10** WB : £6 NB : £3
BIZET Carmen (Highlights) Resnik,Sutherland
Suisse Romande Orchestra

SXL6157 WBg : **£10** WB : £6 NB : £4
TCHAIKOVSKY Symphony No.4
Vienna Philharmonic Orchestra Maazel

SXL6158 WBg : **£14** WB : £8 NB : £3
MILHAUD / POULENC / RACHMANINOV Music For Two Pianos
Eden, Tamir

SXL6159 WBg : **£20** WB : £8 NB : £6
TCHAIKOVSKY Symphony No.1
Vienna Philharmonic Orchestra Maazel

SXL6160 WBg : **£18** WB : £8 NB : £4
BRAHMS Complete Piano Works Vol.4 Katchen

SXL6161 WBg : **£25** WB : £14 NB : £4
SCHUBERT / SCHUMANN Goethe Lieder Prey

SXL6162 WBg : **£12** WB : £8 NB : £4
TCHAIKOVSKY Symphony No.2
Vienna Philharmonic Orchestra Maazel

SXL6163　　　WBg : **£20**　　WB : £8　　　　NB : £4
TCHAIKOVSKY　Symphony No.3
Vienna Philharmonic Orchestra　　　Maazel

SXL6164　　　WBg : **£24**　　WB : £10　　　NB : £6
TCHAIKOVSKY　Symphony No.6
Vienna Philharmonic Orchestra　　　Maazel

SXL6165　　　WBg : **£50**　　WB : £30　　　NB : £5
BERLIOZ　　　Ansermet conducts Berlioz
Suisse Romande Orchestra　　Ansermet

SXL6166　　　WBg : **£60**　　WB : £40　　　NB : £5
MENDELSSOHN　Ansermet conducts Mendelssohn
Suisse Romande Orchestra　　　　Ansermet

SXL6167　　　WBg : **£40**　　WB : £20　　　NB : £5
DEBUSSY　　　Ansermet conducts Debussy
Suisse Romande Orchestra　　　　Ansermet

SXL6168　　　WBg : **£40**　　WB : £20　　　NB : £5
CHABRIER　　Ansermet conducts Chabrier
Suisse Romande Orchestra　　　　Ansermet

SXL6169　　　WBg : **£40**　　WB : £20　　　NB : £4
DVORAK　　　Symphony No.8
Vienna Philharmonic Orchestra　　　Karajan

SXL6170　　　WBg : **£35**　　WB : £20　　　NB : £5
BEETHOVEN　Complete Music for Wind Band
London Wind Soloists　　　Brymer

SXL6171　　　WBg : **£100**　WB : £65　　　NB : £10
STRAVINSKY　Renard, Scherzo a la Russe
Suisse Romande Orchestra　　　Ansermet

SXL6172　　　WBg : **£40**　　WB : £25　　　NB : £5
BRAHMS　　　Symphony No.2
Vienna Philharmonic Orchestra　　　Kertesz

157

SXL6173   WBg : **£60**   WB : £35   NB : £6
SCHUBERT   String Quintet, Trio In B Flat Vienna Piano Quintet

SXL6174   WBg : **£16**   WB : £6   NB : £6
BACH / CHOPIN   Keyboard Concerto No.1, Piano Concerto No.2
Ashkenazy   London Symphony Orchestra

SXL6175   WBg : **£8**   WB : £4   NB : £2
BRITTEN   Cantata Misericordium Etc   Fischer-Dieskau
London Symphony Orchestra   Britten

SXL6176   WBg : **£30**   WB : £12   NB : £4
Various   Neopolitan Songs   Stefano

SXL6177   WBg : **£20**   WB : £5   NB : £2
Various   Classical Stereo Sampler   Various

SXL6178   WBg : **£15**   WB : £5   NB : £3
WAGNER   Tristan und Isolde love duet   Nilsson
Vienna Philharmonic Orchestra   Solti

SXL6179   WBg : **£50**   WB : £35   NB : £8
VIOTTI / BOCCHERINI   Violin Concerto No.3, Symphony in C
Prencipe   Napoli Orchestra   Caracciolo

SXL6180   WBg : **£35**   WB : £25   NB : £5
BLOMDAHL / LEYGRAF   Chamber Concerto, Concerto
London Symphony Orchestra   Ehrling

SXL6181   WBg : **£45**   WB : £30   NB : £7
BEETHOVEN / SCARLATTI   Sonata No.32   Michelangeli

SXL6182   WBg : **£45**   WB : £25   NB : £4
HAYDN   Quartets No.1-3   Weller Quartet

SXL6183   WBg : **£40**   WB : £20   NB : £4
HAYDN   Quartets No.4-6   Weller Quartet

SXL6184   WBg : **£85**   WB : £45   NB : £12
MENDELSSOHN / BRUCH   Violin Concerto   Voicou
London Symphony Orchestra   De Burgos

SXL6185 WBg : **£40** WB : £15 NB : £5
Various Songs from the Land of the Midnight Sun Nilsson
Vienna Opera Orchestra Bokstedt

SXL6186 WBg : **£40** WB : £20 NB : £4
SCHUBERT Symphony No.3 & No.6
Vienna Philharmonic Orchestra Munchinger

SXL6187 WBg : **£25** WB : £10 NB : £4
TCHAIKOVSKY Swan Lake, Sleeping Beauty
Vienna Philharmonic Orchestra Karajan

SXL6188 WBg : **£15** WB : £8 NB : £3
ADAM Le Diable a Quatre
London Symphony Orchestra Bonynge

SXL6189 WBg : **£40** WB : £20 NB : £4
BEETHOVEN Piano Concerto No.1, etc. Katchen
London Symphony Orchestra Gamba

SXL6190 WBg : **£15** WB : £6 NB : £2
VERDI Opera Excerpts Sutherland Various

SXL6191 WBg : **£30** WB : £8 NB : £3
HANDEL Arias Sutherland Various

SXL6192 WBg : **£20** WB : £8 NB : £3
BELLINI Recital Sutherland
London Symphony Orchestra Bonynge

SXL6193 WBg : **£15** WB : £6 NB : £2
Various Christmas Songs Sutherland Philharmonia Orchestra

SXL6194 WBg : **£25** WB : £12 NB : £4
RAMEAU / RAVEL / FRANCK Piano Recital Nishry

SXL6195 WBg : **£30** WB : £15 NB : £5
Various Jenny Lind Songs Soderstrom

SXL6196 WBg : **£90** WB : £65 NB : £12
BERG / SHOSTAKOVICH String Quartet Op 3, String Quartet No.10
Weller Quartet

SXL6197 WBg : **£25** WB : £10 NB : £3
MOZART Complete Dances & Marches Vol.4
Vienna Mozart Ensemble Boskovsky

SXL6198 WBg : **£25** WB : £10 NB : £3
MOZART Complete Dances & Marches Vol.5
Vienna Philharmonic Orchestra Boskovsky

SXL6199 WBg : **£20** WB : £10 NB : £3
MOZART Complete Dances & Marches Vol.6
Vienna Philharmonic Orchestra Boskovsky

SXL6200 WBg : **£15** WB : £10 NB : £5
Spoken Word The Voice of Winston Churchill

SXL6201 WBg : **£18** WB : £10 NB : £3
Various Opera Excerpts McCracken

SXL6202 WBg : **£40** WB : £25 NB : £5
BRUCKNER Symphony No.9
Vienna Philharmonic Orchestra Mehta

SXL6203 WBg : **£14** WB : £8 NB : £3
PROKOFIEV The Stone Flower (Highlights) Varviso
Suisse Romande Orchestra

SXL6204 WBg : **£80** WB : £60 NB : £10
RAVEL Daphnis & Chloe
Suisse Romande Orchestra Ansermet

SXL6205 WBg : **£40** WB : £20 NB : £4
SCHUMANN Ansermet conducts Schumann
Suisse Romande Orchestra Ansermet

SXL6206 WBg : **£20** WB : £8 NB : £3
TCHAIKOVSKY Romeo and Juliet, Hamlet
Vienna Philharmonic Orchestra Maazel

SXL6207 WBg : **£30** WB : £15 NB : £4
WOLF Morike - Leider Prey

SXL6208 WBg : **£50** WB : £30 NB : £6
BRITTEN / HINDEMITH Sinonetta Op 1 OctetVienna Octet

SXL6209　　　　WBg : **£25**　　　WB : £10　　　NB : £4
BARTOK / RAVEL　　　　Piano Concertos　　Katchen
London Symphony Orchestra Kertesz

SXL6210　　　　WBg : **£10**　　　WB : £6　　　NB : £2
ROSSINI　　　　L'italiana In Algeri (Highlights)
Florence Maggio Musicale　　　　　　Varviso

SXL6211　　　　(==== Not Issued ====)

SXL6212　　　　WBg : **£20**　　　WB : £10　　　NB : £3
BARTOK　　　　Concerto for Orchestra
London Symphony Orchestra　　　　Solti

SXL6213　　　　WBg : **£60**　　　WB : £40　　　NB : £8
MENDELSSOHN / SCHUMANN　　　Midsummer Nights Dream,
Symphony No.3　　London Symphony Orchestra De Burgos

SXL6214　　　　WBg : **£20**　　　WB : £10　　　NB : £4
SCHUBERT　　　　Etudes　　Ashkenazy

SXL6215　　　　WBg : **£12**　　　WB : £4　　　NB : £2
CHOPIN / RAVEL　　Scherzo op. 54, Nocturnes op. 62　　Ashkenazy

SXL6216　　　　(==== Not Issued ====)

SXL6217　　　　WBg : **£25**　　　WB : £10　　　NB : £4
BRAHMS　　　　Complete Piano Works Vol.5　　Katchen

SXL6218　　　　WBg : **£25**　　　WB : £8　　　NB : £4
BRAHMS　　　　Complete Piano Works Vol.7　　Katchen

SXL6219　　　　WBg : **£25**　　　WB : £8　　　NB : £4
BRAHMS　　　　Complete Piano Works Vol.6　　Katchen

SXL6220　　　　WBg : **£8**　　　WB : £4　　　NB : £2
WAGNER　　　　Gotterdamerung (Highlights)
Vienna Philharmonic Orchestra　　　　Solti

SXL6221　　　　WBg : **£25**　　　WB : £8　　　NB : £3
Various　　　　Nancy Tatum Recital　　Quadri
Vienna Opera Orchestra

SXL6222-4   (===== Not Issued =====)

SXL6225   WBg : **£30**   WB : £20   NB : £4
MOZART   Symphony No.40 & No.41
New Philharmonia Orchestra   Giulini

SXL6226   WBg : **£40**   WB : £20   NB : £4
HAYDN   Symphony No.22 & No.90 (The Philosopher)
Suisse Romande Orchestra   Ansermet

SXL6227   WBg : **£40**   WB : £20   NB : £4
BRUCKNER   Symphony No.4   London Symphony Orchestra   Kertesz

SXL6228   WBg : **£25**   WB : £8   NB : £4
BRAHMS   Complete Piano Works Vol.8   Katchen

SXL6229   (===== Not Issued =====)

SXL6230   WBg : **£25**   WB : £15   NB : £3
STRAVINSKY   Pulcinella   Suisse Romande Orchestra   Ansermet

SXL6231   WBg : **£20**   WB : £6   NB : £3
LEHAR   Der Graf von Luxenburg (Highlights)   Gueden
Vienna Volksoper Orchestra

SXL6232   WBg : **£40**   WB : £20   NB : £4
BEETHOVEN   Symphony No.3
Vienna Philharmonic Orchestra   Schmitt-Isserstedt

SXL6233   WBg : **£15**   WB : £8   NB : £2
BEETHOVEN   Symphony No.9
Vienna Philharmonic Orchestra   Schmitt-Isserstedt

SXL6234   WBg : **£20**   WB : £6   NB : £2
Various   Popular Recitals   Del Monaco

SXL6235   WBg : **£18**   WB : £8   NB : £2
Various   Favourite Overtures Of The 19th Century
London Symphony Orchestra   Bonynge

SXL6236   WBg : **£16**   WB : £6   NB : £2
SIBELIUS   Symphony No.5 & No.7
Vienna Philharmonic Orchestra   Maazel

SXL6237   WBg : **£20**   WB : £5   NB : £2
Various   Classical Stereo Sampler   Various artists

SXL6238-41   WBg : **£135**   WB : £100   NB : £20
Various   Vienna Chamber Music Festival   Weller Quartet

SXL6242-4   WBg : **£30**   WB : £12   NB : £3
STRAUSS   Invitation to a Strauss Festival
Vienna Philharmonic Orchestra   Boskowsky

SXL6245   WBg : **£20**   WB : £10   NB : £3
Various   Folk songs & Spirituals   Weathers

SXL6246   WBg : **£30**   WB : £12   NB : £3
MOZART   Complete Dances & Marches Vol.7
Vienna Philharmonic Orchestra   Boskowsky

SXL6247   WBg : **£30**   WB : £12   NB : £3
MOZART   Complete Dances & Marches Vol.8
Vienna Philharmonic Orchestra   Boskowsky

SXL6248   WBg : **£30**   WB : £12   NB : £3
MOZART   Complete Dances & Marches Vol.9
Vienna Mozart Ensemble   Boskowsky

SXL6249   WBg : **£30**   WB : £6   NB : £2
Various   Opera Recital   Gwyneth Jones
Vienna Opera Orchestra   Quadri

SXL6250   (==== Not Issued ====)

SXL6251   WBg : **£5**   WB : £4   NB : £2
Various   Easter Mass in St Peters Square   Pope Paul VI

SXL6252   WBg : **£18**   WB : £6   NB : £2
MOZART / BEETHOVEN   Quintets In E Flat Major Ashkenazy
London Wind Soloists

SXL6253   WBg : **£16**   WB : £6   NB : £2
DVORAK   Symphony No.6 "Carnival"
London Symphony Orchestra   Kertesz

SXL6254   WBg : **£20**   WB : £10   NB : £3
SHIELD   Rosina   London Symphony Orchestra   Bonynge

SXL6255   WBg : **£18**   WB : £6   NB : £2
COWARD   Songs of Noel Coward   Sutherland

SXL6256   WBg : **£24**   WB : £10   NB : £3
Various   New Year's Concert
Vienna Philharmonic Orchestra   Boskowsky

SXL6257   WBg : **£16**   WB : £10   NB : £2
DVORAK   Symphony No.4 in Dmin.
London Symphony Orchestra   Kertesz

SXL6258   WBg : **£80**   WB : £50   NB : £10
MOZART   Quartet K575, K590   Weller Quartet

SXL6259   WBg : **£20**   WB : £10   NB : £6
MOZART   Piano Concerto No.8 & No.9   Ashkenazy
London Symphony Orchestra   Kertesz

SXL6260   WBg : **£16**   WB : £5   NB : £2
SCHUBERT   Sonatas D664, D784   Ashkenazy

SXL6261   WBg : **£15**   WB : £6   NB : £3
WAGNER   Gotterdamerung, Salome Scenes   Nilsson
Vienna Philharmonic Orchestra   Solti

SXL6262   WBg : **£10**   WB : £6   NB : £4
Various   Operatic Arias   Geraint Evans

SXL6263   WBg : **£45**   WB : £30   NB : £6
BORODIN / GLINKA   Romantic Russia
London Symphony Orchestra   Solti

SXL6264   WBg : **£10**   WB : £6   NB : £2
BRITTEN   School Concert   Boys of Downside School   Britten

SXL6265   WBg : **£60**   WB : £40   NB : £6
PETTERSSON   Symphony No.2   Sweedish RSO   Westerberg

SXL6266   WBg : **£50**   WB : £35   NB : £5
BACH   Cantatas 45, 105
Suisse Romande Orchestra   Ansermet

SXL6267   WBg : **£24**   WB : £14   NB : £5
Various   Opera Recital   Lorengar
St. Cecilia Academy, Rome   Patane

SXL6268   WBg : **£30**   WB : £15   NB : £3
PIZETTI   La Pisanella   Suisse Romande Orchestra   Gardelli

SXL6269   WBg : **£30**   WB : £20   NB : £3
GLAZUNOV   Ansermet conducts Glazunov
Suisse Romande Orchestra   Ansermet

SXL6270   WBg : **£30**   WB : £20   NB : £4
BEETHOVEN   Symphony No.7, Prometheus
Vienna Philharmonic Orchestra   Abbado

SXL6271   WBg : **£45**   WB : £30   NB : £5
ROSSINI   Introducing..   Rossini de Napoli   Varviso

SXL6272   WBg : **£20**   WB : £8   NB : £3
BACH   St. Matthews Passion (highlights)
Stuttgart Chamber Orchestra   Munchinger

SXL6273   WBg : **£15**   WB : £8   NB : £2
DVORAK   Symphony No.5 in Fmaj
London Symphony Orchestra   Kertesz

SXL6274   WBg : **£20**   WB : £10   NB : £3
BEETHOVEN   Symphony No.4, Consecration House Ov
Vienna Philharmonic Orchestra   Schmitt-Isserstedt

SXL6275   WBg : **£25**   WB : £10   NB : £3
MOZART   Complete Dances & Marches Vol.10
Vienna Philharmonic Orchestra   Boskowsky

SXL6276   WBg : **£8**   WB : £4   NB : £2
BEETHOVEN   Fidelio (Highlights)
Vienna Philharmonic Orchestra   Maazel

SXL6277-80 No Stereo - See LXT6277-80

SXL6281 WBg : **£35** WB : £20 NB : £4
STILL / RUBBRA Elegie, Choral Suit Ambrosian Choir Case

SXL6282-4 WBg : **£45** WB : £30 NB : £10
Various VPO Concert Vienna Philharmonic Orchestra Karajan

SXL6285 WBg : **£65** WB : £20 NB : £9
STRAUSS Horn Concertos Tuckwell
London Symphony Orchestra Kertesz

SXL6286 WBg : **£30** WB : £15 NB : £4
PROKOFIEV Romeo and Juliet, Chout
London Symphony Orchestra Abbado

SXL6287 WBg : **£50** WB : £30 NB : £5
FALLA El Amour Brujo Philharmonia Orchestra de Burgos

SXL6288 WBg : **£18** WB : £8 NB : £2
DVORAK Symphony No.1 London Symphony Orchestra Kertesz

SXL6289 WBg : **£15** WB : £8 NB : £2
DVORAK Symphony No.2 London Symphony Orchestra Kertesz

SXL6290 WBg : **£20** WB : £8 NB : £2
DVORAK Symphony No.3, Hussite Overture
London Symphony Orchestra Kertesz

SXL6291 WBg : **£45** WB : £25 NB : £3
DVORAK Symphony No.9 in Emn, Othello Overture
London Symphony Orchestra Kertesz

SXL6292 WBg : **£40** WB : £15 NB : £4
WAGNER Overtures Vienna Philharmonic Orchestra Kertesz

SXL6293 WBg : **£25** WB : £15 NB : £3
SCHUBERT Symphony No.9
Vienna Philharmonic Orchestra Karajan

SXL6294 WBg : **£30** WB : £15 NB : £3
SIBELIUS Symphony No.2
Vienna Philharmonic Orchestra Maazel

SXL6295 WBg : **£25** WB : £10 NB : £4
BEETHOVEN Piano Concerto Schmit-Isserstedt
Vienna Philharmonic Orchestra

SXL6296 WBg : **£25** WB : £15 NB : £3
Various Munchinger miniatures
Stuttgart Chamber Orchestra Munchinger

SXL6297 WBg : **£25** WB : £10 NB : £3
MOZART Piano Concerto No.20 & No.25 Katchen
Stuttgart Chamber Orchestra Munchinger

SXL6298 WBg : **£30** WB : £10 NB : £3
LISZT / WAGNER Preludes, Lohnegrin, Parsifal
Vienna Philharmonic Orchestra Mehta

SXL6299 WBg : **£25** WB : £8 NB : £3
VERDI / PUCCINI Arias Quadri
Vienna Opera Orchestra Weathers

SXL6300 WBg : **£85** WB : £25 NB : £10
BEETHOVEN Piano Sonatas No.4, 25 & 31 Backhaus

SXL6301 WBg : **£85** WB : £30 NB : £8
MOZART Piano Sonatas Backhaus

SXL6302 WBg : **£40** WB : £25 NB : £4
LALO Ansermet conducts Lalo
Suisse Romande Orchestra Ansermet

SXL6303 WBg : **£10** WB : £6 NB : £3
BRAHMS Sonata for two Pianos, Variations for two Pianos
Eden, Tamir

SXL6304 WBg : **£20** WB : £12 NB : £5
STRAUSS Bourgeois Gentilhomme (Highlights)
Vienna Philharmonic Orchestra Maazel, Gulda, Boskovsky

SXL6305 WBg : **£10** WB : £6 NB : £2
BOITO Mefistofele (Highlights) Ghiaurov
Rome Opera Chorus Varviso

| **SXL6306** | WBg : **£20** | WB : £8 | NB : £3 |
| Various | Operatic Arias | Suliotis Rome Opera Chorus Fabritiis | |

| **SXL6307** | WBg : **£25** | WB : £14 | NB : £4 |
| STRAUSS | Leider | Prey | |

SXL6308	WBg : **£60**	WB : £35	NB : £6
PROKOFIEV	Scythian Suite, Prodigal Son		
Suisse Romande Orchestra		Ansermet	

SXL6309	WBg : **£18**	WB : £8	NB : £4
BRAHMS	Piano Concerto No.2	Ashkenazy	
London Symphony Orchestra		Mehta	

SXL6310	WBg : **£40**	WB : £25	NB : £4
CHAUSSON / FRANCK	Symphony No.in B,		
Suisse Romande Orchestra		Ansermet	

| **SXL6311** | WBg : **£50** | WB : £25 | NB : £5 |
| TCHAIKOVSKY | Suite No.3 | Suisse Romande Orchestra Ansermet | |

SXL6312	WBg : **£100**	WB : £65	NB : £14
TCHAIKOVSKY / RESPIEGHI		Suite No.4, Rossiana	Ricci
Suisse Romande Orchestra		Ansermet	

SXL6313	WBg : **£35**	WB : £20	NB : £4
Various	What Everyone Should Know About Music		
Suisse Romande Orchestra		Ansermet	

| **SXL6314** | WBg : **£15** | WB : £6 | NB : £2 |
| SIBELIUS | Songs | Krause | |

| **SXL6315** | WBg : **£20** | WB : £8 | NB : £2 |
| WILBYE | Madrigals, 3,4,5 and 6 Parts Pears | | |

SXL6316	WBg : **£10**	WB : £6	NB : £2
BRITTEN	Illuminations	Pears	
English Chamber Orchestra		Britten	

| **SXL6317** | (==== Not Issued ====) | | |

| **SXL6318** | WBg : **£20** | WB : £8 | NB : £4 |
| BACH | Music for four Harpsichords | | Malcolm |

SXL6319   WBg : **£50**   WB : £30   NB : £6
SPOHR   Nonet, Double Quartet   Vienna Octet

SXL6320   WBg : **£20**   WB : £10   NB : £3
WEBER / SCHUMANN / SCHUBERT   Romantic Overtures
Vienna Philharmonic Orchestra   Munchinger

SXL6321   WBg : **£35**   WB : £20   NB : £5
BRAHMS   Violin Sonatas No.1, No.2 & No.3   Suk   Katchen

SXL6322   WBg : **£50**   WB : £16   NB : £8
BRAHMS   Piano Concerto No.2   Backhaus
Vienna Philharmonic Orchestra   Bohm

SXL6323   WBg : **£28**   WB : £10   NB : £3
TCHAIKOVSKY   Symphony No.4
Los Angeles Philharmonic Orchestra   Mehta

SXL6324   WBg : **£40**   WB : £20   NB : £4
STRAVINSKY   Petrushka, Circus Polka
Los Angeles Philharmonic Orchestra   Mehta

SXL6325   WBg : **£25**   WB : £12   NB : £3
SCHOENBERG / SCRIABIN   Poem Of Ecstasy, Transfig. Night
Los Angeles Philharmonic Orchestra   Mehta

SXL6326   WBg : **£25**   WB : £14   NB : £4
Various   Operatic Arias   King
Vienna Opera Orchestra   Bernet

SXL6327   WBg : **£15**   WB : £8   NB : £4
Various   Operatic Arias   Krause

SXL6328   WBg : **£28**   WB : £12   NB : £8
MOUSSORGSKY   Pictures at an Exhibition for orch. & piano
Ashkenazy   Los Angeles Philharmonic Orchestra   Mehta

SXL6329   WBg : **£28**   WB : £10   NB : £3
BEETHOVEN   Symphony No.6
Vienna Philharmonic Orchestra   Schmitt-Isserstedt

SXL6330 WBg : **£28** WB : £10 NB : £3
MOZART Serenade No.4, Horn Ronda
Vienna Mozart Ensemble Boskovsky

SXL6331 WBg : **£120** WB : £35 NB : £15
MOZART / HAYDN Dittersdorf Weller Quartet

SXL6332 WBg : **£24** WB : £10 NB : £2
STRAUSS New Year's Concert
Vienna Philharmonic Orchestra Boskovsky

SXL6333 WBg : **£20** WB : £8 NB : £4
Various Song Recital Crespin

SXL6334 WBg : **£15** WB : £8 NB : £4
CHOPIN Piano Recital - 4 Scherzi, Prelude, Barcarolle Ashkenazy

SXL6335 WBg : **£18** WB : £8 NB : £4
BEETHOVEN Hammerklavier Sonata, Op.106 Ashkenazy

SXL6336 WBg : **£25** WB : £15 NB : £5
Various American songs Tatum, Parsons

SXL6337 WBg : **£18** WB : £8 NB : £2
BACH Six Symphonies For Wind
London Wind Soloists Brymer

SXL6338 WBg : **£28** WB : £10 NB : £3
HAYDN The 7 Divertimenti London Wind Soloists Brymer

SXL6339 WBg : **£20** WB : £8 NB : £2
GLUCK Don Juan Complete Ballet
Acadamy of St. Martin in the Fields Marriner

SXL6340 WBg : **£20** WB : £10 NB : £3
BRAHMS Serenade 1 London Symphony Orchestra Kertesz

SXL6341 WBg : **£10** WB : £8 NB : £4
Various Operatic Recital Marimpietri, Benelli

SXL6342 WBg : **£20** WB : £10 NB : £3
RACHMANINOV Symphony No.2
Suisse Romande Orchestra Kletzki

SXL6343   WBg : **£30**   WB : £20   NB : £3
BERLIOZ   Symphonie Fantastique
Suisse Romande Orchestra   Ansermet

SXL6344   WBg : **£15**   WB : £8   NB : £2
SCHUBERT / STRAUSS   Dances of Old Vienna
Vienna Philharmonic Orchestra   Boskovsky

SXL6345   WBg : **£20**   WB : £10   NB : £8
Various   French Operatic Arias   Horne
Vienna Opera Orchestra   Lewis

SXL6346   WBg : **£18**   WB : £8   NB : £4
PROKOFIEV   Piano Sonata No.7   Ashkenazy

SXL6347   WBg : **£12**   WB : £8   NB : £2
SCHUBERT   18 Songs   Krenn

SXL6348   WBg : **£20**   WB : £10   NB : £3
DVORAK   Concert Overtures
Vienna Philharmonic Orchestra   Kertesz

SXL6349   WBg : **£18**   WB : £10   NB : £6
BACH   Arias   Horne

SXL6350   WBg : **£20**   WB : £10   NB : £2
BIZET   Symphony in C, L'Arlesienne Suites
Suisse Romande Orchestra   Gibson

SXL6351   WBg : **£80**   WB : £40   NB : £10
DEBUSSY   Sonata for Violin & Piano   Voicou

SXL6352   WBg : **£25**   WB : £12   NB : £3
BORODIN / TCHAIKOVSKY   Symphony No.2, Francesca Rimini
Suisse Romande Orchestra   Varviso

SXL6353   WBg : **£40**   WB : £12   NB : £8
MOZART   Piano Concerto No.6 & No.20   Ashkenazy
London Symphony Orchestra   Kertesz

SXL6354   WBg : **£30**   WB : £15   NB : £8
MOZART   Piano Concerto K488, K491 Curzon
London Symphony Orchestra   Kertesz

SXL6355   WBg : **£80**   WB : £50   NB : £8
ALBENIZ   Suite Espanola   Philharmonia Orchestra   De Burgos

SXL6356   WBg : **£20**   WB : £6   NB : £2
SCHUMANN   Symphony No.3 & No.4
Vienna Philharmonic Orchestra   Solti

SXL6357   WBg : **£15**   WB : £10   NB : £3
BARTOK / POULENC   Piano & Percussion Sonata, Piano Sonata
Eden, Tamir

SXL6358   WBg : **£50**   WB : £16   NB : £7
BEETHOVEN   Piano Sonatas No.9, No.11 & No.20   Backhaus

SXL6359   WBg : **£50**   WB : £16   NB : £7
BEETHOVEN   Piano Sonatas No.2, No.10 & No.19   Backhaus

SXL6360   WBg : **£20**   WB : £6   NB : £2
HANDEL   Overtures & Sinfonias
English Chamber Orchestra   Bonynge

SXL6361   WBg : **£20**   WB : £10   NB : £3
STRAUSS   Recital   Weathers

SXL6362   WBg : **£30**   WB : £5   NB : £2
Various   Stereo Sampler

SXL6363   WBg : **£20**   WB : £10   NB : £2
MENDELSSOHN   Symphony No.3 & No.4
London Symphony Orchestra   Abbado

SXL6364   WBg : **£20**   WB : £10   NB : £3
SIBELIUS   Symphony No.3 & No.6
Vienna Philharmonic Orchestra   Maazel

SXL6365   WBg : **£18**   WB : £8   NB : £3
SIBELIUS   Symphony No.4
Vienna Philharmonic Orchestra   Maazel

SXL6366   WBg : **£30**   WB : £15   NB : £2
MOZART   Serenades Vol.2
Vienna Mozart Ensemble   Boskovsky

SXL6367   WBg : **£24**   WB : £10   NB : £3
STRAUSS   Don Quixote   Vienna Philharmonic Orchestra   Maazel

SXL6368   WBg : **£15**   WB : £8   NB : £3
BRAHMS / DVORAK   Serenades No.2 , "For Wind"
London Symphony Orchestra   Kertesz

SXL6369   WB : **£15**   NB : £3
HANDEL   12 Grand Concertos Op. 6 Vol.1
Acadamy of St. Martin in the Fields   Marriner

SXL6370   WB : **£15**   NB : £3
HANDEL   12 Grand Concertos Op. 6 Vol.2
Acadamy of St. Martin in the Fields   Marriner

SXL6371   WB : **£15**   NB : £3
HANDEL   12 Grand Concertos Op. 6 Vol.3
Acadamy of St. Martin in the Fields   Marriner

SXL6372   WB : **£50**   NB : £8
MOZART   Symphony No.40, Serenata Notturna
English Chamber Orchestra   Britten

SXL6373   WB : **£15**   NB : £5
BEETHOVEN   Piano Sonata No.32, Bagatelle   Katchen

SXL6374   WB : **£10**   NB : £2
BERWALD   Sinfonie Singulaire
London Symphony Orchestra   Ehrling

SXL6375   WB : **£30**   NB : £3
WEBER / VIVALDI / HUMMEL   Bassoon Concertos, etc.
Suisse Romande Orchestra   Ansermet

SXL6376   WB : **£15**   NB : £4
VERDI   Excerpts   Jones

SXL6377   WB : **£10**   NB : £3
VERDI   Arias   Pavarotti

SXL6378   WB : **£10**   NB : £3
LISZT / MESSIAEN   Piano Recital   Kars

SXL6379   WB : **£30**   NB : £3
STRAUSS   Also Sprach Zarathustra
Los Angeles Philharmonic Orchestra   Mehta

SXL6380   WB : **£25**   NB : £3
TCHAIKOVSKY   Symphony No.5   Israel Philharmonic Orchestra   Mehta

SXL6381   WB : **£25**   NB : £3
DVORAK   Symphony No.7   Israel Philharmonic Orchestra   Mehta

SXL6382   WB : **£28**   NB : £3
STRAUSS   Ein Helden Leben
Los Angeles Philharmonic Orchestra   Mehta

SXL6383   WB : **£18**   NB : £2
Various   Overtures Of Old Vienna
Vienna Philharmonic Orchestra   Boskovsky

SXL6384   WB : **£15**   NB : £2
WEELKES   Madrigals   Pears   Wilbye Consort

SXL6385   WB : **£24**   NB : £6
HAYDN / BACH   Overture In D, Harpsichord Concertos.
Malcolm   Acadamy of St. Martin in the Fields   Marriner

SXL6386   WB : **£15**   NB : £3
BRAHMS   Rinaldo & "Schicksalslied"
New Philharmonia Orchestra   Abbado

SXL6387   WB : **£35**   NB : £12
BRAHMS   Piano Trio No.1 & No.3   Katchen Suk Starker

SXL6388   WB : **£35**   NB : £4
COPELAND   Lincon Portrait
Los Angeles Philharmonic Orchestra   Mehta

SXL6389   WB : **£15**   NB : £4
DVORAK / BRAHMS   Hungarian-Slavonic Dances   Eden, Tamir

SXL6390   WB : **£25**   NB : £3
SCHOENBERG   Variations Op 31, Symphony No.Op 9
Los Angeles Philharmonic Orchestra   Mehta

SXL6391   WB : **£15**   NB : £2
BRITTEN   Songs & Proverbs William Blake   Pears   Dieskau

SXL6392   WB : **£40**   NB : £4
BACH   Cantatas 101, 130
Suisse Romande Orchestra   Ansermet

SXL6393   WB : **£50**   NB : £10
BRITTEN   The 2 Suites for solo Cello   Rostropovich

SXL6394   WB : **£25**   NB : £3
HONEGGER   Symphony No.3 & No.4
Suisse Romande Orchestra   Ansermet

SXL6395   WB : **£40**   NB : £4
LALO / MAGNARD   Scherzo Orch, Symphony No.3
Suisse Romande Orchestra   Ansermet

SXL6396   WB : **£30**   NB : £3
BEETHOVEN   Symphony No.5 & No.8
Vienna Philharmonic Orchestra   Schmitt-Isserstedt

SXL6397   WB : **£24**   NB : £3
BACH / SALLERI   Concerto in C, Sinphony in D etc
English Chamber Orchestra   Bonynge

SXL6398   WB : **£25**   NB : £4
JANACEK   Sinfonetta   London Symphony Orchestra   Abbado

SXL6399   WB : **£30**   NB : £4
RACHMANINOV / MUSSORGSKY   Symphony No.3, Night on Bare
MountainSuisse Romande Orchestra   Kletzki

SXL6400   WB : **£15**   NB : £2
BACH   Magnificat Dmaj, Cantata 10
Stuttgart Chamber Orchestra   Munchinger

SXL6401   WB : **£30**   NB : £3
RESPIGHI   Birds, Pines of Rome, Fountains of Rome
London Symphony Orchestra   Kertesz

SXL6402   WB : **£20**   NB : £3
MOZART   Symphony No.31, No.32 & No.35
Stuttgart Philharmonic Orchestra   Munchinger

SXL6403   WB : **£8**   NB : £3
STRAVINSKY   Rite of Spring etc   Eden, Tamir

SXL6404   WB : **£30**   NB : £3
MENDELSSOHN Midsummer Nights Dream
Philharmonia Orchestra   De Burgos

SXL6405   WB : **£15**   NB : £2
BRITTEN   English Music for Strings
English Chamber Orchestra Britten

SXL6406   WB : **£10**   NB : £2
GLIERE / STRAVINSKY   Russian Rarities
London Symphony Orchestra   Bonynge

SXL6407   WB : **£15**   NB : £2
BURGMULLER   La Peri   London Symphony Orchestra   Bonynge

SXL6408   WB : **£20**   NB : £8
BRAHMS / FRANCK   Horn Trio, Violin Sonata
Ashkenazy Perlman Tuckwell

SXL6409   WB : **£50**   NB : £10
MOZART   Masonic Funeral Music
London Symphony Orchestra   Kertesz

SXL6410   WB : **£10**   NB : £2
BRITTEN   Salute to Percy Grainger   Pears
English Chamber Orchestra Britten

SXL6411   WB : **£30**   NB : £8
PROKOFIEV / RAVEL   Piano Concerto No.3, Piano Concerto for the
Left Hand. Katchen   London Symphony Orchestra Kertesz

SXL6412   (=== Not Issued ===)

SXL6413   WB : **£25**   NB : £3
BRITTEN   A Charm of Lullabies   Greevy

SXL6414   WB : **£60**   NB : £8
MENDELSSOHN / BORODIN   Sextet, Quintet   Vienna Octet

SXL6415   WB : **£20**   NB : £5
LISZT / CHOPIN   Piano Recital   Davies

SXL6416   WB : **£18**   NB : £6
BEETHOVEN   Piano Sonatas No.3, No.13 & No.24   Backhaus

SXL6417   WB : **£18**   NB : £6
BEETHOVEN   Piano Sonatas No.16, No.22 & No.27   Backhaus

SXL6418   WB : **£20**   NB : £3
EINUM / SCHUBERT   Philadelphia Symphony, Symphony No.8
Vienna Philharmonic Orchestra   Mehta

SXL6419   WB : **£10**   NB : £2
STRAUSS   Vienna Imperial, New Years 1969
Vienna Philharmonic Orchestra   Boskovsky

SXL6420   WB : **£30**   NB : £3
MOZART   Serenades Vol.3
Vienna Philharmonic Orchestra   Boskovsky

SXL6421   WB : **£10**   NB : £2
WAGNER   Excerpts from The Ring
Vienna Philharmonic Orchestra   Solti

SXL6422   WB : **£20**   NB : £2
Various   French Opera Overtures
Philharmonia Orchestra   Bonynge

SXL6423   WB : **£80**   NB : £12
BEETHOVEN / HAYDN   String Quartet No.12, String Quartet No.83
Weller Quartet

SXL6424   WB : **£50**   NB : £6
Various   Childrens Songs   Gueden

SXL6425   (==== Not Issued ====)

SXL6426   WB : **£200**   NB : £30
BRIDGE / SCHUBERT   Cello Sonato, Arpeggion   Rostropovich
Britten

SXL6427   WB : **£25**   NB : £2
SCHUBERT   Symphony No.9
Stuttgart Philharmonic Orchestra   Munchinger

SXL6428   WB : **£30**   NB : £8
BRITTEN / TCHAIKOVSKY   Songs By Britten & Tchaikovsky
Vishnevskaya

SXL6429   WB : **£15**   NB : £4
VERDI   Arias   Del Monaco

SXL6430   WB : **£15**   NB : £4
Various   Flute Recital   Pepin

SXL6431   WB : **£40**   NB : £4
SIBELIUS   Symphony No.4
Finnish Symphony Orchestra   Berglund

SXL6432   WB : **£40**   NB : £4
SIBELIUS   Tapiola   Finnish Symphony Orchestra   Berglund

SXL6433   WB : **£40**   NB : £4
SIBELIUS   Symphony No.5   Panula

SXL6434   WB : **£50**   NB : £6
SIBELIUS   Finlandia   Panula

SXL6435   NB : **£12**
DELIUS / DEBUSSY   Piano Concerto   Kars
London Symphony Orchestra   Gibson

SXL6436   WB : **£24**   NB : £3
BEETHOVEN   Dances & Romances
Vienna Mozart Ensemble   Boskovsky

SXL6437   WB : **£20**   NB : £3
BEETHOVEN   Symphony No.1 & No.2   Schmitt-Isserstedt

SXL6438   WB : **£20**   NB : £3
BEETHOVEN   Creatures of Prometheus
Israel Philharmonic Orchestra   Mehta

SXL6439   WB : **£10**   NB : £6
MOZART   Piano Sonata K310, K576   Ashkenazy

SXL6440   WB : **£35**   NB : £25
BLOCH   Voice in Wilderness, Schelmo   Starker
Israel Philharmonic Orchestra   Mehta

SXL6441   WB : **£15**   NB : £8
GABRIELI   Gabrielli Recital   Runnet
Stuttgart Chamber Orchestra   Munchinger

SXL6442   WB : **£20**   NB : £3
STRAUSS   Sinfonia Domestica
Los Angeles Philharmonic Orchestra   Mehta

SXL6443   WB : **£12**   NB : £3
VERDI   Great Scenes   Ghiaurov
London Symphony Orchestra   Abbado

SXL6444   WB : **£30**   NB : £3
STRAVINSKY   Rite of Spring etc
Los Angeles Philharmonic Orchestra   Mehta

SXL6445   WB : **£20**   NB : £3
HINDEMITH / LUTOSLAWSKI   Mathis Der Maler, Conc.For Orch.
Suisse Romande Orchestra   Kletzki

SXL6446   WB : **£12**   NB : £4
MAHLER / WAGNER   Kindertotenleider, Wesendonckleider
Horne   Royal Philharmonic Orchestra   Lewis

SXL6447   NB : **£10**
BEETHOVEN   Symphony No.7
Vienna Philharmonic Orchestra   Schmitt-Isserstedt

SXL6448   WB : **£15**   NB : £3
TCHAIKOVSKY   1812 Overture, Romeo & Juliet
Los Angeles Philharmonic Orchestra   Mehta

SXL6449   NB : **£4**
BRITTEN   Serenade, Illuminations   Pears
London Symphony Orchestra   Britten

SXL6450   NB : **£6**
BRITTEN   Young Persons Guide , Variation on a theme of Frank
Bridge   London Symphony Orchestra   Britten

SXL6451   NB : **£6**
Various   Operatic Recital   Domingo

SXLA6452-61   NB : **£25**
BEETHOVEN   The Complete Piano Sonatas   Backhaus

SXL6462   NB : **£20**
KREUTZER / BERWALD   Grand Septet   Vienna Octet

SXL6463   NB : **£30**
DVORAK / SPOHR   Quintet, Quintet   Vienna Octet

SXL6464   NB : **£25**
BEETHOVEN   String Quintet, String Sextet Vienna Octet

SXL6465   NB : **£18**
BEETHOVEN   Egmont   Vienna Philharmonic Orchestra   Szell

SXL6466   NB : **£8**
GRIEG   Nocturnes etc.   De Larrocha

SXL6467   NB : **£10**
Various   Spanish Music   De Larrocha

SXL6468   NB : **£6**
Various   Welsh Music for Strings
English Chamber Orchestra   Atherton

SXL6469   NB : **£12**
PROKOFIEV   Symphony No.1 & No.3
London Symphony Orchestra   Abbado

SXLB 6470-5   NB : **£20**
BEETHOVEN   The 9 Symphonies
Vienna Philharmonic Orchestra   Schmitt-Isserstedt

SXLC6476-80 NB : **£ 20**
TCHAIKOVSKY The Six Symphonies
Vienna Philharmonic Orchestra Maazel

SXL6481 NB : **£ 35**
SCHUBERT String Quartet No.12 Weller Quartet

SXL6482 NB : **£ 10**
SAINT-SAENS Symphony No.3
Los Angeles Philharmonic Orchestra Mehta

SXL6483 NB : **£ 6**
SCHUBERT Symphony No.4 & No.5
Vienna Philharmonic Orchestra Kertesz

SXL6484 NB : **£ 5**
Various Suite for two Pianos Eden, Tamir

SXL6485 NB : **£ 10**
LISZT Recital Pascal, Roge

SXL6486 NB : **£ 6**
SCHUMANN Symphony No.1, Overture Op.52
Vienna Philharmonic Orchestra Solti

SXL6487 NB : **£ 6**
SCHUMANN Symphony No.2, Ov Julius Caesar
Vienna Philharmonic Orchestra Solti

SXL6488 NB : **£ 15**
RAVEL Daphnis & Chloe
Los Angeles Philharmonic Orchestra Mehta

SXL6489 NB : **£ 15**
BRUCKNER Symphony No.4
Los Angeles Philharmonic Orchestra Mehta

SXL6490 NB : **£ 10**
HAYDN / MOZART Discoveries (Song recital) Peters
Vienna Haydn Orchestra Fischer-Dieskau

SXL6491 NB : **£ 8**
NIELSEN Symphony No.5 Suisse Romande Orchestra Kletzki

SXL6492   (==== Not Issued ====)

SXL6493   NB : **£ 10**
TCHAIKOVSKY / SIBELIUS   Violin Concertos   Chung
London Symphony Orchestra   Previn

SXL6494   NB : **£ 16**
BRUCKNER   Symphony No.1
Vienna Philharmonic Orchestra   Abbado

SXL6495   NB : **£ 6**
Various   New Year's Concert
Vienna Philharmonic Orchestra   Boskovsky

SXL6496   NB : **£ 6**
HANDEL   Overtures   English Chamber Orchestra   Bonynge

SXL6497   NB : **£ 10**
KODALY   Psalmus Hungaricus, Peacock Variations
London Symphony Orchestra   Kertesz

SXL6498   NB : **£ 5**
Various   Operatic Arias   Pavarotti

SXL6499   NB : **£ 6**
MOZART   Serinade in D K.100
Vienna Philharmonic Orchestra   Boskovsky

SXL6500   NB : **£ 6**
MOZART   Divertiment K.63, Cass. K.99
Vienna Mozart Ensemble   Boskovsky

SXL6501   NB : **£ 8**
Various   Operatic Excerpts   Tourango
Suisse Romande Orchestra   Bonynge

SXL6502   NB : **£ 8**
SCHUBERT   Piano Recital   Kars

SXL6503   NB : **£ 10**
BEETHOVEN   Piano Concerto No.3   Lupu
London Symphony Orchestra   Foster

SXL6504   NB : **£10**
SCHUBERT   Piano Sonata Op.143   Lupu

SXL6505   NB : **£8**
BRUCKNER   Symphony No.3   Vienna Philharmonic Orchestra   Bohm

SXL6506   NB : **£8**
SCHUBERT / SCHUMANN 19   Leider   Krenn, Werba

SXL6507   NB : **£8**
JANACEK   Taras Bulba, Lachian Dances
London Philharmonic Orchestra   Huybrechts

SXL6508   NB : **£6**
LISZT   Mephisto Waltz, Etc   Ashkenazy

SXL6509   (==== Not Issued ====)

SXL6510   NB : **£5**
DVORAK   Symphonic Variations, Golden Spinning Wheel
London Symphony Orchestra   Kertesz

SXL6511   (==== Not Issued ====)

SXL6512   NB : **£15**
BRITTEN   Violin Concerto, Piano Concert   Richter, Lubosky
Britten

SXL6513   NB : **£12**
HODDINOTT / MATHIAS   Clarinet Concerto, Piano Concerto No.3
De Peyer   London Symphony Orchestra   Atherton

SXL6514   (==== Not Issued ====)

SXLD6515-21   NB : **£30**
DVORAK   The 9 Symphonies   London Symphony Orchestra   Kertesz

SXL6522   NB : **£6**
SCHUMANN / KILPEN   Songs   Tavela

SXL6523   NB : **£15**
BEETHOVEN / SCHUBERT   Eroica Variations, Moments Music.
Curzon

SXL6524   NB : £10
Various   Christmas Song Festival   Tebaldi

SXL6525   NB : £14
Various   Prima Donna in Vienna   Lorengar
Vienna Opera Orchestra   Weller

SXL6526   NB : £8
STRAUSS   A New Year's Concert
Vienna Philharmonic Orchestra   Boskovsky

SXL6527   NB : £6
SCRIABIN   Prometheus, Piano concerto Ashkenazy
London Philharmonic Orchestra   Maazel

SXL6528   NB : £10
FALLA / CHOPIN   Nights in the Gardens of Spain, Piano Concert No.2
De Larrocha   Suisse Romande Orchestra

SXL6529   NB : £80
HOLST   The Planets
Los Angeles Philharmonic Orchestra   Mehta

SXL6530   NB : £8
Various   Russian Songs   Ghiaurov

SXL6531   NB : £8
Various   18th Century Overtures
English Chamber Orchestra   Bonynge

SXL6532   NB : £15
PROKOFIEV / GLAZUNOV   Violin Concerto No.1, Violin
Concerto   Sivo   Suisse Romande Orchestra   Stein

SXL6533   NB : £6
SUK / WOLF / STRAUSS   Serenade For Strings Etc
London Symphony Orchestra   Munchinger

SXL6534   NB : £8
ROSSINI   Stabat Mater   London Symphony Orchestra   Kertesz

SXL6535   NB : **£15**
LISZT   Battle of the Huns, Mazeppa Orpheus
Los Angeles Philharmonic Orchestra   Mehta

SXL6536   NB : **£10**
BACH   Cimarosa, Flute Concertos   A & C Nicolet
Stuttgart Chamber Orchestra Munchinger

SXL6537   NB : **£4**
Various   Ursula Farr sings Arias Vol.I   Farr

SXL6538   NB : **£15**
PETTERSSON   Symphony No.7
Stockholm Philharmonic Orchestra   Dorati

SXL6539   NB : **£30**
MOZART   Symphonies   English Chamber Orchestra Britten

SXL6540   NB : **£5**
HANDEL   Messiah (Highlights)   Bonynge

SXL6541   NB : **£5**
Various   Ballet music and Entr'actes from French Opera
London Symphony Orchestra   Bonynge

SXL6542   NB : **£10**
SIBELIUS   Finlandia, Pohjola's Daughter
Suisse Romande Orchestra   Stein

SXL6543   NB : **£6**
DVORAK   Symphonic Poems
London Symphony Orchestra   Kertesz

SXL6544   NB : **£7**
SCHMIDT   Symphony No.4
Vienna Philharmonic Orchestra   Mehta

SXL6545   NB : **£20**
BACH   Concerto Italian Style, French Style, etc   De Larrocha

SXL6546   NB : **£14**
SCHUMANN   Schumann Recital   De Larrocha

SXL6547   NB : **£15**
AUBER / MASSENE   Romantic Cello Concertos   Silberstein
Suisse Romande Orchestra   Bonynge

SXL6548   NB : **£8**
DONIZETTI   Arias   Chiara   Vienna Volksoper Orchestra Santi

SXL6549   NB : **£8**
BEETHOVEN / SCHUBERT   Symphony No.8
Vienna Philharmonic Orchestra   Abbado

SXL6550   NB : **£15**
VARESE   Arcana, Ionisation
Los Angeles Philharmonic Orchestra   Mehta

SXL6551   NB : **£6**
POULENC   Concerto for two pianos   Eden, Tamir

SXL6552   NB : **£10**
SCHUBERT   Symphony No.1 & No.2
Vienna Philharmonic Orchestra   Kertesz

SXL6553   NB : **£6**
SCHUBERT   Symphony No.3 & No.6
Vienna Philharmonic Orchestra   Kertesz

SXL6554   NB : **£5**
RACHMANINOV   Piano Concerto No.1 & No.2   Ashkenazy
London Symphony Orchestra   Previn

SXL6555   NB : **£5**
RACHMANINOV Piano Concerto No.3   Ashkenazy
London Symphony Orchestra   Previn

SXL6556   NB : **£5**
RACHMANINOV Piano Concerto No.4, Rhapsody
Ashkenazy   London Symphony Orchestra Previn

SXL6557   NB : **£16**
VIVALDI   Four Seasons
Stuttgart Chamber Orchestra   Munchinger

SXLE6558-61   NB : **£ 15**
SIBELIUS   The 7 Symphonies
Vienna Philharmonic Orchestra   Maazel

SXL6562   NB : **£ 10**
TCHAIKOVSKY   Manfred Symphony
Vienna Philharmonic Orchestra   Maazel

SXL6563   NB : **£ 20**
SHOSTAKOVICH   Symphony No.1 & No.9
Suisse Romande Orchestra   Weller

SXL6564   NB : **£ 10**
BRITTEN   String Quartet No.1 & No.2 Allegri Quartet

SXLF6565-67   NB : **£ 15**
RACHMANINOV   Piano Concerto, Rhapsody on a theme of Paganini
Ashkenazy   London Symphony Orchestra   Previn

SXL6568   NB : **£ 15**
Various   Hits from the Hollywood Bowl
Los Angeles Philharmonic Orchestra   Mehta

SXL6569   NB : **£ 5**
ELGAR   Symphony No.1
London Philharmonic Orchestra   Solti

SXL6570   NB : **£ 25**
HODDINOTT   Orchestral Music
London Symphony Orchestra   Atherton

SXL6571   NB : **£ 8**
BERLIOZ   Symphonie Fantastique
Chicago Symphony Orchestra   Solti

SXL6572   NB : **£ 6**
Various   New Year in Vienna
Vienna Philharmonic Orchestra   Boskovsky

SXL6573   NB : **£ 10**
BRUCH   Violin Concerto No.1, Scottish Fantasia   Chung
Royal Philharmonic Orchestra   Kempe

187

SXL6574   NB : **£15**
TCHAIKOVSKY   Symphony No.4
New Symphony Orchestra London   Dorati

SXL6575   NB : **£6**
CHOPIN   Recital Sonata 2 etc   Ashkenazy

SXL6576   NB : **£10**
BEETHOVEN   Piano Sonata, Moonlight   Lupu

SXL6577   NB : **£5**
Various   Songs   Horne

SXL6578   NB : **£5**
Various   Leider   Horne

SXL6579   NB : **£10**
Various   Italian Songs   Tebaldi

SXL6580   NB : **£6**
SCHUBERT   Sonata Bflat, Impromptu   Curzon

SXL6581   NB : **£15**
Various   Concerto   Chigago Symphony Orchestra   Reiner

SXL6582   NB : **£6**
STRAVINSKY   Firebird Suite, Symphony in C
Suisse Romande Orchestra   Segal

SXL6583   NB : **£8**
RACHMANINOV   Symphony No.1
Suisse Romande Orchestra   Weller

SXL6584   NB : **£5**
ROSSINI   Scenes   Horne

SXL6585   NB : **£12**
Various   Vocal Duets   Correlli, Tebaldi

SXL6586-7   NB : **£38**
ALBENIZ   Iberia   De Larrocha

SXL6588
OFFENBACH
NB : **£18**
Papillon London Symphony Orchestra   Bonynge

SXL6589
BRAHMS
NB : **£40**
Trio in Cmaj.   Starker   Brahms Trio

SXL6590
SCHUBERT
NB : **£8**
Schwanangesang   Krause

SXL6591
(==== Not Issued ====)

SXL6592
ELGAR / IVES
NB : **£45**
Enigms Variations, Symphony No.1
Los Angeles Symphony Orchestra   Mehta

SXL6593
(==== Not Issued ====)

SXLG6594-97
BEETHOVEN
NB : **£10**
The 5 Piano Concertos   Ashkenazy
London Symphony Orchestra Solti

SXL6598
Various
NB : **£4**
Ursula Farr sings Arias Vol.II   Farr

SXL6599
KHACHATURIAN / FRANCK
NB : **£10**
Piano Concerto, Symphonic
Variations   De Larrocha London Philharmonic Orchestra   De Burgos

SXL6600
JANACEK
NB : **£8**
Glogolitic Mass
Royal Philharmonic Orchestra   Kempe

SXL6601
WALTON / STRAVINSKY
London Symphony Orchestra
NB : **£24**
Violin Concertos   Chung
Previn

SXL6602
SCHUBERT
NB : **£6**
Piano Sonatas   Ashkenazy

SXL6603
BEETHOVEN
NB : **£6**
Piano Sonatas No.7 & No.23   Ashkenazy

SXL6604　　NB : **£6**
RACHMANINOV　　　　　Etudes, Tableaux Op 39 etc　Ashkenazy

SXL6605　　NB : **£6**
VERDI　　　　Arias　　　　Chiara

SXL6606　　NB : **£50**
HODDINOTT　　Symphony No.5, etc
Royal Philharmonic Orchestra　　Davis

SXL6607　　NB : **£20**
MATHIAS　　　Dance Overture, Ave Rex
London Symphony Orchestra　　Atherton

SXL6608　　NB : **£6**
PURCELL / BRITTEN　　Songs by Purcell & Britten　Pears, Quirk
Britten

SXL6609　　NB : **£8**
Various　　　Italian Opera Arias　　　Milnes
London Philharmonic Orchestra　　Varviso

SXLH6610-13　NB : **£38**
BRAHMS　　Four Symphonies
Vienna Philharmonic Orchestra　　Kertesz

SXL6614　　NB : **£7**
MOZART　　Haffner Serenade
Vienna Mozart Ensemble　　Boskovsky

SXL6615　　NB : **£8**
MOZART　　Serenades Vol.6
Vienna Mozart Ensemble　　Boskovsky

SXL6616　　NB : **£6**
MOZART　　Symphony No.29, Symphony No.35
Vienna Philharmonic Orchestra　　Boskovsky

SXL6617　　NB : **£8**
MOZART　　Symphony No.25, Symphony No.40
Vienna Philharmonic Orchestra　　Kertesz

SXL6618   NB : £5
RACHMANINOV   Music For Two Pianos   Eden, Tamir

SXL6619   NB : £4
Various   Songs   Sutherland

SXL6620-2   NB : £40
PROKOFIEV   Romeo & Juliet
Chigago Symphony Orchestra   Maazel

SXL6623   NB : £8
RACHMANINOV   Symphony No.2
London Philharmonic Orchestra   Weller

SXL6624   NB : £10
GRIEG / SCHUMANN   Piano Concerto   Lupu
London Symphony Orchestra   Previn

SXL6625   NB : £8
Various   Songs   Hotter

SXL6626   NB : £8
BACH   St. John Passion (Highlights) Harper
English Chamber Orchestra   Britten

SXL6627   NB : £8
TCHAIKOVSKY   Francesca Rimini, Hamlet
New Symphony Orchestra London   Dorati

SXL6628   NB : £15
VIVALDI   Concerto in Bb, Gmaj. F, A & G
Lucerne Festival Orchestra   Baumgartner

SXL6629   NB : £12
Various   18th Century Arias   Tebaldi
New Philharmonia Orchestra   Bonynge

SXL6630   NB : £6
BEETHOVEN   Piano Sonatas No.31 & No.32   Ashkenazy

SXL6631   NB : £10
KODALY   Harry Janos (Highlights)
London Symphony Orchestra   Kurtesz

191

SXL6632   NB : **£14**
BEETHOVEN   Violin Sonatas No.9 & No.2   Perlman

SXL6633   NB : **£12**
NIELSEN   Symphony No.4
Los Angeles Philharmonic Orchestra   Mehta

SXL6634   NB : **£25**
STRAUSS   Don Quixote
Los Angeles Philharmonic Orchestra   Mehta

SXL6635-6   NB : **£30**
DELIBES   Sylvia   Philharmonia Orchestra   Bonynge

SXL6637   NB : **£10**
Various   Arias   Rouleau

SXL6638   NB : **£18**
BACH   Sinfonias For Double Orchestra
Stuttgart Chamber Orchestra   Munchinger

SXL6639   NB : **£10**
WILBYE / GIBBONS / TOMKINS   Madrigals   Wilbye Consort

SXL6640   NB : **£5**
BRITTEN   Cantatas   Fischer-Dieskau
English Chamber Orchestra   Britten

SXL6641   NB : **£22**
BRITTEN   Sinfonia Requiem, Cello Symphony
Rostropovich   English Chamber Orchestra   Britten

SXL6642   NB : **£6**
SCHUMANN   Humoreske   Ashkenazy

SXL6643   NB : **£30**
STRAUSS / MOZART / ROSSINI   Virtuoso Overtures
Los Angeles Philharmonic Orchestra   Mehta

SXLJ6644-8   NB : **£35**
SCHUBERT   The Symphonies
Vienna Philharmonic Orchestra   Kurtesz

SXL6649　　　NB : **£4**
Various　　　　　Operatic Excerpts　　　　Pavarotti

SXL6650　　　NB : **£5**
Various　　　　　Italian Songs　　　Pavarotti Bonynge

SXL6651　　　NB : **£8**
BEETHOVEN　　Piano Concerto No.1, Sonata No.8　　Ashkenazy
Chigago Symphony Orchestra　　　　Solti

SXL6652　　　NB : **£8**
BEETHOVEN　　Piano Concerto No.2, Sonata No.21　　Ashkenazy
Chigago Symphony Orchestra　　　　Solti

SXL6653　　　NB : **£5**
BEETHOVEN　　Piano Concerto No.3, Adieux Son　　Ashkenazy
Chigago Symphony Orchestra　　　　Solti

SXL6654　　　NB : **£8**
BEETHOVEN　　Piano Concerto No.4, Overture In C Maj.
Ashkenazy　　　Chigago Symphony Orchestra　　　Solti

SXL6655　　　NB : **£8**
BEETHOVEN　　Piano Concerto No.5 "Emperor"　　Ashkenazy
Chigago Symphony Orchestra　　　　Solti

SXL6656　　　NB : **£6**
WAGNER　　　Overtures & Preludes
Vienna Philharmonic Orchestra　　　Stein

SXL6657　　　NB : **£10**
BERG / STRAUSS　　　Wazzeck Lulu, Salome　　Silja
Vienna Philharmonic Orchestra　　　Dohnanyi

SXL6658　　　NB : **£5**
Various　　　　　Opera Arias "King of the High C's"　　Pavarotti

SXL6659　　　NB : **£8**
Various　　　　　Popular Russian Songs　　　Ghiaurov

SXLK6660-4　　NB : **£45**
SCHOENBERG　　Complete works for Chamber Ensemble
London Sinfonetta　　　　Atherton

193

SXLM6665-67   NB : **£25**
KODALY   Music Of Kodaly   Philharmonia Orchestra   Dorati

SXL6668   NB : **£7**
PROKOFIEV   Romeo & Juliet (Highlights)
Cleveland Orchestra   Maazel

SXL6669   NB : **£8**
BACH / BUSONI / MOZART   Chaccone, Rondo   De Larrocha

SXL6670   NB : **£7**
MOZART   Divertimento No.7 & 11   Boskovsky

SXL6671-2   NB : **£20**
BRUCKNER   Symphony No.8
Los Angeles Philharmonic Orchestra   Mehta

SXL6673   NB : **£8**
BEETHOVEN   Symphony No.7, Egmont Ov
Los Angeles Philharmonic Orchestra   Mehta

SXL6674   NB : **£8**
RAVEL   Piano Music Vol.1 Sonatine, Valses Nobles   Roge

SXL6675   NB : **£12**
BRAHMS   Symphony No.1 Vienna Philharmonic Orchestra Kertesz

SXL6676   NB : **£16**
BRAHMS   Symphony No.2 Vienna Philharmonic Orchestra Kertesz

SXL6677   NB : **£12**
BRAHMS   Symphony No.3 Vienna Philharmonic Orchestra Kertesz

SXL6678   NB : **£12**
BRAHMS   Symphony No.4 Vienna Philharmonic Orchestra Kertesz

SXL6679   NB : **£12**
MAHLER   The Wayfarer Song   Minton
Chicago Symphony Orchestra   Solti

SXL6680   NB : **£8**
RAVEL / FUARE   Concerto for Left Hand, Fantaisie Op.111
De Larrocha   London Philharmonic Orchestra

SXL6681 NB : **£16**
BRUCKNER Symphony No.2 Vienna Philharmonic Orchestra Stein

SXL6682 NB : **£8**
BRUCKNER Symphony No.6 Vienna Philharmonic Orchestra Stein

SXL6683 NB : **£20**
FALLA Piano Music De Larrocha

SXL6684 NB : **£8**
ROSSINI / BERLIOZ / BEETHOVEN Barber of Seville, etc.
Chigago Symphony Orchestra Solti

SXL6685 (==== Not Issued ====)

SXL6686-7 NB : **£20**
BRUCKNER Symphony No.5
Vienna Philharmonic Orchestra Maazel

SXL6688-9 NB : **£16**
TCHAIKOVSKY Nutcracker New Philharmonia Orchestra Bonynge

SXL6690 NB : **£8**
Various Operatic Recital Caballe

SXL6691 NB : **£45**
STRAVINSKY Rite of Spring Chigago Symphony Orchestra Solti

SXL6692 NB : **£8**
STRAUSS New Year's Concert
Vienna Philharmonic Orchestra Boskovsky

SXL6693 NB : **£6**
CHOPIN Piano Concerto No.2 Ashkenazy
London Symphony Orchestra Zinman

SXL6694 NB : **£8**
TCHAIKOVSKY Romeo & Juliet, Fatum, Tempest
New Symphony Orchestra London Dorati

SXL6695 NB : **£12**
NIELSEN Symphony No.3
London Symphony Orchestra Huybrechts

SXL6696   NB : **£8**
BRAHMS / DVORAK   Slavonic Dances
London Symphony Orchestra   Boskovsky

SXL6697   NB : **£8**
RACHMANINOV   Suite No.1 & 2   Ashkenazy   Previn

SXL6698   NB : **£16**
MOZART   Piano Concerto No.21 & No.12   Lupu
English Chamber Orchestra   Segal

SXL6699   NB : **£4**
MILNER   Roman Spring, Salutio   Pears
London Sinfonetta   Atherton

SXL6700   NB : **£8**
RAVEL   Piano Music Vol.2   Gaspard de la Nuit, Menuet Antique,
Pavane   Roge

SXL6701   NB : **£6**
STRAUSS   Straussiania   New Philharmonia Orchestra   Bonynge

SXL6702   NB : **£25**
PROKOFIEV   Symphony No.1 & No.7
London Philharmonic Orchestra   Weller

SXL6703   NB : **£7**
RAVEL   Daphnis & Chloe
Cleveland Orchestra   Maazel

SXL6704   NB : **£6**
WALDTEUFEL   Waltzes by Emile Waldteufel
New Philharmonia Orchestra   Gamley

SXL6705   NB : **£6**
SCRIABIN   Piano Sonatas No.3, 4, 5 & 9   Ashkenazy

SXL6706   NB : **£6**
BEETHOVEN   Piano Sonatas No.8, 21 & 26   Ashkenazy

SXL6707   NB : **£14**
AUBER   Marco Spada
London Symphony Orchestra   Bonynge

SXL6708 NB : **£6**
LISZT Paraphrases Eden, Tamir

SXL6709 NB : **£10**
LISZT Mephisto Waltz, Tasso Orchestra de Paris Solti

SXL6710 NB : **£8**
CHOPIN Etudes Op.10 & 25 Ashkenazy

SXL6711 NB : **£5**
LEHAR The Magic Of Lehar Paulik Krenn Holm
Vienna Volksoper Orchestra

SXL6712 NB : **£8**
KODALY Orchstral Works Vol.1 Philharmonia Orchestra Dorati

SXL6713 NB : **£8**
KODALY Orchstral Works Vol.2 Philharmonia Orchestra Dorati

SXL6714 NB : **£12**
KODALY Peacock variations, Summer Evening
Philharmonia Orchestra Dorati

SXL6715 NB : **£8**
RAVEL Piano Music Roge

SXL6716 NB : **£8**
MOZART Concerto for 2 Pianos, Concerto for 3 Pianos
Ashkenazy Barenboim Ts'ong English Chamber Orchestra

SXL6717 NB : **£15**
BEETHOVEN / SCHUMANN Music for Horn & Piano
Tuckwell Ashkenazy

SXL6718 NB : **£10**
RACHMANINOV Songs Vol 1 Soderstrom

SXL6719 NB : **£3**
Various Darwin - Song for a city Sutherland
Royal Philharmonic Orchestra Bonynge

SXL6720   NB : **£10**
RACHMANINOV   Symphony No.3, The Rock
London Philharmonic Orchestra   Weller

SXL6721   NB : **£50**
BACH   Partita No.2, Sonata No.3 for Violin   Chung

SXL6722   NB : **£5**
SCHUBERT   Songs   Pears   Britten

SXL6723   NB : **£3**
ELGAR   Symphony No.2
London Philharmonic Orchestra   Solti

SXL6724   NB : **£5**
MOZART   Divertimento 17   Boskovsky

SXL6725   NB : **£8**
GOTTSCHALK   Piano Works   Davies

SXL6726   NB : **£6**
VERDI   Ballet Music From Verdi's Operas
Cleveland Orchestra   Maazel

SXL6727   NB : **£6**
GERSHWIN   Rhapsody in Blue, American in Paris,Cuban Ov.
Cleveland Orchestra   Maazel

SXL6728   NB : **£10**
BRAHMS   Piano Concerto No.1   Lupu
London Philharmonic Orchestra   De Waart

SXL6729   NB : **£25**
SCHUBERT   Symphony No.9
Israel Philharmonic Orchestra   Mehta

SXL6730   NB : **£15**
BARTOK   Concerto for Orchestra, Hungarian Picture
Israel Philharmonic Orchestra   Mehta

SXL6731   NB : **£15**
RIMSKY-KORSAKOV   Scheherezade
Los Angeles Philharmonic Orchestra   Mehta

198

SXL6732 NB : **£10**
BERLIOZ Harold in Italy Israel Philharmonic Orchestra Mehta

SXL6733 NB : **£8**
CHOPIN Preludes De Larrocha

SXL6734 NB : **£15**
Various Favorite Spanish Encores De Larrocha

SXL6735 NB : **£20**
STRAVINSKY Le Sacre Du Printemps (Rite of Spring)
Vienna Philharmonic Orchestra Maazel

SXL6736 NB : **£12**
BEETHOVEN Violin Sonatas No.4 & No.5 Perlman

SXL6737 NB : **£25**
WEBER / HAYDN / VIVA Concertos in Contrast
Los Angeles Philharmonic Orchestra Mehta

SXL6738 NB : **£8**
Various The art of Hans Hotter Vol.II Hotter

SXL6739 NB : **£6**
SCHUBERT Piano Sonatas Ashkenazy

SXL6740 NB : **£6**
STRAUSS New Year's Concert
Vienna Philharmonic Orchestra Boskovsky

SXL6741 NB : **£10**
SCHUBERT Piano Sonata in Gmaj., 2 Scherzi Lupu

SXL6742 NB : **£15**
DEBUSSY Nocturnes
National Symphony Orchestra of Washington Dorati

SXL6743 NB : **£15**
WAGNER Excerpts from The Ring
National Symphony Orchestra of Washington Dorati

SXL6744-5 NB : **£ 12**
MAHLER Symphony No.2 Ludwig
Vienna Philharmonic Orchestra Mehta

SXL6746 NB : **£ 12**
RACHMANINOV Piano Concerto No.3 De Larrocha
London Symphony Orchestra Previn

SXL6747 NB : **£ 8**
MOZART / HAYDN Trinitatis Mass
Vienna Philharmonic Orchestra Munchinger

SXL6748 NB : **£ 6**
SCHUBERT Rosamunde Incidental Music
Vienna Philharmonic Orchestra Munchinger

SXL6749 NB : **£ 12**
STRAUSS Also Sprach Zarathustra, Don Juan, etc.
Chigago Symphony Orchestra Solti

SXL6750 NB : **£ 15**
DVORAK Symphony No.8, The Wood Dove
Los Angeles Philharmonic Orchestra Mehta

SXL6751 NB : **£ 15**
DVORAK Symphony No.9, Carnival
Los Angeles Philharmonic Orchestra Mehta

SXL6752 NB : **£ 15**
STRAUSS Alpine Symphony
Los Angeles Philharmonic Orchestra Mehta

SXL6753 NB : **£ 20**
IVES Variations on America, Symphony No.2 etc
Los Angeles Philharmonic Orchestra Mehta

SXL6754 NB : **£ 6**
TCHAIKOVSKY Symphony No.5 Chigago Symphony Orchestra Solti

SXL6755 NB : **£ 7**
BACH Symphony No.2, No.4 & No.6
Stuttgart Chamber Orchestra Munchinger

200

SXL6756   NB : **£8**
LISZT   Sonata in Bmin   De Larrocha

SXL6757   NB : **£30**
Various   Concertos from Spain
Royal Philharmonic Orchestra   De Burgos

SXL6758   NB : **£10**
DVORAK   Serenade   Suk
Stuttgart Chamber Orchestra   Munchinger

SXL6759   NB : **£35**
SAINT-SAINS / VIEUXTEMPS   Violin Concerto No.3   Chung
London Symphony Orchestra   Foster

SXL6760   NB : **£6**
BEETHOVEN   Symphony No.1 & No.8
Chigago Symphony Orchestra   Solti

SXL6761   NB : **£6**
BEETHOVEN   Symphony No.2
Chigago Symphony Orchestra   Solti

SXL6762   NB : **£6**
BEETHOVEN   Symphony No.5
Chigago Symphony Orchestra   Solti

SXL6763   NB : **£6**
BEETHOVEN   Symphony No.6
Chigago Symphony Orchestra   Solti

SXL6764   NB : **£6**
BEETHOVEN   Symphony No.7, Coriolan
Chigago Symphony Orchestra   Solti

SXL6765   NB : **£15**
MASSENET   Recital   Tourango   Bonynge

SXL6766   NB : **£12**
GRIEG   Grieg Favourites
New Philharmonia Orchestra   Boskovsky

SXL6767   NB : £6
PROKOFIEV   Piano Concerto No.1 & No.2   Ashkenazy
London Symphony Orchestra   Previn

SXL6768   NB : £5
PROKOFIEV   Piano Concerto No.3, Classical Symphony
Ashkenazy   London Symphony Orchestra   Previn

SXL6769   NB : £8
PROKOFIEV   Piano Concerto No.4 & No.5   Ashkenazy
London Symphony Orchestra   Previn

SXL6770   NB : £8
DUKAS   Symphony No.in C, Sorcer's Apprentice
London Philharmonic Orchestra .   Weller

SXL6771   NB : £10
SCHUBERT   Piano Sonatas D557 & D959   Lupu

SXL6772   NB : £10
RACHMANINOV   Song Recital   Soderstrom

SXL6773   NB : £20
PROKOFIEV   Violin Concertos 1, 2   Chung
London Symphony Orchestra   Previn

SXL6774-5   NB : £10
BACH   Brandenburg Concertos
English Chamber Orchestra   Britten

SXL6776   NB : £4
DELIBES   Coppelia (Highlights)
Suisse Romande Orchestra   Bonynge

SXL6777   NB : £8
PROKOFIEV   Symphony No.6
London Philharmonic Orchestra   Weller

SXL6778   NB : £5
BACH   St. Johns Passion (Highlights)
Stuttgart Chamber Orchestra   Munchinger

SXL6779
MAHLER

NB : £ 12
Symphony No.1   Israel Philharmonic Orchestra Mehta

SXL6780

(==== Not Issued ====)

SXL6781
Various

NB : £ 3
Vocal, Sacred Music,   Pavarotti

SXL6782
VERDI / BEETHOVEN / BRAHMS Etc   Overtures
Cleveland Orchestra   Maazel

NB : £ 6

SXL6783
BRAHMS

NB : £ 8
Symphony No.1   Cleveland Orchestra   Maazel

SXL6784
MOZART / HAYDN   Fantasia K397, Sonata K311, K330
De Larrocha

NB : £ 8

SXL6785

NB : £ 8
GRANADOS / GOYESCAS Recital. Volumes 1 & 2, El Pelele De Larrocha

SXL6786
BRAHMS

NB : £ 6
Variation and Fugue on a theme by Handel   Roge

SXL6787
PROKOFIEV

NB : £ 25
Symphony No.5   London Symphony Orchestra Weller

SXL6788
BRITTEN

NB : £ 6
Two Scottish Folk Songs Etc   Pears, Ellis

SXL6789
BEETHOVEN

NB : £ 10
Violin Sonatas Op.12-3 Op.30-3   Perlman

SXL6790
BEETHOVEN

NB : £ 10
Violin Sonatas Op.12-1 Op.96   Perlman

SXL6791
BEETHOVEN

NB : £ 10
Violin Sonatas Op.30-1, 30-2   Perlman

SXL6792
Various

NB : £ 8
Romanzas de Zarzuelas   Caballe

SXL6793 NB : **£4**
BRITTEN Folk Songs Pears

SXL6794 NB : **£6**
SCHUBERT Grand Duo Eden, Tamir

SXL6795 NB : **£12**
ELGAR Enigma Variations
London Philharmonic Orchestra Solti

SXL6796 NB : **£15**
BRAHMS Symphony No.1
Vienna Philharmonic Orchestra Mehta

SXL6797 NB : **£8**
BRAHMS Piano Concerto No.1 Rubenstein
Israel Philharmonic Orchestra Mehta

SXL6798 NB : **£25**
PAGANINI Violin Concerto No.1 & No.6 Belkin

SXL6799 NB : **£15**
SCHUBERT Symphony No.3 & No.5
Israel Philharmonic Orchestra Mehta

SXL6800 NB : **£15**
BERLIOZ Romeo & Juliet orchestral excerpts
Vienna Philharmonic Orchestra Maazel

SXL6801 NB : **£6**
CHOPIN Recital Ashkenazy

SXL6802 NB : **£28**
BARTOK Violin Concerto No.2 Chung
London Philharmonic Orchestra Solti

SXL6803 NB : **£8**
KODALY Missa Brevis, Pange Lingua
Brighton Festival Choir Heltay

SXL6804 NB : **£6**
BEETHOVEN Piano Sonatas No.5, No.6 & No.15 Ashkenazy

SXL6805 NB : **£8**
Various Song Recital Reznik

SXL6806-7 NB : **£30**
MAHLER Symphony No.5, Adagio from Symphony No.10
Los Angeles Philharmonic Orchestra Mehta

SXL6808 NB : **£6**
BEETHOVEN Piano Sonatas No.2 & No.3 Ashkenazy

SXL6809 NB : **£6**
BEETHOVEN Piano Sonatas No.28 & No.30 Ashkenazy

SXL6810 NB : **£6**
CHOPIN Piano works Vol.III Ashkenazy

SXL6811 NB : **£15**
BERNSTEIN / COPELAND Candide, Appachalonian Spring
Los Angeles Symphony Orchestra Mehta

SXL6812 NB : **£6**
MASSENET / MEYERBEER Le Cid, Les Patiners
New Philharmonia Orchestra Bonynge

SXL6813 NB : **£8**
RAVEL / DEBUSSY Bolero, La Mer
Chigago Symphony Orchestra Solti

SXL6814 NB : **£8**
TCHAIKOVSKY Symphony No.6 Chigago Symphony Orchestra Solti

SXL6815 NB : **£10**
BARTOK Piano Concerto No.1, Rhapsody for Piano Roge
London Symphony Orchestra Weller

SXL6816 NB : **£10**
BARTOK Piano Concerto No.3 Roge
London Symphony Orchestra Weller

SXL6817 NB : **£8**
STRAUSS 150 years Of Strauss "Projit!"
Vienna Philharmonic Orchestra Boskovsky

SXL6818   NB : **£6**
MENDELSSOHN Symphony No.1 & No.4
Vienna Philharmonic Orchestra   Dohnanyi

SXL6819   NB : **£10**
SCHUMANN   Symphony No.1 & No.4
Vienna Philharmonic Orchestra   Mehta

SXL6820   NB : **£6**
HOLST / IRELAND etc   Brass Band Classics
Grimethorpe Colliery Band Howarth

SXL6821   NB : **£7**
TCHAIKOVSKY Nutcracker New Philharmonic Orchestra Bonynge

SXL6822   NB : **£25**
RESPIGHI   Pines of Rome   Cleveland Orchestra   Maazel

SXL6823   NB : **£8**
FRANCK   Symphony in D   Cleveland Orchestra   Maazel

SXL6824   NB : **£4**
BACH   The Musical Offering
Stuttgart Chamber Orchestra   Munchinger

SXL6825   (===== Not Issued =====)

SXL6826   NB : **£5**
Various   Grand Opera Choruses
Vienna Philharmonic Orchestra   Various

SXL6827   NB : **£5**
MASSENET   Scenes Alsaciennes, Scenes Dramatiques
New Philharmonia Orchestra   Bonynge

SXL6828   NB : **£4**
Various   Duets   Pavarotti

SXL6829   NB : **£14**
BEETHOVEN   Symphony No.3 Chigago Symphony Orchestra Solti

SXL6830   NB : **£10**
BEETHOVEN / WEBER   Symphony No.4, Oberon Ov.
Chigago Symphony Orchestra   Solti

SXL6831   NB : **£10**
BRAHMS   Seven intermezzi   Lupu

SXL6832   NB : **£5**
RACHMANINOV   Songs Vol.3   Soderstrom

SXL6833   NB : **£18**
MOZART   Symphony No.34 & 39
Israel Philharmonic Orchestra   Mehta

SXL6834   NB : **£12**
BRAHMS   Symphony No.2   Cleveland Orchestra   Maazel

SXL6835   NB : **£12**
BRAHMS   Symphony No.3   Cleveland Orchestra   Maazel

SXL6836   NB : **£12**
BRAHMS   Symphony No.4   Cleveland Orchestra   Maazel

SXL6837   NB : **£6**
BRUCKNER   TeDeum   Blegen
Vienna Philharmonic Orchestra   Mehta

SXL6838   NB : **£8**
SHOSTAKOVICH   Symphony No.10
London Philharmonic Orchestra   Haitink

SXL6839   NB : **£7**
Various   Arias   Pavarotti

SXL6840   NB : **£6**
TCHAIKOVSKY   Piano Concerto No.1   Ashkenazy

SXL6841   NB : **£8**
Various   Sylvia Sass - Opera recital   Sass
London Symphony Orchestra   Gardelli

SXL6842   NB : **£24**
ELGAR   Violin Concerto   Chung
London Philharmonic Orchestra   Solti

SXL6843   NB : **£25**
Various   Showcase Concert Israel Philharmonic Orchestra   Mehta

SXL6844   NB : **£15**
MOZART   Symphony No.40, Eine Kleine Nachtmusik
Israel Philharmonic Orchestra   Mehta

SXL6845   NB : **£8**
SCHUBERT   Symphony No.4 & No.8
Israel Philharmonic Orchestra   Mehta

SXL6846   (==== Not Issued ====)

SXL6847   NB : **£5**
BRITTEN   Phaedra, Sacred & Profane Etc   Baker
English Chamber Orchestra   Britten

SXL6848   NB : **£4**
ELGAR   Pomp & Circumstance Marches, etc.
London Philharmonic Orchestra   Solti

SXL6849   NB : **£8**
SHOSTAKOVICH   Suite on Verses of Michelangelo   Quirk
Ashkenazy

SXL6850   (==== Not Issued ====)

SXL6851   NB : **£25**
SAINT-SAINS / CHAUSSON / RAVEL   Introduction & Rondo,
Poeme, Tzigane   Chung   Royal Philharmonic Orchestra   Dutoit

SXL6852   NB : **£20**
PROKOFIEV   Symphony No.3, Scythian Suite
London Philharmonic Orchestra   Weller

SXL6853   NB : **£8**
TCHAIKOVSKY   Manfred Symphony
New Philharmonia Orchestra   Ashkenazy

SXL6854   NB : **£20**
TCHAIKOVSKY   Violin Concerto   Belkin
Philharmonia Orchestra   Ashkenazy

SXL6855   NB : **£6**
DEBUSSY   Piano Vol.1   Roge

SXL6856   NB : **£8**
WAGNER   Overtures, Preludes & Liebestod
Chigago Symphony Orchestra   Solti

SXL6857   NB : **£10**
TCHAIKOVSKY   Suite No.4
Vienna Philharmonic Orchestra   Maazel

SXL6858   NB : **£5**
Various   Opera Recital   Pavarotti

SXL6859   NB : **£8**
Various   Arias   Ghiaurov

SXL6860   NB : **£4**
WAGNER   Tannhauser & Meistersinger (Highlights)
Vienna Philharmonic Orchestra   Solti

SXL6861   NB : **£6**
SCHUMANN   Piano Concerto   Ashkenazy
London Symphony Orchestra   Segal

SXL6862   NB : **£8**
ALBINONI / PACHABEL   Adagio, Canon etc.
Stuttgart Chamber Orchestra   Munchinger

SXL6863   NB : **£10**
LISZT   Symphonic Poems, Prometheus, Prelude
London Philharmonic Orchestra   Solti

SXL6864   NB : **£8**
Various   Opera Arias   Chiara
New Philharmonia Orchestra   Adler

SXL6865   (==== Not Issued ====)

SXL6866 NB : **£16**
GRANDOS Spanish songs Lorangar, De Larrocha

SXL6867 NB : **£8**
STRAUSS Graduation Ball Vienna Philharmonic Orchestra Dorati

SXL6868 NB : **£6**
SCRIABIN Piano Sonatas Ashkenazy

SXL6869 NB : **£5**
RACHMANINOV Songs Vol.4 Soderstrom

SXL6870 NB : **£5**
Various O Solo Mio Pavarotti

SXL6871 NB : **£6**
BEETHOVEN Piano Sonatas No.17 & No.18 Ashkenazy

SXL6872 NB : **£4**
Various Salute to Percy Grainger
English Chamber Orchestra Bedford

SXL6873 NB : **£12**
BERLIOZ Harold in Italy Cleveland Orchestra Maazel

SXL6874 NB : **£8**
RIMSKY-KORSAKOV Scheherezade Cleveland Orchestra Maazel

SXL6875 NB : **£12**
PROKOFIEV Symphony No.5 Cleveland Orchestra Maazel

SXL6876 NB : **£8**
WEBER Symphony No.1 and overtures
Vienna Philharmonic Orchestra Stein

SXL6877 NB : **£6**
CHOPIN Complete Piano Works Ashkenazy

SXL6878 NB : **£5**
KODALY Hymn of Zinyi, Psalm 114, Laudes Organi
Brighton Festival Choir Luxton

SXL6879   NB : **£5**
MOZART   Symphony No.25 & No.29
English Chamber Orchestra Britten

SXL6880   NB : **£25**
Various   Star Wars' Los Angeles Philharmonic Orchestra Mehta

SXL6881   NB : **£6**
MOZART   Piano Concerto No.21 & No.17   Ashkenazy
Philharmonia Orchestra

SXL6882   (==== Not Issued ====)

SXL6883   NB : **£15**
STRAVINSKY   Petruchka   Vienna Philharmonic Orchestra   Dohnanyi

SXL6884   NB : **£6**
TCHAIKOVSKY Symphony No.5   Ashkenazy Philharmonia Orchestra

SXL6885   NB : **£15**
Various   Suites from Star wars, Close Encounters Etc.
Los Angeles Philharmonic Orchestra   Mehta

SXL6886   NB : **£10**
BEETHOVEN   Piano Concerto No.4, Sonatas. Nos.1 & 2   Lupu
Israel Philharmonic Orchestra   Mehta

SXL6887   NB : **£8**
MOZART   Piano Concerto No.25 & No.27   De Larrocha

SXL6888   NB : **£8**
FALLA   7 Popular Spanish songs   Caballe

SXL6889   NB : **£6**
BEETHOVEN   Piano Sonatas No.13, 14 & 16   Ashkenazy

SXL6890   NB : **£8**
BRAHMS   Symphony No.4 Chigago Symphony Orchestra Solti

SXL6891   NB : **£8**
SCHUBERT   Symphony No.6 Israel Philharmonic Orchestra Mehta

SXL6892 NB : **£8**
SCHUBERT Symphony No.1 & No.3
Israel Philharmonic Orchestra Mehta

SXL6893 NB : **£8**
BRITTEN String Quartet No.2 & No.3 Amadeus String Quartet

SXL6894 NB : **£10**
TCHAIKOVSKY Symphony No.6 Royal Philharmonic Orchestra Kord

SXL6895 NB : **£8**
TCHAIKOVSKY 1812 Overture, Capriccio Italien DSO Dorati

SXL6896 NB : **£8**
DVORAK / ENESCO / RAVEL / LISZT Rhapsody DSO Dorati

SXL6897 NB : **£8**
BARTOK Suite No.1 DSO Dorati

SXL6898 NB : **£5**
MAHLER Song of a Wayfarer, Etc. Horne
Los Angeles Philharmonic Orchestra Mehta

SXL6899 NB : **£15**
BEETHOVEN Piano Concerto No.5 De Larrocha
Los Angeles Philharmonic Orchestra Mehta

SXL6900 NB : **£6**
MUSSORGSKY Songs for Children Soderstrom

SXL6901 NB : **£15**
GRIEG Peer Gynt Royal Philharmonic Orchestra Weller

SXL6902-3 (==== Not Issued ====)

SXL6904 NB : **£15**
DEBUSSY Nocturnes, Iberia, Jeux Cleveland Orchestra Maazel

SXL6905 NB : **£15**
DEBUSSY / SCRIABIN La Mer, Poem of Exstacy
Cleveland Orchestra Maazel

SXL6906   NB : **£ 15**
SHOSTAKOVICH   Symphony No.15
London Philharmonic Orchestra   Haitink

SXL6907   (==== Not Issued ====)

SXL6908   NB : **£ 30**
PROKOFIEV   Symphony No.4, Rusian Overture
London Philharmonic Orchestra   Weller

SXL6909   NB : **£ 8**
NICOLAI / SCHRECA / WOLF   Overtures
New Philharmonia Orchestra Adler

SXL6910-1   (==== Not Issued ====)

SXL6912   NB : **£ 8**
SIBELIUS   Pelias & Melisande
Suisse Romande Orchestra   Stein

SXL6913-18   (==== Not Issued ====)

SXL6919   NB : **£ 6**
TCHAIKOVSKY Symphony No.4   Philharmonia Orchestra   Ashkenazy

SXL6920   (==== Not Issued ====)

SXL6921   NB : **£ 5**
Various   Sylvia Sass Sings Norma, La Traviata, La Gioconda.
Sass   New Philharmonia Orchestra   Gardelli

Decca SET Stereophonic LP's

The Decca SET's have identical labels to the SXL labels, but are Purple rather than Black.

The earliest labels, up until SET 492-3, are the WBg (Wide band grooved) type described previously. Later pressings may be WB (Wide Band) or NB (Narrow Band) types.

From SET 494 onwards, all SET's have the Wide Band without the groove as the first label.

SET 201-3   WBg : **£ 65**   WB : £40   NB : £15
STRAUSS   Die Fledermaus Gala performance   Nilsson
Vienna Philharmonic Orchestra   Karajan

SET 202-3   (==== Not Issued ====)

SET 204-8   WBg : **£ 50**   WB : £35   NB : £12
WAGNER   Tristan und Isolde   Nilsson
Vienna Philharmonic Orchestra   Solti

SET 209-11   WBg : **£ 12**   WB : £8   NB : £3
VERDI   Otello   Vienna Philharmonic Orchestra   Karajan

SET 212-4   WBg : **£ 30**   WB : £20   NB : £5
DONIZETTI   Lucia di Lammermoor   Sutherland
St. Cecilia Academy, Rome   Prichard

SET 215-7   WBg : **£ 30**   WB : £20   NB : £5
VERDI   Un Ballo in Maschera (A Masked Ball)   Nilsson
St. Cecilia Academy, Rome   Solti

SET 218-20   WBg : **£ 30**   WB : £20   NB : £5
HANDEL   Messiah   London Symphony Orchestra   Boult

SET 221-3   WBg : **£ 18**   WB : £12   NB : £3
CILEA   Adriana Lecouvreur St. Cecilia Academy, Rome Capuana

SET 224-6   WBg : **£ 30**   WB : £20   NB : £5
VERDI   Rigoletto   St. Cecilia Academy, Rome   Sanzogno

SET 227   WBg : **£ 18**   WB : £12   NB : £3
WAGNER   Wagner !   Vienna Philharmonic Orchestra   Solti

SET 228-9   WBg : **£ 30**   WB : £20   NB : £5
STRAUSS   Salome   Vienna Philharmonic Orchestra   Solti

SET 230   WBg : **£ 35**   WB : £25   NB : £5
CONFALONIERI   Cosmic Divertissement oh a theme of Dali
Complesso Strumentale Italiano   Confalonieri

SET 231   WBg : **£ 20**   WB : £14   NB : £4
BRAHMS   Symphony No.3
Vienna Philharmonic Orchestra   Karajan

SET 232-4	WBg : **£20**	WB : £14	NB : £4
HANDEL	Alcina London Symphony Orchestra Bonynge		

SET 235	(==== Not Issued ====)

SET 236-8	WBg : **£40**	WB : £25	NB : £8
PUCCINI	Il Triticco Maggio Musici Florence Gardelli		

SET 239-41	WBg : **£25**	WB : £16	NB : £4
BELLINI	La Sonnambula Sutherland		
Maggio Musici Florence Bonynge			

SET 242-6	WBg : **£60**	WB : £40	NB : £15
WAGNER	Siegfried Vienna Philharmonic Orchestra Solti		

SET 247-8	WBg : **£20**	WB : £12	NB : £4
Various	Joan Sutherland Command Performance		
Sutherland	London Symphony Orchestra Bonynge		

SET 249-51	WBg : **£28**	WB : £18	NB : £5
VERDI	La Traviata	Sutherland	
Maggio Musici Florence		Pritchard	

SET 252-3	WBg : **£20**	WB : £10	NB : £4
BRITTEN	War Requiem Melos Ensemble London Britten		

SET 254-5	WBg : **£20**	WB : £10	NB : £4
Various	The Art Of Prima Ballerina Sutherland		
London Symphony Orchestra Bonynge			

SET 256-8	WBg : **£30**	WB : £18	NB : £5
BIZET	Carmen	Sutherland	
Suisse Romande Orchestra		Schippers	

SET 259-61	WBg : **£30**	WB : £18	NB : £5
BELLINI	I Puritani	Sutherland	Bonynge

SET 262-4	WBg : **£35**	WB : £24	NB : £6
ROSSINI	L'italiana In Algeri Maggio Musici Florence Varviso		

SET 265-7	WBg : **£24**	WB : £16	NB : £5
ROSSINI	La Cenerentola Maggio Musici Florence De Fabritiis		

SET 268-9   WBg : **£16**   WB : £10   NB : £4
Various   The age of Bel Canto   Sutherland
London Symphony Orchestra   Bonynge

SET 270-1   WBg : **£20**   WB : £12   NB : £4
SCHUBERT   Winterreise   Pears   Britten

SET 272-3   WBg : **£30**   WB : £20   NB : £5
BEETHOVEN   Fidelio   Vienna Philharmonic Orchestra   Maazel

SET 274-6   WBg : **£20**   WB : £12   NB : £4
BRITTEN   Albert Herring English Chamber Orchestra   Britten

SET 277-9   WBg : **£20**   WB : £12   NB : £4
DEBUSSY   Pelleas et Melisande
Suisse Romande Orchestra   Ansermet

SET 280-1   WBg : **£16**   WB : £10   NB : £3
DONIZETTI   Don Pasquale   Vienna Opera Orchestra   Kertesz

SET 282-4   WBg : **£28**   WB : £18   NB : £7
VERDI   Macbeth   Nilsson
St. Cecilia Academy, Rome   Schippers

SET 285-7   WBg : **£40**   WB : £25   NB : £8
ROSSINI   Barber Of Seville   OCRN   Varviso

SET 288-91   WBg : **£40**   WB : £25   NB : £8
BACH   St Matthew's Passion
Stuttgart Chamber Orchestra   Munchinger

SET 292-7   WBg : **£40**   WB : £25   NB : £8
WAGNER   Gotterdammerung
Vienna Philharmonic Orchestra   Solti

SET 298-300   WBg : **£24**   WB : £15   NB : £3
VERDI   Nabucco   Gobbi
Vienna Opera Orchestra   Gardelli

SET 301   WBg : **£6**   WB : £4   NB : £1
BRITTEN   Curlew River   Britten

218

SET 302-4   WBg : **£ 20**   WB : £12   NB : £3
MOZART   Requiem   Vienna Philharmonic Orchestra   Kertesz

SET 305-8   WBg : **£ 30**   WB : £20   NB : £3
VERDI   Don Carlo   Tebaldi
Royal Opera House, Covent Garden   Solti

SET 309-10   WBg : **£ 24**   WB : £15   NB : £3
Various   Souviner of a Golden era - Sisters Garci   Horne
Suisse Romande Orchestra   Lewis

SET 311   WBg : **£ 10**   WB : £6   NB : £2
BARTOK   Bluebeard's Castle   Ludwig Berry
London Symphony Orchestra   Kertesz

SET 312-6   WBg : **£ 60**   WB : £40   NB : £12
WAGNER   Die Walkure   Vienna Philharmonic Orchestra Solti

SET 317-9   WBg : **£ 20**   WB : £12   NB : £3
ROSSINI   Semiramide   Sutherland
London Symphony Orchestra   Bonynge

SET 320-2   WBg : **£ 35**   WB : £20   NB : £3
BELLINI   Beatrice Di Tenda Sutherland
London Symphony Orchestra   Bonynge

SET 323-4   WBg : **£ 24**   WB : £16   NB : £3
BRUCKNER   Symphony No.7 Vienna Philharmonic Orchestra Solti

SET 325-6   WBg : **£ 30**   WB : £18   NB : £5
MAHLER   Symphony No.2 London Symphony Orchestra Solti

SET 327-30   WBg : **£ 40**   WB : £25   NB : £8
GOUNOD   Faust   Sutherland
London Symphony Orchestra   Bonynge

SET 331   WBg : **£ 18**   WB : £12   NB : £2
MAHLER   Das Lied Von Der Erde
Vienna Philharmonic Orchestra   Bernstein

SET 332   WBg : **£ 15**   WB : £10   NB : £2
MOZART   Symphony No.36, Piano Concerto 15
Vienna Philharmonic Orchestra   Bernstein

SET 333-4   WBg : **£30**   WB : £20   NB : £5
BRAHMS   German Requiem   Suisse Romande Orchestra   Ansermet

SET 335-6   WBg : **£28**   WB : £18   NB : £4
BRUCKNER   Symphony No.8   Vienna Philharmonic Orchestra   Solti

SET 337   (==== Not Issued ====)

SET 338-40   WBg : **£16**   WB : £10   NB : £3
BRITTEN   A Midsummer Night's Dream
London Symphony Orchestra Britten

SET 341-2   WBg : **£40**   WB : £25   NB : £5
PUCCINI   Tosca   St. Cecilia Academy, Rome   Maazel

SET 343-4   WBg : **£22**   WB : £14   NB : £4
MASCAGNI   Cavilleria Rusticana   Del Monaco
Rome Opera   Varviso

SET 345   WBg : **£10**   WB : £5   NB : £2
ROSSINI   La Cenerentola (Highlights)
Maggio Musici Florence   De Fabritiis

SET 346-8   WBg : **£30**   WB : £20   NB : £5
BACH   Weihnachts Oratorium
Stuttgart Chamber Orchestra   Munchinger

SET 349-50   WBg : **£16**   WB : £8   NB : £3
Various   Love Live Forever   Sutherland
Philharmonia Orchestra   Bonynge

SET 351   (==== Not Issued ====)

SET 352   WBg : **£6**   WB : £3   NB : £1
BONONCINI   Griselda   Sutherland
London Philharmonic Orchestra   Bonynge

SET 353   WBg : **£6**   WB : £3   NB : £1
VERDI   Don Carlo (Highlights)
Royal Opera House, Covent Garden   Solti

SET 354-5   WBg : **£30**   WB : £18   NB : £5
STRAUSS   Elektra   Vienna Philharmonic Orchestra   Solti

SET 356   WBg : **£8**   WB : £5   NB : £1
BRITTEN   The Burning Fiery Furnace   English Opera Group Britten

SET 357-9   WBg : **£24**   WB : £15   NB : £4
MOZART   La Clemenza Di Tito
Vienna Philharmonic Orchestra   Kertesz

SET 360-1   WBg : **£25**   WB : £15   NB : £4
MAHLER   Symphony No.9   London Symphony Orchestra Solti

SET 362-3   WBg : **£16**   WB : £10   NB : £3
HAYDN   Die Schopfung
Vienna Philharmonic Orchestra   Munchinger

SET 364-6   WBg : **£20**   WB : £12   NB : £4
PONCHIELLI   La Gioconda   St. Cecilia Academy, Rome Gardelli

SET 367   WBg : **£6**   WB : £3   NB : £1
VERDI   Nabucco (Highlights)   Gobbi
Vienna Opera Orchestra   Gardelli

SET 368-69   WBg : **£30**   WB : £18   NB : £5
BELLINI   Norma   Del Monaco
St. Cecilia Academy, Rome   Varviso

SET 370-71   WBg : **£22**   WB : £15   NB : £4
LISZT   Faust Symphony   Suisse Romande Orchestra Ansermet

SET 372-3   WBg : **£20**   WB : £10   NB : £4
DONIZETTI   La Fille Du Regiment   Sutherland
Rome Opera   Bonynge

SET 374-5   WBg : **£25**   WB : £15   NB : £4
VERDI   Requiem   Pavarotti
Vienna Philharmonic Orchestra   Solti

SET 376-8   (==== Not Issued ====)

SET 379-81   WBg : **£12**   WB : £7   NB : £3
BRITTEN   Billy Budd   London Symphony Orchestra Britten

SET 382-4   WBg : **£35**   WB : £22   NB : £6
WAGNER   Das Rhinegold   Vienna Philharmonic Orchestra Solti

SET 385-6   WBg : **£25**   WB : £15   NB : £5
MAHLER   Symphony No.3   London Symphony Orchestra   Solti

SET 387-389   WBg : **£25**   WB : £15   NB : £5
DELIBES   Lakme   Sutherland   Monte Carlo Opera   Bonynge

SET 390   WBg : **£5**   WB : £3   NB : £1
WAGNER   Die Walkure (Highlights)
Vienna Philharmonic Orchestra   Solti

SET 391   WBg : **£5**   WB : £3   NB : £1
ROSSINI   Semiramide (Highlights)   Sutherland
London Symphony Orchestra   Bonynge

SET 392-393   WBg : **£12**   WB : £6   NB : £3
Various   Opera Excerpts   Royal Opera House, Covent Garden

SET 394-396   WBg : **£25**   WB : £15   NB : £6
CATALANI   La Wally   Tebaldi   Monte Carlo Opera Cleva

SET 397   WBg : **£10**   WB : £6   NB : £2
BRITTEN   Midsummernights Dream
London Symphony Orchestra   Britten

SET 398   WBg : **£10**   WB : £6   NB : £2
BACH   Easter Oratorio
Stuttgart Chamber Orchestra   Munchinger

SET 399-0   WBg : **£35**   WB : £25   NB : £7
KODALY   Hary Janos   London Symphony Orchestra   Kertesz

SET 401-2   WBg : **£20**   WB : £12   NB : £5
VERDI   La Traviata   Fischer-Dieskau   Berlin Opera   Maazel

SET 403-4   WBg : **£30**   WB : £18   NB : £5
LEONCAVALLO   I Pagliacci   Lorengar
St. Cecilia Academy, Rome   Gardelli

SET 405   (==== Not Issued ====)

SET 406-8   WBg : **£40**   WB : £25   NB : £10
WAGNER   An Introduction To The Ring by Deryck Cooke
Vienna Philharmonic Orchestra   Solti

SET 409   WBg : **£6**   WB : £3   NB : £1
VERDI   Macbeth (Highlights)   Nilsson
St. Cecilia Academy, Rome   Schippers

SET 410-11   WBg : **£50**   WB : £30   NB : £12
BACH   Brandenburg Concertos
English Chamber Orchestra   Britten

SET 412-15   WBg : **£40**   WB : £25   NB : £10
MOZART   Don Giovanni   Sutherland
English Chamber Orchestra   Bonynge

SET 416-7   WBg : **£28**   WB : £18   NB : £8
DVORAK   Requiem Mass
London Symphony Orchestra   Kertesz

SET 418-21   WBg : **£20**   WB : £12   NB : £5
STRAUSS   Der Rosenkavalier   Crespin
Vienna Philharmonic Orchestra   Solti

SET 422   WBg : **£16**   WB : £10   NB : £5
ZANDONAI   Ora Andate   del Monaco
Monte Carlo Opera   Rescigno

SET 423   WBg : **£5**   WB : £3   NB : £1
BACH   Christmas Oratorio (Highlights)
Stuttgart Chamber Orchestra   Munchinger

SET 424-26   WBg : **£30**   WB : £18   NB : £7
BELLINI   Norma   Sutherland
London Symphony Orchestra   Bonynge

SET 427-9   WBg : **£25**   WB : £15   NB : £6
VERDI   Aida   Price   Rome Opera   Solti

SET 430-1   (==== Not Issued ====)

SET 432   WBg : **£18**   WB : £12   NB : £3
MOZART   La Clemenza Di Tito
Vienna Symphony Orchestra   Kertesz

SET 433-4   WBg : **£30**   WB : £18   NB : £4
ADAM   Giselle   Monte Carlo Opera   Bonynge

SET 435-6 WBg : **£25** WB : £16 NB : £3
GIORDANO Fedora Del Monaco Monte Carlo Opera Gardelli

SET 437 (==== Not Issued ====)

SET 438 WBg : **£6** WB : £3 NB : £1
BRITTEN The Prodigal Son Pears English Opera Group Britten

SET 439-40 WBg : **£10** WB : £5 NB : £2
Various A Tebaldi festival Suisse Romande Orchestra Bonynge

SET 441-2 (==== Not Issued ====)

SET 443-4 WBg : **£20** WB : £12 NB : £5
GLUCK Orfeo Euridice Horne
Royal Opera House, Covent Garden Solti

SET 445 WBg : **£6** WB : £3 NB : £1
BRITTEN The Golden Vanity Britten

SET 446-9 WBg : **£16** WB : £10 NB : £3
DONIZETTI Anna Bolena Horne
Vienna Opera Orchestra Varviso

SET 450 WBg : **£4** WB : £3 NB : £1
PONCHIELLI La Gioconda (Highlights)
St. Cecilia Academy, Rome Gardelli

SET 451 WBg : **£4** WB : £3 NB : £1
PUCCINI Tosca (Highlights) Nilsson
St. Cecilia Academy, Rome Maazel

SET 452 WBg : **£6** WB : £3 NB : £1
BRITTEN Billy Budd London Symphony Orchestra Britten

SET 453 (==== Not Issued ====)

SET 454-5 WBg : **£10** WB : £5 NB : £2
Various Romantic French Arias Sutherland
Suisse Romande Orchestra Bonynge

SET 456 (==== Not Issued ====)

| **SET 457** | WBg : **£10** | WB : £6 | NB : £2 |
| STRAUSS | Salome Scenes | Vienna Philharmonic Orchestra Solti | |

| **SET 458** | WBg : **£4** | WB : £3 | NB : £1 |
| BELLINI | Norma (Highlights) St. Cecilia Academy, Rome Varviso | | |

SET 459	WBg : **£20**	WB : £14	NB : £3
BRUCKNER	Symphony No.8	Excerpts	
Vienna Philharmonic Orchestra		Solti	

SET 460-3	WBg : **£24**	WB : £14	NB : £4
MEYERBEER	Les Huguenots	Sutherland	
New Philharmonia Orchestra		Bonynge	

SET 464	WBg : **£8**	WB : £4	NB : £1
VERDI	Four Sacred Pieces		
Los Angles Philharmonic Orchestra		Mehta	

SET 465-7	WBg : **£18**	WB : £12	NB : £2
HANDEL	Messiah	Krauss	
English Chamber Orchestra		Bonynge	

SET 468	WBg : **£40**	WB : £25	NB : £5
STRAVINSKY	The Firebird (and Rehersal)		
Suisse Romande Orchestra		Ansermet	

| **SET 469-70** | WBg : **£20** | WB : £12 | NB : £3 |
| MAHLER | Symphony No.6 | Chicago Symphony Orchestra Solti | |

| **SET 471-2** | WBg : **£20** | WB : £12 | NB : £3 |
| MAHLER | Symphony No.5 | Chicago Symphony Orchestra Solti | |

| **SET 473-4** | WBg : **£25** | WB : £14 | NB : £3 |
| DELIBES | Coppelia Suisse Romande Orchestra Bonynge | | |

SET 475	WBg : **£6**	WB : £3	NB : £1
DEBUSSY	Pelleas et Melisande (Highlights)		
Suisse Romande Orchestra		Ansermet	

| **SET 476** | (==== Not Issued ====) | | |

| **SET 477-8** | WBg : **£14** | WB : £9 | NB : £3 |
| BACH | Mass in Bmin. Stuttgart Chamber Orchestra Munchinger | | |

SET 479-81 WBg : **£35** WB : £25 NB : £7
MOZART Magic Flute Fischer-Dieskau
Vienna Philharmonic Orchestra Solti

SET 482 WBg : **£4** WB : £3 NB : £1
WAGNER Das Rhinegold (Highlights)
Vienna Philharmonic Orchestra Solti

SET 483 WBg : **£4** WB : £3 NB : £1
VERDI La Traviata (Highlights) Fischer-Dieskau
Berlin Opera Maazel

SET 484-6 WBg : **£16** WB : £8 NB : £3
VERDI Un Ballo in Maschera Pavarotti
St. Cecilia Academy, Rome Bartoletti

SET 487 WBg : **£4** WB : £3 NB : £1
STRAUSS Der Rosenkavalier (Highlights)
Vienna Philharmonic Orchestra Solti

SET 488 WBg : **£4** WB : £3 NB : £1
DELIBES Lakme (Highlights) Sutherland
Monte Carlo Opera Bonynge

SET 489-1 (==== Not Issued ====)

SET 492-3 WBg : **£6** WB : £3 NB : £1
BRITTEN Rape of Lucretia Pears
English Chamber Orchestra Britten

SET 494 WB : **£4** NB : £2
GIORDANO Fedora (Highlights) ONOMC Gardelli

SET 495 WB : **£4** NB : £2
GLUCK Orfeo ed Euridice (Highlights)
Royal Opera House, Covent Garden Solti

SET 496 (==== Not Issued ====)

SET 497-8 WB : **£10** NB : £5
Various Vienna, Women And Song Arias And Duets Holm
Vienna Volksoper

SET 499-500   WB : **£12**   NB : £6
PURCELL   The Fairy Queen   Vyvian
English Chamber Orchestra   Britten

SET 501-2   WB : **£8**   NB : £4
BRITTEN   Owen Wingrave   Pears
English Chamber Orchestra   Britten

SET 503-5   WB : **£15**   NB : £7
DONIZETTI   L'elisir D'amore
English Chamber Orchestra   Bonynge

SET 506-9   WB : **£25**   NB : £12
WAGNER   Tannhauser   Vienna Philharmonic Orchestra   Solti

SET 510-2   WB : **£15**   NB : £7
VERDI   Macbeth   London Philharmonic Orchestra   Gardelli

SET 513   WB : **£5**   NB : £2
MEYERBEER   Les Huguenots (Highlights)   Sutherland
New Philharmonia Orchestra   Bonynge

SET 514-7   WB : **£20**   NB : £8
MUSSORGSKY   Boris Godunov   Vienna Philharmonic Orchestra Karajan

SET 518-9   WB : **£8**   NB : £3
MAHLER   Symphony No.7   Chicago Symphony Orchestra   Solti

SET 520-21   WB : **£20**   NB : £10
Various   French Opera Excerpts   Crespin   Vienna Volksoper

SET 522   (==== Not Issued ====)

SET 523-24   WB : **£12**   NB : £6
Various   Homage to Pavlova
London Symphony Orchestra   Bonynge

SET 525-6   WB : **£8**   NB : £4
ELGAR   Dream Of Gerontius
London Symphony Orchestra   Britten

SET 527   WB : **£4**   NB : £2
MOZART   Magic Flute (Highlights)   Fischer-Dieskau
Vienna Philharmonic Orchestra   Solti

SET 528-30   WB : **£12**   NB : £6
DONIZETTI   Lucia di Lammermoor   Sutherland
Rome Opera   Bonynge

SET 531-33   WB : **£8**   NB : £4
BACH   St. Johns Passion   English Chamber Orchestra   Britten

SET 534-5   WB : **£16**   NB : £8
MAHLER   Symphony No.8   Chicago Symphony Orchestra   Solti

SET 536-7   (==== Not Issued ====)

SET 538   WB : **£4**   NB : £2
VERDI   Un Ballo in Maschera (Highlights)   Pavarotti
St. Cecilia Academy, Rome   Bartoletti

SET 539   WB : **£4**   NB : £2
VERDI   Macbeth (Highlights)
London Philharmonic Orchestra   Gardelli

SET 540-41   WB : **£14**   NB : £7
STRAUSS   Die Fledermaus   Vienna Philharmonic Orchestra   Bohm

SET 542-4   WB : **£15**   NB : £7
VERDI   Rigoletto   Sutherland
London Symphony Orchestra   Bonynge

SET 545-7   WB : **£12**   NB : £6
OFFENBACH   Tales of Hoffman   Sutherland
Suisse Romande Orchestra   Bonynge

SET 548-9   WB : **£25**   NB : £12
MOZART   Mozart Opera Festival   Krenn
Vienna Haydn Orchestra   Peters

SET 550-4   WB : **£25**   NB : £12
WAGNER   Parsifal   Vienna Philharmonic Orchestra   Solti

228

SET 555   WB : **£6**   NB : £3
MAHLER   Das Lied von der Erde
Chicago Symphony Orchestra   Solti

SET 556   WB : **£4**   NB : £2
WAGNER   Tannhauser (Highlights)
Vienna Philharmonic Orchestra   Solti

SET 557   WB : **£4**   NB : £2
MUSSORGSKY   Boris Godunov (Highlights)
Vienna Philharmonic Orchestra   Karajan

SET 558   (==== Not Issued ====)

SET 559   WB : **£5**   NB : £2
DONIZETTI   Lucis Di Lammermoor (Highlights)   Sutherland
Rome Opera   Bonynge

SET 560   WB : **£4**   NB : £2
PURCELL   The Fairy Queen (Highlights)   Vyvian
English Chamber Orchestra Britten

SET 561-3   WB : **£30**   NB : £12
PUCCINI   Turandot Sutherland
London Philharmonic Orchestra   Mehta

SET 564   (==== Not Issued ====)

SET 565-6   WB : **£30**   NB : £10
PUCCINI   La Boheme   Berlin Philharmonic Orchestra   Karajan

SET 567-8   WB : **£12**   NB : £5
SCHUMANN   Scenes from Goeth's Faust
English Chamber Orchestra   Britten

SET 569   WB : **£4**   NB : £2
OFFENBACH   Tales of Hoffman (Highlights)   Sutherland
Suisse Romande Orchestra   Bonynge

SET 570-71   WB : **£10**   NB : £5
BERLIOZ   Romeo et Juliet   Ludvig
Vienna Philharmonic Orchestra   Maazel

SET 572   WB : **£8**   NB : £4
MASSENET   Therese   Tourengeau
New Philharmonia Orchestra   Bonynge

SET 573   WB : **£4**   NB : £2
PUCCINI   Turandot (Highlights)   Sutherland
London Philharmonic Orchestra   Mehta

SET 574   WB : **£4**   NB : £2
WAGNER   Parsifal (Highlights)
Vienna Philharmonic Orchestra   Solti

SET 575-8   WB : **£28**   NB : £15
MOZART   Cosi Fan Tutte   London Philharmonic Orchestra   Solti

SET 579   WB : **£4**   NB : £2
PUCCINI   La Boheme (Highlights)
Berlin Philharmonic Orchestra   Karajan

SET 580   WB : **£4**   NB : £2
VERDI   Rigoletto (Highlights)   Sutherland   Milnes

SET 581-3   WB : **£10**   NB : £5
BRITTEN   Death in Venice   Quirk
English Chamber Orchestra   Bedford

SET 584-6   WB : **£20**   NB : £8
PUCCINI   Madame Butterfly
Vienna Philharmonic Orchestra   Karajan

SET 587-9   WB : **£12**   NB : £6
BELLINI   I Puritani   Sutherland
London Symphony Orchestra   Bonynge

SET 590-2   WB : **£12**   NB : £6
BACH   St. Johns Passion
Stuttgart Chamber Orchestra   Munchinger

SET 593-4   WB : **£10**   NB : £5
MONTEVERDI   Vespers of 1610
Monteverdi Orchestra & Choir   Gardiner

SET 595   WB : **£5**   NB : £2
MOZART   Cosi fan tutte (Highlights)
London Philharmonic Orchestra   Solti

SET 596-8   WB : **£12**   NB : £6
TCHAIKOVSKY   Eugene Onegin
Royal Opera House, Covent Garden   Solti

SET 599-600   (==== Not Issued ====)

SET 601   WB : **£10**   NB : £5
STRAUSS   Ein Heldenleben   Vienna Philharmonic Orchestra   Solti

SET 602   WB : **£6**   NB : £3
VERDI   4 Sacred Pieces   Chicago Symphony Orchestra   Solti

SET 603-5   (==== Not Issued ====)

SET 606-8   WB : **£16**   NB : £8
VERDI   Luisa Miller   Pavarotti
New Philharmonia Orchestra   Maag

SET 609-11   WB : **£40**   NB : £18
GERSHWIN   Porgy & Bess   Cleveland Orchestra   Maazel

SET 612-4   WB : **£15**   NB : £5
MASSENET   Esclaremonde   Sutherland
New Philharmonia Orchestra   Bonynge

SET 615   WB : **£10**   NB : £5
PURCELL   Dido and Aeneas   Aldeburgh Festival Orchestra   Bedford

SET 616   WB : **£8**   NB : £4
STRAVINSKY   Oedipus Rex   London Philharmonic Orchestra   Solti

SET 617   WB : **£6**   NB : £3
WOLF-FERRARI   Segreto Di Susanna
Royal Opera House, Covent Garden   Gardelli

SET 618   WB : **£8**   NB : £3
WALTON   Belshazzar's Feast
London Philharmonic Orchestra   Solti

SET 619   WB : **£5**   NB : £2
BELLINI   I Puritani (Highlights)   Sutherland
London Symphony Orchestra   Bonynge

SET 620-1   (==== Not Issued ====)

SET 622   WB : **£10**   NB : £5
Various   Carmen, Prince Igor, Etc.
London Symphony Orchestra   Solti

SET 623   WB : **£4**   NB : £2
VERDI   Luisa Miller (Highlights)   Pavarotti
New Philharmonia Orchestra   Maag

SET 624   (==== Not Issued ====)

SET 625   WB : **£4**   NB: £2
WAGNER   Die Meistersinger von Nurnberg
Chicago Symphony Orchestra   Solti

SET 626   WB : **£4**   NB : £2
WAGNER   Flying Dutchman (Highlights)
Chicago Symphony Orchestra   Solti

SET 627   (==== Not Issued ====)

SET 628   WB : **£8**   NB : £3
HOLST   The Planets   London Philharmonic Orchestra   Solti

Columbia 33CX series Monophonic LP's

Launched in 1952, the 33CX series were superbly recorded mono LP's from Columbia records.

The first labels were deep blue with gold writing and this label continued to be the first label up to 33CX1949. This is referred to as **B/Gold** (Blue/Gold) throughout this section of the guide.

From 33CX5251, and later pressed Columbia records, a red background with a black semicircle with the words Columbia printed around it in white is the first label. This is referred to as **Red Semi** throughout this section of the guide.

33CX1001   B/Gold : **£6**   Red Semi : £3
STRAUSS   Don Juan, Til Eulenspiegels
Philharmonia Orchestra   Karajan
No Stereo

33CX1002   B/Gold : **£10**   Red Semi : £5
BALAKIREV   Symphony in Cmaj   Philharmonia Orchestra   Karajan
No Stereo

33CX1003   B/Gold : **£16**   Red Semi : £8
BERLIOZ   Four Overtures
Vienna Philharmonic Orchestra   Karajan
No Stereo

33CX1004   B/Gold : **£8**   Red Semi : £4
BEETHOVEN   Symphony No.5 in Cmin. Op.67
Philharmonia Orchestra   Kletzki
No Stereo

33CX1005   B/Gold : **£6**   Red Semi : £3
WAGNER   Die Walkure (Extracts)
Beyreuth Festival Orchestra   Karajan
No Stereo

33CX1006   B/Gold : **£5**   Red Semi : £3
WAGNER   Die Meistersinger (Extracts)
Beyreuth Festival Orchestra Karajan
No Stereo

33CX1007-9   B/Gold : **£35**   Red Semi : £20
MOZART   Le Nozze di Figaro Seefried
Vienna Philharmonic Orchestra   Karajan
No Stereo

33CX1010   B/Gold : **£30**   Red Semi : £15
BEETHOVEN   Piano Concerto No.5 (Emperor)   Gieseking
Philharmonia Orchestra   Karajan
No Stereo

33CX1011   B/Gold : **£10**   Red Semi : £5
BEETHOVEN   Violin Concerto   Francescatti
Philharmonia Orchestra   Ormandy
No Stereo

33CX1012　　　B/Gold : **£22**　　Red Semi : £12
BRAHMS　　　　Piano Quartet No.1　　　Serkin
Busch String Quartet
No Stereo

33CX1013-5　　B/Gold : **£35**　　Red Semi : £20
MOZART　　　　Die Zauberflote　　Seefried
Vienna Philharmonic Orchestra　　Karajan
No Stereo

33CX1016-8　　B/Gold : **£15**　　Red Semi : £8
BIZET　　　　　Carmen　　　　　Michel
Opera Comique Chorus & Orchestra　　Cluytens
No Stereo

33CX1019　　　B/Gold : **£8**　　Red Semi : £4
BERLIOZ　　　Harold in Italy　　Primrose
Royal Philharmonic Orchestra　　Beecham
No Stereo

33CX1020　　　B/Gold : **£6**　　Red Semi : £3
CASTELNUOVO-TEDESCO　　　Concerto for Guitar and Orchestra
Segovia　New London Orchestra　　Sherman
No Stereo

33CX1021-5　　B/Gold : **£35**　　Red Semi : £20
WAGNER　　　Die Meistersinger　Beyreuth Festival Orchestra　Karajan
No Stereo

33CX1026　　　B/Gold : **£4**　　Red Semi : £2
DVORAK　　　　New World Symphony
Philharmonia Orchestra　　Galliera
No Stereo

33CX1027　　　B/Gold : **£15**　　Red Semi : £8
BRAHMS　　　　Piano Concerto No.2　　Serkin
Philharmonia Orchestra　　Ormandy
No Stereo

33CX1028　　　B/Gold : **£6**　　Red Semi : £3
HAYDN　Symphony No.92, Symphony No.101
Cleveland Orchestra　　Szell
No Stereo

33CX1029   B/Gold : **£ 12**   Red Semi : £6
MOUSSORGSKY / RAVEL   Songs & Dances of Death
Tourel   Columbia Symphony Orchestra   Bernstein
No Stereo

33CX1030   B/Gold : **£ 10**   Red Semi : £5
TCHAIKOVSKY   Romeo & Juliet, Francesca da Rimini
New York PhilharmonicOrchestra   Stokowski
No Stereo

33CX1031   B/Gold : **£ 18**   Red Semi : £10
MOZART   Quintet in D, Quintet in Cmin.   Katims
Budapest String Quartet
No Stereo

33CX1032   B/Gold : **£ 15**   Red Semi : £8
CHOPIN   Waltzes complete   Lipatti
No Stereo

33CX1033   B/Gold : **£ 6**   Red Semi : £3
HANDEL / TCHAIKOVSKY   Water Music, Nutcracker Suite
Philharmonia Orchestra   Karajan
No Stereo

33CX1034   B/Gold : **£ 15**   Red Semi : £8
MAHLER   Symphony No.4
New York Philharmonic Orchestra   Walter
No Stereo

33CX1035   B/Gold : **£ 8**   Red Semi : £4
BEETHOVEN   Symphony No.7   Philharmonia Orchestra   Karajan
No Stereo

33CX1036   B/Gold : **£ 20**   Red Semi : £10
DVORAK   Symphony No.4
Philharmonic Symphony Orchestra of New York   Walter
No Stereo

33CX1037   B/Gold : **£ 8**   Red Semi : £4
BIZET / TCHAIKOVSKY   Carmen Suite, Caprice Italien
Columbia Symphony Orchestra   Beecham
No Stereo

33CX1038   B/Gold : **£6**   Red Semi : £3
HAYDN   Symphony No.31 & 93
Royal Philharmonic Orchestra   Beecham
No Stereo

33CX1039   B/Gold : **£6**   Red Semi : £3
BEETHOVEN / SCHUBERT   Symphony No.8, Symphony No.8
Royal Philharmonic Orchestra   Beecham
No Stereo

33CX1040   B/Gold : **£50**   Red Semi : £30
SCHUBERT   Lieder Recital   Schwarzkopf
No Stereo

33CX1041-2   (==== Not Issued ====)

33CX1043   B/Gold : **£30**   Red Semi : £15
BEETHOVEN   Trio No.5   Busch, Serkin & Adolph
No Stereo

33CX1044   B/Gold : **£12**   Red Semi : £6
Various   Songs   Schwarzkopf
No Stereo

33CX1045   B/Gold : **£30**   Red Semi : £15
SCHUMANN   Symphony No.3
New York Symphony Orchestra   Walter
No Stereo

33CX1046   B/Gold : **£5**   Red Semi : £3
BEETHOVEN   Symphony No.3   Philharmonia Orchestra   Karajan
No Stereo

33CX1047   B/Gold : **£8**   Red Semi : £4
SIBELIUS   Symphony No.5, Finlandia
Philharmonia Orchestra   Karajan
No Stereo

33CX1048   B/Gold : **£8**   Red Semi : £4
BRAHMS   Piano Concerto No.1   Malcuzynski
Philharmonia Orchestra   Reiger
No Stereo

33CX1049   B/Gold : **£8**   Red Semi : £4
PROKOFIEF / FALLA   Symphony No.1, 3-Corn Hat etc
Philharmonia Orchestra   Markevitch
No Stereo

33CX1050   B/Gold : **£25**   Red Semi : £12
SCHUMANN   Piano Quintet in Eb   Curzon   Budapest String Quartet
No Stereo

33CX1051-2   B/Gold : **£18**   Red Semi : £10
LEHAR   The Merry Widow   Schwarzkopf
Philharmonia Orchestra   Ackermann
No Stereo

33CX1053   B/Gold : **£8**   Red Semi : £4
BRAHMS   Symphony No.1   Philharmonia Orchestra   Karajan
No Stereo

33CX1054   B/Gold : **£10**   Red Semi : £5
BARTOK   Concert for Orchestra   Philharmonia Orchestra   Karajan
No Stereo

33CX1055   B/Gold : **£40**   Red Semi : £20
BEETHOVEN   Piano Sonata No.21 & 23   Gieseking
No Stereo

33CX1056-7   B/Gold : **£6**   Red Semi : £3
Spoken Word   Murder in the Cathedral   Various
No Stereo

33CX1058-60   B/Gold : **£60**   Red Semi : £30
BELLINI   I Puritani   Callas
Milan La Scala Orchestra   Serafin
No Stereo

33CX1061   B/Gold : **£25**   Red Semi : £12
HAYDN   Lark & Sunsise Quartets   Budapest String Quartet
No Stereo

33CX1062   B/Gold : **£6**   Red Semi : £3
BEETHOVEN   Symphony No.6
Royal Philharmonic Orchestra   Beecham
No Stereo

33CX1063　　　B/Gold : **£15**　　Red Semi : £8
BAX / TIPPET / FINZI / RUBBRA　　A Garland for the Queen
Cambridge University Madrigal Society　　　Ord
No Stereo

33CX1064　　　B/Gold : **£10**　　Red Semi : £5
FRANCK　　　　Symphony in Dmin.
French National Radio Orchestra　　Cluytens
No Stereo

33CX1065　　　B/Gold : **£2**　　Red Semi : £1
TCHAIKOVSKY　Sleeping Beauty, Swan Lake
Philharmonia Orchestra　　　Karajan
Stereo Issue : SAX2306

33CX1066　　　B/Gold : **£8**　　Red Semi : £4
CHOPIN　　　　Piano Concerto No.2　　　Malcuzynski
Philharmonia Orchestra　　　Kletzki
No Stereo

33CX1067　　　B/Gold : **£6**　　Red Semi : £3
GOLDMARK　　　Rustic Wedding Symphony
Royal Philharmonic Orchestra　　　Beecham
No Stereo

33CX1068　　　B/Gold : **£10**　　Red Semi : £5
MAHLER　　　　Symphony No.1
Minneapolis Symphony Orchestra　　Mitropoulos
No Stereo

33CX1069　　　B/Gold : **£15**　　Red Semi : £8
MOZART　　　　Operatic Arias　　Schwarzkopf
No Stereo

33CX1070　　　B/Gold : **£15**　　Red Semi : £8
BEETHOVEN　　Piano Concerto No.5　　　Serkin
Philharmonia Orchestra　　　Ormandy
No Stereo

33CX1071　　　B/Gold : **£8**　　Red Semi : £4
MENDELSSOHN / MOZART　　Violin Concerto, Violin Concerto No.3
Stern　　Philadelphia Chamber Orchestra　　　Ormandy
No Stereo

33CX1072   B/Gold : **£6**   Red Semi : £3
SCHUMANN / BRAHMS   Symphonic Studies, Paganini Variations Anda
No Stereo

33CX1073   B/Gold : **£40**   Red Semi : £20
BEETHOVEN   Moonlight, Pathetique Sonatas   Gieseking
No Stereo

33CX1074   B/Gold : **£3**   Red Semi : £2
BACH   Fantasia & Fugue in G, Etc.   Schweitzer
No Stereo

33CX1075   B/Gold : **£12**   Red Semi : £6
CHERUBINI   Requiem Mass in Cmin.   Santa Cicilia   Giulini
No Stereo

33CX1076   B/Gold : **£15**   Red Semi : £8
RAVEL   L'Heure Espagnole
Opera Comique Chorus & Orchestra   Cluytens
No Stereo

33CX1077   B/Gold : **£30**   Red Semi : £15
BEETHOVEN   Symphony No.5
New York Philharmonic Orchestra   Walter
No Stereo

33CX1078-9   B/Gold : **£16**   Red Semi : £8
DELIUS   Mass of Life   Raisbeck
Royal Philharmonic Orchestra   Beecham
No Stereo

33CX1080   B/Gold : **£6**   Red Semi : £3
BEETHOVEN   Piano Concerto No.3   Arrau
Philharmonia Orchestra   Ormandy
No Stereo

33CX1081   B/Gold : **£3**   Red Semi : £2
BACH   Choral Preludes   Schweitzer
No Stereo

33CX1082   B/Gold : **£30**   Red Semi : £15
MOZART / SCHUBERT   Symphony No.41, Symphony No.8
Philharmonic Symphony Orchestra of New York   Walter
No Stereo

33CX1083   B/Gold : **£8**   Red Semi : £4
STRAVINSKY   The Rite of Spring
Philharmonic Symphony Orchestra of New York   Stravinsky
No Stereo

33CX1084   B/Gold : **£3**   Red Semi : £2
BACH   Choral Preludes   Schweitzer
No Stereo

33CX1085   B/Gold : **£7**   Red Semi : £4
SIBELIUS   Symphony No.1
Royal Philharmonic Orchestra   Beecham
No Stereo

33CX1086   B/Gold : **£6**   Red Semi : £3
BEETHOVEN   Symphony No.4
Royal Philharmonic Orchestra   Beecham
No Stereo

33CX1087   B/Gold : **£6**   Red Semi : £3
FRANCK / RIMSKY -KORSAKOV   Chasseur Maudit, Coq d'Or
Royal Philharmonic Orchestra   Beecham
No Stereo

33CX1088   B/Gold : **£12**   Red Semi : £6
MOZART   Symphony No.29, Eine Kleine Nachtmusik
Perpignan Festival Orchestra   Casals
No Stereo

33CX1089   B/Gold : **£12**   Red Semi : £6
MOZART   Sinfonia Concertante in Eb   Primrose, Stern
Perpignan Festival Orchestra   Casals
No Stereo

33CX1090   B/Gold : **£14**   Red Semi : £7
MOZART   Divertimento No.11, Quartet in F   Tabuteau,
Tortelier   Perpignan Festival Orchestra   Casals
No Stereo

241

33CX1091   B/Gold : **£16**   Red Semi : £8
MOZART   Piano Concerto No.9 in Eb   Hess
Perpignan Festival Orchestra   Casals
No Stereo

33CX1092   B/Gold : **£15**   Red Semi : £8
MOZART   Piano Concerto No.22 in Eb   Serkin
Perpignan Festival Orchestra   Casals
No Stereo

33CX1093   B/Gold : **£12**   Red Semi : £6
MOZART / BEETHOVEN   Sonata No.2, 7 Variations in Eb, 12 Vars in F
Casals, Serkin   Perpignan Festival Orchestra   Casals
No Stereo

33CX1094-5   B/Gold : **£35**   Red Semi : £20
PUCCINI   Tosca   Callas   Milan La Scala Orchestra   Sabata
No Stereo

33CX1096-7   B/Gold : **£14**   Red Semi : £7
HUMPERDINCK   Hansel & Gretel   Grummer
Philharmonia Orchestra   Karajan
No Stereo

33CX1098   B/Gold : **£40**   Red Semi : £20
DEBUSSY   Preludes 1-12   Gieseking
No Stereo

33CX1099   B/Gold : **£7**   Red Semi : £4
DEBUSSY / RAVEL   La Mer, Rhapsodie Espagnole
Philharmonia Orchestra   Karajan
No Stereo

33CX1100   B/Gold : **£8**   Red Semi : £4
STRAVINSKY   Fireworks, Ode, Ebony Concerto, Russian Maidens song
Woody Herman   Philharmonic Symphony Orchestra of New York   Stravinsky
No Stereo

33CX1101   B/Gold : **£12**   Red Semi : £6
BOCCERINI   Quartet in A, Quartet in Cb   Quartetto Italiano
No Stereo

33CX1102   B/Gold : **£12**   Red Semi : £6
MOZART   String Quartets Gmaj. & Dmin. Quartetto Italiano
No Stereo

33CX1103   B/Gold : **£12**   Red Semi : £6
BEETHOVEN   Quartet No.13   Quartetto Italiano
No Stereo

33CX1104   B/Gold : **£6**   Red Semi : £3
HAYDN   Symphony No.103 & 94
Royal Philharmonic Orchestra   Beecham
No Stereo

33CX1105   B/Gold : **£6**   Red Semi : £3
HANDEL / MOZART   Faithful Shepherd Suite, Symphony No.31
Royal Philharmonic Orchestra   Beecham
No Stereo

33CX1106   B/Gold : **£8**   Red Semi : £4
LISZT   Piano Concerto No.2, Sonata in Bmin.   Malcuzynski
Philharmonia Orchestra   Susskind
No Stereo

33CX1107   B/Gold : **£15**   Red Semi : £8
STRAUSS   Vier Letzte Leider   Schwarzkopf
Philharmonia Orchestra   Ackermann
No Stereo

33CX1108   B/Gold : **£12**   Red Semi : £6
BACH   Orchestral Suites Prades Festival Orchestra   Casals
No Stereo

33CX1109   B/Gold : **£30**   Red Semi : £15
BACH   Piano Concerto No.5, Violin Concerto No.1
Haskil, Stern   Prades Festival Orchestra   Casals
No Stereo

33CX1110   B/Gold : **£12**   Red Semi : £6
BACH   Chromatic fantasia & fuge, Italian Concerto, Sonata No.3
Casals, Baumgartner
No Stereo

33CX1111   B/Gold : **£15**   Red Semi : £8
DEBUSSY / FRANCK   Sonata No.3, Sonata in A for Violin & Piano
Francescatti, Casadesus
No Stereo

33CX1112   B/Gold : **£6**   Red Semi : £3
DELIUS   Appalachia   Royal Philharmonic Orchestra   Beecham
No Stereo

33CX1113   B/Gold : **£75**   Red Semi : £35
BACH   Concerto for Violin, Klavier and Flute, Violin Concerto
Horszowski, Schnieder   Prades Festival Orchestra   Casals
No Stereo

33CX1114-5   B/Gold : **£15**   Red Semi : £8
LEHAR   Land of Smiles   Schwarzkopf
Philharmonia Orchestra   Ackermann
No Stereo

33CX1116   B/Gold : **£15**   Red Semi : £8
SAINT-SAINS   Symphony No.3
New York Symphony Orchestra   Munch
No Stereo

33CX1117   B/Gold : **£30**   Red Semi : £15
BEETHOVEN   Symphony No.3
New York Symphony Orchestra   Walter
No Stereo

33CX1118   B/Gold : **£10**   Red Semi : £5
FRANCK / D'INDY   Symphonic Variations, Chant Montagnard
Casadesus   Philharmonia Orchestra   Weldon, Munch
No Stereo

33CX1119   B/Gold : **£15**   Red Semi : £8
POULENC   Songs   Poulenc, Bernac
No Stereo

33CX1120   B/Gold : **£30**   Red Semi : £15
BEETHOVEN   Symphony No.7
New York Philharmonic Orchestra   Walter
No Stereo

33CX1121-3   B/Gold : **£30**   Red Semi : £15
BACH   Mass in Bmin.   Schwarzkopf   Karajan
No Stereo

33CX1124   B/Gold : **£8**   Red Semi : £4
BEETHOVEN   Symphony No.6   Philharmonia Orchestra   Karajan
No Stereo

33CX1125   B/Gold : **£6**   Red Semi : £3
SIBELIUS   Symphony No.4, Symphonic Poem, Tapiola
Philharmonia Orchestra   Karajan
No Stereo

33CX1126-7   B/Gold : **£4**   Red Semi : £2
Spoken Word   The Importance of Being Earnest   Gielgud
No Stereo

33CX1128   B/Gold : **£30**   Red Semi : £15
MOZART   Complete works of Mozart Vol.1   Gieseking
No Stereo

33CX1129   B/Gold : **£14**   Red Semi : £7
WAGNER   Tannhauser Overture, etc.
Philharmonia Orchestra   Kletzki
No Stereo

33CX1130   B/Gold : **£10**   Red Semi : £5
Various   Operatic Arias   Gedda
No Stereo

33CX1131-2   B/Gold : **£60**   Red Semi : £30
DONIZETTI   Lucia di Lammermoor   Callas
Maggio Musici Florence   Serafin
No Stereo

33CX1133   B/Gold : **£7**   Red Semi : £4
TCHAIKOVSKY   Symphony No.5   Philharmonia Orchestra   Karajan
No Stereo

33CX1134   B/Gold : **£15**   Red Semi : £8
RAVEL   Miroirs No.4
French National Radio Orchestra   Cluytens
No Stereo

33CX1135 B/Gold : **£15** Red Semi : £8
PROKOVIEF Visions Fugitives Francois
No Stereo

33CX1136 B/Gold : **£6** Red Semi : £3
BEETHOVEN Egmont Ovature, Leonora Overture
Philharmonia Orchestra Karajan
No Stereo

33CX1137 B/Gold : **£50** Red Semi : £30
DEBUSSY Piano Works of Debussy Gieseking
No Stereo

33CX1138 B/Gold : **£6** Red Semi : £3
CHOPIN Polonaises & Mazurkas Malcuzynski
No Stereo

33CX1139 B/Gold : **£8** Red Semi : £4
TCHAIKOVSKY Symphony No.4 Philharmonia Orchestra Karajan
No Stereo

33CX1140 B/Gold : **£6** Red Semi : £3
MOZART 4 Horn Concertos Brain
Philharmonia Orchestra Karajan
No Stereo

33CX1141 B/Gold : **£30** Red Semi : £15
KHATCHATURIAN Violin Concerto Igor Oistrakh
Philharmonia Orchestra Goosens
No Stereo

33CX1142 B/Gold : **£30** Red Semi : £15
MOZART Complete works of Mozart Vol.2 Gieseking
No Stereo

33CX1143 B/Gold : **£6** Red Semi : £3
RACHMANINOV Piano Concerto No.2, Preludes Anda
No Stereo

33CX1144 B/Gold : **£8** Red Semi : £4
BACH / BRAHMS / BEETHOVEN Chromatic fantasia ,Intermezzo,
Appasionata Malcuzynski
No Stereo

33CX1145 B/Gold : **£10** Red Semi : £5
FAURE Requiem Angelici
No Stereo

33CX1146-8 B/Gold : **£8** Red Semi : £4
HANDEL Messiah Liverpool Philharmonic Orchestra Sargent
No Stereo

33CX1149 B/Gold : **£30** Red Semi : £15
DEBUSSY Shorter Piano Works Gieseking
No Stereo

33CX1150-2 B/Gold : **£25** Red Semi : £14
OFFENBACH Tales of Hoffmann Jobin TNO Cluytens
No Stereo

33CX1153 B/Gold : **£20** Red Semi : £10
BIZET L'Arlesienne Suites No.1 & 2
French National Radio Orchestra Cluytens
No Stereo

33CX1154 B/Gold : **£20** Red Semi : £10
Various Recital Dobbs
No Stereo

33CX1155 B/Gold : **£12** Red Semi : £6
DEBUSSY / MILHAUD Quartet No.12 in G, Quartet No.12
Quartetto Italiano
No Stereo

33CX1156 B/Gold : **£6** Red Semi : £3
TCHAIKOVSKY / DOHNANYI Piano Concerto No.5, Coppella
Paraphrase Anda
No Stereo

33CX1157 B/Gold : **£7** Red Semi : £4
SCHUBERT Rosamunde Philharmonia Orchestra Kletzki
No Stereo

33CX1158 B/Gold : **£10** Red Semi : £5
SAINT-SAINS Symphonic Poems
Colonne Concert Association Orchestra Fourestier
No Stereo

33CX1159   B/Gold : **£5**   Red Semi : £3
VAUGHAN WILLIAMS / BRITTEN   Fantasia on a Theme of Thomas
Tallis, Frank Bridge   Philharmonia Orchestra   Karajan
No Stereo

33CX1160   B/Gold : **£30**   Red Semi : £15
MOZART   Complete works of Mozart Vol.3   Gieseking
No Stereo

33CX1161   B/Gold : **£6**   Red Semi : £3
RACHMANINOV   Piano Concerto No.3   Malcuzynski
Philharmonia Orchestra   Kletzki
No Stereo

33CX1162   B/Gold : **£14**   Red Semi : £7
WOLF   Leider Recital   Hotter
No Stereo

33CX1163   B/Gold : **£15**   Red Semi : £8
VIVALDI / ALBINONI   Concerto in F for 3 Violins, Strings & Cembalo
I Musici
No Stereo

33CX1164   B/Gold : **£6**   Red Semi : £3
RAVEL / SMETANA   Bolero, Bartered Bride Ov
Philharmonia Orchestra   Kletzki
No Stereo

33CX1165   B/Gold : **£200**   Red Semi : £150
BRAHMS   Violin Concerto   Martzy
Philharmonia Orchestra   Kletzki
No Stereo

33CX1166   B/Gold : **£6**   Red Semi : £3
MENOTTI   Amelia al Ballo   Amandini
Milan La Scala Orchestra   Venez
No Stereo

33CX1167   B/Gold : **£12**   Red Semi : £6
BORODIN / IPPOLITOV-IVANOV   Symphony No.2, Caucasian Sketches
Philharmonia Orchestra   Kletzki
No Stereo

248

33CX1168   B/Gold : **£16**   Red Semi : £8
BEETHOVEN   Quartet No.1 & 2 Hungarian String Quartet
No Stereo

33CX1169   (==== Not Issued ====)

33CX1170   B/Gold : **£15**   Red Semi : £8
VIVALDI   Concerto in A for Strings & Cembalo, Etc.   I Musici
No Stereo

33CX1171   B/Gold : **£10**   Red Semi : £5
CIMAROSA   Concert for 2 Flutes & Orchestra
Alessandra Scarlatti Orchestra   Caracciolo
No Stereo

33CX1172   B/Gold : **£16**   Red Semi : £8
BEETHOVEN   Quartet No.3 & 4 Hungarian String Quartet
No Stereo

33CX1173   B/Gold : **£15**   Red Semi : £8
BIZET   Symphony in G, Patrie Overture
French National Radio Orchestra   Cluytens
No Stereo

33CX1174   B/Gold : **£8**   Red Semi : £4
MENDELSSOHN Midsummernights Dream
Philharmonia Orchestra   Kletzki
No Stereo

33CX1175   B/Gold : **£6**   Red Semi : £3
BRITTEN / SAINT-SAINS Carnival of Animals, Young Persons Guide
Pears, Anda   Philharmonia Orchestra   Markevitch
No Stereo

33CX1176   B/Gold : **£6**   Red Semi : £3
BARTOK   Sonatina   Anda
No Stereo

33CX1177   (==== Not Issued ====)

33CX1178 B/Gold : **£ 10** Red Semi : £5
MOZART Sinfonia Concerto, Eine Kleine Nacht Music
Philharmonia Orchestra Karajan
No Stereo

33CX1179-81 B/Gold : **£ 25** Red Semi : £12
BELLINI Norma Callas Milan La Scala Orchestra Serafin
No Stereo

33CX1182-3 B/Gold : **£ 30** Red Semi : £16
MASCAGNI Cavalleria Rusticana Callas
Milan La Scala Orchestra Serafin
No Stereo

33CX1184 (==== Not Issued ====)

33CX1185 B/Gold : **£ 30** Red Semi : £16
BEETHOVEN Piano Sonata No.31, Piano Sonata No.32 Siki
No Stereo

33CX1186-7 B/Gold : **£ 22** Red Semi : £12
STRAUSS Weiner Blut Schwarzkopf
Philharmonia Orchestra Ackermann
No Stereo

33CX1188 B/Gold : **£ 10** Red Semi : £5
BEETHOVEN Piano Concerto No.3 Gilels
Paris Conservatoire Orchestra Cluytens
No Stereo

33CX1189 B/Gold : **£ 8** Red Semi : £4
TCHAIKOVSKY Symphony Manfred Philharmonia Orchestra Kletzki
No Stereo

33CX1190 B/Gold : **£ 15** Red Semi : £8
D'INDY / FRANCK French Mountain Air Symphony, Variations
Ciccolini Paris Conservatoire Orchestra Cluytens
No Stereo

33CX1191 B/Gold : **£ 16** Red Semi : £8
BEETHOVEN Quartet No.5 & 6 Hungarian String Quartet
No Stereo

33CX1192 B/Gold : **£15** Red Semi : £8
Various Concertos by Vivaldi, Rossini Etc I Musici
No Stereo

33CX1193 B/Gold : **£5** Red Semi : £3
Various English Church Music book 2 St Pauls Cathedral Choir
No Stereo

33CX1194 B/Gold : **£25** Red Semi : £14
BEETHOVEN Violin Concerto Oistrakh SFO Erhling
No Stereo

33CX1195-6 B/Gold : **£20** Red Semi : £10
VERDI Requiem Mass Schwarzkopf
No Stereo

33CX1197-9 B/Gold : **£8** Red Semi : £4
Various Homage to Diaghilev
Philharmonia Orchestra Markevitch
No Stereo

33CX1200 (==== Not Issued ====)

33CX1201 B/Gold : **£40** Red Semi : £20
FRANCK / SZYMONOWSKI Violin Sonata in A & Dmin. Oistrakh
No Stereo

33CX1202 B/Gold : **£6** Red Semi : £3
LISZT Recital Anda
No Stereo

33CX1203 B/Gold : **£16** Red Semi : £8
BEETHOVEN Quartet No.7 Hungarian String Quartet
No Stereo

33CX1204 B/Gold : **£15** Red Semi : £8
PUCCINI Operatic Arias Callas
Philharmonic Orchestra & Chorus Serafin
No Stereo

33CX1205   B/Gold : **£10**   Red Semi : £5
BLISS   Miracle in the Gorbals, Music for Strings
Philharmonic Orchestra & Chorus   Bliss
No Stereo

33CX1206   B/Gold : **£8**   Red Semi : £4
BERLIOZ   Symphony Fantastique
Philharmonia Orchestra   Karajan
No Stereo

33CX1207   B/Gold : **£8**   Red Semi : £4
MAHLER   Symphony No.1   Israel Philharmonic Orchestra   Kletzki
No Stereo

33CX1208   B/Gold : **£12**   Red Semi : £6
TCHAIKOVSKY / BORODIN / MOUSSORGSKY   Romeo, Polov, Bare
Orchestre National de la Radiodiffusion Francaise   Markevitch
No Stereo

33CX1209-10   (==== Not Issued ====)

33CX1211-2   B/Gold : **£30**   Red Semi : £16
LEONCAVALLO   I Pagliacci   Callas
Milan La Scala Orchestra   Serafin
No Stereo

33CX1213   B/Gold : **£14**   Red Semi : £7
Various   Recital of French Songs   Merriman
No Stereo

33CX1214   (==== Not Issued ====)

33CX1215-6   B/Gold : **£20**   Red Semi : £10
ROSSINI   L'Italiana in Algeri   Petri   Giulini
No Stereo

33CX1217   B/Gold : **£8**   Red Semi : £4
MOZART / SAINT-SAINS   Piano Concerto No.2, Sonata No.16   Gilels
Paris Conservatoire Orchestra   Cluytens
No Stereo

33CX1218   B/Gold : **£15**   Red Semi : £8
POULENC   Mamelles de Tiresias
Opera Comique Chorus & Orchestra   Cluytens
No Stereo

33CX1219   B/Gold : **£6**   Red Semi : £3
MENDELSSOHN Symphony No.3 Israel Philharmonic Orchestra Kletzki
No Stereo

33CX1220   B/Gold : **£30**   Red Semi : £15
MOZART   Complete works of Mozart Vol.4   Gieseking
No Stereo

33CX1221   B/Gold : **£15**   Red Semi : £8
FALLA   Nights in the Gardens of Spain   Ciccolini
French National Radio Orchestra   Halffter
No Stereo

33CX1222-3   B/Gold : **£25**   Red Semi : £14
SCHUBERT   Winterreise   Hotter
No Stereo

33CX1224-5   B/Gold : **£15**   Red Semi : £8
STRAUSS   Eine Nacht in Veredig   Schwarzkopf
Philharmonia Orchestra   Ackermann
No Stereo

33CX1226   B/Gold : **£4**   Red Semi : £2
STRAUSS   Arabella (Highlights)   Schwarzkopf
Philharmonia Orchestra   Matacic
No Stereo

33CX1227   B/Gold : **£7**   Red Semi : £4
BEETHOVEN   Symphony No.2, Coriolan Overture
Philharmonia Orchestra   Karajan
No Stereo

33CX1228   B/Gold : **£12**   Red Semi : £6
STRAVINSKY   le Balser de la Fee, Divertimento
French National Radio Orchestra   Markevitch
No Stereo

33CX1229   B/Gold : **£35**   Red Semi : £20
DEBUSSY   March Ecossaise, Nocturnes No.1
French National Radio Orchestra   Inghelbrecht
No Stereo

33CX1230   B/Gold : **£12**   Red Semi : £6
HAYDN   Quartet in Fmaj. & Dmin.   Quartetto Italiano
No Stereo

33CX1231   B/Gold : **£15**   Red Semi : £8
Various   Opera Recital   Callas
Philharmonia Orchestra   Serafin
No Stereo

33CX1232-3   B/Gold : **£15**   Red Semi : £8
BIZET   Les Pecheurs Perles   Angelici   Cluytens
No Stereo

33CX1234   (═══ Not Issued ═══)

33CX1235   B/Gold : **£15**   Red Semi : £8
MOZART   Piano Concertos 20,25   Gieseking
Philharmonia Orchestra   Rosbaud
No Stereo

33CX1236   B/Gold : **£16**   Red Semi : £8
BEETHOVEN   Quartet No.8 & 11   Hungarian String Quartet
No Stereo

33CX1237   B/Gold : **£6**   Red Semi : £3
Various   English Madrigals   St Pauls Cathedral Choir
No Stereo

33CX1238   B/Gold : **£15**   Red Semi : £8
CHOPIN / LISZT   Piano Concerto No.1 in E   Francois
Paris Conservatoire Orchestra   Tzipine
No Stereo

33CX1239   B/Gold : **£15**   Red Semi : £8
BACH   Suite No.1 & 2   Philharmonia Orchestra   Klemperer
No Stereo

33CX1240   B/Gold : **£15**   Red Semi : £8
BACH   Suite No.3 & 4   Philharmonia Orchestra   Klemperer
No Stereo

33CX1241   B/Gold : **£8**   Red Semi : £4
BRAHMS   Haydn Variations, St Anthony Chorale
Philharmonia Orchestra   Klemperer
No Stereo

33CX1242   B/Gold : **£30**   Red Semi : £15
MOZART   Complete works of Mozart Vol.5   Gieseking
No Stereo

33CX1243   B/Gold : **£14**   Red Semi : £7
Various   Recital of Spanish Songs   Merriman
No Stereo

33CX1244   B/Gold : **£12**   Red Semi : £6
BRAHMS   Quartet No.3   Quartetto Italiano
No Stereo

33CX1245   B/Gold : **£20**   Red Semi : £10
BARTOK   Quartet No.1, Quartet No.2   Vegh String Quartet
No Stereo

33CX1246   B/Gold : **£45**   Red Semi : £25
LALO   Symphonie Espagnole   Oistrakh
Philharmonia Orchestra   Martinon
No Stereo

33CX1247-8   B/Gold : **£6**   Red Semi : £3
ELGAR   Dream of Gerontius   Lewis
Liverpool Philharmonic Orchestra   Sargent
No Stereo

33CX1249   B/Gold : **£3**   Red Semi : £2
BACH   Organ Recital   Schweitzer
No Stereo

33CX1250-1   B/Gold : **£8**   Red Semi : £4
MAHLER / SCHONBERG   Symphony No.9, Verklarte Nacht Op.4
Israel Philharmonic Orchestra   Kletzki
No Stereo

33CX1252-3 B/Gold : **£40** Red Semi : £20
AURIC / DUREY / HONEGGER / MILHAUD Le Groupe des Six
Paris Conservatoire Orchestra Tzipine
No Stereo

33CX1254 B/Gold : **£16** Red Semi : £8
BEETHOVEN Quartet No.9 & 10 Hungarian String Quartet
No Stereo

33CX1255 B/Gold : **£25** Red Semi : £14
BRAHMS Piano Works Vol.1 Gieseking
No Stereo

33CX1256 B/Gold : **£25** Red Semi : £14
BRAHMS Piano Works Vol.2 Gieseking
No Stereo

33CX1257 B/Gold : **£8** Red Semi : £4
MOZART Symphonie No.29 & 41
Philharmonia Orchestra Klemperer
No Stereo

33CX1258-60 B/Gold : **£30** Red Semi : £16
VERDI Forza del Destino Callas
Milan La Scala Orchestra Serafin
No Stereo

33CX1261 B/Gold : **£35** Red Semi : £20
DEBUSSY Etudes 1-12 Gieseking
No Stereo

33CX1262-4 B/Gold : **£50** Red Semi : £30
MOZART Cosi Fan Tutti Schwarzkopf
Philharmonia Orchestra Karajan
No Stereo

33CX1265 B/Gold : **£7** Red Semi : £4
Various Operatic Intermezzi Philharmonia Orchestra Karajan
No Stereo

33CX1266
BEETHOVEN
Schwarzkopf
No Stereo

B/Gold : **£ 8**   Red Semi : £4
Symphonie 5, Abscheulicher -recital
            Karajan

33CX1267
BARTOK
No Stereo

B/Gold : **£ 20**   Red Semi : £10
Quartet No.3 & 4 Vegh String Quartet

33CX1268
BRUCH / PROKOFIEV
London Symphony Orchestra
No Stereo

B/Gold : **£ 40**   Red Semi : £20
        Violin Concerto No.1   Oistrakh
                    Matacic

33CX1269
SCHUBERT
No Stereo

B/Gold : **£ 14**   Red Semi : £7
Schwanengesang   Hotter

33CX1270
BEETHOVEN
Philharmonia Orchestra
No Stereo

B/Gold : **£ 8**   Red Semi : £4
Overtures Leonore 1-3, Fedelio
        Klemperer

33CX1271
MOZART
No Stereo

B/Gold : **£ 30**   Red Semi : £15
Complete works of Mozart Vol.6   Gieseking

33CX1272
BEETHOVEN
No Stereo

B/Gold : **£ 16**   Red Semi : £8
String Quartet No.12 & 16   Hungarian String Quartet

33CX1273
Various
No Stereo

B/Gold : **£ 6**   Red Semi : £3
La Valse   Philharmonia Orchestra   Markevitch

33CX1274-5
BRUCKNER
No Stereo

B/Gold : **£ 12**   Red Semi : £6
Symphony No.4   Philharmonia Orchestra   Matacic

33CX1276-7
Various
No Stereo

B/Gold : **£ 20**   Red Semi : £10
Concert   Alessandra Scarlatti Orchestra   Caracciolo

33CX1278 B/Gold : **£8** Red Semi : £4
BEETHOVEN Symphony No.4, Perfido Schwarzkopf
Philharmonia Orchestra Karajan
No Stereo

33CX1279 B/Gold : **£10** Red Semi : £5
TCHAIKOVSKY Quartet No.2 Armenian String Quartet
No Stereo

33CX1280 B/Gold : **£12** Red Semi : £6
BALAKIREV Islamey, Russia, Thamar Philharmonia Orchestra Matacic
No Stereo

33CX1281 B/Gold : **£130** Red Semi : £75
GLAZOUNOV / PAGANINI Violin Concertos Rabin
Philharmonia Orchestra Matacic
No Stereo

33CX1282 B/Gold : **£15** Red Semi : £8
DEBUSSY La Boite a Joujoux, Childrens Corner
Orchestre National de la Radiodiffusion Francaise Cluytens
No Stereo

33CX1283 B/Gold : **£6** Red Semi : £3
SCHUMANN Carnival, Kreisleriana Anda
No Stereo

33CX1284 B/Gold : **£10** Red Semi : £5
SCHUBERT String Quartet No.14 Armenian String Quartet
No Stereo

33CX1285 B/Gold : **£20** Red Semi : £10
BARTOK Quartet No.5 & 6 Vegh String Quartet
No Stereo

33CX1286-8 B/Gold : **£3,500** Red Semi : £3,000
BACH Unaccompanied Violin Partias and Sonatas Martzy
No Stereo

33CX1289-1 B/Gold : **£45** Red Semi : £25
ROSSINI Il Turco in Italia Callas
Milan La Scala Orchestra Gavanezzi
No Stereo

33CX1292-4   B/Gold : **£30**   Red Semi : £15
STRAUSS   Ariadne auf Naxos   Streich
Philharmonia Orchestra   Karajan
No Stereo

33CX1295   B/Gold : **£12**   Red Semi : £6
PROKOFIEV / MALIPIERO   String Quartets No.2, No.4
Quartetto Italiano
No Stereo

33CX1296-8   B/Gold : **£35**   Red Semi : £20
PUCCINI   Madame Butterfly   Callas
Milan La Scala Orchestra   Karajan
No Stereo

33CX1299-01   B/Gold : **£30**   Red Semi : £15
GOUNOD   Mireille   Gedda
Paris Conservatoire Orchestra   Cluytens
No Stereo

33CX1302   B/Gold : **£6**   Red Semi : £3
BEETHOVEN   Piano Concerto No.1, Piano Concerto No.14   Anda
No Stereo

33CX1303   B/Gold : **£30**   Red Semi : £15
KHATCHATURIAN   Violin Concerto   Oistrakh
Philharmonia Orchestra   Khatchaturian
No Stereo

33CX1304   B/Gold : **£40**   Red Semi : £20
DEBUSSY   Preludes Book 2   Gieseking
No Stereo

33CX1305   B/Gold : **£15**   Red Semi : £8
Various   Operatic Recital, Arias & Duets   Dobbs, Panerai
Philharmonia Orchestra   Galliera
No Stereo

33CX1306-7   B/Gold : **£20**   Red Semi : £10
PERGOLESI   Music of Pergolesi   I Musici
No Stereo

33CX1308 B/Gold : **£15** Red Semi : £8
Various Spanish Classical & Traditional Music
Capilla Clasica Polifonica Ribo
No Stereo

33CX1309-10 B/Gold : **£24** Red Semi : £12
STRAUSS Die Fledermaus Streich
Philharmonia Orchestra Karajan
No Stereo

33CX1311 B/Gold : **£8** Red Semi : £4
SIBELIUS Symphony No.1 Philharmonia Orchestra Kletzki
No Stereo

33CX1312 (==== Not Issued ====)

33CX1313 B/Gold : **£14** Red Semi : £7
WALTON Troilus & Cressida Schwarzkopf
Philharmonia Orchestra Walton
No Stereo

33CX1314 (==== Not Issued ====)

33CX1315 B/Gold : **£30** Red Semi : £15
MOZART Complete works of Mozart Vol.7 Gieseking
No Stereo

33CX1316 B/Gold : **£6** Red Semi : £3
BARTOK Sonatina for Children Anda
No Stereo

33CX1317 B/Gold : **£15** Red Semi : £8
Various An Evening with Robert Burns Various
Zorian String Quartet
No Stereo

33CX1318-20 B/Gold : **£60** Red Semi : £30
VERDI Aida Callas Milan La Scala Orchestra Serafin
No Stereo

33CX1321 B/Gold : **£16** Red Semi : £8
MOZART Mozart Songs Schwarzkopf
No Stereo

33CX1322 B/Gold : **£20** Red Semi : £10
BEETHOVEN / MOZART Quintet Op 61, Quintet K452
Gieseking, Brain
No Stereo

33CX1323 B/Gold : **£8** Red Semi : £4
RACHMANINOV Piano Concerto No.3 Gilels
Paris Conservatoire Orchestra Cluytens
No Stereo

33CX1324-6 B/Gold : **£30** Red Semi : £16
VERDI Rigoletto Callas
Milan La Scala Orchestra Serafin
No Stereo

33CX1327 B/Gold : **£5** Red Semi : £3
Various Ballet Music from the Opera
Philharmonia Orchestra Karajan
No Stereo

33CX1328 B/Gold : **£7** Red Semi : £4
TCHAIKOVSKY / STRAUSS Romeo & Juliet, Death &
Transfiguration Philharmonia Orchestra Galliera
No Stereo

33CX1329-30 B/Gold : **£5** Red Semi : £3
STRAUSS Gypsy Baron Prey
Philharmonia Orchestra Ackermann
No Stereo

33CX1331 B/Gold : **£5** Red Semi : £3
Various Duets Schwarzkopf
No Stereo

33CX1332 B/Gold : **£10** Red Semi : £5
SIBELIUS Symphony No.2 Philharmonia Orchestra Kletski
Stereo Issue : SAX2280

33CX1333   B/Gold : **£6**   Red Semi : £3
BEETHOVEN   Piano Concerto No.4   Arrau
Philharmonia Orchestra   Galliera
No Stereo

33CX1334   B/Gold : **£10**   Red Semi : £5
BORODIN / SHOSTAKOVITCH   Quartet No.12, Quartet No.2
Armenian String Quartet
No Stereo

33CX1335   B/Gold : **£4**   Red Semi : £2
Various   Promenade Concert   Philharmonia Orchestra   Karajan
No Stereo

33CX1336   (==== Not Issued ====)

33CX1337   B/Gold : **£25**   Red Semi : £14
CHOPIN / ENESCO   Piano Sonata No.3   Lipatti
No Stereo

33CX1338   B/Gold : **£6**   Red Semi : £3
CHOPIN   Recital   Malcuzynski
No Stereo

33CX1339   B/Gold : **£6**   Red Semi : £3
RESPIGHI   Fountains of Rome, Brazillian
Philharmonia Orchestra   Galliera
No Stereo

33CX1340   B/Gold : **£20**   Red Semi : £10
PERGOLESI   La Serva Padronia   Carteri
Milan La Scala Orchestra   Giulini
No Stereo

33CX1341   B/Gold : **£7**   Red Semi : £4
SIBELIUS   Symphony No.6 & 7   Philharmonia Orchestra   Karajan
No Stereo

33CX1342   B/Gold : **£35**   Red Semi : £20
PROKOFIEV / KHATCHATURIAN   Violin Sonata No.2, Violin Sonata
Oistrakh
No Stereo

33CX1343 B/Gold : **£15** Red Semi : £8
Various Piano Recital Malinin
No Stereo

33CX1344 B/Gold : **£10** Red Semi : £5
Various Recital Maldonado
No Stereo

33CX1345 B/Gold : **£30** Red Semi : £15
MOZART Complete works of Mozart Vol.8 Gieseking
No Stereo

33CX1346 B/Gold : **£5** Red Semi : £3
BEETHOVEN Symphony No.3
Philharmonia Orchestra Klemperer
No Stereo

33CX1347-9 B/Gold : **£12** Red Semi : £6
HANDEL Israel in Egypt
Liverpool Philharmonic Orchestra Sargent
No Stereo

33CX1349 B/Gold : **£4** Red Semi : £2
SCHUBERT / BRAHMS Symphony No.8,Var.On A Theme By Haydn
Philharmonia Orchestra Karajan
No Stereo

33CX1350-2 B/Gold : **£40** Red Semi : £20
RAVEL Piano Works of Ravel Gieseking
No Stereo

33CX1353 B/Gold : **£25** Red Semi : £14
DALLAPICCOLA / GUARNIERI Canti di Prigonia, String Quartet No.2
Pascal Quartet
No Stereo

33CX1354 B/Gold : **£10** Red Semi : £5
RESPIGHI The Birds Alessandra Scarlatti Orchestra Caracciolo
No Stereo

33CX1355 B/Gold : **£6** Red Semi : £3
BRAHMS Symphony No.2 Philharmonia Orchestra Karajan
No Stereo

33CX1356   B/Gold : **£6**   Red Semi : £3
BORODIN / RIMSKY-KORSAKOV   Symphony No.1, Capriccio Espagnol
Philharmonia Orchestra   Galliera
No Stereo

33CX1357   B/Gold : **£15**   Red Semi : £8
Various   I Musici Concert   I Musici
No Stereo

33CX1358   B/Gold : **£30**   Red Semi : £15
MOZART   Complete works of Mozart Vol.9   Gieseking
No Stereo

33CX1359   B/Gold : **£400**   Red Semi : £300
SCHUBERT   Sonatina No.1 & 2   Martzy
No Stereo

33CX1360   (=== Not Issued ===)

33CX1361   B/Gold : **£8**   Red Semi : £4
MOZART   Clarinet Concerto, Symphony No.39   Walton
Philharmonia Wind Quartet   Karajan
No Stereo

33CX1362   B/Gold : **£8**   Red Semi : £4
BRAHMS   Symphony No.4   Philharmonia Orchestra   Karajan
No Stereo

33CX1363   B/Gold : **£6**   Red Semi : £3
GRIEG / SCHUBERT   Symphony No.6, Etc.
Royal Philharmonic Orchestra   Beecham
No Stereo

33CX1364   B/Gold : **£8**   Red Semi : £4
BACH / CHOPIN / SHOSTAKOVICH   Piano Recital   Gilels
No Stereo

33CX1365   B/Gold : **£8**   Red Semi : £4
VIVALDI   4 Seasons   Philharmonia Orchestra   Giulini
No Stereo

33CX1366   B/Gold : **£6**   Red Semi : £3
LISZT   Piano Concerto No.1, Hungarian Fantasia   Anda
No Stereo

33CX1367   B/Gold : **£12**   Red Semi : £6
SCHUBERT / MOZART   Quartet No.2, Quartet No.17 Quartetto Italiano
No Stereo

33CX1368   B/Gold : **£45**   Red Semi : £25
Various   Iturbi Treasures   Iturbi
No Stereo

33CX1369   B/Gold : **£15**   Red Semi : £8
RACHMANANOV / CHOPIN   Piano Concerto No.2, Nocturne No.8
Malinin   Philharmonia Orchestra   Ackermann
No Stereo

33CX1370-1   B/Gold : **£20**   Red Semi : £10
VERDI   La Traviata   Stella
Milan La Scala Orchestra   Serafin
No Stereo

33CX1372   B/Gold : **£350**   Red Semi : £250
SCHUBERT   Violin Sonatas   Martzy
No Stereo

33CX1373   B/Gold : **£150**   Red Semi : £75
BACH   Double Concerto, Violin Concerto BWV 1042
Kogan, Gilels   Philharmonia Orchestra   Ackermann
No Stereo

33CX1374   B/Gold : **£25**   Red Semi : £14
BEETHOVEN   Piano Sonata No.30 & 31   Gieseking
No Stereo

33CX1375   B/Gold : **£7**   Red Semi : £4
Spoken Word   Shakespeare As You Like It Various
No Stereo

33CX1376   B/Gold : **£10**   Red Semi : £5
VERDI   Operatic Choruses   Milan La Scala Orchestra   Serafin
No Stereo

33CX1377 B/Gold : **£7** Red Semi : £4
TCHAIKOVSKY Symphony No.6, Etc. Philharmonia Orchestra Karajan
No Stereo

33CX1378 B/Gold : **£10** Red Semi : £5
HAYDN Symphonie No.86 & 92
Alessandra Scarlatti Orchestra Caracciolo
No Stereo

33CX1379 B/Gold : **£6** Red Semi : £3
BEETHOVEN Symphony No.7 Philharmonia Orchestra Klemperer
No Stereo

33CX1380 B/Gold : **£35** Red Semi : £20
MOZART Piano Recital Iturbi
No Stereo

33CX1381 B/Gold : **£100** Red Semi : £50
BRAHMS Violin Sonatas No.1 & 2 Kogan Mytnik
No Stereo

33CX1382 B/Gold : **£6** Red Semi : £3
BRAHMS Piano Recital Malcuzynski
No Stereo

33CX1383 B/Gold : **£12** Red Semi : £6
HAYDN Quartet No.17 Quartetto Italiano
No Stereo

33CX1384 B/Gold : **£4** Red Semi : £2
Spoken Word 18th Century Comedy Dame Edith Evans
No Stereo

33CX1385 B/Gold : **£6** Red Semi : £3
DONIZETTI Lucia di Lammermoor (Highlights) Callas
Maggio Musici Florence
No Stereo

33CX1386 B/Gold : **£30** Red Semi : £16
BACH / SCARLATTI / CHOPIN / RAVEL Recital Lipatti
No Stereo

33CX1387-9 B/Gold : **£ 15** Red Semi : £ 8
Spoken Word Sheridan - The School for Scandel Dame Edith Evans
No Stereo

33CX1390 B/Gold : **£ 65** Red Semi : £20
TANEIEV Concert Suite for Violin & Orchestra Oistrakh
Philharmonia Orchestra Malko
No Stereo

33CX1391-2 B/Gold : **£ 80** Red Semi : £45
BEETHOVEN Symphonie No.8 & 9 Schwarzkopf
Vienna Philharmonic Orchestra Karajan
No Stereo

33CX1393 B/Gold : **£ 6** Red Semi : £3
STRAUSS A Strauss Concert Philharmonia Orchestra Karajan
No Stereo

33CX1394 B/Gold : **£ 12** Red Semi : £6
MENDELSSOHN / SCHUBERT Symphony No.4, Symphony No.8
Orchestre National de la Radiodiffusion Francaise Markevitch
No Stereo

33CX1395 B/Gold : **£ 85** Red Semi : £50
PROKOFIEV / MOZART Violin Concerto No.2 & No.3 Kogan
London Symphony Orchestra Cameron
No Stereo

33CX1396 B/Gold : **£ 12** Red Semi : £6
BEETHOVEN Quartet No.10 Quartetto Italiano
No Stereo

33CX1397-8 B/Gold : **£ 4** Red Semi : £2
HANDEL Solomon Cameron
Royal Philharmonic Orchestra Beecham
Stereo Issue : SAX2499-500

33CX1399 B/Gold : **£ 500** Red Semi : £400
SCHUBERT Violin Sonata No.3 Martzy
No Stereo

33CX1400-1 B/Gold : **£20** Red Semi : £10
CORNELIUS Barber von Bagdad Schwarzkopf
Philharmonia Orchestra Leinsdorf
No Stereo

33CX1402 B/Gold : **£6** Red Semi : £3
LEONCAVALLO / MASCAGNI I Pagliacci, (Highlights) Callas
Milan La Scala Orchestra Serafin
No Stereo

33CX1403 B/Gold : **£35** Red Semi : £20
MOZART / BACH Concertos for 2 Pianos Haskil Anda
Philharmonia Orchestra Galliera
No Stereo

33CX1404 B/Gold : **£2** Red Semi : £1
Various Songs You Love Schwarzkopf
Stereo Issue : SAX2265

33CX1405 B/Gold : **£16** Red Semi : £8
BEETHOVEN String Quartet No.13 & 17, Grosse Fugue
Hungarian String Quartet
No Stereo

33CX1406 B/Gold : **£2** Red Semi : £1
Various Hoffnung Music Festival Hoffnung
No Stereo

33CX1407 B/Gold : **£7** Red Semi : £4
TCHAIKOVSKY / SCHUMANN Rococco Variations, Cello Concerto
Fournier Philharmonia Orchestra Sargent
Stereo Issue : SAX2282

33CX1408 B/Gold : **£12** Red Semi : £6
GLUPPI / BOCCHERINI String Quartet in Gmin., La Tiranna Spagnola
Quartetto Italiano
No Stereo

33CX1409 B/Gold : **£14** Red Semi : £7
GRIEG / STRAUSS Recital of songs by Grieg & Strauss Aase
No Stereo

33CX1410-2 B/Gold : **£3** Red Semi : £2
VERDI Falstaff Schwarzkopf
Philharmonia Chorus & Orchestra Karajan
Stereo Issue : SAX2254-6

33CX1413 B/Gold : **£8** Red Semi : £4
SAINT-SAINS Symphony No.3
Paris Conservatoire Orchestra Cluytens
No Stereo

33CX1414 B/Gold : **£10** Red Semi : £5
PETRASSI / MALIPIERO Sesta Sinfonia, Don Chisciotte
Alessandro Scarlatti Orchestra Caracciolo
No Stereo

33CX1415 B/Gold : **£25** Red Semi : £14
MOZART / TARTINI Violin Sonata No.32, Violin Sonata in Gmin.
Oistrakh
No Stereo

33CX1416 B/Gold : **£25** Red Semi : £14
LISZT Petrarch Sonnets No.47, No.104, etc. Siki
No Stereo

33CX1417 B/Gold : **£35** Red Semi : £20
BEETHOVEN Sonata No.17 & 18 Gieseking
No Stereo

33CX1418 B/Gold : **£7** Red Semi : £4
Various Ceremonial Music of the Synagogue Kacmann
No Stereo

33CX1419 B/Gold : **£6** Red Semi : £3
SCHUMANN Symphonie No.1 & 4
Israel Philharmonic Orchestra Kletzki
No Stereo

33CX1420 B/Gold : **£7** Red Semi : £4
TCHAIKOVSKY / BALAKIREV Hamlet Overture, Overture on Russian
Themes Philharmonia Orchestra Matacic
No Stereo

33CX1421   B/Gold : **£8**   Red Semi : £4
MUSSORGSKY   Pictures at an Exhibition
Philharmonia Orchestra   Karajan
Stereo Issue : SAX2261

33CX1422   B/Gold : **£120**   Red Semi : £60
TCHAIKOVSKY / SAINT-SAINS   Violin Concerto, Intro & Rondo
Rabin   Philharmonia Orchestra   Galliera
No Stereo

33CX1423   B/Gold : **£150**   Red Semi : £75
SCHUBERT   Octet   Oistrakh   Oistrakh Octet
No Stereo

33CX1424   B/Gold : **£40**   Red Semi : £20
MOZART   String Quartet K421 & K428   Smetana Quartet
No Stereo

33CX1425   B/Gold : **£60**   Red Semi : £40
MILHAUD / PROKOFIEV   Cello Concerto No. 1, Cello Concerto
Starker   Philharmonia Orchestra   Susskind
No Stereo

33CX1426   (==== Not Issued ====)

33CX1427   B/Gold : **£6**   Red Semi : £3
BEETHOVEN   Piano Sonata Op.10/3, Op.101   Anda
No Stereo

33CX1428   B/Gold : **£30**   Red Semi : £15
MOZART   Complete works of Mozart Vol.10   Gieseking
No Stereo

33CX1429   B/Gold : **£8**   Red Semi : £4
BRAHMS / LISZ   Song Destiny, Acad Fest Ov
Royal Philharmonic Orchestra   Beecham
No Stereo

33CX1430   B/Gold : **£12**   Red Semi : £6
Various   Italian String Quartets in the 17th Century
Quartetto Italiano
No Stereo

33CX1431-3 B/Gold : **£8** Red Semi : £4
MENDELSSOHN Elijah Liverpool Philharmonic Orchestra Sargent
No Stereo

33CX1434-6 B/Gold : **£30** Red Semi : £16
CIMAROSA Il Matrimonia Segresto Calabrese
Milan La Scala Orchestra Stignani
No Stereo

33CX1437 B/Gold : **£10** Red Semi : £5
STRAVINSKY The Nightingale
French National Radio Orchestra Cluytens
No Stereo

33CX1438 B/Gold : **£10** Red Semi : £5
BEETHOVEN / MOZART Grosse Fugue, Serinade No.6
Philharmonia Orchestra Klemperer
No Stereo

33CX1439 B/Gold : **£30** Red Semi : £15
BERLIOZ Symphonie Fantastique
French National Radio Orchestra Cluytens
No Stereo

33CX1440 B/Gold : **£20** Red Semi : £10
SHOSTAKOVICH / PROKOFIEV Symphony No.1, Scythian Suite
Orchestre National de Francaise Markevitch
No Stereo

33CX1441 (==== Not Issued ====)

33CX1442 B/Gold : **£16** Red Semi : £8
BEETHOVEN Quartet Op.131 Hungarian String Quartet
No Stereo

33CX1443-4 B/Gold : **£20** Red Semi : £10
CHOPIN Etudes complete Arrau
No Stereo

33CX1445 B/Gold : **£25** Red Semi : £14
SCHUBERT 4 Impromptus, Siki
No Stereo

33CX1446-7   B/Gold : **£7**   Red Semi : £4
ORFF   Die Kluge   Schwarzkopf
Philharmonia Orchestra   Sawalisch
Stereo Issue : SAX2257-8

33CX1448   B/Gold : **£14**   Red Semi : £7
BRAHMS   Leider Recital   Hotter
No Stereo

33CX1449   B/Gold : **£6**   Red Semi : £3
SCHUMANN   Symphony No.2   Israel Philharmonic Orchestra   Kletzki
No Stereo

33CX1450   B/Gold : **£6**   Red Semi : £3
BALAKIREV   Symphony No.1
Royal Philharmonic Orchestra   Beecham
No Stereo

33CX1451   B/Gold : **£10**   Red Semi : £5
SALIERI / VIVALDI   Overtures Axer, Re d'Ormus, Concerto
Alessandro Scarlatti Orchestra   Schippers
No Stereo

33CX1452   (==== Not Issued ====)

33CX1453   B/Gold : **£30**   Red Semi : £15
MOZART   Complete works of Mozart Vol.11   Gieseking
No Stereo

33CX1454-5   (==== Not Issued ====)

33CX1456   B/Gold : **£8**   Red Semi : £4
BARTOK   Bluebeards Castle   Budapest Opera   Ferencsik
No Stereo

33CX1457   B/Gold : **£8**   Red Semi : £4
MOZART   Symphony No.25, Symphony No.40
Philharmonia Orchestra   Klemperer
Stereo Issue : SAX2278

33CX1458   B/Gold : **£15**   Red Semi : £8
HAYDN   Symphony No.101, Symphony No.102
French National Radio Orchestra   Markevitch
No Stereo

33CX1459   B/Gold : **£6**   Red Semi : £3
CHOPIN   Etudes, Ballade No.1   Anda
No Stereo

33CX1460   B/Gold : **£16**   Red Semi : £8
BEETHOVEN   String Quartet Op.132   Hungarian String Quartet
No Stereo

33CX1461   (==== Not Issued ====)

33CX1462-3   B/Gold : **£4**   Red Semi : £2
MOZART   Abduction from the Seraglio   Frick
Royal Philharmonic Orchestra   Beecham
Stereo Issue : SAX2427-9

33CX1464-5   B/Gold : **£20**   Red Semi : £10
PUCCINI   La Boheme   Callas
Milan La Scala Orchestra   Votto
No Stereo

33CX1466   B/Gold : **£14**   Red Semi : £7
Various   Encores Oistrakh
Stereo Issue : SAX2253

33CX1467-8   B/Gold : **£60**   Red Semi : £30
GRIEG   Lyric Pieces   Gieseking
No Stereo

33CX1469-1   B/Gold : **£60**   Red Semi : £30
BELLINI   La Somnambula   Callas
Milan La Scala Orchestra   Votto
No Stereo

33CX1472-4   B/Gold : **£60**   Red Semi : £30
VERDI   Un Ballo in Maschera   Callas
Milan La Scala Orchestra   Votto
No Stereo

33CX1475   B/Gold : **£7**   Red Semi : £4
SCHUMANN   Symphony No.3, Manfred Overture
Israel Philharmonic Orchestra   Kletzki
No Stereo

33CX1476   B/Gold : **£10**   Red Semi : £5
BOCCERINI   Synphony in Amaj. & Cmin.
Alessandra Scarlatti Orchestra   Caracciolo
No Stereo

33CX1477   B/Gold : **£30**   Red Semi : £20
DVORAK / FAURE   Cello Concerto, Elegie   Starker
Philharmonia Orchestra   Susskind
Stereo Issue : SAX2263

33CX1478   B/Gold : **£7**   Red Semi : £4
BACH   Toccata & Fugue, Fantasia, Choral Preludes   Commette
No Stereo

33CX1479   B/Gold : **£15**   Red Semi : £8
MENDELSSOHN   Songs without words   Gieseking
No Stereo

33CX1480   B/Gold : **£16**   Red Semi : £8
ORFF   Carmina Burana
Colonne Royal Symphony Orchestra   Sawallisch
No Stereo

33CX1481   B/Gold : **£8**   Red Semi : £4
TCHAIKOVSKY   Piano Concerto No.1   Malcuzynski
French National Radio Orchestra   Malko
No Stereo

33CX1482   B/Gold : **£6**   Red Semi : £3
Various   Christmas Songs   Schwarzkopf
No Stereo

33CX1483-5   B/Gold : **£60**   Red Semi : £30
VERDI   Il Trovatore   Callas
Milan La Scala Orchestra   Karajan
No Stereo

33CX1486   B/Gold : **£8**   Red Semi : £4
MOZART   Symphonie No.38 & 39
Philharmonia Orchestra   Klemperer
No Stereo

33CX1487   B/Gold : **£8**   Red Semi : £4
BRAHMS   Double Concerto, Tragic Overture   Oistrakh, Fournier
Philharmonia Orchestra
Stereo Issue : SAX2264

33CX1488   B/Gold : **£25**   Red Semi : £14
BEETHOVEN   Piano Sonatas Op.21 etc.   Gieseking
No Stereo

33CX1489   B/Gold : **£6**   Red Semi : £3
BELLINI   Norma (Highlights)   Callas
Milan La Scala Orchestra   Serafin
No Stereo

33CX1490   B/Gold : **£4**   Red Semi : £2
BEETHOVEN   Piano concerto No.5   Ludwig
Philharmonia Orchestra   Gilels
Stereo Issue : SAX2252

33CX1491   B/Gold : **£8**   Red Semi : £4
STRAUSS   Horn Concs   Brain
Philharmonia Orchestra   Sawallisch
No Stereo

33CX1492-5   B/Gold : **£5**   Red Semi : £3
STRAUSS   Der Rosenkavalier   Schwarzkopf
Philharmonia Orchestra   Karajan
Stereo Issue : SAX2269-72

33CX1496   B/Gold : **£7**   Red Semi : £4
WAGNER   Wagner Overtures
Berlin Philharmonic Orchestra   Karajan
No Stereo

33CX1497   B/Gold : **£250**   Red Semi : £175
MENDELSSOHN   Violin Concerto   Martzy
Philharmonia Orchestra   Kletzki
No Stereo

33CX1498   B/Gold : **£30**   Red Semi : £15
BEETHOVEN   Piano Sonata Op.10/3, Op.22   Gieseking
No Stereo

33CX1499-00   B/Gold : **£100**   Red Semi : £40
Various   His Last Recital-Besancon Festival 1950   Lipatti
No Stereo

33CX1501   B/Gold : **£4**   Red Semi : £2
Various   Tito Gobi at La Scalla   Gobbi
Milan La Scala Orchestra
No Stereo

33CX1502   B/Gold : **£6**   Red Semi : £3
VERDI   La Forza del Destino (Highlights)   Callas
Milan La Scala Orchestra   Serafin
No Stereo

33CX1503   B/Gold : **£12**   Red Semi : £6
ROUSSEAU   Le Devin du Village   Gedda
Chamber Orchestra   Froment
No Stereo

33CX1504   B/Gold : **£6**   Red Semi : £3
BRAHMS   Symphony No.1   Philharmonia Orchestra   Klemperer
Stereo Issue : SAX2262

33CX1505   B/Gold : **£15**   Red Semi : £8
DELIBES   Copelia, Sylva
Orchestre National de la Radiodiffusion Francaise   Cluytens
No Stereo

33CX1506   B/Gold : **£100**   Red Semi : £50
BRAHMS   Violin Concerto   Kogan
Paris Conservatoire Orchestra   Bruck
No Stereo

33CX1507-9   B/Gold : **£30**   Red Semi : £15
ROSSINI   The Barber of Seville   Callas
Philharmonia Orchestra & Chorus   Galliera
Stereo Issue : SAX2266-8

33CX1510   (==== Not Issued ====)

33CX1511   B/Gold : **£8**   Red Semi : £4
MOZART   Symphony No.35, Divertimento
Philharmonia Orchestra   Karajan
No Stereo

33CX1512   B/Gold : **£15**   Red Semi : £8
HINDEMITH   Concert Music for Brass & Strings
Philharmonia Orchestra   Hindemith
No Stereo

33CX1513   B/Gold : **£10**   Red Semi : £5
BEETHOVEN   Piano Sonata No.21 & 28   Arrau
No Stereo

33CX1514   B/Gold : **£14**   Red Semi : £7
BEETHOVEN   Violin Concerto   Igor Oistrakh   Schuchter
No Stereo

33CX1515   B/Gold : **£75**   Red Semi : £45
BACH   Cello Suites   Starker
No Stereo

33CX1516   B/Gold : **£6**   Red Semi : £3
STRAUSS   Die Fledermaus (Highlights) Streich
Philharmonia Orchestra   Karajan
No Stereo

33CX1517   B/Gold : **£7**   Red Semi : £4
BRAHMS   Symphony No.2, Tragic Overture
Philharmonia Orchestra   Klemperer
Stereo Issue : SAX2362

33CX1518   B/Gold : **£6**   Red Semi : £3
STRAVINSKY   Firebird Suite   Philharmonia Orchestra   Giulini
Stereo Issue : SAX2279

33CX1519   B/Gold : **£7**   Red Semi : £4
BEETHOVEN   Sonata No.9, No.10, No.13 & No.14   Gieseking
Stereo Issue : SAX2259

33CX1520-1　　　B/Gold : **£10**　　　Red Semi : £5
GLUCK　　　　　Orphee　Gedda
Societe des Concertes du Conservatoire　　　　　De Froment
No Stereo

33CX1522　　　B/Gold : **£15**　　　Red Semi : £8
Various　　　　　Recital　　　　　Nilsson
No Stereo

33CX1523　　　B/Gold : **£2**　　　Red Semi : £1
TCHAIKOVSKY / MOUSSORGSKY Symphony No.2, Night on Bare
Mountain　　　　　Philharmonia Orchestra　　　Giulini
Stereo Issue : SAX2416

33CX1524　　　B/Gold : **£14**　　　Red Semi : £7
BERLIOZ　　　　Overtures　Paris Conservatoire Orchestra　　　Cluytens
No Stereo

33CX1525　　　B/Gold : **£35**　　　Red Semi : £20
TCHAIKOVSKY　　　　　Piano Concerto No.1　　　　　Iturbi
Colonne Royal Symphony Orchestra
No Stereo

33CX1526　　　B/Gold : **£30**　　　Red Semi : £15
MOZART / CHOPIN　　　Piano Concerto K491, Barcarolle
Gieseking　　　Philharmonia Orchestra　　　Karajan
No Stereo

33CX1527　　　B/Gold : **£16**　　　Red Semi : £8
HAYDN　　　　String Quatet Op64/5　　　Hungarian String Quartet
No Stereo

33CX1528　　　B/Gold : **£14**　　　Red Semi : £7
MOZART　　　Arias　　　　　Gedda
Paris Conservatoire Orchestra　　　Cluytens
No Stereo

33CX1529-30　　　B/Gold : **£15**　　　Red Semi : £8
Various　　　　Playboy Jazz　　　Various
No Stereo

33CX1531   B/Gold : **£6**   Red Semi : £3
GRIEG / SCHUMANN   Piano Concertos   Arrau
Philharmonia Orchestra   Galliera
No Stereo

33CX1532   B/Gold : **£2**   Red Semi : £1
BEETHOVEN   Symphony No.6   Philharmonia Orchestra   Klemperer
Stereo Issue : SAX2260

33CX1533   B/Gold : **£18**   Red Semi : £9
HINDEMITH   Concerto for Clarinet & Orchestra
Philharmonia Orchestra   Hindemith
No Stereo

33CX1534-5   B/Gold : **£16**   Red Semi : £8
ORFF   Der Mond   Christ
Philharmonia Orchestra   Sawallisch
No Stereo

33CX1536   B/Gold : **£7**   Red Semi : £4
BRAHMS   Symphony No.3, Academic Fest Ov
Philharmonia Orchestra   Klemperer
Stereo Issue : SAX2351

33CX1537   B/Gold : **£30**   Red Semi : £15
BEETHOVEN   Piano Sonatas Op.2/2 & Op.2/3   Gieseking
No Stereo

33CX1538   B/Gold : **£100**   Red Semi : £50
BRUCH / WIENIAWSKI   Scottish Fantasie, Violin Concerto No.1Rabin
Philharmonia Orchestra   Boult
No Stereo

33CX1539   B/Gold : **£8**   Red Semi : £4
BOCCHERINI / HAYDN   Overture in Dmaj., Symphony in Cmin.
Philharmonia Orchestra   Giulini
No Stereo

33CX1540   B/Gold : **£15**   Red Semi : £8
Various   Callas at La Scalla - Opera Revivals   Callas
Milan La Scala Orchestra   Serafin
No Stereo

33CX1541 B/Gold : **£7** Red Semi : £4
MAHLER Symphony No.4 Philharmonia Orchestra Kletski
Stereo Issue : SAX2345

33CX1542 B/Gold : **£5** Red Semi : £3
WAGNER Wagner Recital Hotter
Philharmonia Orchestra Ludwig
Stereo Issue : SAX2296

33CX1543 B/Gold : **£12** Red Semi : £6
MENOTTI The Unicorn,the Gorgon and the Manticore
New York Ballet Schippers
No Stereo

33CX1544 B/Gold : **£14** Red Semi : £7
BERLIOZ Romeo et Juliet Suite, Damnation of Faust Suite
Paris Conservatoire Orchestra Cluytens
No Stereo

33CX1545 B/Gold : **£6** Red Semi : £3
Various Concert of Italian Opera Intermezzi
Philharmonia Orchestra Galliera
No Stereo

33CX1546 B/Gold : **£100** Red Semi : £50
LOCATELLI / VIVALDI / TCHAIKOVSKY Violin Sonata in F, Violin
Concerto in G Kogan Vandernoot
No Stereo

33CX1547 B/Gold : **£40** Red Semi : £20
BARTOK Mikrocosmos, Rumanian Dances, etc. Solchany
No Stereo

33CX1548 B/Gold : **£7** Red Semi : £4
RESPIGHI / BERLIOZ Pines of Rome, Carnival Romain
Philharmonia Orchestra Karajan
No Stereo

33CX1549-50 B/Gold : **£10** Red Semi : £5
ORFF Music for Children
Childrens Choir and Instrument Ensemble Jellinek
No Stereo

33CX1551   B/Gold : **£10**   Red Semi : £5
FALLA   3 Cornered Hat   French National Radio Orchestra Toldra
No Stereo

33CX1552   B/Gold : **£12**   Red Semi : £6
Various   Recital   Ludwig
No Stereo

33CX1553   B/Gold : **£14**   Red Semi : £7
Various   Song Recital   Farrell
No Stereo

33CX1554   B/Gold : **£4**   Red Semi : £2
BEETHOVEN   Symphony No.1, Symphony No.8
Philharmonia Orchestra   Klemperer
Stereo Issue : SAX2318

33CX1555-7   B/Gold : **£60**   Red Semi : £30
PUCCINI   Turnadot   Callas
Milan La Scala Orchestra   Serafin
No Stereo

33CX1558   B/Gold : **£5**   Red Semi : £3
MOZART   Marriage of Figaro (Highlights)   Seefried
Vienna Philharmonic Orchestra   Karajan
No Stereo

33CX1559   B/Gold : **£4**   Red Semi : £2
PROKOFIEV / MOZART   Peter & Wolf, Toy Symphony
Philharmonia Orchestra   Karajan
Stereo Issue : SAX2375

33CX1560   B/Gold : **£15**   Red Semi : £8
ROSSINI   Overtures
French National Radio Orchestra   Markevich
No Stereo

33CX1561   B/Gold : **£10**   Red Semi : £5
PROKOFIEV   Symphony No.5   Philharmonia Orchestra Schippers
No Stereo

33CX1562   B/Gold : **£100**   Red Semi : £50
PAGANINI   Violin Concerto No.1, Cantabile in Dmaj.   Kogan
Paris Conservatoire Orchestra   Bruck
No Stereo

33CX1563   B/Gold : **£10**   Red Semi : £5
CHOPIN   Piano Concerto No.2   Ashkenazy
Warsaw Philharmonic Orchestra   Gorzynski
No Stereo

33CX1564   B/Gold : **£20**   Red Semi : £10
BEETHOVEN   Sonata No.4, 5 & 6   Gieseking
No Stereo

33CX1565   B/Gold : **£7**   Red Semi : £4
TCHAIKOVSKY   Overtures   Royal Philharmonic Orchestra   Kletski
No Stereo

33CX1566   B/Gold : **£16**   Red Semi : £8
SCHUBERT   Quartet in Gmaj.   Hungarian String Quartet
No Stereo

33CX1567   B/Gold : **£12**   Red Semi : £6
PALESTRINA / MONTEVERDI   Church Music, Madrigals
Netherlands Chambre Choir   Nobel
No Stereo

33CX1568   B/Gold : **£10**   Red Semi : £5
Various   An Edelmann Recital   Edelmann
No Stereo

33CX1569   B/Gold : **£8**   Red Semi : £4
SCHUBERT   Impromptus 1-3, Fantasea in C   Arrau
No Stereo

33CX1570   B/Gold : **£2**   Red Semi : £1
Various   Elisabeth Schwartzkopf Sings Operetta   Schwarzkopf
Philharmonia Orchestra   Ackermann
Stereo Issue : SAX2283

33CX1571   B/Gold : **£2**   Red Semi : £1
TCHAIKOVSKY / BERLIOZ / SIBELIUS   1812, Hungarian March,
Rhapsody ,Valse Etc   Philharmonia Orchestra   Karajan
Stereo Issue : SAX2302

33CX1572   B/Gold : **£5**   Red Semi : £3
MOZART   Magic Flute (Highlights)   Seefried
Vienna Philharmonic Orchestra   Karajan
No Stereo

33CX1573   B/Gold : **£8**   Red Semi : £4
BRAHMS   Symphony No.1   Royal Philharmonic Orchestra   Kletski
No Stereo

33CX1574-5   B/Gold : **£15**   Red Semi : £8
BEETHOVEN   Symphony No.9   Philharmonia Orchestra   Klemperer
Stereo Issue : SAX2276-7

33CX1576   (==== Not Issued ====)

33CX1577   B/Gold : **£12**   Red Semi : £6
FAURE   Suites   Opera Comique   Tzipine
No Stereo

33CX1578   B/Gold : **£35**   Red Semi : £20
MOZART   Piano Concerto No.22   Iturbi
Colonne Royal Symphony Orchestra
No Stereo

33CX1579   B/Gold : **£10**   Red Semi : £5
HAYDN   String Quatet No.57, String Quartet No.65
Amadeus Quartet
No Stereo

33CX1580   B/Gold : **£25**   Red Semi : £14
BRAHMS / BEETHOVEN   Violin Sonata No.3   Oistrakh
No Stereo

33CX1581   B/Gold : **£16**   Red Semi : £8
BORODIN / TCHAIKOVSKY   String Quartet No.2, String Quartet No.1
Hungarian String Quartet
No Stereo

33CX1582   B/Gold : **£4**   Red Semi : £2
VERDI   Rigoletto (Highlights)   Callas
Milan La Scala Orchestra   Serafin
No Stereo

33CX1583-5   B/Gold : **£60**   Red Semi : £30
PUCCINI   Manon Lescaut   Callas
Milan La Scala Orchestra   Serafin
No Stereo

33CX1586-7   B/Gold : **£16**   Red Semi : £8
BRUCKNER   Symphony No.8   Philharmonia Orchestra   Karajan
No Stereo

33CX1588   B/Gold : **£5**   Red Semi : £3
OFFENBACH / ROSSINI / GOUNOD   Ballet Music
Philharmonia Orchestra   Karajan
Stereo Issue : SAX2274

33CX1589   B/Gold : **£8**   Red Semi : £4
FRANCK   Symphony, Psyche et Eros
Philharmonia Orchestra   Giulini
No Stereo

33CX1590   B/Gold : **£15**   Red Semi : £8
BACH   Musical Offering
French National Radio Orchestra   Markevich
No Stereo

33CX1591   B/Gold : **£5**   Red Semi : £3
BRAHMS   Symphony No.4
Philharmonia Orchestra   Klemperer
Stereo Issue : SAX2350

33CX1592   B/Gold : **£10**   Red Semi : £5
HAYDN   String Quartet No.72, String Quartet No.74
Amadeus Quartet
No Stereo

33CX1593   B/Gold : **£75**   Red Semi : £45
BEETHOVEN   Piano Sonata No.8, Piano Sonata No.21   Annie Fischer
No Stereo

33CX1594   B/Gold : **£45**   Red Semi : £25
TCHAIKOVSKY   Violin Concerto   Igor Oistrakh
Pro Arte Orchestra   Schuchter
No Stereo

33CX1595   B/Gold : **£75**   Red Semi : £45
DOHNANYI / KODALY   Konzertstuck Op.12, Sonata for Cello   Starker
Philharmonia Orchestra   Susskind
No Stereo

33CX1596   B/Gold : **£14**   Red Semi : £7
Various   Opera Excerpts   Farrell
Philharmonia Orchestra   Schippers
No Stereo

33CX1597   B/Gold : **£85**   Red Semi : £50
MENDELSSOHN   Violin Concerto   Rabin
Philharmonia Orchestra   Boult
No Stereo

33CX1598   B/Gold : **£10**   Red Semi : £5
Various   Love Duets   Di Stefano
No Stereo

33CX1599   B/Gold : **£25**   Red Semi : £12
MOZART   String Quartet K428 & K464   Hungarian String Quartet
No Stereo

33CX1600-2   B/Gold : **£45**   Red Semi : £25
STRAUSS   Capriccio   Schwarzkopf
Philharmonia Orchestra   Sawallisch
No Stereo

33CX1603   B/Gold : **£30**   Red Semi : £15
BEETHOVEN   Piano Sonata Op.26, Piano Sonata Op.28   Gieseking
No Stereo

33CX1604-5   B/Gold : **£35**   Red Semi : £20
SHOSTAKOVICH   Symphony No.11
French National Radio Orchestra   Cluytens
No Stereo

33CX1606   B/Gold : **£35**   Red Semi : £20
Various   Recital by Fournier   Fournier
No Stereo

33CX1607   B/Gold : **£15**   Red Semi : £8
CHOPIN   17 Polish Songs   Zareska
No Stereo

33CX1608   B/Gold : **£8**   Red Semi : £4
BIZET   Arlesienne Suites 1,2, Carmen Suitet 1
Philharmonia Orchestra   Karajan
Stereo Issue : SAX2289

33CX1609   B/Gold : **£12**   Red Semi : £6
TCHAIKOVSKY   Symphony No.4   Philharmonia Orchestra   Schippers
No Stereo

33CX1610   B/Gold : **£6**   Red Semi : £3
BEETHOVEN   Piano Sonata Op.110, Op.111   Arrau
No Stereo

33CX1611-2   B/Gold : **£40**   Red Semi : £20
SCHUBERT   Impromptus 1-4, Drei Klavistuck   Gieseking
No Stereo

33CX1613   B/Gold : **£2**   Red Semi : £1
HANDEL   Messiah (Highlights)
Royal Liverpool Philharmonic Orchestra   Sargent
No Stereo

33CX1614   B/Gold : **£16**   Red Semi : £8
KODALY / VILLA-LOBOS   Quartet No.2 , Quartet No.6
Hungarian String Quartet
No Stereo

33CX1615   B/Gold : **£6**   Red Semi : £3
BEETHOVEN   Symphony No.2, Coriolan, Prometheus
Philharmonia Orchestra   Klemperer
Stereo Issue : SAX2331

33CX1616   B/Gold : **£6**   Red Semi : £3
BEETHOVEN   Piano ConcertoNo.3,   Arrau
Philharmonia Orchestra   Galliera
No Stereo

33CX1617   B/Gold : **£2**   Red Semi : £1
Various   Hoffnung Interplanetary Music Festival 1958 Hoffnung
No Stereo

33CX1618-20   B/Gold : **£30**   Red Semi : £16
CHERUBINI   Medea   Callas   Milan La Scala Orchestra   Serafin
Stereo Issue : SAX2290-2

33CX1621   B/Gold : **£8**   Red Semi : £4
CHOPIN   Chopin Recital   Ashkenazy
No Stereo

33CX1622   B/Gold : **£14**   Red Semi : £7
BACH   Concerto in Dmin., etc.   Casadesus
Paris Conservatoire Orchestra   Vandernoot
No Stereo

33CX1623   B/Gold : **£3**   Red Semi : £2
TCHAIKOVSKY   Swan Lake & Nutcracker
Philharmonia Orchestra   Sawalisch
Stereo Issue : SAX2285

33CX1624   B/Gold : **£6**   Red Semi : £3
BRAHMS   Piano Concert No.3, Intermezzi   Anda
No Stereo

33CX1625   B/Gold : **£6**   Red Semi : £3
BEETHOVEN   Piano Concerto No.1, Piano Sonata Op.78   Arrau
Philharmonia Orchestra   Galliera
No Stereo

33CX1626   B/Gold : **£14**   Red Semi : £7
Various   Leider Recital No.1   Hotter
No Stereo

33CX1627   B/Gold : **£7**   Red Semi : £4
SCHUBERT   Trio in Bb Op.99   Oborin   Oistrakh Trio
Stereo Issue : SAX2281

33CX1628   B/Gold : **£7**   Red Semi : £4
VERDI   Callas Portrays Verdi Heroines   Callas
Stereo Issue : SAX2293

33CX1629   B/Gold : **£3**   Red Semi : £2
Various   Recital   Nilsson   Philharmonia Orchestra   Wallberg
Stereo Issue : SAX2284

33CX1630   B/Gold : **£30**   Red Semi : £18
MOZART   Concerto No.21 & 22   Annie Fischer
No Stereo

33CX1631-3   B/Gold : **£15**   Red Semi : £8
PUCCINI   La Fanciulla del West   Nilsson
Milan La Scala Orchestra   Matatic
Stereo Issue : SAX2286-8

33CX1634-5   B/Gold : **£30**   Red Semi : £15
BEETHOVEN   Missa Solemnis   Schwarzkopf
Philharmonia Orchestra   Karajan
No Stereo

33CX1636   B/Gold : **£7**   Red Semi : £4
RIMSKY-KORSAKOV   Scheherazade, Symphonic Suite Op.35
Philharmonia Orchestra   Matatic
No Stereo

33CX1637   B/Gold : **£10**   Red Semi : £5
BRAHMS   PianoConcerto No.2   Ashkenazy
German State Opera Orchestra   Ludwig
No Stereo

33CX1638   B/Gold : **£22**   Red Semi : £12
Various   Renata Scotto Operatic Arias   Scotto
Philharmonia Orchestra   Ferrari
No Stereo

33CX1639   B/Gold : **£6**   Red Semi : £3
CHOPIN   Recital   Malcuzynski
No Stereo

33CX1640   (==== Not Issued ====)

33CX1641   B/Gold : **£6**   Red Semi : £3
Various   Victorian Chorale Music   Netherlands Choir
Choir Nobel
No Stereo

33CX1642   B/Gold : **£3**   Red Semi : £2
DVORAK   New World Symphony
Berlin Philharmonic Orchestra   Karajan
Stereo Issue : SAX2275

33CX1643   B/Gold : **£14**   Red Semi : £7
BEETHOVEN   Archduke Trio Op.97   Oistrakh   David Oistrakh Trio
Stereo Issue : SAX2352

33CX1644   B/Gold : **£25**   Red Semi : £14
Various   Cello Encores   Fournier
No Stereo

33CX1645   B/Gold : **£5**   Red Semi : £3
Various   Mad Scenes   Callas
Philharmonia Orchestra   Rescigno
Stereo Issue : SAX2320

33CX1646   (==== Not Issued ====)

33CX1647   B/Gold : **£8**   Red Semi : £4
STRAUSS   Le Bourgeois Gentilhomme, Intermezzo Suite
Philharmonia Orchestra   Sawallisch
No Stereo

33CX1648   B/Gold : **£15**   Red Semi : £8
VILLA-LOBOS   Banchianas, Brazileiras
French National Radio Orchestra   Villa-Lobos
No Stereo

33CX1649-50   B/Gold : **£6**   Red Semi : £3
DONIZETTI   L'Elisor D'Amore (Love Potion)   Alva
Milan La Scala Orchestra   Serafin
Stereo Issue : SAX2298-9

33CX1651   B/Gold : **£6**   Red Semi : £3
WAGNER / VERDI   Soprano Arias from Wagner & Verdi   Lovberg
Philharmonia Orchestra   Susskind
Stereo Issue : SAX2353

33CX1652   B/Gold : **£3**   Red Semi : £2
WEBER   Overtures   Philharmonia Orchestra   Sawalisch
Stereo Issue : SAX2343

33CX1653   B/Gold : **£2**   Red Semi : £1
BEETHOVEN   Piano Concerto 5   Arrau
Philharmonia Orchestra   Galliera
Stereo Issue : SAX2297

33CX1654   B/Gold : **£12**   Red Semi : £6
BORODIN   Prince Igor   Philharmonia Orchestra   Matatic
Stereo Issue : SAX2327

33CX1655   B/Gold : **£10**   Red Semi : £5
WAGNER   Concert   Philharmonia Orchestra   Sawallisch
No Stereo

33CX1656   B/Gold : **£75**   Red Semi : £45
BACH   Cello Suites   Starker
No Stereo

33CX1657   B/Gold : **£3**   Red Semi : £2
Various   Goeth Leider   Schwarzkopf
Philharmonia Orchestra   Boult
Stereo Issue : SAX2333

33CX1658   B/Gold : **£7**   Red Semi : £4
Various   Schwartzkopf portrays Romantic Heroines
Schwarzkopf   Philharmonia Orchestra   Ludwig
Stereo Issue : SAX2300

33CX1659   (=== Not Issued ===)

33CX1660   B/Gold : **£7**   Red Semi : £4
MOZART / PROKOFIEV   Violin Concerto No.3, Violin Conerto No.2
Oistrakh   Philharmonia Orchestra   Galliera
Stereo Issue : SAX2304

33CX1661　　B/Gold : **£14**　　Red Semi : £7
Various　　　　Leider Recital No.2　　Hotter　Philharmonia Orchestra
No Stereo

33CX1662　　B/Gold : **£8**　　Red Semi : £4
SCHUMANN　　Symphony No.3, Manfred Overture
Philharmonia Orchestra　　Giulini
No Stereo

33CX1663　　B/Gold : **£4**　　Red Semi : £2
Various　　　　Philharmonia Concert　Philharmonia Orchestra　Karajan
Stereo Issue : SAX2303

33CX1664　　B/Gold : **£50**　　Red Semi : £30
Various　　　　Fantasia, Carnival　　　Annie Fischer
No Stereo

33CX1665　　B/Gold : **£60**　　Red Semi : £40
BOCCERINI / HAYDN　　Cello Concerto　　Starker
Philharmonia Orchestra　　Giulini
No Stereo

33CX1666　　B/Gold : **£6**　　Red Semi : £3
BEETHOVEN　　Sonata No.31 & 32　　　Richter-Haaser
No Stereo

33CX1667　　B/Gold : **£6**　　Red Semi : £3
BEETHOVEN　　Concerto No.1 & 2　　Gilels
Paris Conservatoire Orchestra　　Vandernoot
No Stereo

33CX1668-70　　B/Gold : **£5**　　Red Semi : £3
HANDEL　　　Messiah
Royal Liverpool Philharmonic Orchestra　　Sargent
Stereo Issue : SAX2308-10

33CX1671　　B/Gold : **£4**　　Red Semi : £2
MAHLER　　　Fahrendedn Gesellen
Philharmonia Orchestra　　Boult
Stereo Issue : SAX2321

33CX1672 B/Gold : **£8** Red Semi : £4
BEETHOVEN Violin concerto Oistrakh
French Narional Radio Orchestra Cluytens
Stereo Issue : SAX2315

33CX1673 B/Gold : **£12** Red Semi : £6
BERLIOZ Symphony Fantastique
Philharmonia Orchestra Cluytens
No Stereo

33CX1674 B/Gold : **£10** Red Semi : £5
TCHAIKOVSKY Francesca Da Rimini, Romeo et Juliet, Ovs.
Philharmonia Orchestra Wallberg
No Stereo

33CX1675 B/Gold : **£75** Red Semi : £45
BEETHOVEN Piano Sonata Op.27, Op.78 & Op.109 Annie Fischer
No Stereo

33CX1676 B/Gold : **£30** Red Semi : £15
HINDEMITH Symphonia Serina, Concerto for Horn & Orchestra
Brain Philharmonia Orchestra Hindemith
No Stereo

33CX1677 B/Gold : **£3** Red Semi : £2
DVORAK New World Symphony
Philharmonia Orchestra Sawalisch
Stereo Issue : SAX2322

33CX1678 B/Gold : **£12** Red Semi : £6
Various Bass Operatic Arias Ladysz
Philharmonia Orchestra Fistoulari
No Stereo

33CX1679 B/Gold : **£2** Red Semi : £1
WALTON Belshazzar's Feast Philharmonia Orchestra Walton
Stereo Issue : SAX2319

33CX1680 B/Gold : **£5** Red Semi : £3
BRAHMS Piano Concerto No.2 Richter-Haaser
Berlin Philharmonic Orchestra Karajan
Stereo Issue : SAX2328

33CX1681   B/Gold : **£15**   Red Semi : £8
VERDI   Arias at La Scala   Callas
Milan La Scala Orchestra   Serafin
No Stereo

33CX1682   B/Gold : **£6**   Red Semi : £3
VERDI   Il Trovatore (Highlights)   Callas
Milan La Scala Orchestra   Karajan
No Stereo

33CX1683   B/Gold : **£10**   Red Semi : £5
LALO / TCHAIKOVSKY   Symphonie Espagnole   Kogan
Philharmonia Orchestra   Kondrashin
Stereo Issue : SAX2329

33CX1684   B/Gold : **£4**   Red Semi : £2
VERDI   Overtures   Philharmonia Orchestra   Serafin
Stereo Issue : SAX2324

33CX1685   B/Gold : **£2**   Red Semi : £1
CHOPIN   Waltzes 1-14   Malcuzynski
Stereo Issue : SAX2332

33CX1686   B/Gold : **£8**   Red Semi : £4
MOZART   Piano concerto No.20, Piano concerto No.23
Annie Fischer   Philharmonia Orchestra   Boult
Stereo Issue : SAX2335

33CX1687   B/Gold : **£20**   Red Semi : £10
MOZART / IBERT   Divertimento K270, 3 Pieces
Dennis Brain Ensemble

33CX1688-9   B/Gold : **£3**   Red Semi : £2
STRAUSS   Die Fledermaus   Lipp
Philharmonia Orchestra   Ackermann
Stereo Issue : SAX2336-7

33CX1690   B/Gold : **£2**   Red Semi : £1
CHOPIN   The Six Polonaises   Malcuzynski
Stereo Issue : SAX2338

33CX1691   B/Gold : **£7**   Red Semi : £4
TCHAIKOVSKY   Romeo & Juliet   Philharmonia Orchestra   Markevitch
Stereo Issue : SAX2339

33CX1692   B/Gold : **£12**   Red Semi : £6
BRAHMS   Violin concerto   Kogan
Philharmonia Orchestra   Kondrashin
Stereo Issue : SAX2307

33CX1693   B/Gold : **£2**   Red Semi : £1
SCHUMANN   Frauenliebe und Leben   Ludwig
Stereo Issue : SAX2340

33CX1694   B/Gold : **£3**   Red Semi : £2
FALLA / RAVEL   3 Cornered Hat, Daphnis Et Chloe
Philharmonia Orchestra   Giulini
Stereo Issue : SAX2341

33CX1695   B/Gold : **£3**   Red Semi : £2
CHOPIN   Piano Concerto No.2, Fantaisie in Fmin.
Malcuzynski   London Symphony Orchestra   Susskind
Stereo Issue : SAX2344

33CX1696   B/Gold : **£2**   Red Semi : £1
BEETHOVEN   Piano Concerto No.2   Arrau
Philharmonia Orchestra   Galliera
Stereo Issue : SAX2346

33CX1697   B/Gold : **£3**   Red Semi : £2
WAGNER   Klemperer conducts Wagner Vol.1
Philharmonia Orchestra   Klemperer
Stereo Issue : SAX2347

33CX1698   B/Gold : **£3**   Red Semi : £2
WAGNER   Klemperer conducts Wagner Vol.2
Philharmonia Orchestra   Klemperer
Stereo Issue : SAX2348

33CX1699   B/Gold : **£12**   Red Semi : £6
RIMSKY-KORSAKOV / RAVEL   Caprice Espagnol, La Valse
Philharmonia Orchestra   Cluytens
Stereo Issue : SAX2355

33CX1700   B/Gold : **£ 85**   Red Semi : £50
Various   Transcriptions for Cello & Piano   Starker
No Stereo

33CX1701   B/Gold : **£ 15**   Red Semi : £8
CHOPIN   Recital   Iturbi
No Stereo

33CX1702   B/Gold : **£ 7**   Red Semi : £4
BEETHOVEN   Symphony No.4, Consecration of the House
Philharmonia Orchestra   Klemperer
Stereo Issue : SAX2354

33CX1703   B/Gold : **£ 5**   Red Semi : £3
MOZART   Symphony No.29, Symphony No.38
Berlin Philharmonic Orchestra   Karajan
Stereo Issue : SAX2356

33CX1704   B/Gold : **£ 6**   Red Semi : £3
TCHAIKOVSKY   Symphony No.4
Berlin Philharmonic Orchestra   Karajan
Stereo Issue : SAX2357

33CX1705   B/Gold : **£ 2**   Red Semi : £1
MAHLER   Songs   Ludwig
Stereo Issue : SAX2358

33CX1706-8   B/Gold : **£ 16**   Red Semi : £8
PONCHIELLI   La Gioconda   Callas
Milan La Scala Orchestra   Votto
Stereo Issue : SAX2359-61

33CX1709   B/Gold : **£ 2**   Red Semi : £1
SCHUBERT   Moments Musicaux, March in E   Arrau
Stereo Issue : SAX2363

33CX1710   B/Gold : **£ 4**   Red Semi : £2
BEETHOVEN   Symphony No.3
Philharmonia Orchestra   Klemperer
Stereo Issue : SAX2364

33CX1711   B/Gold : **£20**   Red Semi : £10
TCHAIKOVSKY   Violin Concerto, Meditation   Kogan
Paris Conservatoire Orchestra   Silvestri
Stereo Issue : SAX2323

33CX1712   B/Gold : **£6**   Red Semi : £3
LEHAR   Land of Smiles, Merry Widow (Highlights)
Schwarzkopf   Philharmonia Orchestra   Ackermann
No Stereo

33CX1713   B/Gold : **£1**   Red Semi : £1
HANDEL   Messiah (Highlights)
Huddersfield Choral Society   Sargent
Stereo Issue : SAX2365

33CX1714   B/Gold : **£7**   Red Semi : £4
WOLF   Aus dem Italiensch Leiderbuch   Schwarzkopf
Stereo Issue : SAX2366

33CX1715   B/Gold : **£8**   Red Semi : £4
STRAUSS   Don Juan. Till Eulenspiegel
Philharmonia Orchestra   Klemperer
Stereo Issue : SAX2367

33CX1716   B/Gold : **£4**   Red Semi : £2
TCHAIKOVSKY   Symphony No.6   Philharmonia Orchestra   Giulini
Stereo Issue : SAX2368

33CX1717-20   B/Gold : **£20**   Red Semi : £10
MOZART   Don Giovanni   Schwarzkopf
Philharmonia Orchestra   Giulini
Stereo Issue : SAX2369-72

33CX1721   B/Gold : **£7**   Red Semi : £4
BEETHOVEN   Symphony No.5   Philharmonia Orchestra   Klemperer
Stereo Issue : SAX2373

33CX1722   B/Gold : **£12**   Red Semi : £6
STRAVINSKY / SCHUMANN   Pieces, Quartet No.3   Quartetto Italiano
No Stereo

33CX1723-4   B/Gold : **£16**   Red Semi : £8
DONIZETTI   Lucia di Lammermore   Callas
Philharmonic Orchestra & Chorus   Serafin
Stereo Issue : SAX2316-17

33CX1725   B/Gold : **£15**   Red Semi : £8
Various   Opera Duets   Callas, Stefano
Milan La Scala Orchestra
No Stereo

33CX1726   B/Gold : **£4**   Red Semi : £2
ROSSINI / VERDI Overtures   Philharmonia Orchestra   Giulini
Stereo Issue : SAX2377

33CX1727   B/Gold : **£12**   Red Semi : £6
MOZART / RAVEL   String Quartet in G, String Quartet in F
Quartetto Italiano
No Stereo

33CX1728   B/Gold : **£2**   Red Semi : £1
Various   Recital   Moffo
Stereo Issue : SAX2376

33CX1729   B/Gold : **£5**   Red Semi : £3
ROSSINI   Rossini Overtures   Philharmonia Orchestra   Karajan
Stereo Issue : SAX2378

33CX1730   B/Gold : **£5**   Red Semi : £3
SIBELIUS   Symphony No.2   Philharmonia Orchestra   Karajan
Stereo Issue : SAX2379

33CX1731   B/Gold : **£4**   Red Semi : £2
TCHAIKOVSKY / WEBER Piano Concerto No.1, Konzertst   Arrau
Philharmonia Orchestra   Galliera
Stereo Issue : SAX2380

33CX1732-5   B/Gold : **£16**   Red Semi : £8
MOZART   Marriage of Figaro   Schwarzkopf
Philharmonia Orchestra   Giulini
Stereo Issue : SAX2381-4

33CX1736   B/Gold : **£10**   Red Semi : £5
MENDELSSOHN   Symphony No.3, Hebrides
Philharmonia Orchestra   Klemperer
Stereo Issue : SAX2342

33CX1737   B/Gold : **£3**   Red Semi : £2
BEETHOVEN   Piano Sonata No.17, Piano Sonata No.30   Richter-Haaser
Stereo Issue : SAX2385

33CX1738   B/Gold : **£8**   Red Semi : £4
BEETHOVEN   Violin Concerto   Kogan
Paris Conservatoire Orchestra   Silvestri
Stereo Issue : SAX2386

33CX1739   B/Gold : **£5**   Red Semi : £3
BRAHMS   Piano Concerto No.1   Arrau
Philharmonia Orchestra   Giulini
Stereo Issue : SAX2387

33CX1740   B/Gold : **£10**   Red Semi : £5
BRAHMS   Violin & Piano Sonatas No.1 & 2   Oistrakh
Stereo Issue : SAX2388

33CX1741   B/Gold : **£3**   Red Semi : £2
MOZART / HANDEL   Kleine Nachtmusik, Ave Verum Co
Berlin Philharmonic Orchestra   Karajan
Stereo Issue : SAX2389

33CX1742   B/Gold : **£4**   Red Semi : £2
Various   Piano Recital   Arrau
Stereo Issue : SAX2390

33CX1743   B/Gold : **£12**   Red Semi : £6
Various   Spanish Music   Iturbi
Stereo Issue : SAX2391

33CX1745   B/Gold : **£75**   Red Semi : £45
BACH   Cello Suites   Starker
No Stereo

33CX1746   B/Gold : **£7**   Red Semi : £4
MENDELSSOHN Midsummernights Dream
Philharmonia Orchestra   Klemperer
Stereo Issue : SAX2393

33CX1747   B/Gold : **£6**   Red Semi : £3
RAVEL   Piano Concerto In G And D   Francois
Paris Conservatoire Orchestra   Cluytens
Stereo Issue : SAX2394

33CX1748   B/Gold : **£6**   Red Semi : £3
HAYDN   Symphony No.98, Symphony No.101
Philharmonia Orchestra   Klemperer
Stereo Issue : SAX2395

33CX1749   B/Gold : **£15**   Red Semi : £8
SCHUBERT   String Quartet No.14   Hungarian String Quartet
No Stereo

33CX1750   B/Gold : **£5**   Red Semi : £3
SIBELIUS   Symphony No.5, Finlandia
Philharmonia Orchestra   Karajan
Stereo Issue : SAX2392

33CX1751   B/Gold : **£7**   Red Semi : £4
MENDELSSOHN / SCHUMANN   Symphony No.4
Philharmonia Orchestra   Klemperer
Stereo Issue : SAX2398

33CX1752-3   B/Gold : **£6**   Red Semi : £3
LEONCAVALLO I Pagliacci   Gobbi
Milan La Scala Orchestra   Matatic
Stereo Issue : SAX2399-2400

33CX1754   B/Gold : **£7**   Red Semi : £4
SCHUBERT   Symphony In C   Philharmonia Orchestra   Klemperer
Stereo Issue : SAX2397

33CX1755   B/Gold : **£5**   Red Semi : £3
CHOPIN   Piano Sonata No.3, Fantasie in Fmaj.   Arrau
Stereo Issue : SAX2401

33CX1756   B/Gold : **£3**   Red Semi : £2
SCHUBERT   Recital   Fischer-Diesku
Stereo Issue : SAX2402

33CX1757   B/Gold : **£4**   Red Semi : £2
BEETHOVEN   Piano Concerto No.4   Richter-Haaser
Philharmonia Orchestra   Kertesz
Stereo Issue : SAX2403

33CX1758   B/Gold : **£3**   Red Semi : £2
Various   Promenade Concert Philharmonia Orchestra   Karajan
Stereo Issue : SAX2404

33CX1759   B/Gold : **£2**   Red Semi : £1
DVORAK   New World Symphony
Philharmonia Orchestra   Giulini
Stereo Issue : SAX2405

33CX1760   B/Gold : **£5**   Red Semi : £3
MOZART   Horn Concertos   Civil
Philharmonia Orchestra   Klemperer
Stereo Issue : SAX2406

33CX1761   B/Gold : **£30**   Red Semi : £15
Various   Piano Recital   Gieseking
No Stereo

33CX1762   B/Gold : **£9**   Red Semi : £5
BEETHOVEN   Piano Sonata No.27, Piano Sonata No.29 Richter-Haaser
Stereo Issue : SAX2407

33CX1763-4   B/Gold : **£8**   Red Semi : £4
BACH   Brandenburg Concerto
Philharmonia Orchestra   Klemperer
Stereo Issue : SAX2408-9

33CX1765   B/Gold : **£5**   Red Semi : £3
BRAHMS   Violin Concerto   Oistrakh
Philharmonia Orchestra   Klemperer
Stereo Issue : SAX2411

33CX1766-8   B/Gold : **£20**   Red Semi : £10
BELLINI   Norma   Callas   Milan La Scala Orchestra   Serafin
Stereo Issue : SAX2412-4

33CX1769   B/Gold : **£6**   Red Semi : £3
BEETHOVEN   Symphony No.7
Philharmonia Orchestra   Klemperer
Stereo Issue : SAX2415

33CX1770   B/Gold : **£4**   Red Semi : £2
WEBER   Overtures   Philharmonia Orchestra   Klemperer
Stereo Issue : SAX2417

33CX1771   B/Gold : **£6**   Red Semi : £3
Various   French Operatic Arias   Callas
Stereo Issue : SAX2410

33CX1772   B/Gold : **£16**   Red Semi : £8
TCHAIKOVSKY   Capriccio Italien etc
Milan La Scala Orchestra   Matatic
Stereo Issue : SAX2418

33CX1773   B/Gold : **£5**   Red Semi : £3
BRAHMS   Symphony No.1   Philharmonia Orchestra   Giulini
Stereo Issue : SAX2420

33CX1774   B/Gold : **£5**   Red Semi : £3
Various   Ballet Music from the Opera
Philharmonia Orchestra   Karajan
Stereo Issue : SAX2421

33CX1775   B/Gold : **£2**   Red Semi : £1
BEETHOVEN   Piano Concerto No.5, Rondo in C   Richter-Haaser
Philharmonia Orchestra   Kertesz
Stereo Issue : SAX2422

33CX1776   B/Gold : **£5**   Red Semi : £3
ROSSINI / RESPIEGHI / DUKAS   La Boutique Fantastique, L'apprenti
Sorcier   Philharmonia Orchestra   Galliera
Stereo Issue : SAX2419

33CX1777   B/Gold : **£1**   Red Semi : £1
STRAUSS   Der Rosenkavalier (Highlights)
Philharmonia Orchestra   Karajan
Stereo Issue : SAX2423

33CX1778   B/Gold : **£4**   Red Semi : £2
SCHUBERT / BRAHMS   Symphony No.8, Variations On Theme By
Haydn   Philharmonia Orchestra   Giulini
Stereo Issue : SAX2424

33CX1779   (==== Not Issued ====)

33CX1780   B/Gold : **£7**   Red Semi : £4
MOZART   Piano concerto No.17, Piano Concerto No.26   Richter-
Haaser   Philharmonia Orchestra   Kertesz
Stereo Issue : SAX2426

33CX1781-2   B/Gold : **£9**   Red Semi : £5
BRAHMS   German Requiem   Philharmonia Orchestra   Klemperer
Stereo Issue : SAX2430-1

33CX1783   B/Gold : **£4**   Red Semi : £2
BARTOK / HINDEMITH   Music For Strings,Perc & Celest, Mathis De
Maler   Berlin Philharmonic Orchestra   Karajan
Stereo Issue : SAX2432

33CX1784   B/Gold : **£12**   Red Semi : £6
Various   Opera Excerpts   Stefano
No Stereo

33CX1785   B/Gold : **£2**   Red Semi : £1
Various   The Hoffnung Astronautical Music Festival   Hoffnung
Stereo Issue : SAX2433

33CX1786   B/Gold : **£7**   Red Semi : £4
MOZART   Symphony No.35, Symphony No.36
Philharmonia Orchestra   Klemperer
Stereo Issue : SAX2436

33CX1787   B/Gold : **£10**   Red Semi : £5
PUCCINI   Madame Butterfly excerpts   Callas
Philharmonia Orchestra   Karajan
No Stereo

33CX1788   B/Gold : **£12**   Red Semi : £6
DEBUSSY   Recital   Iturbi
Stereo Issue : SAX2434

33CX1789   B/Gold : **£6**   Red Semi : £3
STRAUSS   Tod Verklarung, Metamorphosis
Philharmonia Orchestra   Klemperer
Stereo Issue : SAX2437

33CX1790   B/Gold : **£2**   Red Semi : £1
ROSSINI   Barber Of Seville (Highlights)   Callas
Philharmonia Orchestra   Galliera
Stereo Issue : SAX2438

33CX1791   B/Gold : **£5**   Red Semi : £3
Various   Overtures   Berlin Philharmonic Orchestra   Karajan
Stereo Issue : SAX2439

33CX1792   B/Gold : **£2**   Red Semi : £1
PUCCINI   Turnadot (Highlights)   Callas
Milan La Scala Orchestra
Stereo Issue : SAX2440

33CX1793   B/Gold : **£7**   Red Semi : £4
MAHLER   Symphony No.4   Schwarzkopf
Philharmonia Orchestra   Klemperer
Stereo Issue : SAX2441

33CX1794   (==== Not Issued ====)

33CX1795-6   B/Gold : **£3**   Red Semi : £2
BIZET   The Pearl Fishers
Orchestra of the Theatre National de L'Opera   Dervaux
Stereo Issue : SAX2442-3

33CX1797   B/Gold : **£4**   Red Semi : £2
CHOPIN   Piano Sonata No.2, Piano Sonata No.3 Malcuzynski
Stereo Issue : SAX2444

33CX1798   B/Gold : **£4**   Red Semi : £2
POULENC   Gloria, Organ Concerto,Gloria In G Maj   Druffel
French National Radio Orchestra   Pretre
Stereo Issue : SAX2445

33CX1799-03 B/Gold : **£20** Red Semi : £10
BACH St. Mathews passion
Philharmonia Orchestra Klemperer
Stereo Issue : SAX2446-50

33CX1804-6 B/Gold : **£9** Red Semi : £5
BEETHOVEN Fidelio Philharmonia Orchestra Klemperer
Stereo Issue : SAX2451-3

33CX1807 B/Gold : **£9** Red Semi : £5
BEETHOVEN Piano Sonata No.18, Piano Sonata No.32 Annie Fischer
Stereo Issue : SAX2435

33CX1808-9 B/Gold : **£14** Red Semi : £7
BRUCKNER Symphony No.7 Philharmonia Orchestra Klemperer
Stereo Issue : SAX2454-5

33CX1810 B/Gold : **£2** Red Semi : £1
ORFF Die Kluge (Highlights) Schwarzkopf
Philharmonia Orchestra Sawalisch
Stereo Issue : SAX2456

33CX1811 B/Gold : **£2** Red Semi : £1
ORFF Der Mond (Highlights) Christ
Philharmonia Orchestra Sawalisch
Stereo Issue : SAX2457

33CX1812 B/Gold : **£8** Red Semi : £4
TCHAIKOVSKY Symphony No.6 Philharmonia Orchestra Klemperer
Stereo Issue : SAX2458

33CX1813 B/Gold : **£15** Red Semi : £8
Various Piano Recital Ashkenazy
No Stereo

33CX1814 B/Gold : **£3** Red Semi : £2
WEILL Threepenny Opera Philharmonia Orchestra Klemperer
Stereo Issue : SAX2460

33CX1815 B/Gold : **£4** Red Semi : £2
SCHUBERT Symphony No.8 Philharmonia Orchestra Giulini
Stereo Issue : SAX2461

33CX1816   B/Gold : **£2**   Red Semi : £1
WALTON   Symphony No.2, Partita   Cleveland Orchestra   Szell
Stereo Issue : SAX2459

33CX1817   B/Gold : **£7**   Red Semi : £4
BRAHMS / WAGNER   Alto Rhapsody, Wesendonk Leider   Ludwig
Philharmonia Orchestra   Klemperer
Stereo Issue : SAX2462

33CX1818   B/Gold : **£3**   Red Semi : £2
DEBUSSY   La Mer   Philharmonia Orchestra   Giulini
Stereo Issue : SAX2463

33CX1819   B/Gold : **£8**   Red Semi : £4
HUMPERDINCK   Hansel & Gretel (Highlights)   Schwarzkopf
Philharmonia Orchestra   Karajan
No Stereo

33CX1820   B/Gold : **£3**   Red Semi : £2
WAGNER   Klemperer Conducts More Wagner
Philharmonia Orchestra   Klemperer
Stereo Issue : SAX2464

33CX1821   B/Gold : **£4**   Red Semi : £2
CHOPIN   Mazurkas   Malcuzynski
Stereo Issue : SAX2465

33CX1822   B/Gold : **£4**   Red Semi : £2
BRAHMS   Piano Concerto No.2   Arrau
Philharmonia Orchestra   Giulini
Stereo Issue : SAX2466

33CX1823   B/Gold : **£7**   Red Semi : £4
STRAUSS   Also Sprach Zarathustra Philharmonia Orchestra   Maazel
Stereo Issue : SAX2467

33CX1824   B/Gold : **£8**   Red Semi : £4
MOZART   Symphony No.38, Symphony No.39
Philharmonia Orchestra   Klemperer
Stereo Issue : SAX2468

33CX1825　　B/Gold : **£5**　　Red Semi : £3
DEBUSSY　　L'Isle Joyeuse　　Francois
Stereo Issue : SAX2469

33CX1826-8　　B/Gold : **£20**　　Red Semi : £10
MOZART　　The Haydn Quartets　　Juilliard Quartet
Stereo Issue : SAX2470-2

33CX1829-30　　B/Gold : **£10**　　Red Semi : £5
MAHLER　　Symphony No.2　　Philharmonia Orchestra　Klemperer
Stereo Issue : SAX2473-4

33CX1831　　B/Gold : **£4**　　Red Semi : £2
SCHUMANN　　Symphony No.3　　Cleveland Orchestra　　Szell
Stereo Issue : SAX2475

33CX1832　　B/Gold : **£7**　　Red Semi : £4
RAVEL　　Complete Orchestral Works V.1
Paris Conservatoire Orchestra　　Cluytens
Stereo Issue : SAX2476

33CX1833　　B/Gold : **£7**　　Red Semi : £4
RAVEL　　Complete Orchestral Works V.2
Paris Conservatoire Orchestra　　Cluytens
Stereo Issue : SAX2477

33CX1834　　B/Gold : **£7**　　Red Semi : £4
RAVEL　　Complete Orchestral Works V.3
Paris Conservatoire Orchestra　　Cluytens
Stereo Issue : SAX2478

33CX1835　　B/Gold : **£7**　　Red Semi : £4
RAVEL　　Complete Orchestral Works V.4
Paris Conservatoire Orchestra　　Cluytens
Stereo Issue : SAX2479

33CX1836　　B/Gold : **£5**　　Red Semi : £3
SCHOENBERG / STRAVINSKY　　Modern Music　　Rosen
Stereo Issue : SAX2480

33CX1837 B/Gold : **£8** Red Semi : £4
Various Gedda A Paris Gedda
French Narional Radio Orchestra Pretre
Stereo Issue : SAX2481

33CX1838 B/Gold : **£2** Red Semi : £1
CHERUBINI Medea (Highlights) Gorr Paris Opera Pretre
Stereo Issue : SAX2482

33CX1839 B/Gold : **£6** Red Semi : £3
BRAHMS Piano Music Fleisher
No Stereo

33CX1840 B/Gold : **£2** Red Semi : £1
TCHAIKOVSKY Romeo & Juliet Philharmonia Orchestra Giulini
Stereo Issue : SAX2483

33CX1841 B/Gold : **£7** Red Semi : £4
MOUSSORGSKY / RAVEL Pictures Exhibition
Philharmonia Orchestra Maazel
Stereo Issue : SAX2484

33CX1842 B/Gold : **£12** Red Semi : £6
SCHUMANN Piano Concerto Annie Fischer
Philharmonia Orchestra Klemperer
Stereo Issue : SAX2485

33CX1843 B/Gold : **£9** Red Semi : £5
MOZART Symphony No.40, Symphony No.41
Philharmonia Orchestra Klemperer
Stereo Issue : SAX2486

33CX1844 B/Gold : **£4** Red Semi : £2
Various The Red Army Ensemble Choral Concert
Red Army Ensemble
Stereo Issue : SAX2487

33CX1845 B/Gold : **£4** Red Semi : £2
MAHLER / STRAUSS Symphony No.10, Death & Transfiguration
Cleveland Orchestra Szell
Stereo Issue : SAX2488

33CX1846   B/Gold : **£2**   Red Semi : £1
Various   Opera Excerpts   Prey
Berlin Symphony Orchestra   Stein
Stereo Issue : SAX2489

33CX1847   B/Gold : **£8**   Red Semi : £4
Various   Szell conducts Russian Music
Cleveland Orchestra   Szell
Stereo Issue : SAX2490

33CX1848   B/Gold : **£3**   Red Semi : £2
PONCHIELLI   La Gioconda (Highlights)   Callas
Milan La Scala Orchestra   Votto
Stereo Issue : SAX2491

33CX1849   B/Gold : **£3**   Red Semi : £2
DEBUSSY   12 Etudes   Rosen
Stereo Issue : SAX2492

33CX1850   B/Gold : **£4**   Red Semi : £2
BEETHOVEN / SCHUBERT   Symphony No.8, Symphony No.8
Cleveland Orchestra   Szell
Stereo Issue : SAX2493

33CX1851   B/Gold : **£6**   Red Semi : £3
TCHAIKOVSKY   Symphony No.4   Philharmonia Orchestra   Klemperer
Stereo Issue : SAX2494

33CX1852   B/Gold : **£4**   Red Semi : £2
STRAUSS   Don Quixote, Don Juan   Fournier
Cleveland Orchestra   Szell
Stereo Issue : SAX2495

33CX1853   B/Gold : **£4**   Red Semi : £2
SCHUMANN   Symphony No.2   Cleveland Orchestra   Szell
Stereo Issue : SAX2496

33CX1854   B/Gold : **£8**   Red Semi : £4
TCHAIKOVSKY   Symphony No.5   Philharmonia Orchestra   Klemperer
Stereo Issue : SAX2497

33CX1855   B/Gold : **£5**   Red Semi : £3
BRAHMS   Symphony No.2   Philharmonia Orchestra   Giulini
Stereo Issue : SAX2498

33CX1856   B/Gold : **£3**   Red Semi : £2
STRAUSS   Till Eulenspiegel   Cleveland Orchestra   Szell
Stereo Issue : SAX2501

33CX1857   B/Gold : **£5**   Red Semi : £3
SCHUBERT   Piano Sonata in A   Rosen
Stereo Issue : SAX2502

33CX1858   B/Gold : **£3**   Red Semi : £2
Various   Callas a Paris   Callas
Stereo Issue : SAX2503

33CX1859   B/Gold : **£6**   Red Semi : £3
BEETHOVEN   String Quartet No.3, String Quartet No.6   Drolc Quartet
Stereo Issue : SAX2504

33CX1860   B/Gold : **£3**   Red Semi : £2
BEETHOVEN   Songs   Prey
Stereo Issue : SAX2505

33CX1861   B/Gold : **£4**   Red Semi : £2
SCHUMANN   Symphony No.3   Cleveland Orchestra   Szell
Stereo Issue : SAX2506

33CX1862   B/Gold : **£5**   Red Semi : £3
BRAHMS   Leider   Prey
No Stereo

33CX1863   B/Gold : **£7**   Red Semi : £4
BEETHOVEN   Violin concerto   Milstein   Philharmonia Orchestra
Stereo Issue : SAX2508

33CX1864   B/Gold : **£4**   Red Semi : £2
CHOPIN   The four Ballades   Malcuzynski
Stereo Issue : SAX2509

33CX1865   B/Gold : **£7**   Red Semi : £4
PROKOFIEV / TCHAIKOVSKY   String Quartet No.1, String Quartet
No.1   Kroll Quartet
Stereo Issue : SAX2507

33CX1866   B/Gold : **£3**   Red Semi : £2
LOEWE   Carl Loewe Ballads   Prey
Stereo Issue : SAX2511

33CX1867-8   B/Gold : **£7**   Red Semi : £4
BEETHOVEN   Symphony No.9   Cleveland Orchestra   Szell
Stereo Issue : SAX2512-3

33CX1869   B/Gold : **£5**   Red Semi : £3
BEETHOVEN   Symphony No.7   Cleveland Orchestra   Szell
Stereo Issue : SAX2510

33CX1870   B/Gold : **£4**   Red Semi : £2
SCHUBERT   Symphony No.5, Symphony No.8
Philharmonia Orchestra   Klemperer
Stereo Issue : SAX2514

33CX1871   B/Gold : **£4**   Red Semi : £2
RACHMANINOV Piano Concerto No.3   Malcuzynski
Warsaw Philharmonic Orchestra   Rowiki
Stereo Issue : SAX2515

33CX1872   B/Gold : **£5**   Red Semi : £3
BRAHMS   Symphony No.3   Philharmonia Orchestra   Giulini
Stereo Issue : SAX2516

33CX1873   (===== Not Issued =====)

33CX1874   B/Gold : **£9**   Red Semi : £5
SCHUBERT   Symphony No.9   Cleveland Orchestra   Szell
Stereo Issue : SAX2517

33CX1875   B/Gold : **£10**   Red Semi : £5
VIVALDI   Four Concerti   Milstein Milstein Chamber Orchestra
Stereo Issue : SAX2518

33CX1876   B/Gold : **£7**   Red Semi : £4
SCHUBERT / HAYDN   String Quartet No.14, String Quartet
Kroll Quartet
Stereo Issue : SAX2519

33CX1877   B/Gold : **£7**   Red Semi : £4
BEETHOVEN   String Quartet 11   Kroll Quartet
Stereo Issue : SAX2520

33CX1878   B/Gold : **£4**   Red Semi : £2
CHOPIN   Preludes   Francois
Stereo Issue : SAX2521

33CX1879   B/Gold : **£4**   Red Semi : £2
SCHUMANN   Carnival, Davidsbundlertanze   Rosen
Stereo Issue : SAX2522

33CX1880   B/Gold : **£6**   Red Semi : £3
BEETHOVEN   Piano Sonata No.16, Piano Sonata No.18   Richter-Haaser
Stereo Issue : SAX2523

33CX1881   B/Gold : **£7**   Red Semi : £4
MENDELSSOHN   Symphony No.4, Hebrides Ov etc
Cleveland Orchestra   Szell
Stereo Issue : SAX2524

33CX1882   B/Gold : **£2**   Red Semi : £1
BRAHMS   Piano concerto 1   Fleisher
Cleveland Orchestra   Szell
Stereo Issue : SAX2526

33CX1883   B/Gold : **£2**   Red Semi : £1
WALTON   Shakespeare Film Scores
Philharmonia Orchestra   Walton
Stereo Issue : SAX2527

33CX1884   B/Gold : **£10**   Red Semi : £5
FRANCK   Symphonic Poems
Belgium National Orchestra Cluytens
Stereo Issue : SAX2528

33CX1885   B/Gold : **£5**   Red Semi : £3
MOZART / HAYDN   Symphony No.35, Symphony No.92
Cleveland Orchestra   Szell
Stereo Issue : SAX2529

33CX1886   B/Gold : **£6**   Red Semi : £3
BEETHOVEN   Quartet No.4, Quartet No.5   Drolc Quartet
Stereo Issue : SAX2530

33CX1887   B/Gold : **£30**   Red Semi : £20
Various   Sonatas for two Violins   Kogan
Stereo Issue : SAX2531

33CX1888   B/Gold : **£7**   Red Semi : £4
RAVEL   Piano Works   Rosen
No Stereo

33CX1889   B/Gold : **£5**   Red Semi : £3
PROKOFIEV   Piano Concerto No.3, Piano Concerto No.5   Francois
Philharmonia Orchestra   Rowiki
Stereo Issue : SAX2533

33CX1890   B/Gold : **£3**   Red Semi : £2
BRAHMS   Piano Concerto No.2   Fleisher
Cleveland Orchestra   Szell
Stereo Issue : SAX2534

33CX1891   B/Gold : **£9**   Red Semi : £5
SCHUBERT   String Quartet 15   Juilliard Quartet
Stereo Issue : SAX2535

33CX1892   B/Gold : **£3**   Red Semi : £2
STRAUSS   Horn Concerto No.1   Cleveland Orchestra   Szell
Stereo Issue : SAX2536

33CX1893   B/Gold : **£3**   Red Semi : £2
PUCCINI   Tosca (Highlights) Callas
Milan La Scala Orchestra   De Sabata
No Stereo

33CX1894   B/Gold : **£4**   Red Semi : £2
MOZART   Mass in C
South West German Chamber Orchestra   Gonnenwein
Stereo Issue : SAX2544

33CX1895   B/Gold : **£2**   Red Semi : £1
HANDEL   Dettingen Te Deum   German Madrigal Choir
Stereo Issue : SAX2538

33CX1896   B/Gold : **£3**   Red Semi : £2
DEBUSSY / RAVEL   La Mer, Daphnis et Chloe
Cleveland Orchestra   Szell
Stereo Issue : SAX2532

33CX1897   B/Gold : **£3**   Red Semi : £2
STRAUSS   Arabella (Highlights)   Schwarzkopf
Philharmonia Orchestra   Matacic
No Stereo

33CX1898   B/Gold : **£2**   Red Semi : £1
BERLIOZ   Symphony Fantastique
Philharmonia Orchestra   Klemperer
Stereo Issue : SAX2537

33CX1899   B/Gold : **£2**   Red Semi : £1
Various   Bohemian Carnival   Cleveland Orchestra   Szell
Stereo Issue : SAX2539

33CX1900   B/Gold : **£5**   Red Semi : £3
MOZART / WEBER / BEETHOVEN   Callas Sings   Callas
Stereo Issue : SAX2540

33CX1901   B/Gold : **£3**   Red Semi : £2
BRAHMS   Piano Quintet Op 34   Fleisher Juilliard Quartet
Stereo Issue : SAX2541

33CX1902   B/Gold : **£2**   Red Semi : £1
BEETHOVEN   Leonore Nos.1-3, Fidelio Over.
Philharmonia Orchestra   Klemperer
Stereo Issue : SAX2542

33CX1903 B/Gold : **£6** Red Semi : £3
BEETHOVEN Piano Concerto No.3 Richter-Haaser
Philharmonia Orchestra Giulini
Stereo Issue : SAX2543

33CX1904 B/Gold : **£2** Red Semi : £1
STRAUSS Sinfonia Domestica Cleveland Orchestra Szell
Stereo Issue : SAX2545

33CX1905 B/Gold : **£9** Red Semi : £5
BEETHOVEN Symphony No.6 Cleveland Orchestra Szell
Stereo Issue : SAX2549

33CX1906 B/Gold : **£2** Red Semi : £1
MOZART Symphony No.31, Symphony No.34
Philharmonia Orchestra Klemperer
Stereo Issue : SAX2546

33CX1907 B/Gold : **£1** Red Semi : £1
BEETHOVEN Fidelio (Highlights)Ludwig
Philharmonia Orchestra Klemperer
Stereo Issue : SAX2547

33CX1908 B/Gold : **£8** Red Semi : £4
DEBUSSY Jeux Enfants Paris Conservatoire Orchestra Cluytens
Stereo Issue : SAX2548

33CX1909 (==== Not Issued ====)

33CX1910 B/Gold : **£4** Red Semi : £2
VERDI Arias Callas
Stereo Issue : SAX2550

33CX1911 B/Gold : **£4** Red Semi : £2
BEETHOVEN Diabelli Variations Richter-Haaser
Stereo Issue : SAX2557

33CX1912 B/Gold : **£7** Red Semi : £4
MOZART Symphony No.41 Cleveland Orchestra Szell
Stereo Issue : SAX2552

33CX1913   B/Gold : **£ 7**   Red Semi : £4
MOZART   Symphony No.33 Cleveland Orchestra   Szell
Stereo Issue : SAX2553

33CX1914   B/Gold : **£ 4**   Red Semi : £2
DVORAK   New World Symphony
Philharmonia Orchestra   Klemperer
Stereo Issue : SAX2554

33CX1915   B/Gold : **£ 2**   Red Semi : £1
BRITTEN   4 Sea Interludes, Variations & Fugue from Purcel
Philharmonia Orchestra   Giulini
Stereo Issue : SAX2555

33CX1916   B/Gold : **£ 4**   Red Semi : £2
MOUSSORGSKY / STRAVINSKY Pictures at an Exhibition, Fairies Kiss
Cleveland Orchestra   Szell
Stereo Issue : SAX2556

33CX1917   B/Gold : **£ 3**   Red Semi : £2
MENDELSSOHN Quartets In A & D   Juilliard Quartet
Stereo Issue : SAX2558

33CX1918   B/Gold : **£ 1**   Red Semi : £1
MOZART   Don Giovanni (Highlights)
Philharmonia Orchestra   Giulini
Stereo Issue : SAX2559

33CX1919   B/Gold : **£ 2**   Red Semi : £1
ROSSINI   Overtures   Philharmonia Orchestra   Giulini
Stereo Issue : SAX2560

33CX1920   B/Gold : **£ 3**   Red Semi : £2
BEETHOVEN   Piano Sonata No.3, No.22 & No.26   Richter-Haaser
Stereo Issue : SAX2561

33CX1921   B/Gold : **£ 6**   Red Semi : £3
ROUSSEL   Bacchus & Ariadne, Spiders Banquet
Paris Conservatoire Orchestra   Cluytens
Stereo Issue : SAX2562

33CX1922   B/Gold : **£10**   Red Semi : £5
Various   Music of Old Russia   Milstein   Irving
Stereo Issue : SAX2563

33CX1923   B/Gold : **£4**   Red Semi : £2
ROSSINI / DONIZETTI   Rossini and Donizetti Arias   Callas
Stereo Issue : SAX2564

33CX1924   B/Gold : **£4**   Red Semi : £2
BEETHOVEN   Symphony No.1, Symphony No.2
Cleveland Orchestra   Szell
Stereo Issue : SAX2565

33CX1925   B/Gold : **£20**   Red Semi : £10
BIZET   L'Arlesienne Suites 1 & 2, Carmen Suite 1
Paris Conservatoire Orchestra   Cluytens
Stereo Issue : SAX2566

33CX1926   B/Gold : **£5**   Red Semi : £3
Spoken Word   Hagadah - The telling   Kossoff
No Stereo

33CX1927   B/Gold : **£2**   Red Semi : £1
SCHUMANN   Dichterliebe   Prey
Stereo Issue : SAX2567

33CX1928   B/Gold : **£2**   Red Semi : £1
BRUCKNER   Symphony No.4   Philharmonia Orchestra   Klemperer
Stereo Issue : SAX2569

33CX1929   (==== Not Issued ====)

33CX1930   B/Gold : **£2**   Red Semi : £1
BEETHOVEN   Overtures Consec, Coriolan, Prometheus
Philharmonia Orchestra   Klemperer
Stereo Issue : SAX2570

33CX1931   B/Gold : **£2**   Red Semi : £1
HAYDN   Symphony No.88, Symphony No.104
Philharmonia Orchestra   Klemperer
Stereo Issue : SAX2571

33CX1932   B/Gold : **£3**   Red Semi : £2
VERDI   Aida (Highlights) Callas
Milan La Scala Orchestra   Serafin
No Stereo

33CX1933   B/Gold : **£6**   Red Semi : £3
BRAHMS   Symphony No.3   Cleveland Orchestra   Szell
Stereo Issue : SAX2572

33CX1934   B/Gold : **£1**   Red Semi : £1
MOZART   Figaro (Highlights)   Schwarzkopf
Philharmonia Orchestra   Giulini
Stereo Issue : SAX2573

33CX1935   B/Gold : **£2**   Red Semi : £1
WALTON / HINDEMITH   Variations On A Theme By Hindemith Etc
Cleveland Orchestra   Szell
Stereo Issue : SAX2576

33CX1936   B/Gold : **£3**   Red Semi : £2
BEETHOVEN   Piano Sonata No.1, Piano Sonata No.2 Richter-Haaser
Stereo Issue : SAX2574

33CX1937   B/Gold : **£2**   Red Semi : £1
BARBER / SCHUMANN   Piano Concerto,Song Of Orpheus
Browning, Rose   Cleveland Orchestra   Szell
Stereo Issue : SAX2575

33CX1938   B/Gold : **£2**   Red Semi : £1
BEETHOVEN   Symphony No.3   Cleveland Orchestra   Szell
Stereo Issue : SAX2577

33CX1939   B/Gold : **£1**   Red Semi : £1
VERDI   Falstaff (Highlights)   Schwarzkopf
Philharmonia Orchestra   Karajan
Stereo Issue : SAX2578

33CX1940   B/Gold : **£18**   Red Semi : £10
BACH   Concerto for 2 Violins   Morini, Milstein
Stereo Issue : SAX2579

317

33CX1941   B/Gold : **£1**   Red Semi : £1
GOUNOD   Romeo et Juliette (highlights)   Gedda
Orchestra of the Theatre National de L'Opera   Lombard
Stereo Issue : SAX2580

33CX1942   (===== Not Issued =====)

33CX1943   B/Gold : **£2**   Red Semi : £1
BRUCKNER   Symphony No.6 in A major
New Philharmonia Orchestra   Klemperer
Stereo Issue : SAX2582

33CX1944   B/Gold : **£10**   Red Semi : £5
SCHUMANN   Kinderszenen, Kreileriana   Annie Fischer
Stereo Issue : SAX2583

33CX1945   B/Gold : **£2**   Red Semi : £1
SCHUTZ   Christmas Oratio   Thamm
Stereo Issue : SAX2584

33CX1946   B/Gold : **£2**   Red Semi : £1
WOLF   Songs from the Romantic Poets   Schwarzkopf
Stereo Issue : SAX2589

33CX1947   (===== Not Issued =====)

33CX1948   B/Gold : **£2**   Red Semi : £1
MOZART   Overtures Figaro, Giovanni, Magic Flute
Cleveland Orchestra   Szell
Stereo Issue : SAX2587

33CX1949   B/Gold : **£9**   Red Semi : £5
STRAVINSKY   Symphony No.3 Movements, Pulchinella St
Philharmonia Orchestra   Klemperer
Stereo Issue : SAX2588

33CX5251   Red Semi : **£5**
ROUSSEL   Symphony No.3, Symphony No.4
Paris Conservatoire Orchestra   Cluytens
Stereo Issue : SAX5251

33CX5252 Red Semi : **£2**
MOZART Eine Kleine,Symphony No.25
Philharmonia Orchestra Klemperer
Stereo Issue : SAX5252

33CX5253 Red Semi : **£1**
BACH Arias from St Matthew Passion Schwarzkopf
Philharmonia Orchestra Klemperer
Stereo Issue : SAX5253

33CX5254 Red Semi : **£9**
MOZART Violin Concerto No.4, Violin Concerto No.5 Milstein
Stereo Issue : SAX5254

33CX5255 Red Semi : **£2**
SCHUBERT Piano Sonata No.14 & 19 Richter-Haaser
Stereo Issue : SAX5255

33CX5256 Red Semi : **£2**
MOZART Symphony No.29, Symphony No.33
Philharmonia Orchestra Klemperer
Stereo Issue : SAX5256

33CX5257 Red Semi : **£2**
BEETHOVEN Piano Sonatas Rosen
Stereo Issue : SAX5257

33CX5258 Red Semi : **£2**
STRAUSS Four Last Songs Schwarzkopf
Belgium Radio Symphony Orchestra Szell
Stereo Issue : SAX5258

33CX5259 Red Semi : **£2**
MOZART Serenade For 13 Wind Instruments
London Wind Quartet Klemperer
Stereo Issue : SAX5259

33CX5260 Red Semi : **£4**
BARTOK String quartet No.1 & 2 Juilliard Quartet
Stereo Issue : SAX5260

33CX5261   Red Semi : **£4**
BARTOK   String quartet No.3 & 4   Juilliard Quartet
Stereo Issue : SAX5261

33CX5262   Red Semi : **£4**
BARTOK   String quartet No.5 & 6   Juilliard Quartet
Stereo Issue : SAX5262

33CX5263   Red Semi : **£2**
BARTOK   Concert for Orchestra
Cleveland Orchestra   Szell
Stereo Issue : SAX5263

33CX5264   Red Semi : **£8**
VIVALDI   Concerto for Violin & Strings in D & A   Milstein
Milstein Chamber Orchestra
Stereo Issue : SAX5264

33CX5265   Red Semi : **£4**
RAVEL / FALLA   Rapsody Espagnola, Pavane, Love & the Magician
De Los Angles   Philharmonia Orchestra   Giulini
Stereo Issue : SAX5265

33CX5266   Red Semi : **£2**
HAYDN   Symphony No.100, Symphony No.102
Philharmonia Orchestra   Klemperer
Stereo Issue : SAX5266

33CX5267   Red Semi : **£2**
Various   Transcriptions for Piano   Rosen
Stereo Issue : SAX5267

33CX5268   Red Semi : **£2**
Various   Song Book   Schwarzkopf
Stereo Issue : SAX5268

33CX5269   Red Semi : **£2**
SCHUMANN   Symphony No.1   Philharmonia Orchestra   Klemperer
Stereo Issue : SAX5269

33CX5270   (===== Not Issued =====)

33CX5271   Red Semi : **£2**
SCHUBERT   String quartet No.9 & No.13   Juilliard Quartet
Stereo Issue : SAX5271

33CX5272   Red Semi : **£2**
SCHUBERT   Christa Ludwig Recital   Ludwig
Stereo Issue : SAX5272

33CX5273   Red Semi : **£2**
CHOPIN / LISZT   Piano Concerto No.2, Piano Concerto No.1   Rosen
Philharmonia Orchestra   Pritchard
Stereo Issue : SAX5273

33CX5274   Red Semi : **£2**
Various   Song Recital   Ludwig
Stereo Issue : SAX5274

33CX5275   Red Semi : **£12**
PROKOFIEV   Concerto for Violin & Orchestra No.1 & 2   Milstein
New Philharmonia Orchestra Giulini
Stereo Issue : SAX5275

33CX5276   Red Semi : **£2**
FRANCK   Symphony In D   Philharmonia Orchestra   Klemperer
Stereo Issue : SAX5276

33CX5277   Red Semi : **£7**
WAGNER   Szell Conducts Wagner Overtures
Cleveland Orchestra   Szell
Stereo Issue : SAX5277

33CX5278   Red Semi : **£2**
Various   Songs & Arias   Gedda
Stereo Issue : SAX5278

33CX5279   Red Semi : **£7**
BRAHMS   Symphony No.1   Cleveland Orchestra   Szell
Stereo Issue : SAX5279

33CX5280   Red Semi : **£5**
MOZART   Overtures, Symphony No.28, Symphonia Concertina
Cleveland Orchestra, Philharmonia Orchestra   Szell, Fruhbeck
Stereo Issue : SAX5280

33CX5281-2　　Red Semi : **£10**
MAHLER　　Symphony No.9
New Philharmonia Orchestra　　Klemperer
Stereo Issue : SAX5281-2

33CX5283　　Red Semi : **£2**
BRUCKNER　　Symphony No.6
New Philharmonia Orchestra　　Klemperer
Stereo Issue : SAX5283

33CX5284　　Red Semi : **£5**
BRAHMS　　Symphony No.2, Tragic Overture
Cleveland Orchestra　　Szell
Stereo Issue : SAX5284

33CX5285　　Red Semi : **£8**
BACH / VIVALDI　　Concerto in Amin., Concerto in Dmin. & A
Milstein　　Milstein Chamber Orchestra
Stereo Issue : SAX5285

33CX5286　　Red Semi : **£2**
Various　　Favorite Scenes of Otello, Boheme, Eug Oneg　　Schwarzkopf
Stereo Issue : SAX5286

33CX5287　　Red Semi : **£10**
MOZART　　Piano Concerto No.24 & No.27　　Annie Fischer
New Philharmonia Orchestra　　Kurtz
Stereo Issue : SAX5287

33CX5288-9　　Red Semi : **£15**
BRUCKNER　　Symphony No.5　　Philharmonia Orchestra　　Klemperer
Stereo Issue : SAX5288-9

33CX5290　　Red Semi : **£1**
MOZART　　Piano Concerto 25, Serenade No.12　　Barenboim
Philharmonia Orchestra　　Klemperer
Stereo Issue : SAX5290

33CX5291　　Red Semi : **£2**
DEBUSSY　　Piano Recital　　Rosen
Stereo Issue : SAX5291

33CX5292   Red Semi : **£4**
BRAHMS   Symphony No.4   Cleveland Orchestra   Szell
Stereo Issue : SAX5292

33CX5293   Red Semi : **£2**
Various   Recital   Prey
Stereo Issue : SAX5293

33CX5294   Red Semi : **£4**
BRUCKNER   Symphony No.3   Cleveland Orchestra   Szell
Stereo Issue : SAX5294

Columbia SAX series Stereophonic LP's

The Columbia SAX series of stereophonic LP's were launched in 1958. With the exception of SAX2526 and SAX2532, the earliest labels, from SAX2252 until SAX2539, are pale blue with silver lines and black lettering. These are referred to as **B/s** (Blue / silver) throughout this guide.

SAX2526, SAX2532 and all labels from SAX2540 onwards, have a red background with a black semicircle with the words Columbia printed around it in white. This is referred to as **Red Semi** throughout this section of the guide.

A third label, again red, but with a boxed logo and no semicircle was only used on later re-pressed records. Records with this label are generally worth about 10% of the first label price.

SAX2252 B/s : **£55** S/c : £15
BEETHOVEN Piano concerto No.5 Ludwig
Philharmonia Orchestra Gilels
Mono Issue : 33CX1490

SAX2253 B/s : **£250** S/c : £85
Various Encores Oistrakh
Mono Issue : 33CX1466

SAX2254-6 B/s : **£120** S/c : £40
VERDI Falstaff Schwarzkopf
Philharmonia Orchestra Karajan
Mono Issue : 33CX1410-2

SAX2257-8 B/s : **£80** S/c : £25
ORFF Die Kluge Schwarzkopf
Philharmonia Orchestra Sawalisch
Mono Issue : 33CX1446-7

SAX2259 B/s : **£80** S/c : £25
BEETHOVEN Sonata No.9, No.10, No.13 & No.14 Gieseking
Mono Issue : 33CX1519

SAX2260 B/s : **£35** S/c : £10
BEETHOVEN Symphony No.6 Philharmonia Orchestra Klemperer
Mono Issue : 33CX1532

SAX2261 B/s : **£100** S/c : £25
MUSSORGSKY Pictures at an Exhibition
Philharmonia Orchestra Karajan
Mono Issue : 33CX1421

SAX2262 B/s : **£75** S/c : £25
BRAHMS Symphony No.1 Philharmonia Orchestra Klemperer
Mono Issue : 33CX1504

SAX2263 B/s : **£300** S/c : £85
DVORAK / FAURE Cello Concerto, Elegie Starker
Philharmonia Orchestra Susskind
Mono Issue : 33CX1477

SAX2264   B/s : **£140**   S/c : £45
BRAHMS   Double Concerto, Tragic Overture   Oistrakh, Fournier
Philharmonia Orchestra
Mono Issue : 33CX1487

SAX2265   B/s : **£30**   S/c : £10
Various   Songs You Love   Schwarzkopf
Mono Issue : 33CX1404

SAX2266-8   B/s : **£300**   S/c : £80
ROSSINI   Barber Of Seville   Callas
Philharmonia Orchestra   Galliera
Mono Issue : 33CX1507-9

SAX2269-72   B/s : **£60**   S/c : £15
STRAUSS   Der Rosenkavalier Schwarzkopf
Philharmonia Orchestra   Karajan
Mono Issue : 33CX1492-5

SAX2273   (==== Not Issued ====)

SAX2274   B/s : **£65**   S/c : £20
OFFENBACH / ROSSINI / GOUNOD   Ballet Music
Philharmonia Orchestra   Karajan
Mono Issue : 33CX1588

SAX2275   B/s : **£45**   S/c : £15
DVORAK   New World Symphony
Berlin Philharmonic Orchestra   Karajan
Mono Issue : 33CX1642

SAX2276-7   B/s : **£175**   S/c : £50
BEETHOVEN   Symphony No.9   Philharmonia Orchestra   Klemperer
Mono Issue : 33CX1574-5

SAX2278   B/s : **£100**   S/c : £25
MOZART   Symphony No.25, Symphony No.40
Philharmonia Orchestra   Klemperer
Mono Issue : 33CX1457

SAX2279   B/s : **£70**   S/c : £15
STRAVINSKY   Firebird Suite   Philharmonia Orchestra   Giulini
Mono Issue : 33CX1518

SAX2280 B/s : **£150** S/c : £40
SIBELIUS Symphony No.2 Philharmonia Orchestra Kletski
Mono Issue : 33CX1332

SAX2281 B/s : **£85** S/c : £20
SCHUBERT Trio in Bb Op.99 Oborin Oistrakh Trio
Mono Issue : 33CX1627

SAX2282 B/s : **£85** S/c : £18
SCHUMANN / TCHAIKOVSKY Cello Concerto Fournier
Philharmonia Orchestra Sargent
Mono Issue : 33CX1407

SAX2283 B/s : **£25** S/c : £5
Various Elisabeth Schwartzkopf Sings Operetta
Schwarzkopf Philharmonia Orchestra Ackermann
Mono Issue : 33CX1570

SAX2284 B/s : **£45** S/c : £10
Various Recital Nilsson
Philharmonia Orchestra Wallberg
Mono Issue : 33CX1629

SAX2285 B/s : **£40** S/c : £10
TCHAIKOVSKY Swan Lake & Nutcracker
Philharmonia Orchestra Sawalisch
Mono Issue : 33CX1623

SAX2286-8 B/s : **£250** S/c : £75
PUCCINI Fanciulla del West Nilsson
Milan La Scala Orchestra Matatic
Mono Issue : 33CX1631-3

SAX2289 B/s : **£100** S/c : £20
BIZET Arlesienne Suites 1,2, Carmen Suitet 1
Philharmonia Orchestra Karajan
Mono Issue : 33CX1608

SAX2290-2 B/s : **£300** S/c : £75
CHERUBINI Medea Callas
Milan La Scala Orchestra Serafin
Mono Issue : 33CX1618-20

SAX2293 B/s : **£80** S/c : £15
VERDI Callas Portrays Verdi Heroines Callas
Mono Issue : 33CX1628

SAX2294 B/s : **£65** S/c : £12
Various Opera Intermezzi
Philharmonia Orchestra Karajan
Mono Issue : No 33CX

SAX2295 (═══ Not Issued ═══)

SAX2296 B/s : **£60** S/c : £12
WAGNER Wagner Recital Hotter
Philharmonia Orchestra Ludwig
Mono Issue : 33CX1542

SAX2297 B/s : **£35** S/c : £10
BEETHOVEN Piano Concerto 5 Arrau
Philharmonia Orchestra Galliera
Mono Issue : 33CX1653

SAX2298-9 B/s : **£70** S/c : £15
DONIZETTI L'Elisor D'Amore (Love Potion) Alva
Milan La Scala Orchestra Serafin
Mono Issue : 33CX1649-50

SAX2300 B/s : **£85** S/c : £20
Various Schwartzkopf portrays Romantic Heroines
Schwarzkopf Philharmonia Orchestra Ludwig
Mono Issue : 33CX1658

SAX2301 (═══ Not Issued ═══)

SAX2302 B/s : **£35** S/c : £10
TCHAIKOVSKY / BERLIOZ / SIBELIUS 1812, Hungarian March,
Rhapsody, Valse Etc Philharmonia Orchestra Karajan
Mono Issue : 33CX1571

SAX2303 B/s : **£55** S/c : £12
Various Philharmonia Concert
Philharmonia Orchestra Karajan
Mono Issue : 33CX1663

SAX2304   B/s : **£140**   S/c : £50
MOZART   Concerto No.3   Oistrakh
Philharmonia Orchestra   Galliera
Mono Issue : 33CX1660

SAX2305   (==== Not Issued ====)

SAX2306   B/s : **£30**   S/c : £8
TCHAIKOVSKY   Sleeping Beauty, Swan Lake
Philharmonia Orchestra   Karajan
Mono Issue : 33CX1065

SAX2307   B/s : **£500**   S/c : £80
BRAHMS   Violin concerto   Kogan
Philharmonia Orchestra   Kondrashin
Mono Issue : 33CX1692

SAX2308-10   B/s : **£60**   S/c : £15
HANDEL   Messiah
Royal Liverpool Philharmonic Orchestra   Sargent
Mono Issue : 33CX1668-70

SAX2311-14   (==== Not Issued ====)

SAX2315   B/s : **£150**   S/c : £45
BEETHOVEN   Violin concerto   Oistrakh
French Narional Radio Orchestra   Cluytens
Mono Issue : 33CX1672

SAX2316-17   B/s : **£200**   S/c : £45
DONIZETTI   Lucia di Lammermore   Callas
Philharmonic Orchestra & Chorus   Serafin
Mono Issue : 33CX1723-4

SAX2318   B/s : **£50**   S/c : £10
BEETHOVEN   Symphony No.1, Symphony No.8
Philharmonia Orchestra   Klemperer
Mono Issue : 33CX1554

SAX2319   B/s : **£20**   S/c : £4
WALTON   Belshazzar's Feast   Philharmonia Orchestra   Walton
Mono Issue : 33CX1679

SAX2320   B/s : **£ 65**   S/c : £15
Various   Mad Scenes   Callas
Mono Issue : 33CX1645

SAX2321   B/s : **£ 50**   S/c : £12
MAHLER   Fahrendedn Gesellen   Philharmonia Orchestra Boult
Mono Issue : 33CX1671

SAX2322   B/s : **£ 40**   S/c : £8
DVORAK   New World Symphony   Philharmonia Orchestra   Sawalisch
Mono Issue : 33CX1677

SAX2323   B/s : **£ 300**   S/c : £85
TCHAIKOVSKY   Violin Concerto   Kogan
Paris Conservatoire Orchestra   Silvestri
Mono Issue : 33CX1711

SAX2324   B/s : **£ 50**   S/c : £10
VERDI   OverturesPhilharmonia Orchestra   Serafin
Mono Issue : 33CX1684

SAX2325-6   (===== Not Issued =====)

SAX2327   B/s : **£ 200**   S/c : £50
BORODIN   Prince Igor   Philharmonia Orchestra   Matatic
Mono Issue : 33CX1654

SAX2328   B/s : **£ 65**   S/c : £15
BRAHMS   Piano Concerto No.2   Richter-Haaser
Berlin Philharmonic Orchestra   Karajan
Mono Issue : 33CX1680

SAX2329   B/s : **£ 150**   S/c : £45
LALO   Symphonie Espagnole   Kogan
Philharmonia Orchestra   Kondrashin
Mono Issue : 33CX1683

SAX2330   (===== Not Issued =====)

SAX2331   B/s : **£ 70**   S/c : £20
BEETHOVEN   Symphony No.2, Coriolan, Prometheus
Philharmonia Orchestra   Klemperer
Mono Issue : 33CX1615

SAX2332   B/s : **£30**   S/c : £6
CHOPIN   Waltzes 1-14   Malcuzynski
Mono Issue : 33CX1685

SAX2333   B/s : **£45**   S/c : £10
Various   Goeth Leider   Schwarzkopf
Philharmonia Orchestra   Boult
Mono Issue : 33CX1657

SAX2334   (==== Not Issued ====)

SAX2335   B/s : **£150**   S/c : £45
MOZART   Piano concerto No.20, Piano concerto No.23
Annie Fischer   Philharmonia Orchestra   Boult
Mono Issue : 33CX1686

SAX2336-7   B/s : **£40**   S/c : £10
STRAUSS   Die Fledermaus   Lipp
Philharmonia Orchestra   Ackermann
Mono Issue : 33CX1688-9

SAX2338   B/s : **£30**   S/c : £8
CHOPIN   The Six Polonaises   Malcuzynski
Mono Issue : 33CX1690

SAX2339   B/s : **£80**   S/c : £18
TCHAIKOVSKY   Romeo & Juliet   Philharmonia Orchestra   Markevitch
Mono Issue : 33CX1691

SAX2340   B/s : **£35**   S/c : £8
SCHUMANN   Frauenliebe und Leben   Ludwig
Mono Issue : 33CX1693

SAX2341   B/s : **£40**   S/c : £10
FALLA / RAVEL   3 Cornered Hat, Daphnis Et Chloe
Philharmonia Orchestra   Giulini
Mono Issue : 33CX1694

SAX2342   B/s : **£160**   S/c : £40
MENDELSSOHN   Symphony No.3, Hebrides
Philharmonia Orchestra   Klemperer
Mono Issue : 33CX1736

SAX2343   B/s : **£45**   S/c : £10
WEBER   Overtures Philharmonia Orchestra   Sawalisch
Mono Issue : 33CX1652

SAX2344   B/s : **£40**   S/c : £8
CHOPIN Piano Concerto No.2, Fantaisie in Fmin.
Malcuzynski   London Symphony Orchestra Susskind
Mono Issue : 33CX1695

SAX2345   B/s : **£85**   S/c : £18
MAHLER   Symphony No.4   Philharmonia Orchestra   Kletski
Mono Issue : 33CX1541

SAX2346   B/s : **£35**   S/c : £8
BEETHOVEN   Piano concerto 2   Arrau
Philharmonia Orchestra   Galliera
Mono Issue : 33CX1696

SAX2347   B/s : **£40**   S/c : £8
WAGNER   Klemperer conducts Wagner Vol.1
Philharmonia Orchestra   Klemperer
Mono Issue : 33CX1697

SAX2348   B/s : **£40**   S/c : £8
WAGNER   Klemperer conducts Wagner Vol.2
Philharmonia Orchestra   Klemperer
Mono Issue : 33CX1698

SAX2349   (==== Not Issued ====)

SAX2350   B/s : **£60**   S/c : £15
BRAHMS   Symphony No.4   Philharmonia Orchestra   Klemperer
Mono Issue : 33CX1591

SAX2351   B/s : **£80**   S/c : £18
BRAHMS   Symphony No.3, Academic Festival Overture
Philharmonia Orchestra   Klemperer
Mono Issue : 33CX1536

SAX2352   B/s : **£250**   S/c : £80
BEETHOVEN   Archduke Trio Op.97   Oistrakh   David Oistrakh Trio
Mono Issue : 33CX1643

SAX2353   B/s : **£75**   S/c : £15
WAGNER / VERDI   Soprano Arias from Wagner & Verdi
Lovberg   Philharmonia Orchestra   Susskind
Mono Issue : 33CX1651

SAX2354   B/s : **£80**   S/c : £15
BEETHOVEN   Symphony No.4, Consn of the House
Philharmonia Orchestra   Klemperer
Mono Issue : 33CX1702

SAX2355   B/s : **£200**   S/c : £50
RIMSKY-KORSAKOV / RAVEL   Caprice Espagnol, La Valse
Philharmonia Orchestra   Cluytens
Mono Issue : 33CX1699

SAX2356   B/s : **£60**   S/c : £14
MOZART   Symphony No.29, Symphony No.38
Berlin Philharmonic Orchestra   Karajan
Mono Issue : 33CX1703

SAX2357   B/s : **£70**   S/c : £14
TCHAIKOVSKY   Symphony No.4 Berlin Philharmonic Orchestra Karajan
Mono Issue : 33CX1704

SAX2358   B/s : **£35**   S/c : £7
MAHLER   Songs   Ludwig
Mono Issue : 33CX1705

SAX2359-61   B/s : **£200**   S/c : £45
PONCHIELLI   La Gioconda   Callas
Milan La Scala Orchestra   Votto
Mono Issue : 33CX1706-8

SAX2362   B/s : **£80**   S/c : £15
BRAHMS   Symphony No.2, Tragic Overture
Philharmonia Orchestra   Klemperer
Mono Issue : 33CX1517

SAX2363   B/s : **£35**   S/c : £7
SCHUBERT   Moments Musicaux, March in E   Arrau
Mono Issue : 33CX1709

SAX2364   B/s : **£55**   S/c : £10
BEETHOVEN   Symphony No.3   Philharmonia Orchestra   Klemperer
Mono Issue : 33CX1710

SAX2365   B/s : **£10**   S/c : £2
HANDEL   Messiah (Highlights)   Huddersfield Choral Society   Sargent
Mono Issue : 33CX1713

SAX2366   B/s : **£85**   S/c : £16
WOLF   Aus dem Italiensch Leiderbuch   Schwarzkopf
Mono Issue : 33CX1714

SAX2367   B/s : **£100**   S/c : £25
STRAUSS   Don Juan. Till Eulenspiegel
Philharmonia Orchestra   Klemperer
Mono Issue : 33CX1715

SAX2368   B/s : **£55**   S/c : £12
TCHAIKOVSKY   Symphony No.6   Philharmonia Orchestra   Giulini
Mono Issue : 33CX1716

SAX2369-72   B/s : **£200**   S/c : £45
MOZART   Don Giovanni   Schwarzkopf
Philharmonia Orchestra   Giulini
Mono Issue : 33CX1717-20

SAX2373   B/s : **£85**   S/c : £18
BEETHOVEN   Symphony No.5   Philharmonia Orchestra   Klemperer
Mono Issue : 33CX1721

SAX2374   B/s : **£75**   S/c : £20
Various   Light Music   Philharmonia Orchestra   Karajan
Mono Issue : No CX

SAX2375   B/s : **£50**   S/c : £10
PROKOFIEV / MOZART   Peter & Wolf, Toy Symphony
Philharmonia Orchestra   Karajan
Mono Issue : 33CX1559

SAX2376   B/s : **£35**   S/c : £8
Various   Recital   Moffo
Mono Issue : 33CX1728

SAX2377   B/s : **£50**   S/c : £10
ROSSINI / VERDI   Overtures
Philharmonia Orchestra   Giulini
Mono Issue : 33CX1726

SAX2378   B/s : **£60**   S/c : £12
ROSSINI   Overtures   Philharmonia Orchestra   Karajan
Mono Issue : 33CX1729

SAX2379   B/s : **£65**   S/c : £12
SIBELIUS   Symphony No.2
Philharmonia Orchestra   Karajan
Mono Issue : 33CX1730

SAX2380   B/s : **£50**   S/c : £10
TCHAIKOVSKY / WEBER   Piano Concerto No.1, Konzertst
Arrau   Philharmonia Orchestra   Galliera
Mono Issue : 33CX1731

SAX2381-4   B/s : **£175**   S/c : £45
MOZART   Marriage of Figaro   Schwarzkopf
Philharmonia Orchestra   Giulini
Mono Issue : 33CX1732-5

SAX2385   B/s : **£45**   S/c : £10
BEETHOVEN   Piano Sonata No.17, Piano Sonata No.30
Richter-Haaser
Mono Issue : 33CX1737

SAX2386   B/s : **£140**   S/c : £45
BEETHOVEN   Violin concerto   Kogan
Paris Conservatoire Orchestra   Silvestri
Mono Issue : 33CX1738

SAX2387   B/s : **£65**   S/c : £12
BRAHMS   Piano Concerto No.1   Arrau
Philharmonia Orchestra   Giulini
Mono Issue : 33CX1739

SAX2388   B/s : **£175**   S/c : £45
BRAHMS   Violin & Piano Sonatas No.1 & 2   Oistrakh
Mono Issue : 33CX1740

SAX2389   B/s : **£40**   S/c : £10
MOZART   Kleine Nachtmusik, Ave Verum Co
Berlin Philharmonic Orchestra   Karajan
Mono Issue : 33CX1741

SAX2390   B/s : **£50**   S/c : £12
Various   Piano Recital   Arrau
Mono Issue : 33CX1742

SAX2391   B/s : **£160**   S/c : £60
Various   Spanish Music   Iturbi
Mono Issue : 33CX1743

SAX2392   B/s : **£60**   S/c : £12
SIBELIUS   Symphony No.5, Finlandia
Philharmonia Orchestra   Karajan
Mono Issue : 33CX1750

SAX2393   B/s : **£90**   S/c : £20
MENDELSSOHN Midsummernights Dream
Philharmonia Orchestra   Klemperer
Mono Issue : 33CX1746

SAX2394   B/s : **£75**   S/c : £20
RAVEL   Piano Concerto In G And D   Francois
Paris Conservatoire Orchestra   Cluytens
Mono Issue : 33CX1747

SAX2395   B/s : **£75**   S/c : £15
HAYDN   Symphony No.98, Symphony No.101
Philharmonia Orchestra   Klemperer
Mono Issue : 33CX1748

SAX2396   (==== Not Issued ====)

SAX2397   B/s : **£85**   S/c : £18
SCHUBERT   Symphony In C   Philharmonia Orchestra Klemperer
Mono Issue : 33CX1754

SAX2398   B/s : **£80**   S/c : £18
MENDELSSOHN / SCHUMANN   Symphony No.4
Philharmonia Orchestra   Klemperer
Mono Issue : 33CX1751

SAX2399-2400   B/s : **£ 75**   S/c : £15
LEONCAVALLO   I Pagliacci   Gobbi
Milan La Scala Orchestra   Matatic
Mono Issue : 33CX1752-3

SAX2401   B/s : **£ 60**   S/c : £12
CHOPIN   Piano Sonata No.3, Fantasie in Fmaj.   Arrau
Mono Issue : 33CX1755

SAX2402   B/s : **£ 45**   S/c : £10
SCHUBERT   Recital   Fischer-Diesku
Mono Issue : 33CX1756

SAX2403   B/s : **£ 55**   S/c : £12
BEETHOVEN   Piano Concerto No.4   Richter-Haaser
Philharmonia Orchestra   Kertesz
Mono Issue : 33CX1757

SAX2404   B/s : **£ 45**   S/c : £10
Various   Promenade Concert   Philharmonia Orchestra   Karajan
Mono Issue : 33CX1758

SAX2405   B/s : **£ 30**   S/c : £7
DVORAK   New World Symphony   Philharmonia Orchestra Giulini
Mono Issue : 33CX1759

SAX2406   B/s : **£ 60**   S/c : £15
MOZART   Horn Concertos   Civil
Philharmonia Orchestra   Klemperer
Mono Issue : 33CX1760

SAX2407   B/s : **£ 125**   S/c : £25
BEETHOVEN   Piano Sonata No.27, Piano Sonata No.29 Richter-Haaser
Mono Issue : 33CX1762

SAX2408-9   B/s : **£ 100**   S/c : £20
BACH   Brandenburg Concerto
Philharmonia Orchestra   Klemperer
Mono Issue : 33CX1763-4

SAX2410   B/s : **£ 75**   S/c : £15
Various   French Operatic Arias   Callas
Mono Issue : 33CX1771

SAX2411   B/s : **£65**   S/c : £15
BRAHMS   Violin Concerto   Oistrakh
Philharmonia Orchestra   Klemperer
Mono Issue : 33CX1765

SAX2412-4   B/s : **£250**   S/c : £50
BELLINI   Norma   Callas
Milan La Scala Orchestra   Serafin
Mono Issue : 33CX1766-8

SAX2415   B/s : **£75**   S/c : £15
BEETHOVEN   Symphony No.7
Philharmonia Orchestra   Klemperer
Mono Issue : 33CX1769

SAX2416   B/s : **£35**   S/c : £8
TCHAIKOVSKY / MOUSSORGSKY Symphony No.2, Night on Bare
Mountain   Philharmonia Orchestra   Giulini
Mono Issue : 33CX1523

SAX2417   B/s : **£55**   S/c : £12
WEBER   Overtures Philharmonia Orchestra   Klemperer
Mono Issue : 33CX1770

SAX2418   B/s : **£200**   S/c : £55
TCHAIKOVSKY   Capriccio Italien etc
Milan La Scala Orchestra   Matatic
Mono Issue : 33CX1772

SAX2419   B/s : **£65**   S/c : £14
ROSSINI / RESPIEGHI / DUKAS   La Boutique Fantastique, L'apprenti
Sorcier   Philharmonia Orchestra   Galliera
Mono Issue : 33CX1776

SAX2420   B/s : **£60**   S/c : £14
BRAHMS   Symphony No.1   Philharmonia Orchestra   Giulini
Mono Issue : 33CX1773

SAX2421   B/s : **£60**   S/c : £12
Various   Ballet Music from the Opera
Philharmonia Orchestra   Karajan
Mono Issue : 33CX1774

SAX2422 B/s : **£35** S/c : £8
BEETHOVEN Piano Concerto No.5, Rondo in C Richter-Haaser
Philharmonia Orchestra Kertesz
Mono Issue : 33CX1775

SAX2423 B/s : **£18** S/c : £4
STRAUSS Der Rosenkavalier (Highlights)
Philharmonia Orchestra Karajan
Mono Issue : 33CX1777

SAX2424 B/s : **£50** S/c : £10
SCHUBERT / BRAHMS Symphony No.8, Variations On Theme By
Haydn Philharmonia Orchestra Giulini
Mono Issue : 33CX1778

SAX2425 (==== Not Issued ====)

SAX2426 B/s : **£80** S/c : £20
MOZART Piano concerto No.17, Piano Concerto No.26
Richter-Haaser Philharmonia Orchestra Kertesz
Mono Issue : 33CX1780

SAX2427-9 B/s : **£90** S/c : £25
MOZART Abduction from the Seraglio
Royal Philharmonic Orchestra Beecham
Mono Issue : 33CX1462-3

SAX2430-1 B/s : **£120** S/c : £35
BRAHMS German Requiem Philharmonia Orchestra Klemperer
Mono Issue : 33CX1781-2

SAX2432 B/s : **£55** S/c : £12
BARTOK / HINDEMITH Music For Strings,Perc & Celest, Mathis De
Maler Berlin Philharmonic Orchestra Karajan
Mono Issue : 33CX1783

SAX2433 B/s : **£10** S/c : £5
Various The Hoffnung Astronautical Music Festival Hoffnung
Mono Issue : 33CX1785

SAX2434 B/s : **£150** S/c : £50
DEBUSSY Recital Iturbi
Mono Issue : 33CX1788

SAX2435   B/s : **£130**   S/c : £40
BEETHOVEN   Piano Sonata No.18, Piano Sonata No.32   Annie Fischer
Mono Issue : 33CX1807

SAX2436   B/s : **£85**   S/c : £20
MOZART   Symphony No.35, Symphony No.36
Philharmonia Orchestra   Klemperer
Mono Issue : 33CX1786

SAX2437   B/s : **£75**   S/c : £18
STRAUSS   Tod Verklarung, Metamorphosis
Philharmonia Orchestra   Klemperer
Mono Issue : 33CX1789

SAX2438   B/s : **£30**   S/c : £8
ROSSINI   Barber Of Seville (Highlights)   Callas
Philharmonia Orchestra   Galliera
Mono Issue : 33CX1790

SAX2439   B/s : **£60**   S/c : £12
Various   Overtures   Berlin Philharmonic Orchestra   Karajan
Mono Issue : 33CX1791

SAX2440   (==== Not Issued ====)

SAX2441   B/s : **£80**   S/c : £20
MAHLER   Symphony No.4   Schwarzkopf
Philharmonia Orchestra   Klemperer
Mono Issue : 33CX1793

SAX2442-3   B/s : **£40**   S/c : £10
BIZET   The Pearl Fishers
Orchestra of the Theatre National de L'Opera   Dervaux
Mono Issue : 33CX1795-6

SAX2444   B/s : **£50**   S/c : £12
CHOPIN   Piano Sonata No.2, Piano Sonata No.3   Malcuzynski
Mono Issue : 33CX1797

SAX2445   B/s : **£50**   S/c : £10
POULENC   Gloria, Organ Concerto,Gloria In G Maj   Druffel
French National Radio Orchestra   Pretre
Mono Issue : 33CX1798

SAX2446-50   B/s : **£250**   S/c : £80
BACH   St. Mathews passion   Philharmonia Orchestra Klemperer
Mono Issue : 33CX1799-03

SAX2451-3   B/s : **£130**   S/c : £40
BEETHOVEN   Fidelio   Philharmonia Orchestra   Klemperer
Mono Issue : 33CX1804-6

SAX2454-5   B/s : **£175**   S/c : £60
BRUCKNER   Symphony No.7   Philharmonia Orchestra   Klemperer
Mono Issue : 33CX1808-9

SAX2456   B/s : **£20**   S/c : £5
ORFF   Die Kluge (Highlights)   Schwarzkopf
Philharmonia Orchestra   Sawalisch
Mono Issue : 33CX1810

SAX2457   B/s : **£25**   S/c : £5
ORFF   Der Mond (Highlights)   Christ
Philharmonia Orchestra   Sawalisch
Mono Issue : 33CX1811

SAX2458   B/s : **£100**   S/c : £20
TCHAIKOVSKY   Symphony No.6   Philharmonia Orchestra   Klemperer
Mono Issue : 33CX1812

SAX2459   B/s : **£30**   S/c : £6
WALTON   Symphony No.2, Partita   Cleveland Orchestra   Szell
Mono Issue : 33CX1816

SAX2460   B/s : **£40**   S/c : £8
WEILL   Threepenny Opera   Philharmonia Orchestra Klemperer
Mono Issue : 33CX1814

SAX2461   B/s : **£50**   S/c : £10
SCHUBERT   Symphony No.8   Philharmonia Orchestra   Giulini
Mono Issue : 33CX1815

SAX2462   B/s : **£85**   S/c : £15
BRAHMS / WAGNER   Alto Rhapsody, Wesendonk Leider
Ludwig   Philharmonia Orchestra   Klemperer
Mono Issue : 33CX1817

SAX2463   B/s : **£40**   S/c : £12
DEBUSSY   La Mer   Philharmonia Orchestra   Giulini
Mono Issue : 33CX1818

SAX2464   B/s : **£40**   S/c : £10
WAGNER   Klemperer Conducts More Wagner
Philharmonia Orchestra   Klemperer
Mono Issue : 33CX1820

SAX2465   B/s : **£50**   S/c : £10
CHOPIN   Mazurkas   Malcuzynski
Mono Issue : 33CX1821

SAX2466   B/s : **£50**   S/c : £12
BRAHMS   Piano Concerto No.2   Arrau
Philharmonia Orchestra   Giulini
Mono Issue : 33CX1822

SAX2467   B/s : **£80**   S/c : £18
STRAUSS   Also Sprach Zarathustra
Philharmonia Orchestra   Maazel
Mono Issue : 33CX1823

SAX2468   B/s : **£100**   S/c : £25
MOZART   Symphony No.38, Symphony No.39
Philharmonia Orchestra   Klemperer
Mono Issue : 33CX1824

SAX2469   B/s : **£60**   S/c : £20
DEBUSSY   L'Isle Joyeuse   Francois
Mono Issue : 33CX1825

SAX2470-2   B/s : **£250**   S/c : £85
MOZART   The Haydn Quartets   Juilliard Quartet
Mono Issue : 33CX1826-8

SAX2473-4   B/s : **£150**   S/c : £40
MAHLER   Symphony No.2   Philharmonia Orchestra   Klemperer
Mono Issue : 33CX1829-30

SAX2475   B/s : **£50**   S/c : £10
SCHUMANN   Symphony No.3   Cleveland Orchestra   Szell
Mono Issue : 33CX1831

SAX2476 B/s : **£85** S/c : £20
RAVEL Complete Orchestral Works V.1
Paris Conservatoire Orchestra Cluytens
Mono Issue : 33CX1832

SAX2477 B/s : **£85** S/c : £20
RAVEL Complete Orchestral Works V.2
Paris Conservatoire Orchestra Cluytens
Mono Issue : 33CX1833

SAX2478 B/s : **£85** S/c : £20
RAVEL Complete Orchestral Works V.3
Paris Conservatoire Orchestra Cluytens
Mono Issue : 33CX1834

SAX2479 B/s : **£85** S/c : £20
RAVEL Complete Orchestral Works V.4
Paris Conservatoire Orchestra Cluytens
Mono Issue : 33CX1835

SAX2480 B/s : **£60** S/c : £14
SCHOENBERG / STRAVINSKY Modern Music Rosen
Mono Issue : 33CX1836

SAX2481 B/s : **£100** S/c : £20
Various Gedda A Paris Gedda
French Narional Radio Orchestra Pretre
Mono Issue : 33CX1837

SAX2482 B/s : **£30** S/c : £8
CHERUBINI Medea (Highlights)Gorr Paris Opera Pretre
Mono Issue : 33CX1838

SAX2483 B/s : **£30** S/c : £8
TCHAIKOVSKY Romeo & Juliet
Philharmonia Orchestra Giulini
Mono Issue : 33CX1840

SAX2484 B/s : **£80** S/c : £18
MOUSSORGSKY / RAVEL Pictures at an Exhibition
Philharmonia Orchestra Maazel
Mono Issue : 33CX1841

SAX2485   B/s : **£160**   S/c : £50
SCHUMANN   Piano Concerto   Annie Fischer
Philharmonia Orchestra   Klemperer
Mono Issue : 33CX1842

SAX2486   B/s : **£120**   S/c : £25
MOZART   Symphony No.40, Symphony No.41
Philharmonia Orchestra   Klemperer
Mono Issue : 33CX1843

SAX2487   B/s : **£50**   S/c : £10
Various   The Red Army Ensemble Choral Concert
Red Army Ensemble
Mono Issue : 33CX1844

SAX2488   B/s : **£55**   S/c : £10
MAHLER / STRAUSS   Symphony No.10, Death & Transfiguration
Cleveland Orchestra   Szell
Mono Issue : 33CX1845

SAX2489   B/s : **£35**   S/c : £8
Various   Opera Excerpts   Prey
Berlin Symphony Orchestra   Stein
Mono Issue : 33CX1846

SAX2490   B/s : **£100**   S/c : £20
Various   Szell conducts Russian Music
Cleveland Orchestra   Szell
Mono Issue : 33CX1847

SAX2491   B/s : **£60**   S/c : £15
PONCHIELLI   La Gioconda (Highlights)   Callas
Milan La Scala Orchestra   Votto
Mono Issue : 33CX1848

SAX2492   B/s : **£45**   S/c : £10
DEBUSSY   12 Etudes   Rosen
Mono Issue : 33CX1849

SAX2493   B/s : **£50**   S/c : £12
BEETHOVEN / SCHUBERT   Symphony No.8, Symphony No.8
Cleveland Orchestra   Szell
Mono Issue : 33CX1850

SAX2494   B/s : **£70**   S/c : £15
TCHAIKOVSKY   Symphony No.4
Philharmonia Orchestra   Klemperer
Mono Issue : 33CX1851

SAX2495   B/s : **£50**   S/c : £15
STRAUSS   Don Quixote, Don Juan   Fournier
Cleveland Orchestra   Szell
Mono Issue : 33CX1852

SAX2496   B/s : **£50**   S/c : £10
SCHUMANN   Symphony No.2   Cleveland Orchestra   Szell
Mono Issue : 33CX1853

SAX2497   B/s : **£100**   S/c : £20
TCHAIKOVSKY   Symphony No.5   Philharmonia Orchestra   Klemperer
Mono Issue : 33CX1854

SAX2498   B/s : **£60**   S/c : £12
BRAHMS   Symphony No.2   Philharmonia Orchestra   Giulini
Mono Issue : 33CX1855

SAX2499-500   B/s : **£80**   S/c : £18
HANDEL   Solomon   Royal Philharmonic Orchestra   Beecham
Mono Issue : 33CX1397-8

SAX2501   B/s : **£45**   S/c : £10
STRAUSS   Till Eulenspiegel   Cleveland Orchestra   Szell
Mono Issue : 33CX1856

SAX2502   B/s : **£60**   S/c : £12
SCHUBERT   Piano Sonata in A   Rosen
Mono Issue : 33CX1857

SAX2503   B/s : **£45**   S/c : £12
Various   Callas a Paris   Callas
Mono Issue : 33CX1858

SAX2504   B/s : **£75**   S/c : £20
BEETHOVEN   String Quartet No.3, String Quartet No.6
Drolc Quartet
Mono Issue : 33CX1859

SAX2505　　B/s : **£40**　　S/c : £8
BEETHOVEN　　Songs　　Prey
Mono Issue : 33CX1860

SAX2506　　B/s : **£50**　　S/c : £10
SCHUMANN　　Symphony No.3　　Cleveland Orchestra　　Szell
Mono Issue : 33CX1861

SAX2507　　B/s : **£80**　　S/c : £20
PROKOFIEV / TCHAIKOVSKY　　String Quartet No.1, String Quartet No.1
Kroll Quartet
Mono Issue : 33CX1865

SAX2508　　B/s : **£90**　　S/c : £20
BEETHOVEN　　Violin concerto　　Milstein Philharmonia Orchestra
Mono Issue : 33CX1863

SAX2509　　B/s : **£50**　　S/c : £12
CHOPIN　　The four Ballades　　Malcuzynski
Mono Issue : 33CX1864

SAX2510　　B/s : **£60**　　S/c : £12
BEETHOVEN　　Symphony No.7　　Cleveland Orchestra　　Szell
Mono Issue : 33CX1869

SAX2511　　B/s : **£40**　　S/c : £10
LOEWE　　Carl Loewe Ballads　　Prey
Mono Issue : 33CX1866

SAX2512-3　　B/s : **£90**　　S/c : £20
BEETHOVEN　　Symphony No.9　　Cleveland Orchestra　　Szell
Mono Issue : 33CX1867-8

SAX2514　　B/s : **£50**　　S/c : £12
SCHUBERT　　Symphony No.5, Symphony No.8
Philharmonia Orchestra　　Klemperer
Mono Issue : 33CX1870

SAX2515　　B/s : **£50**　　S/c : £12
RACHMANINOV Piano Concerto No.3　　Malcuzynski
Warsaw Philharmonic Orchestra　　Rowiki
Mono Issue : 33CX1871

SAX2516   B/s : **£60**   S/c : £12
BRAHMS   Symphony No.3   Philharmonia Orchestra   Giulini
Mono Issue : 33CX1872

SAX2517   B/s : **£125**   S/c : £25
SCHUBERT   Symphony No.9   Cleveland Orchestra   Szell
Mono Issue : 33CX1874

SAX2518   B/s : **£160**   S/c : £50
VIVALDI   Four Concerti   Milstein Milstein Chamber Orchestra
Mono Issue : 33CX1875

SAX2519   B/s : **£80**   S/c : £20
SCHUBERT / HAYDN   String Quartet No.14, String Quartet
Kroll Quartet
Mono Issue : 33CX1876

SAX2520   B/s : **£80**   S/c : £20
BEETHOVEN   String Quartet 11   Kroll Quartet
Mono Issue : 33CX1877

SAX2521   B/s : **£50**   S/c : £15
CHOPIN   Preludes   Francois
Mono Issue : 33CX1878

SAX2522   B/s : **£50**   S/c : £12
SCHUMANN   Carnival, Davidsbundlertanze   Rosen
Mono Issue : 33CX1879

SAX2523   B/s : **£75**   S/c : £12
BEETHOVEN   Piano Sonata No.16, Piano Sonata No.18 Richter-Haaser
Mono Issue : 33CX1880

SAX2524   B/s : **£80**   S/c : £16
MENDELSSOHN Symphony No.4, Hebrides Overture
Cleveland Orchestra   Szell
Mono Issue : 33CX1881

SAX2525   B/s : **£30**   S/c : £6
BACH   Choruses & Chorales From St.Mathew's Passion
Philharmonia Orchestra   Klemperer
Mono Issue : No CX

SAX2526   S/c : **£30**
BRAHMS   Piano concerto 1   Fleisher
Cleveland Orchestra   Szell
Mono Issue : 33CX1882

SAX2527   B/s : **£20**   S/c : £5
WALTON   Shakespeare Film Scores
Philharmonia Orchestra   Walton
Mono Issue : 33CX1883

SAX2528   B/s : **£150**   S/c : £40
FRANCK   Symphonic Poems
Belgium National Orchestra Cluytens
Mono Issue : 33CX1884

SAX2529   B/s : **£65**   S/c : £12
MOZART / HAYDN   Symphony No.35, Symphony No.92
Cleveland Orchestra   Szell
Mono Issue : 33CX1885

SAX2530   B/s : **£75**   S/c : £20
BEETHOVEN   Quartet No.4, Quartet No.5   Drolc Quartet
Mono Issue : 33CX1886

SAX2531   B/s : **£350**   S/c : £100
Various   Sonatas for two Violins   Kogan
Mono Issue : 33CX1887

SAX2532   S/c : **£40**
DEBUSSY / RAVEL   La Mer, Daphnis et Chloe
Cleveland Orchestra   Szell
Mono Issue : 33CX1896

SAX2533   B/s : **£65**   S/c : £20
PROKOFIEV   Piano Concerto No.3, Piano Concerto No.5
Francois   Philharmonia Orchestra   Rowiki
Mono Issue : 33CX1889

SAX2534   B/s : **£40**   S/c : £10
BRAHMS   Piano Concerto No.2   Fleisher
Cleveland Orchestra   Szell
Mono Issue : 33CX1890

SAX2535 B/s : **£125** S/c : £40
SCHUBERT String Quartet 15 Juilliard Quartet
Mono Issue : 33CX1891

SAX2536 B/s : **£45** S/c : £12
STRAUSS Horn Concerto No.1 Cleveland Orchestra Szell
Mono Issue : 33CX1892

SAX2537 B/s : **£35** S/c : £10
BERLIOZ Symphonie Fantastique
Philharmonia Orchestra Klemperer
Mono Issue : 33CX1898

SAX2538 B/s : **£25** S/c : £6
HANDEL Dettingen Te Deum German Madrigal Choir
Mono Issue : 33CX1895

SAX2539 B/s : **£35** S/c : £12
Various Bohemian Carnival Cleveland Orchestra Szell
Mono Issue : 33CX1899

SAX2540 S/c : **£65**
MOZART / WEBER / BEETHOVEN Callas Sings Callas
Mono Issue : 33CX1900

SAX2541 S/c : **£40**
BRAHMS Piano Quintet Op 34 Fleisher Juilliard Quartet
Mono Issue : 33CX1901

SAX2542 S/c : **£35**
BEETHOVEN Leonore Nos.1-3, Fidelio Overture
Philharmonia Orchestra Klemperer
Mono Issue : 33CX1902

SAX2543 S/c : **£70**
BEETHOVEN Piano Concerto No.3 Richter-Haaser
Philharmonia Orchestra Giulini
Mono Issue : 33CX1903

SAX2544 S/c : **£50**
MOZART Mass in C
South West German Chamber Orchestra Gonnenwein
Mono Issue : 33CX1894

SAX2545   S/c : **£ 20**
STRAUSS   Sinfonia Domestica   Cleveland Orchestra   Szell
Mono Issue : 33CX1904

SAX2546   S/c : **£ 25**
MOZART   Symphony No.31, Symphony No.34
Philharmonia Orchestra   Klemperer
Mono Issue : 33CX1906

SAX2547   S/c : **£ 10**
BEETHOVEN   Fidelio (Highlights)Ludwig
Philharmonia Orchestra   Klemperer
Mono Issue : 33CX1907

SAX2548   S/c : **£ 100**
DEBUSSY   Jeux Enfants   Paris Conservatoire Orchestra Cluytens
Mono Issue : 33CX1908

SAX2549   S/c : **£ 125**
BEETHOVEN   Symphony No.6   Cleveland Orchestra   Szell
Mono Issue : 33CX1905

SAX2550   S/c : **£ 50**
VERDI   Arias   Callas
Mono Issue : 33CX1910

SAX2551   S/c : **£ 40**
LISZT   Don Juan Fantasy, Hungarian Rhapsody   Rosen
Mono Issue : No CX

SAX2552   S/c : **£ 85**
MOZART   Symphony No.41   Cleveland Orchestra   Szell
Mono Issue : 33CX1912

SAX2553   S/c : **£ 85**
MOZART   Symphony No.33   Cleveland Orchestra   Szell
Mono Issue : 33CX1913

SAX2554   S/c : **£ 50**
DVORAK   New World Symphony
Philharmonia Orchestra   Klemperer
Mono Issue : 33CX1914

SAX2555   S/c : **£ 35**
BRITTEN   4 Sea Interludes, Variations & Fugue from Purcel
Philharmonia Orchestra   Giulini
Mono Issue : 33CX1915

SAX2556   S/c : **£ 50**
MOUSSORGSKY / STRAVINSKY   Pictures at an Exhibition, Fairies Kiss
Cleveland Orchestra   Szell
Mono Issue : 33CX1916

SAX2557   S/c : **£ 50**
BEETHOVEN   Diabelli Variations   Richter-Haaser
Mono Issue : 33CX1911

SAX2558   S/c : **£ 40**
MENDELSSOHN   Quartets In A & D   Juilliard Quartet
Mono Issue : 33CX1917

SAX2559   S/c : **£ 10**
MOZART   Don Giovanni (Highlights)
Philharmonia Orchestra   Giulini
Mono Issue : 33CX1918

SAX2560   S/c : **£ 20**
ROSSINI   Overtures   Philharmonia Orchestra   Giulini
Mono Issue : 33CX1919

SAX2561   S/c : **£ 45**
BEETHOVEN   Piano Sonata No.3, No.22 & No.26   Richter-Haaser
Mono Issue : 33CX1920

SAX2562   S/c : **£ 70**
ROUSSEL   Bacchus & Ariadne, Spiders Banquet
Paris Conservatoire Orchestra   Cluytens
Mono Issue : 33CX1921

SAX2563   S/c : **£ 150**
Various   Music of Old Russia   Milstein   Irving
Mono Issue : 33CX1922

SAX2564   S/c : **£ 50**
ROSSINI / DONIZETTI   Rossini and Donizetti Arias   Callas
Mono Issue : 33CX1923

SAX2565   S/c : **£ 50**
BEETHOVEN   Symphony No.1, Symphony No.2
Cleveland Orchestra   Szell
Mono Issue : 33CX1924

SAX2566   S/c : **£ 250**
BIZET   L'Arlesienne Suites 1 & 2, Carmen Suite 1
Paris Conservatoire Orchestra   Cluytens
Mono Issue : 33CX1925

SAX2567   S/c : **£ 35**
SCHUMANN   Dichterliebe   Prey
Mono Issue : 33CX1927

SAX2568   (==== Not Issued ====)

SAX2569   S/c : **£ 30**
BRUCKNER   Symphony No.4   Philharmonia Orchestra Klemperer
Mono Issue : 33CX1928

SAX2570   S/c : **£ 35**
BEETHOVEN   Overtures Consec, Coriolan, Prometheus
Philharmonia Orchestra   Klemperer
Mono Issue : 33CX1930

SAX2571   S/c : **£ 30**
HAYDN   Symphony No.88, Symphony No.104
Philharmonia Orchestra   Klemperer
Mono Issue : 33CX1931

SAX2572   S/c : **£ 75**
BRAHMS   Symphony No.3   Cleveland Orchestra   Szell
Mono Issue : 33CX1933

SAX2573   S/c : **£ 10**
MOZART   Figaro Excerpts   Schwarzkopf
Philharmonia Orchestra   Giulini
Mono Issue : 33CX1934

SAX2574   S/c : **£ 45**
BEETHOVEN   Piano Sonata No.1, Piano Sonata No.2   Richter-Haaser
Mono Issue : 33CX1936

SAX2575   S/c : **£30**
BARBER / SCHUMANN   Piano Concerto,Song Of Orpheus
Browning, Rose   Cleveland Orchestra   Szell
Mono Issue : 33CX1937

SAX2576   S/c : **£25**
WALTON / HINDEMITH   Variations On A Theme By Hindemith Etc
Cleveland Orchestra   Szell
Mono Issue : 33CX1935

SAX2577   S/c : **£30**
BEETHOVEN   Symphony No.3   Cleveland Orchestra   Szell
Mono Issue : 33CX1938

SAX2578   S/c : **£10**
VERDI   Falstaff (Highlights)   Schwarzkopf
Philharmonia Orchestra   Karajan
Mono Issue : 33CX1939

SAX2579   S/c : **£200**
BACH   Concerto for 2 Violins   Morini, Milstein
Mono Issue : 33CX1940

SAX2580   S/c : **£12**
GOUNOD   Romeo et Juliette (highlights)Gedda
Orchestra of the Theatre National de L'Opera   Lombard
Mono Issue : 33CX1941

SAX2581   (===== Not Issued =====)

SAX2582   S/c : **£30**
BRUCKNER   Symphony No.6 in A major
New Philharmonia Orchestra   Klemperer
Mono Issue : 33CX1943

SAX2583   S/c : **£150**
SCHUMANN   Kinderszenen, Kreileriana   Annie Fischer
Mono Issue : 33CX1944

SAX2584   S/c : **£25**
SCHUTZ   Christmas Oratio   Thamm
Mono Issue : 33CX1945

SAX2585-6   (===== Not Issued =====)

SAX2587   S/c : **£ 30**
MOZART   Overtures Figaro, Giovanni, Magic Flute
Cleveland Orchestra   Szell
Mono Issue : 33CX1948

SAX2588   S/c : **£ 125**
STRAVINSKY   Symphony No.3 Movements, Pulchinella St
Philharmonia Orchestra   Klemperer
Mono Issue : 33CX1949

SAX2589   S/c : **£ 25**
WOLF   Songs from the Romantic Poets   Schwarzkopf
Mono Issue : 33CX1946

SAX5251   S/c : **£ 60**
ROUSSEL   Symphony No.3, Symphony No.4
Paris Conservatoire Orchestra   Cluytens
Mono Issue : 33CX5251

SAX5252   S/c : **£ 20**
MOZART   Eine Kleine,Symphony No.25
Philharmonia Orchestra   Klemperer
Mono Issue : 33CX5252

SAX5253   S/c : **£ 15**
BACH   Arias from St Matthew Passion   Schwarzkopf
Philharmonia Orchestra   Klemperer
Mono Issue : 33CX5253

SAX5254   S/c : **£ 125**
MOZART   Violin Concerto No.4, Violin Concerto No.5 Milstein
Mono Issue : 33CX5254

SAX5255   S/c : **£ 25**
SCHUBERT   Piano Sonata No.14 & 19   Richter-Haaser
Mono Issue : 33CX5255

SAX5256   S/c : **£ 25**
MOZART   Symphony No.29, Symphony No.33
Philharmonia Orchestra   Klemperer
Mono Issue : 33CX5256

SAX5257   S/c : **£25**
BEETHOVEN   Piano Sonatas   Rosen
Mono Issue : 33CX5257

SAX5258   S/c : **£25**
STRAUSS   Four Last Songs   Schwarzkopf
Belgium Radio Symphony Orchestra   Szell
Mono Issue : 33CX5258

SAX5259   S/c : **£20**
MOZART   Serenade For 13 Wind Instruments
London Wind Quartet   Klemperer
Mono Issue : 33CX5259

SAX5260   S/c : **£55**
BARTOK   String quartet No.1 & 2   Juilliard Quartet
Mono Issue : 33CX5260

SAX5261   S/c : **£55**
BARTOK   String quartet No.3 & 4   Juilliard Quartet
Mono Issue : 33CX5261

SAX5262   S/c : **£55**
BARTOK   String quartet No.5 & 6   Juilliard Quartet
Mono Issue : 33CX5262

SAX5263   S/c : **£30**
BARTOK   Concert for Orchestra
Cleveland Orchestra   Szell
Mono Issue : 33CX5263

SAX5264   S/c : **£100**
VIVALDI   Concerto for Violin & Strings in D & A
Milstein   Milstein Chamber Orchestra
Mono Issue : 33CX5264

SAX5265   S/c : **£50**
RAVEL / FALLA   Rapsody Espagnola, Pavane, Love & the Magician
De Los Angles   Philharmonia Orchestra   Giulini
Mono Issue : 33CX5265

SAX5266   S/c : **£30**
HAYDN   Symphony No.100, Symphony No.102
Philharmonia Orchestra   Klemperer
Mono Issue : 33CX5266

SAX5267   S/c : **£30**
Various   Transcriptions for Piano   Rosen
Mono Issue : 33CX5267

SAX5268   S/c : **£30**
Various   Song Book   Schwarzkopf
Mono Issue : 33CX5268

SAX5269   S/c : **£35**
SCHUMANN   Symphony No.1
Philharmonia Orchestra   Klemperer
Mono Issue : 33CX5269

SAX5270   (==== Not Issued ====)

SAX5271   S/c : **£30**
SCHUBERT   String quartet No.9 & No.13   Juilliard Quartet
Mono Issue : 33CX5271

SAX5272   S/c : **£38**
SCHUBERT   Christa Ludwig Recital   Ludwig
Mono Issue : 33CX5272

SAX5273   S/c : **£30**
CHOPIN / LISZT   Piano Concerto No.2, Piano Concerto No.1
Rosen   Philharmonia Orchestra   Pritchard
Mono Issue : 33CX5273

SAX5274   S/c : **£20**
Various   Song Recital   Ludwig
Mono Issue : 33CX5274

SAX5275   S/c : **£250**
PROKOFIEV   Concerto for Violin & Orchestra No.1 & 2
Milstein   New Philharmonia Orchestra   Giulini
Mono Issue : 33CX5275

SAX5276   S/c : **£35**
FRANCK   Symphony In D
Philharmonia Orchestra   Klemperer
Mono Issue : 33CX5276

SAX5277   S/c : **£80**
WAGNER   Szell Conducts Wagner Overtures
Cleveland Orchestra   Szell
Mono Issue : 33CX5277

SAX5278   S/c : **£20**
Various   Songs & Arias   Gedda
Mono Issue : 33CX5278

SAX5279   S/c : **£80**
BRAHMS   Symphony No.1   Cleveland Orchestra   Szell
Mono Issue : 33CX5279

SAX5280   S/c : **£65**
MOZART   Overtures, Symphony No.28, Symphonia Concertina
Cleveland Orchestra, Philharmonia Orchestra   Szell, Fruhbeck
Mono Issue : 33CX5280

SAX5281-2   S/c : **£140**
MAHLER   Symphony No.9
New Philharmonia Orchestra   Klemperer
Mono Issue : 33CX5281-2

SAX5283   S/c : **£20**
BRUCKNER   Symphony No.6
New Philharmonia Orchestra   Klemperer
Mono Issue : 33CX5283

SAX5284   S/c : **£60**
BRAHMS   Symphony No.2, Tragic Overture
Cleveland Orchestra   Szell
Mono Issue : 33CX5284

SAX5285   S/c : **£100**
BACH / VIVALDI Concerto in Amin., Concerto in Dmin. & A
Milstein   Milstein Chamber Orchestra
Mono Issue : 33CX5285

SAX5286   S/c : **£ 20**
Various   Favorite Scenes of Otello, Boheme, Eug Oneg
Schwarzkopf
Mono Issue : 33CX5286

SAX5287   S/c : **£ 150**
MOZART   Piano Concerto No.24 & No.27   Annie Fischer
New Philharmonia Orchestra   Kurtz
Mono Issue : 33CX5287

SAX5288-9   S/c : **£ 160**
BRUCKNER   Symphony No.5   Philharmonia Orchestra   Klemperer
Mono Issue : 33CX5288-9

SAX5290   S/c : **£ 15**
MOZART   Piano Concerto 25, Serenade No.12   Barenboim
Philharmonia Orchestra   Klemperer
Mono Issue : 33CX5290

SAX5291   S/c : **£ 30**
DEBUSSY   Piano Recital   Rosen
Mono Issue : 33CX5291

SAX5292   S/c : **£ 55**
BRAHMS   Symphony No.4   Cleveland Orchestra   Szell
Mono Issue : 33CX5292

SAX5293   S/c : **£ 35**
Various   Recital   Prey
Mono Issue : 33CX5293

SAX5294   S/c : **£ 50**
BRUCKNER   Symphony No.3   Cleveland Orchestra   Szell
Mono Issue : 33CX5294

HMV ALP series Monophonic LP's

The HMV ALP series of LP's were launched in 1952 and have red labels with gold lettering and the famous 'Nipper' picture in the top half of the label with the words 'His Masters Voice' printed in gold in a semi-circle around the picture. This label is the first label in all of the ALP series and are referred to as **Gold/Red** in this guide.

Later re-pressed copies of a few of the ALP series may be found to have the second ALP label. This is a red label with the words 'His Masters Voice' printed in bold white letters around the slightly reduced 'Nipper' picture and the lettering on the label is printed in Black. Although these are not common, they are not popular with collectors and as such, only have a nominal value of about 10% of the original label price.

With many of the earlier ALP records, the earliest outer jackets were Red and Cream gatefold sleeves, with a cloth strengthening strip on the hinged edge. The familiar 'Nipper' Logo is printed centrally in the upper red section and is flanked by royal 'by appointment' crests on both sides. The prices listed in this guide can be increased by 10% if the record is in its original Red and Cream outer sleeve.

ALP1001   Gold/Red : **£16**
TCHAIKOVSKY Symphony No. 5 in Emin.   La Scalla   Cantelli
No Stereo

ALP1002   Gold/Red : **£8**
TCHAIKOVSKY Sleeping Princess Ballet (Highlights)
Stokowski Orchestra   Stokowski
No Stereo

ALP1003   Gold/Red : **£16**
RAVEL   Mother Goose Suite
Boston Symphony Orchestra   Koussevitzky
No Stereo

ALP1004-6   Gold/Red : **£30**
VERDI   Rigoletto   Peerce
RCA Victrola Orchestra   Cellini
No Stereo

ALP1007   Gold/Red : **£10**
ROSSINI   Overtures
NBC Symphony Orchestra   Toscanini
No Stereo

ALP1008   Gold/Red : **£8**
BEETHOVEN   Symphony No.3
NBC Symphony Orchestra   Toscanini
No Stereo

ALP1009   Gold/Red : **£65**
MENDELSSOHN / RAVEL Piano Trio No.1, Piano Trio in Amin.
Heifetz, Piatigorsky
No Stereo

ALP1010   Gold/Red : **£12**
NIELSEN   Symphony No.4   Danish State Radio Orchestra Britten
No Stereo

ALP1011   Gold/Red : **£80**
HAYDN / BRAHMS   Symphony No.94 G, Variation Theme Haydn
Vienna Philharmonic Orchestra   Furtwangler
No Stereo

ALP1012 Gold/Red : **£8**
BRAHMS Symphony No.1
NBC Symphony Orchestra Toscanini
No Stereo

ALP1013 Gold/Red : **£8**
BRAHMS Symphony No.2
NBC Symphony Orchestra Toscanini
No Stereo

ALP1014 Gold/Red : **£15**
ELGAR Violin Concerto in Bmin op 61 Heifetz
London Symphony Orchestra Sargent
No Stereo

ALP1015 Gold/Red : **£8**
CHOPIN Concerto No.1 RCA Symphony Orchestra Steinberg
No Stereo

ALP1016 Gold/Red : **£30**
WAGNER Gotterdamerung Flagstad
Philharmonia Orchestra Furtwangler
No Stereo

ALP1017 Gold/Red : **£16**
RACHMANINOV Piano Concerto No.3 Horowitz
RCA Victrola Orchestra Reiner
No Stereo

ALP1018 Gold/Red : **£18**
DVORAK Symphony No.5
Chicago Symphony Orchestra Kubelik
No Stereo

ALP1019 Gold/Red : **£10**
FRANCK Symphony in Dmin.
San Fransisco Symphony Orchestra Monteux
No Stereo

ALP1020-1 Gold/Red : **£20**
PUCCINI Tosca Gigli
Orchestra of Rome Opera House De Fabritiis
No Stereo

ALP1022-4   Gold/Red : **£18**
ROSSINI   The Barber of Seville   De Los Angeles
Milan Symphony Orchestra   Serafin
No Stereo

ALP1025   Gold/Red : **£80**
TCHAIKOVSKY   Symphony No.4 Fmin Op 36
Vienna Philharmonic Orchestra   Furtwangler
No Stereo

ALP1026   Gold/Red : **£10**
PURCELL   Dido & Aeneas   Flagstad   Schwartz
No Stereo

ALP1027   Gold/Red : **£6**
WALTON   Symphony in Bbmin.   Philharmonia Orchestra Walton
No Stereo

ALP1028   Gold/Red : **£8**
CHOPIN   Polonaises   Rubinstein
No Stereo

ALP1029   Gold/Red : **£8**
BRAHMS   Symphony No.4
NBC Symphony Orchestra   Toscanini
No Stereo

ALP1030-5   Gold/Red : **£250**
WAGNER   Tristan & Isolde   Flagstad
Philharmonia Orchestra   Furtwangler
No Stereo

ALP1036-7   Gold/Red : **£20**
SCHUBERT   Die Schone Mullerin   Fischer-Dieskau
No Stereo

ALP1038   Gold/Red : **£10**
HAYDN   Symphony No.83, Symphony No.96
Halle Orchestra   Barbirolli
No Stereo

ALP1039-40 Gold/Red : **£12**
BEETHOVEN Symphony No.1 , Symphony No.9 Dmin Op125
NBC Symphony Orchestra Toscanini
No Stereo

ALP1041 Gold/Red : **£50**
BEETHOVEN Symphony No.6 F Op 68
Vienna Philharmonic Orchestra Furtwangler
No Stereo

ALP1042 Gold/Red : **£15**
TCHAIKOVSKY Symphony No.6 Bmin Op 74
Philharmonia Orchestra Cantelli
No Stereo

ALP1043 Gold/Red : **£6**
Various Through Childhood to the Throne Queen Elizabeth II
No Stereo

ALP1044-7 Gold/Red : **£28**
MOUSSORGSKY Boris Godunov Christoff
Orchestre National de la Radiodiffusion Francaise Dobrowen
No Stereo

ALP1048 ==== Not Issued ====)

ALP1049 Gold/Red : **£6**
SMETANA / MENDELSSOHN The Bartered Bride (Highlights)
Philharmonia Orchestra Kubelik
No Stereo

ALP1050 Gold/Red : **£30**
BEETHOVEN Violin Sonatas Menhuin, Kentner
No Stereo

ALP1051 Gold/Red : **£30**
BEETHOVEN Piano Concerto No.5 Edwin Fischer
Philharmonia Orchestra Furtwangler
No Stereo

ALP1052   Gold/Red : £5
ELGAR   Symphony No.1 Ab Op55
London Philharmonic Orchestra   Boult
No Stereo

ALP1053-5   Gold/Red : £12
SHAKESPEARE   Romeo & Juliet   Whelen
No Stereo

ALP1056-8   Gold/Red : £15
Various   Coronation Service of HM Queen Elizabeth II
No Stereo

ALP1059   Gold/Red : £75
BEETHOVEN   Symphony No.4
Vienna Philharmonic Orchestra   Furtwangler
No Stereo

ALP1060   Gold/Red : £80
BEETHOVEN   Symphony No.3 Eb Op 55
Vienna Philharmonic Orchestra   Furtwangler
No Stereo

ALP1061   Gold/Red : £10
HAYDN / SCHUBERT   Symphony No.10
Boston Symphony Orchestra   Munch
No Stereo

ALP1062   Gold/Red : £10
BEETHOVEN   Piano Sonata No.30 in E, No. 8 in Cmn   Solomon
No Stereo

ALP1063   Gold/Red : £12
Various   Traditional Spanish Songs   De Los Angeles
No Stereo

ALP1064   Gold/Red : £12
DVORAK   Symphony No.4   Philharmonia Orchestra   Kubelik
No Stereo

ALP1065   Gold/Red : **£10**
GRIEG / FALLA   Piano Concerto in Amin, Noches Jardin
Rubinstein   RCA Victrola Orchestra   Dorati
No Stereo

ALP1066   Gold/Red : **£15**
BEETHOVEN / SCHUBERT   Ferne Geliebte, Schwwanengesang
Fischer-Dieskau
No Stereo

ALP1067-8   Gold/Red : **£20**
DONIZETTI   L'elisiir D'amore   Santini
No Stereo

ALP1069   Gold/Red : **£8**
CHOPIN / SCHUMANN   Mazurkas, Kinderscenen   Horowitz
No Stereo

ALP1070   Gold/Red : **£8**
DEBUSSY / RAVEL   La Mer, Daphnis et Chloe
NBC Symphony Orchestra   Toscanini
No Stereo

ALP1071   Gold/Red : **£10**
Various   The Great Caruso (Soundtrack)   Lanza
No Stereo

ALP1072-3   Gold/Red : **£14**
VERDI   La Traviata   Albanese
NBC Symphony Orchestra   Toscanini
No Stereo

ALP1074   Gold/Red : **£15**
ROSSINI / BELLINI   Operatic Arias   Rossi-Lemeni
No Stereo

ALP1075   Gold/Red : **£12**
DVORAK   Symphony No.2   Philharmonia Orchestra   Kubelik
No Stereo

ALP1076   Gold/Red : **£6**
BRUCH   Ave Maria   Hammond
No Stereo

ALP1077-80   Gold/Red : **£12**
HANDEL   Messiah
Philharmonia Orchestra & Luton Choir   Beecham
No Stereo

ALP1081-2   Gold/Red : **£14**
PUCCINI   La Boheme   Albanese
NBC Symphony Orchestra   Toscanini
No Stereo

ALP1083   Gold/Red : **£12**
TCHAIKOVSKY   Symphony No.4
Chicago Symphony Orchestra   Kubelik
No Stereo

ALP1084   Gold/Red : **£50**
BACH   Brandenburg Concerto No.5 in D, No.2 in F   E. Fischer
No Stereo

ALP1085   Gold/Red : **£10**
MENDELSSOHN   Violin Concerto in Dmin., Violin Sonata in F
Menuhin   Philharmonia Orchestra   Boult
No Stereo

ALP1086   Gold/Red : **£10**
WAGNER / TCHAIKOVSKY   Siegfried Idyll, Rom
Philharmonia Orchestra   Cantelli
No Stereo

ALP1087   Gold/Red : **£10**
CHOPIN   Sonata Op.35, Ballade Op.23, Nocturne Op.15
Horowitz
No Stereo

ALP1088   Gold/Red : **£12**
SCHUBERT   String Quartet, Death & the Maiden
Amadeus String Quartet
No Stereo

ALP1089   Gold/Red : **£6**
WALTON   Belshazzars Feast
Liverpool Philharmonic Oirchestra   Walton
No Stereo

ALP1090-2   Gold/Red : **£15**
VERDI   Otello   Nelli
NBC Symphony Orchestra   Toscanini
No Stereo

ALP1093   Gold/Red : **£50**
BEETHOVEN   Violin Sonata No.9 in A Op 47   Heifetz
Moisewitche
No Stereo

ALP1094   Gold/Red : **£45**
BEETHOVEN   Sonata Pathetique, Sonata Appassionata
Edwin Fischer
No Stereo

ALP1095-8   Gold/Red : **£60**
WAGNER   Lohengrin   Frick
Hamburg State Opera Orchestra   Schuchter
No Stereo

ALP1099   Gold/Red : **£15**
VERDI   Operatic Arias   Rossi-Lemeni
Philharmonia Orchestra   Fistoulari
No Stereo

ALP1100   Gold/Red : **£15**
BEETHOVEN   Violin Concerto in D Op 61   Menuhin
Philharmonia Orchestra   Furtwangler
No Stereo

ALP1101   Gold/Red : **£8**
RESPIGHI   Fountains & Pines of Rome
NBC Symphony Orchestra   Toscanini
No Stereo

ALP1102   Gold/Red : **£10**
VAUGHAN-WILLIAMS   Symphony No.7   Halle Orchestra   Barbirolli
No Stereo

ALP1103   Gold/Red : **£35**
BACH / SCHUBERT   Concerto for 3 Pianos, Moments Musiceaux
Edwin Fischer   Philharmonia Orchestra
No Stereo

ALP1104   Gold/Red : **£250**
BRAHMS   Violin Concerto   De Vito
Philharmonia Orchestra   Schwartz
No Stereo

ALP1105   Gold/Red : **£20**
BEETHOVEN   Violin Sonata No.5 in F, Violin Sonata No.10 in G Op 96
     Menuhin
No Stereo

ALP1106   Gold/Red : **£6**
CHERUBINI / BEETHOVEN   Symphony No.D, Septet Efl
NBC Symphony Orchestra   Toscanini
No Stereo

ALP1107   Gold/Red : **£5**
PROKOFIEV / GERSHWIN Classical Symphony, American in Paris
NBC Symphony Orchestra   Toscanini
No Stereo

ALP1108   Gold/Red : **£6**
BEETHOVEN   Symphony No.5, Symphony No.8
NBC Symphony Orchestra   Toscanini
No Stereo

ALP1109   Gold/Red : **£20**
MOZART   Overtures
Philharmonia Orchestra   Kubelik
No Stereo

ALP1110   Gold/Red : **£10**
LISZT   Mephisto Waltz, Hungarian Rhapsody etc   Brailowsky
No Stereo

ALP1111   Gold/Red : **£10**
CHOPIN Ballades No.3 & No.4, Etudes etc   Horowitz
No Stereo

ALP1112-3   Gold/Red : **£20**
VERDI   Il Trovatore   Bjorling
RCA Victrola Orchestra   Cellini
No Stereo

ALP1114　　　Gold/Red : **£10**
MOZART / HAYDN　　　Symphony No.38, Symphony No.60
Glyndenbourne Festival Orchestra　　　　Gui
No Stereo

ALP1115-7　　　Gold/Red : **£30**
BIZET　　　Carmen　　　Merrill
RCA Victrola Orchestra　　　Reiner
No Stereo

ALP1118　　　Gold/Red : **£10**
RACHMANINOV　　　Symphony No. 3 in Amin.
BBC Symphony Orchestra　　　　Sargent
No Stereo

ALP1119　　　Gold/Red : **£6**
BEETHOVEN　　　Symphony No. 7 in A
NBC Symphony Orchestra　　　　Toscanini
No Stereo

ALP1120　　　Gold/Red : **£8**
SCHUBERT　　　Symphony No.9 in C
NBC Symphony Orchestra　　　　Toscanini
No Stereo

ALP1121　　　Gold/Red : **£80**
BARTOK　　　Violin Concerto　　　Menuhin
Philharmonia Orchestra　　　Furtwangler
No Stereo

ALP1122　　　Gold/Red : **£6**
SIBELIUS　　　Symphony No.2 D Op 43　　Halle Orchestra　Barbirolli
No Stereo

ALP1123　　　Gold/Red : **£6**
BRAHMS　　　Piano Concerto No.2 in Bb Op.83　　　Rubinstein
Boston Symphony Orchestra　　　Munch
No Stereo

ALP1124　　　Gold/Red : **£15**
BRUCH /MOZART　Violin Concerto No.1 in Gmin, Violin concerto No.5
Heifetz　　　London Symphony Orchestra　　　Sargent
No Stereo

371

ALP1125   Gold/Red : **£20**
MOZART   String Quintet in C K515   Amadeus Quartet   Aronowitz
No Stereo

ALP1126-8   Gold/Red : **£8**
MASCAGNI / LEONCAVALLO   Cavalleria Rusticana, I Pagliacci
Bjorling   RCA Victrola Orchestra   Cellini
No Stereo

ALP1129   Gold/Red : **£6**
BEETHOVEN   Symphony No.6
NBC Symphony Orchestra   Toscanini
No Stereo

ALP1130-2   Gold/Red : **£120**
BEETHOVEN   Fidelio   Jurinac
Vienna Philharmonic Orchestra   Furtwangler
No Stereo

ALP1133   Gold/Red : **£15**
ADAM / CHOPIN   Heart of the Ballet   Stokowski
No Stereo

ALP1134   Gold/Red : **£6**
BEETHOVEN   Symphony No.2
ABC Symphony Orchestra   Goossens
No Stereo

ALP1135   Gold/Red : **£10**
MENDELSSOHN / BEETHOVEN   Violin Concerto, Romance
Menuhin Philharmonia Orchestra   Furtwangler
No Stereo

ALP1136   Gold/Red : **£12**
CHOPIN   The 4 scherzi   Rubinstein
No Stereo

ALP1137   Gold/Red : **£20**
BERLIOZ   Symphonie Fantastique
San Fransisco Symphony Orchestra   Monteux
No Stereo

ALP1138   Gold/Red : **£10**
BRAHMS / MAHLER   Alto Rhapsody, Kindertotenleider
Anderson   RCA Symphony Orchestra   Monteux
No Stereo

ALP1139   Gold/Red : **£12**
BACH   Goldberg Variations   Landowska
No Stereo

ALP1140   Gold/Red : **£10**
Various   A Recital of Songs by the Scandanavian Dorumsgaard
Flagstad
No Stereo

ALP1141   Gold/Red : **£10**
BEETHOVEN   Piano Sonata No.29   Solomon
No Stereo

ALP1142   Gold/Red : **£120**
SCHUMANN   Carnival   Cortot
No Stereo

ALP1143   Gold/Red : **£10**
WOLF   Leider Recital   Fischer-Dieskau
No Stereo

ALP1144   Gold/Red : **£10**
BOCCHERINI   Quintet in Cmin Op.29, Quintet in G Op.60
Quintetto Boccherini
No Stereo

ALP1145   Gold/Red : **£5**
BEETHOVEN   Symphony No.2, Symphony No.4
NBC Symphony Orchestra   Toscanini
No Stereo

ALP1146   (===== Not Issued =====)

ALP1147-9   Gold/Red : **£30**
ROSSINI   La Cenerentola   Gabarain
Glyndenbourne Festival Orchestra   Gui
No Stereo

ALP1150-1 Gold/Red : **£30**
FALLA Vida Breve. Song Recital   De Los Angeles
No Stereo

ALP1152 Gold/Red : **£30**
BRAHMS Symphony No.1 in Cmin. Op.68
Philharmonia Orchestra   Cantelli
No Stereo

ALP1153 Gold/Red : **£18**
ELGAR Enigma Variations, Wand of Youth Suite
Philharmonia Orchestra   Cantelli
No Stereo

ALP1154 Gold/Red : **£10**
LISZT Piano Sonata in Bmin., Don Juan Fantasy   Cherkassky
No Stereo

ALP1155 Gold/Red : **£10**
MOZART / HAYDN   Symphony No.39, Symphony No.95
Glyndenbourne Festival Orchestra   Gui
No Stereo

ALP1156   (==== Not Issued ====)

ALP1157 Gold/Red : **£6**
CHOPIN Nocturnes   Rubinstein
No Stereo

ALP1158 Gold/Red : **£12**
DEBUSSY / LISZT / BEETHOVEN   Piano Recital   Iturbi
No Stereo

ALP1159 Gold/Red : **£6**
Various Christmas Carols   Royal Choral Society   Sargent
No Stereo

ALP1160 Gold/Red : **£10**
BEETHOVEN Piano Sonata No.21, Piano Sonata No.32   Solomon
No Stereo

ALP1161   (==== Not Issued ====)

ALP1162-5   Gold/Red : **£25**
GOUNOD   Faust   De Los Angeles
Paris Conservatoire Orchestra   Cluytens
No Stereo

ALP1166   Gold/Red : **£8**
BRAHMS   Symphony No.3 Fmin Op 90
NBC Symphony Orchestra   Toscanini
No Stereo

ALP1167   (==== Not Issued ====)

ALP1168   Gold/Red : **£10**
SCHUMANN   Fantasia, Carnival   Brailowsky
No Stereo

ALP1169   Gold/Red : **£25**
BEETHOVEN   Piano Sonata No. 30 in E, Piano Sonata No.31 in Ab
Hess
No Stereo

ALP1170   Gold/Red : **£6**
CHOPIN   Nocturnes Vol.2   Rubinstein
No Stereo

ALP1171   (==== Not Issued ====)

ALP1172   Gold/Red : **£10**
BRAHMS   Piano Concerto No.1   Solomon
Philharmonia Orchestra   Kubelik
No Stereo

ALP1173   Gold/Red : **£6**
STRAUSS / WAGNER   Don Juan Symphony No.Poem,
Gotterdammerung NBC Symphony Orchestra   Toscanini
No Stereo

ALP1174   Gold/Red : **£12**
Various   Italian Classic Songs of the 17th & 18th Century Gigli
No Stereo

ALP1175 Gold/Red : £8
RODGERS Victory at Sea   NBC Symphony Orchestra   Bennett
No Stereo

ALP1176-7 Gold/Red : £10
Spoken Word Shakespeare Macbeth   Alec Guiness   Old Vic
No Stereo

ALP1178 Gold/Red : £6
SCHUBERT Symphony No.9 in C   Halle Orchestra   Barbirolli
No Stereo

ALP1179-0 Gold/Red : £10
BERLIOZ Romeo & Juliet   Boston Symphony Orchestra Munch
No Stereo

ALP1181 Gold/Red : £12
BIZET Symphony in C, L'Arlesienne Suites
Stokowski Orchestra   Stokowski
No Stereo

ALP1182-3 Gold/Red : £12
BEETHOVEN   Missa Solemnis   Merriman
NBC Symphony Orchestra   Toscanini
No Stereo

ALP1184 Gold/Red : £15
BEETHOVEN   Archduke trio   Heifetz
No Stereo

ALP1185 Gold/Red : £15
ROMAN-TURINA   Canto a Sevilla   De Los Angeles
London Philharmonic Orchestra   Fistoulari
No Stereo

ALP1186 Gold/Red : £10
ROMBERG The Student Prince   Lanza
No Stereo

ALP1187 Gold/Red : £15
Various Song Recital by Bjorling   Bjorling
No Stereo

ALP1188-90   Gold/Red : **£16**
BACH   St. Johns Passion   Addison
RCA Symphony Orchestra   Shaw
No Stereo

ALP1191   Gold/Red : **£20**
Various   Song Recital   Flagstad
No Stereo

ALP1192   Gold/Red : **£6**
CHOPIN   24 Preludes   Rubinstein
No Stereo

ALP1193   Gold/Red : **£12**
SCHUBERT / TCHAIKOVSKY   Rosamunde, Nutcracker Suite
Stokowski Orchestra   Stokowski
No Stereo

ALP1194   Gold/Red : **£10**
MOZART   Piano Concerto K.450, Sonata K.331   Solomon
Philharmonia Orchestra   Ackermann
No Stereo

ALP1195   Gold/Red : **£80**
BEETHOVEN   Symphony No.5 Cmin Op 67
Vienna Philharmonic Orchestra   Furtwangler
No Stereo

ALP1196   Gold/Red : **£8**
MENOTTI   Amahl and the Night Visitors   Schippers
No Stereo

ALP1197   Gold/Red : **£60**
Various   Alfred Cortot plays Popular Encores   Cortot
No Stereo

ALP1198   (==== Not Issued ====)

ALP1199-1201   Gold/Red : **£100**
MOZART   Don Giovanni   Souez
Glyndenbourne Festival Orchestra   Busch
No Stereo

ALP1202   Gold/Red : **£10**
BIZET / FLOTOW / DONIZETTI   Operatic Arias   Lanza
RCA Victrola Orchestra
No Stereo

ALP1203   Gold/Red : **£10**
SCHUMANN   Symphony No.1   Boston Symphony Orchestra   Munch
No Stereo

ALP1204   Gold/Red : **£8**
BRAHMS / ELGAR   Haydn Variations, Enigma Variations
NBC Symphony Orchestra   Toscanini
No Stereo

ALP1205   Gold/Red : **£12**
SCHONBERG / VAUGHAN-WILLIAMS   Verklarte Nacht, Thomas
Tallis Fantasia   Stokowski Orchestra   Stokowski
No Stereo

ALP1206   Gold/Red : **£80**
Various   Encores   Heifetz
No Stereo

ALP1207   Gold/Red : **£50**
RAVEL / DUKAS Pavanne, Three Cornered Hat, Infante Defunte
Philharmonia Orchestra   Cantelli
No Stereo

ALP1208   Gold/Red : **£80**
STRAUSS   Don Juan, Till Eulenspiegel
Vienna Philharmonic Orchestra   Furtwangler
No Stereo

ALP1209   Gold/Red : **£15**
STRAUSS   Ein Heldenleben
Chicago Symphony Orchestra   Reiner
No Stereo

ALP1210   Gold/Red : **£12**
SIBELIUS   Symphony No.1   Stokowski Orchestra Stokowski
No Stereo

ALP1211 Gold/Red : **£20**
STRAUSS Don Quixote Piatigorsky
Boston Symphony Orchestra Munch
No Stereo

ALP1212 (==== Not Issued ====)

ALP1213 Gold/Red : **£8**
BRAHMS Piano Recital Rubinstein
No Stereo

ALP1214 Gold/Red : **£15**
STRAUSS Also Spracht Zarathustra, Dance of the 7 Veils
Chicago Symphony Orchestra Reiner
No Stereo

ALP1215-7 Gold/Red : **£16**
PUCCINI Madame Butterfly De Los Angeles
Orchestra & Chorus of the Opera House Rome Gavazzeni
No Stereo

ALP1218 Gold/Red : **£8**
MUSSORGSKY / FRANCK Pictures at an Exhibition, Psyche
NBC Symphony Orchestra Toscanini
No Stereo

ALP1219 Gold/Red : **£40**
FRANCK Symphony in Dmn
NBC Symphony Orchestra Cantelli
No Stereo

ALP1220 Gold/Red : **£60**
WAGNER / LISZT Lohengrin, Tannhauser Ov
Vienna Philharmonic Orchestra Furtwangler
No Stereo

ALP1221 (==== Not Issued ====)

ALP1222 Gold/Red : **£5**
DVORAK Symphony No.9 Emin Op 95
NBC Symphony Orchestra Toscanini
No Stereo

ALP1223   Gold/Red : £12
BUSONI   Arlecchino   Evans
Glyndenbourne Festival Orchestra   Pritchard
No Stereo

ALP1224   Gold/Red : £10
SAINT-SAINS / STRAUSS Carnival of the Animals, Fantasy
Rawicz   Halle Orchestra Barbirolli
No Stereo

ALP1225-7   Gold/Red : £15
BERLIOZ   Damnation Faust   Danco
Boston Symphony Orchestra   Munch
No Stereo

ALP1228   Gold/Red : £50
DEBUSSY   La Mer, Martyre St Se
Philharmonia Orchestra   Cantelli
No Stereo

ALP1229-31   Gold/Red : £15
VERDI   Falstaff   Valdengo
NBC Symphony Orchestra   Toscanini
No Stereo

ALP1232   Gold/Red : £6
GROFE   Grand Canyon Suite
NBC Symphony Orchestra   Toscanini
No Stereo

ALP1233   Gold/Red : £25
BRAHMS   Cello Sonata Op.38, Cello Sonata Op.99   Tortelier
No Stereo

ALP1234   Gold/Red : £18
VIVALDI   The Seasons   Virtuosi di Roma   Fasano
No Stereo

ALP1235   Gold/Red : £6
BEETHOVEN / BERLIOZ / SIBELIUS   Egmont, Carnival Romain,
Finlandia   NBC Symphony Orchestra Toscanini
No Stereo

ALP1236　　　Gold/Red : **£4**
TCHAIKOVSKY　Symphony No.5
BBC Symphony Orchestra　　　　Sargent
No Stereo

ALP1237-8　　(═══ Not Issued ═══)

ALP1239　　　Gold/Red : **£14**
MOZART　　　Symphony No.34, Symphony No.39
Chicago Symphony Orchestra　　Kubelik
No Stereo

ALP1240　　　Gold/Red : **£16**
STRAVINSKY　Petruchka　　　Stokowski Orchestra　Stokowski
No Stereo

ALP1241　　　Gold/Red : **£15**
VIEUXTEMPS / SAINT SAENS　　Violin Concerto No.5 in Amin
Menuhin　　　London Symphony Orchestra　　Fistoulari
No Stereo

ALP1242　　　Gold/Red : **£4**
ELGAR　　　Symphony No.2　Halle Orchestra　Barbirolli
No Stereo

ALP1243　　　Gold/Red : **£20**
CHOPIN　　　Piano Sonata No.2, Piano Sonata No.3　Schioler
No Stereo

ALP1244　　　Gold/Red : **£10**
IBERT / FAURE　Divertissement, Pelleas et Melisande
Halle Orchestra　Barbirolli
No Stereo

ALP1245　　　Gold/Red : **£10**
Various　　　French Music　Boston Symphony Orchestra　Munch
No Stereo

ALP1246　　　Gold/Red : **£12**
Various　　　A Recital of Harpsichord Music　Landowska
No Stereo

ALP1247   Gold/Red : **£15**
Various   Operatic Arias   Zinka
RCA Victrola Orchestra   Cellini
No Stereo

ALP1248   (==== Not Issued ====)

ALP1249   Gold/Red : **£8**
MOZART / HAYDN   String Quartet No. 15 in Dmin, String Quartet No.58
Amadeus Quartet
No Stereo

ALP1250   Gold/Red : **£10**
CHOPIN   Piano Concerto No.1   Rubinstein
Los Angeles Philharmonic Orchestra   Wallenstein
No Stereo

ALP1251   Gold/Red : **£8**
SCHONBERG / HINDEMITH   5 Pieces for Orchestra
Chicago Symphony Orchestra   Kubelik
No Stereo

ALP1252-4   Gold/Red : **£15**
VERDI   Ballo in Maschera   Peerce
NBC Symphony Orchestra   Toscanini
No Stereo

ALP1255-6   Gold/Red : **£5**
GILBERT & SULLIVAN   The Mikado   D'oyly Carte Opera
No Stereo

ALP1257-61   Gold/Red : **£120**
WAGNER   Die Walkure   Modl
Vienna Philharmonic Orchestra   Furtwangler
No Stereo

ALP1262-4   Gold/Red : **£15**
SHAKESPEARE MENDELSSOHN   Midsummer Nights Dream
Helpman   BBC Symphony Orchestra   Sargent
No Stereo

ALP1265
Various
No Stereo
Gold/Red : **£6**
Shakespear Songs and Lute Songs
Deller

ALP1266
Various
No Stereo
Gold/Red : **£14**
Russian Folk Songs
Christoff

ALP1267
MENDELSSOHN Symphony No.4, Symphony No.5
NBC Symphony Orchestra
Toscanini
No Stereo
Gold/Red : **£6**

ALP1268
BEETHOVEN Symphony No.6
NBC Symphony Orchestra Toscanini
No Stereo
Gold/Red : **£6**

ALP1269
CHAUSSON
Swarthout
No Stereo
Gold/Red : **£18**
Poeme de L'Amor et de la Mer, French Song Recital
RCA Symphony Orchestra
Monteux

ALP1270
MAHLER / BRAHMS
Fischer-Dieskau Philharmonia Orchestra
No Stereo
Gold/Red : **£30**
Lieder Fahrenden, Song Re
Furtwangler

ALP1271
BEETHOVEN
Edwin Fischer
No Stereo
Gold/Red : **£30**
Piano Sonata No.7, Piano Sonata No.32

ALP1272
BEETHOVEN
No Stereo
Gold/Red : **£10**
Piano Sonata No.23, Piano Sonata No.28 Solomon

ALP1273-5
MOZART The Magic Flute Berger
Berlin Philharmonic Orchestra Beecham
No Stereo
Gold/Red : **£12**

ALP1276   Gold/Red : **£14**
WAGNER   Parsifal (Act 2), Lohengrin (Act 3)   Flagstad
RCA Symphony Orchestra   Mc Arthur
No Stereo

ALP1277   Gold/Red : **£15**
Various   Italian Operatic Choruses
Rome Opera Orchestra   Morelli
No Stereo

ALP1278-9   Gold/Red : **£20**
ROSSINI   Petite Messe Solenelle   Acadamy St Cecil RO   Fasano
No Stereo

ALP1280   Gold/Red : **£16**
BEETHOVEN   Piano Concerto No.5   Horowitz
RCA Victrola Orchestra   Reiner
No Stereo

ALP1281   Gold/Red : **£10**
MOZART   Violin Concerto No.4 in D, Violin Conc.No.5 in A
Menuhin Philharmonia Orchestra   Pritchard
No Stereo

ALP1282   Gold/Red : **£350**
BRAHMS   Violin Sonata No.1, Violin Sonata No.3   De Vito
No Stereo

ALP1283   Gold/Red : **£8**
MOZART   String Quartet No.19 in C, String Quartet No.21 in D
Amadeus Quartet
No Stereo

ALP1284   Gold/Red : **£14**
Various   Recital   De Los Angeles
No Stereo

ALP1285   Gold/Red : **£20**
CHAUSSON   Violin Concerto   Menhuin
No Stereo

ALP1286-7   Gold/Red : **£400**
BEETHOVEN   Symphony No.9 Dmin Op 125   Schwarzkopf
Bayreuth Festival Orchestra   Furtwangler
No Stereo

ALP1288   Gold/Red : **£40**
BRUCH / KORNGOLD   Scottish Fantasia, Violin Concerto in D
Heifetz   Los Angeles Philharmonic Orchestra   Wallenstein
No Stereo

ALP1289-92   Gold/Red : **£30**
VERDI   Don Carlos   Christoff
Orchestra of Rome Opera House   Santini
No Stereo

ALP1293-4   Gold/Red : **£8**
GILBERT & SULLIVAN   HMS Pinafore   Sargent
No Stereo

ALP1295   Gold/Red : **£8**
SCHUBERT   Song Recital   Fischer-Dieskau
No Stereo

ALP1296   Gold/Red : **£8**
SAINT-SAINS   Symphony No.3
NBC Symphony Orchestra   Toscanini
No Stereo

ALP1297   Gold/Red : **£8**
BRAHMS   Piano Concerto No.1 in Dmin Op 15   Rubinstein
Chicago Symphony Orchestra   Reiner
No Stereo

ALP1298-9   Gold/Red : **£12**
SCHUBERT   Winterreise   Fischer-Dieskau
No Stereo

ALP1300   Gold/Red : **£8**
BEETHOVEN   Emperor Concerto   Solomon
Philharmonia Orchestra
No Stereo

ALP1301   Gold/Red : **£10**
Various   Homage to Pavlova
Philharmonia Orchestra   Kurtz
No Stereo

ALP1302   Gold/Red : **£8**
SEIBER   String Quartet No.2, Quartetto Lirico   Amedeus Quartet
No Stereo

ALP1303   Gold/Red : **£20**
BEETHOVEN   Piano Sonata No.17, Piano Sonata No.18   Solomon
No Stereo

ALP1304-5   Gold/Red : **£15**
BEETHOVEN   Fidelio   Peerce
NBC Symphony Orchestra   Toscanini
No Stereo

ALP1306   Gold/Red : **£15**
DVORAK   Cello Concerto in Bmin Op 104   Tortelier
Philharmonia Orchestra   Sargent
No Stereo

ALP1307   Gold/Red : **£8**
MOZART   String Quartet in Dmaj. , String Quartet in Bbmaj
Amadeus String Quartet
No Stereo

ALP1308   Gold/Red : **£16**
SAINT-SAINS   Sceanes from Sampson & Delilah   Peerce
NBC Symphony Orchestra   Stokowski
No Stereo

ALP1309   Gold/Red : **£14**
Various   Song Recital   Flagstad
No Stereo

ALP1310   Gold/Red : **£6**
CHOPIN Etudes Opus 10 No.1 - 12   Cherkassky
No Stereo

ALP1311 Gold/Red : **£6**
CHOPIN Etudes Opus 25 No.1 - 13 Cherkassky
No Stereo

ALP1312-15 Gold/Red : **£16**
MOZART Marriage of Figaro Glyndebourne Orchestra Gui
Stereo Issue : ASD 274-7

ALP1316 Gold/Red : **£10**
MOZART Piano Concerto K.448 & K.491 Solomon
Philharmonia Orchestra Menges
No Stereo

ALP1317-8 Gold/Red : **£20**
BEETHOVEN Songs Vol.1 & 2 Fischer-Dieskau
No Stereo

ALP1319 Gold/Red : **£300**
BEETHOVEN Violin Sonata No.9 in A, Op.47 De Vito Aprea
No Stereo

ALP1320 Gold/Red : **£20**
GRANADOS Goyescas Iturbi
No Stereo

ALP1321 Gold/Red : **£8**
SAINT-SAINS / CHOPIN Piano Concerto No.4, Piano Concerto No.2
Brailowsky Boston Symphony Orchestra Munch
No Stereo

ALP1322 Gold/Red : **£10**
SHOSTAKOVICH Symphony No.10 Philharmonia Orchestra Kurtz
No Stereo

ALP1323 Gold/Red : **£12**
RIMSKY-KORSAKOV Boris Godunov
French Nationl Radio Orchestra Dobrowen
No Stereo

ALP1324 Gold/Red : **£100**
BEETHOVEN Symphony No.1, Leonore Overture
Vienna Philharmonic Orchestra Furtwangler
No Stereo

ALP1325   Gold/Red : **£10**
SCHUBERT / MENDELSSOHN   Symphony No.8 Bmin, Symphony No.4 A
Philharmonia Orchestra   Cantelli
No Stereo

ALP1326-9   Gold/Red : **£30**
PUCCINI / ALBANES   Manon Lescaut,
Orchestra of Rome Opera House   Perlea
No Stereo

ALP1330   Gold/Red : **£15**
MOZART   Symphony No.40, Symphony No.41
Chicago Symphony Orchestra   Reiner
No Stereo

ALP1331   Gold/Red : **£20**
MOZART   Violin Sonata No.10 Bb K378,Violin Sonata No.15
Heifetz   Brookes-Smith
No Stereo

ALP1332   Gold/Red : **£8**
BOCCHERINI   Quintet Op.13/3 & 18/1   Quintetto Boccherini
No Stereo

ALP1333   Gold/Red : **£6**
CHOPIN   Valses 1-14   Rubinstein
No Stereo

ALP1334   Gold/Red : **£15**
BRAHMS   Violin Concerto in D Op 77   Heifetz
Chicago Symphony Orchestra   Reiner
No Stereo

ALP1335   Gold/Red : **£10**
VILLA-LOBOS / SIBELIUS / STRAUSS   Bachianas, Swan, Die Leibe
der Danae   Halle Orchestra   Barbirolli
No Stereo

ALP1336   Gold/Red : **£15**
TCHAIKOVSKY / SAINT-SAENS   Variations on a Rococco Theme
Tortelier   Philharmonia Orchestra   Menges
No Stereo

ALP1337
SCHUBERT
No Stereo

Gold/Red : £8
Quartet No.10   Amedeus Quartet

ALP1338
BEETHOVEN
Menuhin
No Stereo

Gold/Red : £15
Violin Sonata No.2 in A, Violin Sonata No.4 Amn

ALP1339
RIMSKY-KORSAKOV
Philharmonia Orchestra
No Stereo

Gold/Red : £8
Scheherazade   Parikian
Stokowski

ALP1340
CLEMENTI
No Stereo

Gold/Red : £16
Piano Sonatas   Horowitz

ALP1341-3
Spoken Word
No Stereo

Gold/Red : £12
Shakespeare Richard III   London Film Production

ALP1344
Various
No Stereo

Gold/Red : £20
Concertos   Virtuosi di Roma   Fasano

ALP1345
BEETHOVEN
No Stereo

Gold/Red : £30
Cello Sonata Op 5/1   Piatigorsky

ALP1346
BEETHOVEN
No Stereo

Gold/Red : £30
Cello Sonata Op.5/2 and Op.69   Piatigorsky

ALP1347
BEETHOVEN
Piatigorsky
No Stereo

Gold/Red : £30
Cello Sonata Op 102/1, Cello Sonata Op. 102/2

ALP1348   (==== Not Issued ====)

389

ALP1349   Gold/Red : **£ 12**
PROKOFIEV / SHOSTAKOVITCH   Piano Concerto No.2, Concerto for
Piano Trumpet & Strings   Cherkassky
Philharmonia Orchestra   Menges
No Stereo

ALP1350   Gold/Red : **£ 15**
SIBELIUS / PAGANINI   Violin Concerto in Dmin, Violin Concerto
Menuhin   London Philharmonic Orchestra   Boult
No Stereo

ALP1351-2   Gold/Red : **£ 18**
BRAHMS   German Requiem Grummer
Berlin Philharmonic Orchestra   Kempe
No Stereo

ALP1353   Gold/Red : **£ 18**
BIZET / DONIZETTI / MASCAGNINI   Operatic Duets   Carosio
No Stereo

ALP1354   Gold/Red : **£ 25**
BEETHOVEN   Violin Sonatas   Menuhin
No Stereo

ALP1355   Gold/Red : **£ 8**
PUCCINI   Il Tabarro   Gobbi
Orchestra of Rome Opera House   Belezza
No Stereo

ALP1356   Gold/Red : **£ 6**
TCHAIKOVSKY   Symphony No.6 Bmin Op 74
Boston Symphony Orchestra   Monteux
No Stereo

ALP1357   Gold/Red : **£ 12**
GLUCK   Orfeo ed Euridice (Act 2)   Merriman
NBC Symphony Orchestra   Toscanini
No Stereo

ALP1358   Gold/Red : **£ 16**
BRAHMS   Piano Sonata Op.5   Solomon
No Stereo

ALP1359   Gold/Red : **£5**
ELGAR   Overture "In The South"
London Philharmonic Orchestra   Boult
No Stereo

ALP1360   Gold/Red : **£8**
BACH / SCUBERT / BRAHMS   Komm Jesu komm, Mass No.2, Three
songs   Robert Shaw Chorale   Shaw
No Stereo

ALP1361   Gold/Red : **£8**
BOCCHERINI   Quintet Op.28, 10/5 & 41/2   Quintetto Boccherini
No Stereo

ALP1362   Gold/Red : **£30**
BRUCH / WIENIAWSKI   Violin Concerto No.2 in Dmin, Violin Concerto
Heifetz   RCA Victrola Orchestra   Soloman
No Stereo

ALP1363   Gold/Red : **£8**
VERDI / BOITO   Te Deum, Mefistofele prolog
NBC Symphony Orchestra   Toscanini
No Stereo

ALP1364   (==== Not Issued ====)

ALP1365   Gold/Red : **£10**
Soundtrack   Serenade   Lanza
No Stereo

ALP1366   Gold/Red : **£18**
VERDI   Soprano Arias   Stella   Curiel
No Stereo

ALP1367   (==== Not Issued ====)

ALP1368   Gold/Red : **£10**
DEBUSSY / BERLIOZ   La Damoiselle Elue, Les Nuits d'ete
De Los Angeles   Boston Symphonu Orchestra   Munch
No Stereo

ALP1369-70   Gold/Red : £16
BOITO   Mefistofele   Christoff
Rome Opera Orchestra   Gui
No Stereo

ALP1371   Gold/Red : £6
VERDI   Forza del Destino (Highlights)   Milanov
No Stereo

ALP1372   Gold/Red : £8
TCHAIKOVSKY / DVORAK   Suite No.3, Symphonic Variations
Philharmonia Orchestra   Sargent
No Stereo

ALP1373   Gold/Red : £8
SCHUBERT   Quintet in C Op.163   Quintetto Boccherini
No Stereo

ALP1374   Gold/Red : £12
RAVEL   Daphnis et Chloe   Boston Symphony Orchestra   Munch
No Stereo

ALP1375   Gold/Red : £6
Spoken Word   Shakespeare : Hamlet, Henry V, etc.   Olivier
Philharmonia Orchestra   Mathieson
No Stereo

ALP1376   Gold/Red : £15
BEETHOVEN   Violin Sonata No.8 in G, No.9 in A   Menuhin
No Stereo

ALP1377   Gold/Red : £8
STRAVINSKY   The Soldiers Tale   Prichard
No Stereo

ALP1378   Gold/Red : £8
FRIMI   Vagabond King   Rene
No Stereo

ALP1379   Gold/Red : £5
ELGAR   Marches, Froissart, Dream Children
London Philharmonic Orchestra   Boult
No Stereo

ALP1380-1   Gold/Red : **£16**
VERDI   Requiem Mass   Stefano
NBC Symphony Orchestra   Toscanini
No Stereo

ALP1382-3   Gold/Red : **£25**
BACH   Suites No.1 - 4
Chicago Symphony Orchestra   Reiner
No Stereo

ALP1384   Gold/Red : **£12**
BERLIOZ   Symphonie Fantastique
Boston Symphony Orchestra   Munch
No Stereo

ALP1385   Gold/Red : **£8**
BOCCHERINI   Quintet Op.11/6, Largo Op.12/1, Quintet Op.40/4
Quintetto Boccherini
No Stereo

ALP1386   Gold/Red : **£50**
BRAHMS   Symphony No.2 D Op 73
Berlin Philharmonic Orchestra   Kempe
No Stereo

ALP1387   Gold/Red : **£8**
Various   Restful Music   NBC Symphony Orchestra   Toscanini
No Stereo

ALP1388-90   Gold/Red : **£20**
VERDI   Aida   Bjorling
Rome Opera Orchestra   Perlea
No Stereo

ALP1391   Gold/Red : **£2**
VERDI   Il Trovatore (Highlights)   Bjorling
RCA Victrola Orchestra   Cellini
No Stereo

ALP1392   Gold/Red : **£3**
VERDI   Rigoletto (Highlights)   Peerce
RCA Victrola Orchestra   Cellini
No Stereo

ALP1393
Various
No Stereo
Gold/Red : £12
Five Centures Of Spanish Song   De Los Angeles

ALP1394-7
MASSENET
No Stereo
Gold/Red : £35
Manon   De Los Angeles   Opera Comique   Monteux

ALP1398-1400
CHOPIN
No Stereo
Gold/Red : £6
Mazurkas No.1 – 51   Rubinstein

ALP1401
CHOPIN
No Stereo
Gold/Red : £10
Piano Sonata No.2, Piano Sonata No.3   Brailowsky

ALP1402
TCHAIKOVSKY   Piano Concerto No.1   Gilels
Chicago Symphony Orchestra   Reiner
No Stereo

ALP1403
MOZART   Symphony No.36, Symphony No.39
Chicago Symphony Orchestra   Reiner
No Stereo

ALP1404
STRAUSS   Till Eulenspiegel, Death and Transfiguration
NBC Symphony Orchestra   Toscanini
No Stereo

ALP1405
Various
No Stereo
Gold/Red : £18
The Magic Mario   Lanza

ALP1406
BOCCHERINI   Quintet Op.25/3, Largo, Cantabile, Quintet Op.25/1
Quintetto Boccherini
No Stereo

ALP1407   Gold/Red : **£ 8**
VERDI   Opera Recital   Hammond
Philharmonia Orchestra   Curiel
No Stereo

ALP1408   Gold/Red : **£ 9**
BEETHOVEN   Symphony No.6 F Op 68
Berlin Philharmonic Orchestra   Cluytens
No Stereo

ALP1409-10   Gold/Red : **£ 10**
PUCCINI   La Boheme   De Los Angeles
No Stereo

ALP1411   Gold/Red : **£ 70**
PROKOFIEV / LECLAIR / LOCAT   Violin Sonata No.1, Violin Sonata
No.3   Oistrakh   Yampolsky
No Stereo

ALP1412   Gold/Red : **£ 6**
CHERUBINI   Requiem   NBC Symphony Orchestra   Toscanini
No Stereo

ALP1413   Gold/Red : **£ 12**
RACHMANINOV / LISZT   Piano Concerto No.2, Piano Concerto No.1
Rubinstein   Chicago Symphony Orchestra   Reiner
No Stereo

ALP1414   Gold/Red : **£ 12**
RACHMANINOV / GRIEG   Rhapsody on a theme of Paganini, Piano
Concerto Rubinstein   Chicago Symphony Orchestra   Reiner
No Stereo

ALP1415   Gold/Red : **£ 8**
BEETHOVEN / SCHUBERT   Symphony No.5, Symphony No.8
Boston Symphony Orchestra   Munch
No Stereo

ALP1416   Gold/Red : **£ 4**
BIZET   Carmen (Highlights)   Merrill
RCA Victrola Orchestra   Reiner
No Stereo

ALP1417   Gold/Red : **£8**
Various   Carmen, Oberon, Force of Destiny Etc.
NBC Symphony Orchestra   Toscanini
No Stereo

ALP1418   Gold/Red : **£10**
HUMPERDINCK / THOMAS   Hansel & Gretel, Migno
NBC Symphony Orchestra   Toscanini
No Stereo

ALP1419-21   Gold/Red : **£20**
VERDI   La Traviata   Carteri
Orchestra of Rome Opera House   Monteux
No Stereo

ALP1422   Gold/Red : **£50**
BEETHOVEN   Sonata No.1 in D, Op.12/1.1, Sonata No.2 in A, Op.12/1.2
Heifetz
No Stereo

ALP1423   Gold/Red : **£50**
BEETHOVEN   Sonata No.3 in Eb, Op.12/3, Sonata No.4 in Amin, Op.23
Heifetz
No Stereo

ALP1424   Gold/Red : **£50**
BEETHOVEN   Sonata No.5 in F, Op.24, Sonata No.6 in A, Op.30/1
Heifetz
No Stereo

ALP1425   Gold/Red : **£50**
BEETHOVEN   Sonata No.7 in Cmin, Op.30/2, Sonata No.8 in G, Op.30/2
Heifetz
No Stereo

ALP1426   Gold/Red : **£50**
BEETHOVEN   Sonata No.9 in A, Op.47, Sonata No.10 in G, Op.96
Heifetz
No Stereo

ALP1427   Gold/Red : **£80**
SAINT-SAENS / MIASKOVSY   Cello Concerto 1 Amin
Rostropovitch   Philharmonia Orchestra   Sargent
No Stereo

ALP1428   Gold/Red : **£18**
PUCCINI   Operatic Arias   Stella
London Symphony Orchestra   Erede
No Stereo

ALP1429   Gold/Red : **£14**
SCRIABIN   Piano Sonata Op.23, Preludes   Horowitz
No Stereo

ALP1430-1   Gold/Red : **£14**
Various   Piano Recital   Horowitz
No Stereo

ALP1432   Gold/Red : **£5**
Various   Toscanini Anthology Vol.3
NBC Symphony Orchestra   Toscanini
No Stereo

ALP1433-4   (==== Not Issued ====)

ALP1435-6   Gold/Red : **£15**
Spoken Word   Speeches of Winston Churchill
No Stereo

ALP1437   Gold/Red : **£40**
BEETHOVEN   Violin Concerto   Heifetz
Boston Symphony Orchestra   Munch
No Stereo

ALP1438   Gold/Red : **£8**
BERLIOZ   Harold in Italy
NBC Symphony Orchestra   Toscanini
No Stereo

ALP1439   Gold/Red : **£15**
VIVALDI   Concertos   Virtuosi di Roma   Fasano
No Stereo

ALP1440   Gold/Red : **£ 20**
SIBELIUS   Symphony No.2
NBC Symphony Orchestra   Stokowski
No Stereo

ALP1441   Gold/Red : **£ 8**
TCHAIKOVSKY / WALDTEUFEL / ROSSINI Nutcracker suite, Skaters
Waltz, William Tell overture   NBC Symphony Orchestra   Toscanini
No Stereo

ALP1442   (==== Not Issued ====)

ALP1443   Gold/Red : **£ 6**
TCHAIKOVSKY Swan Lake (Highlights)
NBC Symphony Orchestra   Stokowski
No Stereo

ALP1444   Gold/Red : **£ 20**
MOZART   Requiem   Berlin Philharmonic Orchestra   Kempe
No Stereo

ALP1445   (==== Not Issued ====)

ALP1446   Gold/Red : **£ 8**
LISZT   Hungarian Rhapsodies No.2, 6, 12 & 15   Cziffra
No Stereo

ALP1447-8   (==== Not Issued ====)

ALP1449   Gold/Red : **£ 60**
BACH   Sonatas for Solo Violin No.1 & 2   Heifetz
No Stereo

ALP1450   Gold/Red : **£ 60**
BACH   Sonatas for Solo Violin No.3 & 4   Heifetz
No Stereo

ALP1451   Gold/Red : **£ 60**
BACH   Sonatas for Solo Violin No.5 & 6   Heifetz
No Stereo

ALP1452   Gold/Red : **£8**
VERDI   Highlights from the Operas   Peerce
NBC Symphony Orchestra   Toscanini
No Stereo

ALP1453   Gold/Red : **£5**
VERDI   Rigoletto (Highlights)   Peerce
NBC Symphony Orchestra   Toscanini
No Stereo

ALP1454   Gold/Red : **£10**
MOZART   Piano Concerto No.11, Piano Concerto No.24
Kirkpatrick   Geraint Jones Orchestra   Jones
No Stereo

ALP1455   Gold/Red : **£8**
LISZT   Piano Concerto No.1 in Eflat G124, Hungarian Fantasy.
Cziffra   Paris Conservatoire Orchestra   Dervaux
No Stereo

ALP1456   Gold/Red : **£8**
ELGAR   Violin Concerto in Bmin op 61   Menuhin
London Symphony Orchestra   Elgar
No Stereo

ALP1457-9   (==== Not Issued ====)

ALP1460   Gold/Red : **£60**
CHAUSSON / BERLIOZ / SAINT-SAINS   Poeme, Intro, Romeo et
Juliet   Oistrakh   Boston Symphony Orchestra   Munch
No Stereo

ALP1461   Gold/Red : **£16**
MOZART   Symphony No.29   Philharmonia Orchestra   Cantelli
No Stereo

ALP1462   Gold/Red : **£400**
PURCELL / HANDEL / VIOTTI / SPOHR   Sonatas and Duos   De Vito
No Stereo

ALP1463   (==== Not Issued ====)

ALP1464 Gold/Red : **£8**
ELGAR Enigma Variations, Serenade, Cockaigne Elgar
No Stereo

ALP1465 Gold/Red : **£8**
SCHUMANN / CHOPIN Piano concerto in Amin, Piano Concerto 2
Rubinstein NBC Symphony Orchestra Steinberg
No Stereo

ALP1466-8 (==== Not Issued ====)

ALP1469 Gold/Red : **£8**
BERLIOZ / TCHAIKOVSKY Romeo & Juliet
NBC Symphony Orchestra Toscanini
No Stereo

ALP1470 Gold/Red : **£8**
ALBINEZ Iberia, Poeme de L'Extase
Philharmonia Orchestra Goossens
No Stereo

ALP1471 Gold/Red : **£20**
MOZART / HAYDN Symphony No.34, Symphony No.104
Philharmonia Orchestra Kempe
No Stereo

ALP1472 Gold/Red : **£30**
BEETHOVEN Symphony No.7 Philharmonia Orchestra Cantelli
Stereo Issue : ASD 254

ALP1473-4 Gold/Red : **£16**
ROSSINI Le Compte Ory Barabas
Glyndenbourne Festival Orchestra Gui
No Stereo

ALP1475 Gold/Red : **£12**
DELIBES Sylvia & Coppelia
Boston Symphony Orchestra Monteux
No Stereo

ALP1476   Gold/Red : **£3**
VERDI   Ballo in Maschera (Highlights)   Peerce
Metropolitan Opera Orchestra   Mitropoulos
No Stereo

ALP1477   Gold/Red : **£6**
CHOPIN / DEBUSSY   Piano Sonata No.2, Preludes   Rubinstein
No Stereo

ALP1478   (==== Not Issued ====)

ALP1479   Gold/Red : **£250**
SIBELIUS / SUK   Violin Concerto in Dmin, 4 Pieces
Neveu   Philharmonia Orchestra   Susskind
No Stereo

ALP1480   Gold/Red : **£4**
SIBELIUS   Symphony No.7, Pelleas Melisande etc
Royal Philharmonic Orchestra   Beecham
Stereo Issue : ASD 468

ALP1481   Gold/Red : **£4**
MASCAGNI / LEONCAVELLO   Cavalleria Rusticana, I Pagliacci
(Highlights)   De Los Angeles RCA Victrola Orchestra   Cellini
No Stereo

ALP1482-4   Gold/Red : **£12**
Spoken Word   Shakespeare Hamlet   Gielgud Old Vic
No Stereo

ALP1485-6   Gold/Red : **£3**
GILBERT & SULLIVAN   The Mikado
Glyndenbourne Festival Orchestra   Sargent
Stereo Issue : ASD 256-7

ALP1487   Gold/Red : **£10**
STRAUSS   Song Recital   Fischer-Dieskau
No Stereo

ALP1488   Gold/Red : **£8**
MOZART / HAYDN   String Quartet K.458, String Quartet Op.77/1
Amadeus Quartet
No Stereo

ALP1489   Gold/Red : **£6**
CHOPIN   Ballades, Mazurkas, Nocturnes   Cherkassky
No Stereo

ALP1490   Gold/Red : **£5**
Various   Russian Easter Festival
Philharmonia Orchestra   Goossens
Stereo Issue : ASD 262

ALP1491   Gold/Red : **£5**
TCHAIKOVSKY   Symphony No.5   Philharmonia Orchestra   Silvestri
Stereo Issue : ASD 261

ALP1492   Gold/Red : **£8**
MOZART   Symphony No.39, Divertimento No.15
NBC Symphony Orchestra   Toscanini
No Stereo

ALP1493   Gold/Red : **£6**
STRAUSS   Don Quixote   NBC Symphony Orchestra   Toscanini
No Stereo

ALP1494   Gold/Red : **£15**
BARTOK   Concerto for Orchestra
Chicago Symphony Orchestra   Reiner
No Stereo

ALP1495   Gold/Red : **£6**
TCHAIKOVSKY   Symphony No.6   Philharmonia Orchestra   Silvestri
Stereo Issue : ASD 273

ALP1496   Gold/Red : **£8**
MOZART   Exsultate Jubilate, Benedictus Sit DeusBerger
Berlin Philharmonic Orchestra   Forster
No Stereo

ALP1497   Gold/Red : **£3**
BIZET   L'Arlesienne
Royal Philharmonic Orchestra   Beecham
Stereo Issue : ASD 252

ALP1498   Gold/Red : **£60**
MOZART   Symphony No.40, Eine Kleine Nachtmusik
Vienna Philharmonic Orchestra   Furtwangler
No Stereo

ALP1499   Gold/Red : **£6**
VAUGHAN-WILLIAMS   Serenade, Greensleeves, etc.
London Symphony Orchestra   Sargent
No Stereo

ALP1500   (══ Not Issued ══)

ALP1501   Gold/Red : **£20**
HAYDN   Concerto in D for Cello and Orchestra   Vival
Danish State Radio Orchestra   Woldyke
No Stereo

ALP1502   (══ Not Issued ══)

ALP1503   Gold/Red : **£16**
STRAVINSKY   Petrushka   Philharmonia Orchestra   Kurtz
No Stereo

ALP1504-5   Gold/Red : **£1**
GILBERT & SULLIVAN   The Gondoliers
Glyndebourne Pro Arte   Sargent
Stereo Issue : ASD 265-6

ALP1506-10   Gold/Red : **£50**
WAGNER   Meistersinger Nurnberg   Frantz
Berlin Philharmonic Orchestra   Kempe
No Stereo

ALP1511   Gold/Red : **£3**
TCHAIKOVSKY   Symphony No.4   Philharmonia Orchestra   Silvestri
Stereo Issue : ASD 253

ALP1512   Gold/Red : **£20**
BACH   Sonatas & Partitas (solo violin)   Menuhin
No Stereo

ALP1513   Gold/Red : **£ 40**
WAGNER   Fliegende Hollander Ov,Tannhaus
Berlin Philharmonic Orchestra   Kempe
No Stereo

ALP1514   Gold/Red : **£ 4**
DOHNANYI   Nursary Song, Concerto No.2Dohnanyi
Royal Philharmonic Orchestra   Boult
No Stereo

ALP1515-7   Gold/Red : **£ 30**
MOZART   Idomenco   Jurinac
Glyndenbourne Festival Orchestra   Pritchard
No Stereo

ALP1518   Gold/Red : **£ 10**
Various   Recital   Kirkpatrick
No Stereo

ALP1519   (═══ Not Issued ═══)

ALP1520   Gold/Red : **£ 350**
DEBUSSY / CHAUSSON   Sonata in Gmin., Poeme, Tzigane   Neveu
No Stereo

ALP1521   Gold/Red : **£ 300**
BEETHOVEN   Violin Sonata No.8   De Vito   Aprea
No Stereo

ALP1522-4   Gold/Red : **£ 20**
DEBUSSY   Pelleas & Melisande   De Los Angeles
Orchestre National de la Radiodiffusion Francaise   Cluytens
No Stereo

ALP1525   (═══ Not Issued ═══)

ALP1526   Gold/Red : **£ 80**
Various   Pops Concert
Vienna Philharmonic Orchestra   Furtwangler
No Stereo

ALP1527
Various
No Stereo
Gold/Red : **£8**
Popular Piano Recital   Cherkassky

ALP1528
BACH
Danish State Radio Orchestra
No Stereo
Gold/Red : **£8**
Cantata No.33, Cantata No.105
Woldike

ALP1529   (==== Not Issued ====)

ALP1530
GRIEG
Stereo Issue : ASD 258
Gold/Red : **£3**
Peer Gynt   Royal Philharmonic Orchestra   Beecham

ALP1531
BACH
No Stereo
Gold/Red : **£20**
Sonatas & Partitas (solo violin)   Menuhin

ALP1532
BACH
No Stereo
Gold/Red : **£20**
Sonatas & Partitas (solo violin)   Menuhin

ALP1533
Various
Royal Philharmonic Orchestra
Stereo Issue : ASD 259
Gold/Red : **£1**
Beecham Lollipops
Beecham

ALP1534
LISZT
Cziffra
No Stereo
Gold/Red : **£8**
Mephisto Waltz, Valse Oubliee No.1, Rhapsody Espagnol

ALP1535
Various
Philharmonia Orchestra
No Stereo
Gold/Red : **£14**
The Art of Guido Cantelli
Cantelli

ALP1536
MOZART
Royal Philharmonic Orchestra
No Stereo
Gold/Red : **£6**
Symphony No.41 in C, Divertiment No.2 in D
Beecham

405

ALP1537   Gold/Red : **£4**
DVORAK   Symphony No.8, Carnival Overture
London Philharmonic Orchestra   Silvestri
Stereo Issue : ASD 470

ALP1538   Gold/Red : **£14**
RAVEL / RACHMANINOV   Piano Concerto in G, Piano Concerto No.4
Michelangeli   Philharmonia Orchestra   Gracis
Stereo Issue : ASD 255

ALP1539   Gold/Red : **£8**
MOZART   String Quintet in D K593, String Quintet in Eb K614
Amadeus Quartet   Aronowitz
No Stereo

ALP1540   Gold/Red : **£14**
Various   Recital   Loose
No Stereo

ALP1541   Gold/Red : **£25**
BOCCHERINI / HAYDN   Cello Concerto   Baldovino
Pro Arte   Previtali
No Stereo

ALP1542   Gold/Red : **£3**
SIBELIUS   Symphony No.1
BBC Symphony Orchestra   Sargent
Stereo Issue : ASD 260

ALP1543   Gold/Red : **£4**
MENDELSSOHN / TCHAIKOVSKY   Violin Concertos   Ferras
Philharmonia Orchestra   Silvestri
Stereo Issue : ASD 278

ALP1544   Gold/Red : **£10**
SCHUBERT   Octet in F Op.166
Berlin Philharmonic Chamber Music Ensemble
No Stereo

ALP1545   Gold/Red : **£30**
BRAHMS   Symphony No.4
Berlin Philharmonic Orchestra   Kempe
No Stereo

ALP1546   Gold/Red : **£8**
BEETHOVEN   Piano Concerto No.3   Solomon
Philharmonia Orchestra   Menges
No Stereo

ALP1547   Gold/Red : **£25**
MOZART   Violin Sonata No.32, Violin Sonata No.34   Menhuin
No Stereo

ALP1548-9   Gold/Red : **£100**
BACH   Goldberg Variations   Tureck
No Stereo

ALP1550   Gold/Red : **£10**
DVORAK   Symphony No.9
French National Radio Orchestra   Silvestri
No Stereo

ALP1551   Gold/Red : **£10**
SCHUMANN   Songs   Fischer-Dieskau
No Stereo

ALP1552   Gold/Red : **£10**
DOHNANYI   6 Pieces, Intermezzo, Pastorale, etc.   Dohnanyi
No Stereo

ALP1553   Gold/Red : **£10**
DOHNANYI   Winterreigen, Suite in Olden Style   Dohnanyi
No Stereo

ALP1554   Gold/Red : **£4**
PROKOFIEV / SHOSTAKOVITCH   Classical Symphony, Symphony No.1
Philharmonia Orchestra   Kurtz
Stereo Issue : ASD 263

ALP1555-63   Gold/Red : **£60**
Spoken Word   Winston Churchill Speeches
No Stereo

ALP1564   Gold/Red : **£3**
RIMSKY-KORSAKOV   Scheherezade
Royal Philharmonic Orchestra   Beecham
Stereo Issue : ASD 251

ALP1565 Gold/Red : **£18**
BEETHOVEN / CHOPIN Andante Favori, Impromptus Kentner
No Stereo

ALP1566 Gold/Red : **£40**
TCHAIKOVSKY Symphony No.6 Bmin Op 74
Philharmonia Orchestra Kempe
No Stereo

ALP1567 Gold/Red : **£6**
BRUCKNER Te Deum, Mass in Emin
Berlin Philharmonic Orchestra Forster
No Stereo

ALP1568 Gold/Red : **£4**
BRAHMS Violin Concerto Menuhin
Berlin Philharmonic Orchestra Kempe
Stereo Issue : ASD 264

ALP1569 Gold/Red : **£14**
MENDELSSOHN Symphony No.3
Royal Philharmonic Orchestra Previtali
No Stereo

ALP1570 Gold/Red : **£15**
GRIEG Holberg St Op 40, 2 Elegiac Melo
Philharmonia Orchestra Fistoulari
No Stereo

ALP1571 Gold/Red : **£4**
LALO / SAINT-SAINS Symphony Espagnole, Intro & Rondo Capricio
Menuhin Philharmonia Orchestra Goossens
Stereo Issue : ASD 290

ALP1572 Gold/Red : **£3**
BACH St. Matthews Passion (Highlights)
St. Hedwigs Choir Forster
No Stereo

ALP1573 Gold/Red : **£10**
BEETHOVEN Piano Sonata No.1, Piano Sonata No.7 Solomon
No Stereo

ALP1574   Gold/Red : **£8**
BACH / SCHUBERT / HINDEMITH Chaconne, Impromptu in Ab, Sonata
No.3   Cherkassky
No Stereo

ALP1575   Gold/Red : **£2**
HANDEL   Airs   Lewis
London Symphony Orchestra   Sargent
Stereo Issue : ASD 291

ALP1576   Gold/Red : **£10**
BEETHOVEN   Symphony No.7 A Op 92, Egmont Ov Op84
Berlin Philharmonic Orchestra   Cluytens
No Stereo

ALP1577   Gold/Red : **£15**
PUCCINI   Suor Angelica   De Los Angeles
Orchestra of Rome Opera House   Serafin
No Stereo

ALP1578   Gold/Red : **£10**
SIBELIUS   Karelia, en Saga, Swan of Tuonela, etc.
Royal Philharmonic Orchestra   Collins
No Stereo

ALP1579   Gold/Red : **£8**
HAYDN   String Quartet No.57 in G, String Quartet No.65 in Bb
Amadeus Quartet
No Stereo

ALP1580   Gold/Red : **£6**
CHOPIN   Piano Concertos Nos.1 & 2   Simon
Royal Philharmonic Orchestra   Goossens
No Stereo

ALP1581   Gold/Red : **£50**
SCHUMANN   Symphony No.1 Bb Op 38, Manfred Overture
Berlin Philharmonic Orchestra   Kempe
No Stereo

ALP1582   Gold/Red : **£15**
TCHAIKOVSKY / GLAZUNOV / BORODIN   The Tempest, Stenka Razin
Philharmonia Orchestra   Fistoulari
No Stereo

ALP1583   Gold/Red : **£3**
BEETHOVEN   Piano Concerto No.1   Solomon
Philharmonia Orchestra   Menges
Stereo Issue : ASD 294

ALP1584   Gold/Red : **£10**
BRAHMS   Songs   Fischer-Dieskau
No Stereo

ALP1585   Gold/Red : **£16**
Various   Opera Recital   Christoff
Rome Opera Orchestra   Gui
No Stereo

ALP1586   Gold/Red : **£3**
DELIUS   Brigg Fair Etc
Royal Philharmonic Orchestra   Beecham
Stereo Issue : ASD 357

ALP1587   Gold/Red : **£12**
SCHUMANN / MENDELSSOHN   Frauenliebe und Leben, Songs
Berger
No Stereo

ALP1588   Gold/Red : **£80**
BARTOK   Piano Concerto No.3, Dance Suite   Annie Fischer
Philharmonia Orchestra   Markevitch
No Stereo

ALP1589   Gold/Red : **£15**
Various   Concert   Virtuosi di Roma   Fasano
No Stereo

ALP1590   Gold/Red : **£10**
BRAHMS   Serenade No.1 Op.11
Paris Conservatoire Orchestra   Vandernoot
No Stereo

ALP1591   Gold/Red : **£25**
STRAUSS / SMETANA   Feuersnot, Ma Vlast
Vienna Philharmonic Orchestra   Cluytens
No Stereo

ALP1592   Gold/Red : **£8**
HAYDN   String Quartet No.72 in C, String Quartet No.74 in Gmin
Amadeus Quartet
No Stereo

ALP1593   Gold/Red : **£12**
SAINT-SAENS   Piano Concerto No.1, Piano Concerto No.3   Darre
French National Radio Orchestra   Fourestier
No Stereo

ALP1594   Gold/Red : **£6**
PAISELLO / BELLINI   Concerto No.5 in Eflat, Concerto in C
Virtuosi di Roma   Zanfini
No Stereo

ALP1595   Gold/Red : **£4**
DVORAK   Cello Concerto   Rostropovitch
Royal Philharmonic Orchestra   Boult
Stereo Issue : ASD 358

ALP1596   Gold/Red : **£2**
BEETHOVEN   Symphony No.2
Royal Philharmonic Orchestra   Beecham
Stereo Issue : ASD 287

ALP1597   Gold/Red : **£14**
BARTOK / HINDEMITH   Divertimento, Mathis der Maler
Philharmonia Orchestra   Silvestri
No Stereo

ALP1598   Gold/Red : **£8**
BEETHOVEN   Symphony No.4 Bb, Leonore Overture No.1 Op138
BBC Symphony Orchestra   Toscanini
No Stereo

ALP1599   Gold/Red : **£4**
Test Record   Microgroove Frequency Test record
No Stereo

ALP1600   Gold/Red : **£1**
HOLST   The Planets
BBC Symphony Orchestra   Sargent
Stereo Issue : ASD 269

ALP1601-2   Gold/Red : **£3**
GILBERT & SULLIVAN   Yeomen of the Guard
Glyndebourne Pro Arte   Sargent
Stereo Issue : ASD 364-5

ALP1603   Gold/Red : **£15**
VILLA-LOBOS   Bachianas Brasilieras No.2, 5, 6 & 9
De Los Angeles   Orchestre National de la Radiodiffusion Francaise
Villa-Lobos
No Stereo

ALP1604   Gold/Red : **£12**
Various   Piano Recital   Cziffra
No Stereo

ALP1605   Gold/Red : **£9**
STRAUSS   Tod und Verk, Dance of the 7 Veils
Philharmonia Orchestra   Rodzinsky
Stereo Issue : ASD 270

ALP1606-8   Gold/Red : **£9**
HAYDN   The Seasons
Royal Philharmonic Orchestra   Beecham
Stereo Issue : ASD 282-4

ALP1609   Gold/Red : **£2**
TCHAIKOVSKY   Nutcracker extracts
Philharmonia Orchestra   Kurtz
Stereo Issue : ASD 289

ALP1610-12   Gold/Red : **£20**
MASCAGNI / LEONCAVALLO   Cavalleria Rusticana, I Pagliacci
Gigli   La Scalla   Ghione
No Stereo

ALP1613-5   Gold/Red : **£16**
GLINKA   A Life for the Tsar   Christoff
Lamoureux Orchestra   Markevitch
No Stereo

ALP1616   Gold/Red : **£12**
RACHMANINOV / STRAVINSKY   Rhapsody, Petrushka
Cherkassky   London Symphony Orchestra Menges
No Stereo

ALP1617-9   Gold/Red : **£10**
WOLF   Morike Leider   Fischer-Dieskau
No Stereo

ALP1620   Gold/Red : **£15**
Various   Recital of Operatic Arias   Bjorling
No Stereo

ALP1621   Gold/Red : **£18**
BEETHOVEN   Waldstein Sonata, Appassionata Sonata
Kentner
No Stereo

ALP1622   Gold/Red : **£8**
DVORAK / JANACEK   String Quartet Op.96, String Quartet No.2
Vlach Quartet
No Stereo

ALP1623   Gold/Red : **£10**
DVORAK   Symphony No.5 (New World)
Berlin Philharmonic Orchestra   Kempe
Stereo Issue : ASD 380

ALP1624-6   Gold/Red : **£15**
HAYDN   Symphony No.93 - 98
Royal Philharmonic Orchestra   Beecham
No Stereo

ALP1627   Gold/Red : **£8**
MOUSSORGSKY / RAVEL Pictures at an Exhibition, Bolero
Royal Philharmonic Orchestra   Goossens
No Stereo

ALP1628   Gold/Red : **£10**
WALTON   Belshazzars Feast, Zadok
Royal Liverpool Philharmonic Orchestra   Sargent
No Stereo

ALP1629   Gold/Red : **£16**
VIVALDI   L'Estro Armonico, Concertos
Virtuosi di Roma   Fasano
No Stereo

ALP1630   Gold/Red : **£16**
RACHMANINOV Piano Concerto No.2   Rachmaninov
Philadelphia Orchestra   Stokowski
No Stereo

ALP1631   Gold/Red : **£15**
MOZART   Piano Double Concertos K242,365   Vronsky, Babin
No Stereo

ALP1632   Gold/Red : **£6**
RIMSKY-KORSAKOV / PROKOFIEV / LIAD   Caprice Espagnol
Royal Philharmonic Orchestra   Kurtz
No Stereo

ALP1633   Gold/Red : **£3**
BERLIOZ   Symphonie Fantastique
French National Radio Orchestra   Beecham
Stereo Issue : ASD 399

ALP1634-6   Gold/Red : **£16**
VERDI   Simon Boccanegra   Gobbi
Orchestra of Rome Opera House   Santini
No Stereo

ALP1637   Gold/Red : **£8**
LEHAR / STRAUSS / SUPPE   Nights in Vienna
Vienna Philharmonic Orchestra   Kempe
Stereo Issue : ASD 279

ALP1638   Gold/Red : **£30**
WAGNER   Tristan Isolde, Lohengrin Prelude
Vienna Philharmonic Orchestra   Kempe
No Stereo

ALP1639   Gold/Red : **£14**
SIBELIUS   Symphony No.2
BBC Symphony Orchestra   Sargent
No Stereo

ALP1640   Gold/Red : **£50**
PROKOFIEV / RACHMANINOV   Sinfonia Concert, etc.
Rostropovitch
No Stereo

ALP1641   Gold/Red : **£20**
Various   Orchestral Concert   Virtuosi di Roma   Fasano
No Stereo

ALP1642   Gold/Red : **£12**
Various   Opera Recital   Marshall
London Symphony Orchestra   Pedrazzoli
No Stereo

ALP1643   Gold/Red : **£3**
GRIEG / SCHUMANN   Piano Concertos   Solomon
Philharmonia Orchestra   Menges
Stereo Issue : ASD 272

ALP1644   Gold/Red : **£2**
TCHAIKOVSKY   Swan Lake   Menuhin
Philharmonia Orchestra   Kurtz
Stereo Issue : ASD 271

ALP1645   Gold/Red : **£50**
BACH   Partita No.1, Partita No.2   Tureck
No Stereo

ALP1646-7   (==== Not Issued ====)

ALP1648   Gold/Red : **£8**
LISZT   Symphonic Poems   Philharmonia Orchestra   Silvestri
No Stereo

ALP1649   Gold/Red : **£6**
SIBELIUS / WEBER   Finlandia, etc.
Royal Philharmonic Orchestra   Collins
No Stereo

ALP1650-1   Gold/Red : **£3**
GILBERT & SULLIVAN   HMS Pinafore
Glyndebourne Pro Arte   Sargent
Stereo Issue : ASD 415-6

ALP1652-5   Gold/Red : **£14**
MOUSSORGSKY Songs   Christoff
No Stereo

ALP1656   Gold/Red : **£6**
Various   French Ballet Music
Royal Philharmonic Orchestra   Beecham
No Stereo

ALP1657   Gold/Red : **£6**
BEETHOVEN   Symphony No.5, Leonora 3 Ov
Berlin Philharmonic Orchestra   Cluytens
Stereo Issue : ASD 267

ALP1658   Gold/Red : **£3**
Various   An Evening at the Proms
BBC Symphony Orchestra   Sargent
Stereo Issue : ASD 536

ALP1659-0   Gold/Red : **£28**
PUCCINI   Madama Butterfly
Orchestra of Rome Opera House   De Fabritiis
No Stereo

ALP1661-2   Gold/Red : **£16**
GALUPPI / CIMAROSA   Filosofo Campagna
Collegium Musicum Italicum   Fasano
No Stereo

ALP1663   Gold/Red : **£4**
BEETHOVEN   Overtures Berlin Philharmonic Orchestra   Kempe
Stereo Issue : ASD 336

ALP1664   Gold/Red : **£6**
BEETHOVEN   Symphony No.6 F Op 68
BBC Symphony Orchestra   Toscanini
No Stereo

ALP1665 Gold/Red : **£10**
Various   Music of India   Shankar
No Stereo

ALP1666 Gold/Red : **£45**
FRANCK / FAURE   Violin Sonata in Amaj.   Ferras
No Stereo

ALP1667 Gold/Red : **£6**
TCHAIKOVSKY   Symphony No.4
Royal Philharmonic Orchestra   Beecham
No Stereo

ALP1668 Gold/Red : **£10**
TCHAIKOVSKY   Manfred Symphony
French National Radio Orchestra   Silvestri
No Stereo

ALP1669 Gold/Red : **£3**
MENDELSSOHN / BRUCH   Violin Concertos In E & G Minor
Menuhin   Philharmonia Orchestra   Susskind
Stereo Issue : ASD 334

ALP1670 Gold/Red : **£8**
BACH   Cantata No.56, Cantata No.82   Souzay
Gerraint Jones Orchestra   Jones
No Stereo

ALP1671 Gold/Red : **£10**
Various   British Folk Songs   Marshall
No Stereo

ALP1672 Gold/Red : **£12**
Various   Opera Excerpts   Rome Opera Orchestra   Santini
No Stereo

ALP1673 Gold/Red : **£8**
SCHUBERT / BRAHMS   String Quartets   Amadeus Quartet
No Stereo

ALP1674 Gold/Red : **£3**
BEETHOVEN   Mass in C   Royal Philharmonic Orchestra   Beecham
Stereo Issue : ASD 280

417

ALP1675 Gold/Red : **£20**
JANACEK / MARTINU   Taras Bulba, Frescoes
Royal Philharmonic Orchestra   Kubelik
No Stereo

ALP1676 Gold/Red : **£6**
MOZART   Flute Concertos   Schaffer
Philharmonia Orchestra   Kurtz
No Stereo

ALP1677 Gold/Red : **£10**
SCHUBERT   Lieder Recital No.2   Fischer-Dieskau
No Stereo

ALP1678 Gold/Red : **£3**
GRIEG / LISZT   Piano Concerto, Piano Concerto No.2   Cziffra
Philharmonia Orchestra   Vandernoot
Stereo Issue : ASD 301

ALP1679 Gold/Red : **£4**
TCHAIKOVSKY   Capriccio Italiano   Philharmonia Orchestra   Kletzki
Stereo Issue : ASD 343

ALP1680 Gold/Red : **£2**
Various   Operatic Arias   Hammond
Philharmonia Orchestra   Susskind
Stereo Issue : ASD 302

ALP1681 Gold/Red : **£10**
Various   The Best of Gigli   Gigli
No Stereo

ALP1682-4   (══ Not Issued ══)

ALP1684 Gold/Red : **£15**
RAVEL / SAINT-SAINS / DUKAS   Bolero, Danse Macabre, L'appreni
Paris Conservatoire Orchestra   Silvestri
No Stereo

ALP1686 Gold/Red : **£3**
FRANCK   Symphony in Dmin.
French National Radio Orchestra   Beecham
Stereo Issue : ASD 458

418

ALP1687
KODALY
No Stereo
Gold/Red : **£18**
Missa Brevis   Hungarian State Orchestra   Kodaly

ALP1688
FALLA
Royal Philharmonic Orchestra   Rodzinsky
Stereo Issue : ASD 281
Gold/Red : **£4**
Three cornered hat

ALP1689
DEBUSSY
Paris Conservatoire Orchestra   Silvestri
No Stereo
Gold/Red : **£10**
La Mer, Nocturnes

ALP1690
Various
No Stereo
Gold/Red : **£100**
Cello Recital   Rostropovitch

ALP1691
Various
No Stereo
Gold/Red : **£12**
Cziffra Plays Minatures   Cziffra

ALP1692
BACH
No Stereo
Gold/Red : **£50**
Partita No.3, Partita No.6   Tureck

ALP1693
HAYDN
Royal Philharmonic Orchestra   Beecham
Stereo Issue : ASD 339
Gold/Red : **£2**
Symphony No.99, Symphony No.100

ALP1694
HAYDN
Royal Philharmonic Orchestra   Beecham
Stereo Issue : ASD 340
Gold/Red : **£2**
Symphony No.101, Symphony No.102

ALP1695
HAYDN
Royal Philharmonic Orchestra   Beecham
Stereo Issue : ASD 341
Gold/Red : **£2**
Symphony No.103, Symphony No.104

ALP1696   Gold/Red : **£4**
BRAHMS / WAGNER   St. Anthony Variations, Siegfried Idyll
Philharmonia Orchestra   Kletzki
No Stereo

ALP1697   Gold/Red : **£3**
DELIUS   Florida Suite, Over the Hills
Royal Philharmonic Orchestra   Beecham
Stereo Issue : ASD 329

ALP1698-9   Gold/Red : **£20**
BEETHOVEN   Symphony No.8, Symphony No.9
Berlin Philharmonic Orchestra   Cluytens
No Stereo

ALP1700   Gold/Red : **£5**
VERDI   Don Carlos (Highlights)   Stella
Rome Opera Orchestra   Santini
No Stereo

ALP1701-2   Gold/Red : **£16**
CHOPIN   Nocturnes 1-19   Rubinstein
No Stereo

ALP1703   Gold/Red : **£3**
BACH   Cantata Arias   Fischer-Dieskau
Berlin Philharmonic Orchestra   Forster
Stereo Issue : ASD 342

ALP1704   Gold/Red : **£4**
BRAHMS   Piano Concerto No.2   Kentner   Boult
Stereo Issue : ASD 268

ALP1705   Gold/Red : **£30**
BARTOK   Violin Sonata No.1, Sonata for Solo Violin   Menuhin
No Stereo

ALP1706   Gold/Red : **£8**
DEBUSSY / RAVEL   Iberia, Rapsodie Espagnole
Royal Philharmonic Orchestra   Goossens
No Stereo

ALP1707   Gold/Red : **£40**
BEETHOVEN   Symphony No.7
Paris Conservatoire Orchestra   Schuricht
No Stereo

ALP1708   Gold/Red : **£30**
LISZT / SCHUBERT   Piano Sonata in Bmin., Wanderer Fantasy Gheorghiu
No Stereo

ALP1709   Gold/Red : **£15**
BRAHMS / MENDELSSOHN   Songs of Many Lands   Baldwin
No Stereo

ALP1710   Gold/Red : **£2**
HANDEL   Water Music, Fireworks Music
Royal Philharmonic Orchestra   Sargent
Stereo Issue : ASD 286

ALP1711   Gold/Red : **£4**
TCHAIKOVSKY   Romeo & Juliet
Royal Philharmonic Orchestra   Rodzinsky
Stereo Issue : ASD 288

ALP1712   Gold/Red : **£70**
GRIEG   Violin Sonata No.1, No.2 & No.3   Menuhin, Levin
No Stereo

ALP1713   Gold/Red : **£8**
SCHUMANN / CHOPIN   Fantasiestucke, Fantasie in Fmin.   Cziffra
No Stereo

ALP1714   Gold/Red : **£50**
BACH   Partita No.4, Partita No.5   Tureck
No Stereo

ALP1715-6   (==== Not Issued ====)

ALP1717   Gold/Red : **£12**
BEETHOVEN   Piano Variations   Cziffra
No Stereo

ALP1718   Gold/Red : **£3**
TCHAIKOVSKY   Piano Concerto No.1   Cziffra
Philharmonia Orchestra   Vandernoot
Stereo Issue : ASD 315

ALP1719   Gold/Red : **£6**
LISZT /FRANCK / SCHUMANN   Paganini Studies, Prelude, Choral &
Fugue   Simon
No Stereo

ALP1720   Gold/Red : **£8**
Various   Operatic Highlights Rome Opera Orchestra   Santini
No Stereo

ALP1721-4   Gold/Red : **£6**
GOUNOD   Faust
Orchestra of the Theatre National de L'Opera   Cluytens
Stereo Issue : ASD 307-10

ALP1725   Gold/Red : **£4**
SCHUBERT   Symphony No.8 (Unfinished), Rosamunde
Royal Philharmonic Orchestra   Kletzki
Stereo Issue : ASD 296

ALP1726   Gold/Red : **£4**
PUCCINI   Gianni Schicchi   Gobbi
Orchestra of Rome Opera House   Santini
Stereo Issue : ASD 295

ALP1727   Gold/Red : **£5**
FALLA   El Amor Brujo Philharmonia Orchestra   Vandernoot
Stereo Issue : ASD 297

ALP1728   Gold/Red : **£4**
SAINT-SAENS   Carnival of the Animals, Peter & Wolf
Philharmonia Orchestra   Kurtz
Stereo Issue : ASD 299

ALP1729   Gold/Red : **£2**
HANDEL - BEECHAM   Love In Bath
Royal Philharmonic Orchestra   Beecham
Stereo Issue : ASD 298

ALP1730   (==== Not Issued ====)

ALP1731   Gold/Red : **£8**
Various   Glyndebourne - Memories of 1st 25 Years
Glyndenbourne Festival Orchestra   Pritchard, Gui
No Stereo

ALP1732   Gold/Red : **£2**
SIBELIUS   Symphony No.5 In E Flat
BBC Symphony Orchestra   Sargent
Stereo Issue : ASD 303

ALP1733   Gold/Red : **£3**
SCHUBERT   Trout Quintet   H. Menuhin
Amadeus String Quartet
Stereo Issue : ASD 322

ALP1734-5   Gold/Red : **£16**
SCHUBERT   Die Winterreisse   Souzay
No Stereo

ALP1736   Gold/Red : **£5**
Various   Popular Movements from the Symphonies
Vienna Philharmonic Orchestra   Cluytens
Stereo Issue : ASD 304

ALP1737-8   Gold/Red : **£4**
LISZT   Faust Symphony, Orpheus
Royal Philharmonic Orchestra   Beecham
Stereo Issue : ASD 317-8

ALP1739   Gold/Red : **£3**
BEETHOVEN   Spring & Kreutzer Sonatas   Yehudi & Hepzi Menuhin
Stereo Issue : ASD 389

ALP1740-2   (==== Not Issued ====)

ALP1743   Gold/Red : **£2**
SCHUBERT   Symphony No.3, Symphony No.5
Royal Philharmonic Orchestra   Beecham
Stereo Issue : ASD 345

ALP1744   Gold/Red : **£3**
BARTOK   Concerto for Orchestra
Royal Philharmonic Orchestra   Kubelik
Stereo Issue : ASD 312

ALP1745   Gold/Red : **£10**
STRAVINSKY   Rite of Spring   Philharmonia Orchestra   Markevitch
Stereo Issue : ASD 313

ALP1746   Gold/Red : **£6**
BRUCH   Violin Concerto   Ferras
Philharmonia Orchestra   Susskind
Stereo Issue : ASD 314

ALP1747   Gold/Red : **£50**
BACH   Introduction to Bach, Books 1-3   Tureck
No Stereo

ALP1748   Gold/Red : **£2**
BEETHOVEN   Symphony No.7
Royal Philharmonic Orchestra   Beecham
Stereo Issue : ASD 311

ALP1749   Gold/Red : **£5**
Various   Overtures Hansel Gretal, Midsummer Nights Dream
Philharmonia Orchestra   Silvestri
Stereo Issue : ASD 338

ALP1750   Gold/Red : **£3**
WOLF   Lieder Recital of Spanish Songs   Moore Dieskau
Stereo Issue : ASD 378

ALP1751   Gold/Red : **£6**
SCHUBERT   Symphony No.9
Royal Philharmonic Orchestra   Kubelik
Stereo Issue : ASD 325

ALP1752-4   Gold/Red : **£9**
WEBER   Der Freischutz   Grummer
Berlin Philharmonic Orchestra   Keilberth
Stereo Issue : ASD 319-21

ALP1755-6   Gold/Red : **£3**
BACH   Brandenburg Concertos
Bath Festival Chamber Orchestra   Menhuin
Stereo Issue : ASD 327-8

ALP1757-8   Gold/Red : **£2**
GILBERT & SULLIVAN   Iolanthe
Glyndenbourne Festival Orchestra   Sargent
Stereo Issue : ASD 323-4

ALP1759   Gold/Red : **£5**
STRAUSS   Don Quixote, Till Eulenspiegel   Tortelier
Berlin Philharmonic Orchestra   Kempe
Stereo Issue : ASD 326

ALP1760   Gold/Red : **£3**
BACH   Violin Concerto, Double Concerto   Ferras, Menuhin
Bath Festival Chamber Orchestra
Stereo Issue : ASD 346

ALP1761   Gold/Red : **£2**
BIZET / LALO   Symphony In C
Orchestre National de la Radiodiffusion Francaise   Beecham
Stereo Issue : ASD 388

ALP1762-4   Gold/Red : **£3**
BIZET   Carmen   Callas
French National Radio Orchestra   Beecham
Stereo Issue : ASD 331-3

ALP1765   Gold/Red : **£5**
Various   Overtures Bartered Bride, Oberon, Hebrides
Vienna Philharmonic Orchestra   Kempe
Stereo Issue : ASD 330

ALP1766   Gold/Red : **£3**
Various   Recitals   Ambrosian Singers   Goldsbrough
Stereo Issue : ASD 335

ALP1767   Gold/Red : **£3**
SCHUBERT   Leider Recital   Fischer-Dieskau
Stereo Issue : ASD 337

ALP1768   Gold/Red : **£2**
MOZART   Clarinet concerto
Royal Philharmonic Orchestra   Beecham
Stereo Issue : ASD 344

ALP1769   Gold/Red : **£9**
BRAHMS / DVORAK   Hungarian Dances, Scherzo Caprico
Royal Philharmonic Orchestra   Kubelik
Stereo Issue : ASD 347

ALP1770   Gold/Red : **£2**
BRAHMS   Symphony No.2
Royal Philharmonic Orchestra   Beecham
Stereo Issue : ASD 348

ALP1771   Gold/Red : **£9**
BEETHOVEN   Symphony No.6
Philharmonia Orchestra   Kubelik
Stereo Issue : ASD 349

ALP1772   Gold/Red : **£6**
BRAHMS   Symphony No.1
Berlin Philharmonic Orchestra   Kempe
Stereo Issue : ASD 350

ALP1773-4   Gold/Red : **£9**
MAHLER   Das lied von der erde
Philharmonia Orchestra   Kletzki
Stereo Issue : ASD 351-2

ALP1775-6   Gold/Red : **£8**
VERDI   Requiem Christoff
Royal Philharmonic Orchestra   Serafin
Stereo Issue : ASD 353-4

ALP1777   Gold/Red : **£10**
Various   Folksongs of the British Isles   Mackerras
No Stereo

ALP1778   Gold/Red : **£4**
WOLF   Lieder Recital   Fischer-Dieskau
Stereo Issue : ASD 356

ALP1779   Gold/Red : **£12**
SCHUMANN   Symphony No.3
Berlin Philharmonic Orchestra   Cluytens
No Stereo

ALP1780-2   Gold/Red : **£8**
VERDI   La Traviata   De Los Angeles
Orchestra of Rome Opera House   Serafin
Stereo Issue : ASD 359-61

ALP1783   Gold/Red : **£3**
WOLF   Leider Recital   Fischer-Dieskau
Stereo Issue : ASD 362

ALP1784   Gold/Red : **£3**
WAGNER   Tannhauser, Gotterdammerung (Highlights) Grummer
Stereo Issue : ASD 363

ALP1785   Gold/Red : **£4**
RESPIGHI   Fountains Of Rome
Philharmonia Orchestra   Goossens
Stereo Issue : ASD 366

ALP1786-8   Gold/Red : **£5**
VIVALDI   Concertos 1 - 12   Ferro, Mozzato
Virtuosi di Roma   Fasano
Stereo Issue : ASD 367-9

ALP1789   Gold/Red : **£10**
BRAHMS   Liebeslieder Waltzer Op 52, 65   Lewis
No Stereo

ALP1790   Gold/Red : **£3**
TCHAIKOVSKY Sleeping Beauty   Philharmonia Orchestra   Kurtz
Stereo Issue : ASD 371

ALP1791   Gold/Red : **£5**
BACH   Overtures in a French Style, Italian Conerto   Tureck
Stereo Issue : ASD 372

ALP1792   Gold/Red : **£4**
Various   Christmas Carols   Royal Choral Society   Sargent
Stereo Issue : ASD 383

ALP1793   Gold/Red : £4
TCHAIKOVSKY   Songs   Christoff
Stereo Issue : ASD 390

ALP1794   Gold/Red : £3
CHOPIN   Piano Concerto No.1   Pollini
Philharmonia Orchestra   Kletzki
Stereo Issue : ASD 370

ALP1795-7   Gold/Red : £6
PUCCINI   Madama Butterfly
Orchestra of Rome Opera House   Santini
Stereo Issue : ASD 373-5

ALP1798   Gold/Red : £5
Various   Orchestral Marches   Philharmonia Orchestra   Kurtz
Stereo Issue : ASD 376

ALP1799   Gold/Red : £4
BEETHOVEN   Violin Concerto   Menuhin
Vienna Philharmonic Orchestra   Silvestri
Stereo Issue : ASD 377

ALP1800   Gold/Red : £9
TCHAIKOVSKY   Symphony No.5
Berlin Philharmonic Orchestra   Kempe
Stereo Issue : ASD 379

ALP1801-2   Gold/Red : £3
GILBERT & SULLIVAN   Pirates of Penzance   Sargent
Stereo Issue : ASD 381-2

ALP1803   Gold/Red : £8
Various   A Cziffra Recital   Cziffra
No Stereo

ALP1804   Gold/Red : £3
BACH / HANDEL Cantata No.203, Arias   Fischer-Dieskau
Stereo Issue : ASD 397

ALP1805   Gold/Red : £1
Various   Love Duets   Hammond
Stereo Issue : ASD 384

ALP1806-8   Gold/Red : **£10**
WAGNER   Flying Dutchman   Fischer-Dieskau
German State Opera, Berlin   Konwitschny
Stereo Issue : ASD 385-7

ALP1809-11   Gold/Red : **£10**
VIVALDI   L'Estro Armonico Collegium Musicum Italicum Fasano
Stereo Issue : ASD 391-3

ALP1812-3   Gold/Red : **£5**
STRAUSS   Gypsy Barron
Vienna Philharmonic Orchestra   Hollreiser
Stereo Issue : ASD 394-5

ALP1814   Gold/Red : **£5**
DVORAK   Symphony No.2
Vienna Philharmonic Orchestra   Silvestri
Stereo Issue : ASD 396

ALP1815   Gold/Red : **£6**
TCHAIKOVSKY   Symphony No.4
Vienna Philharmonic Orchestra   Kubelik
Stereo Issue : ASD 398

ALP1816   Gold/Red : **£10**
LISZT   Transcendental Studies No.1-8   Cziffra
No Stereo

ALP1818   Gold/Red : **£5**
Various   Russian Music, Capriccio Espagnol Op.34 Etc
Vienna Philharmonic Orchestra   Silvestri
Stereo Issue : ASD 400

ALP1819   Gold/Red : **£6**
STRAVINSKY   Symphony in 3 movements
Philharmonia Orchestra   Silvestri
Stereo Issue : ASD 401

ALP1820-1   Gold/Red : **£10**
DVORAK   Slavonic Dances
BBC Symphony Orchestra   Schwartz
Stereo Issue : ASD 402-3

ALP1822-3   Gold/Red : **£3**
BACH   Suites
Bath Festival Chamber Orchestra   Menhuin
Stereo Issue : ASD 404-5

ALP1824   Gold/Red : **£6**
BRAHMS   Symphony No.3
Berlin Philharmonic Orchestra   Kempe
Stereo Issue : ASD 406

ALP1825   Gold/Red : **£2**
VERDI   Operatic Arias   Fischer-Dieskau
Berlin Philharmonic Orchestra   Erede
Stereo Issue : ASD 407

ALP1826   (=== Not Issued ===)

ALP1827   Gold/Red : **£10**
SCHUBERT   Lieder Recital 4   Fischer-Dieskau
No Stereo

ALP1828   Gold/Red : **£8**
BACH   Cantata No.11, Cantata No.140   Gewandhaus
No Stereo

ALP1829   Gold/Red : **£10**
HAYDN   Songs   Fischer-Dieskau
No Stereo

ALP1830   Gold/Red : **£10**
RACHMANINOV   Songs   Christoff
No Stereo

ALP1831   Gold/Red : **£5**
FRANCK   Symphony in Dmin.   Philharmonia Orchestra   Silvestri
Stereo Issue : ASD 408

ALP1832-3   Gold/Red : **£12**
VERDI   Il Trovatore   Bjorling
RCA Symphony Orchestra   Cellini
No Stereo

ALP1834-6   Gold/Red : **£6**
HAYDN   Die Schopfung (The Creation)   Grummer
Berlin Symphony Orchestra   Forster
Stereo Issue : ASD 409-11

ALP1837   Gold/Red : **£3**
GOUNOD   Faust (Highlights)
Orchestra of the Theatre National de L'Opera   Cluytens
Stereo Issue : ASD 412

ALP1838   Gold/Red : **£3**
Various   The Fabulous De Los Angeles   De Los Angeles
Stereo Issue : ASD 413

ALP1839   Gold/Red : **£3**
BACH   The Musical Offering   Shaffer
Bath Festival Chamber Orchestra   Menhuin
Stereo Issue : ASD 414

ALP1840   Gold/Red : **£12**
SCHUMANN   Carnival, Carnival of Vienna   Cziffra
No Stereo

ALP1841   Gold/Red : **£15**
MASCAGNI / PUCCINI / VERDI   Operatic Recital   Bjorling
No Stereo

ALP1842   Gold/Red : **£5**
LISZT / RAVEL   Rhapsodies
Vienna Philharmonic Orchestra   Silvestri
Stereo Issue : ASD 417

ALP1843   Gold/Red : **£15**
FAURE   French Romantic Music
French National Radio Orchestra   Beecham
No Stereo

ALP1844   Gold/Red : **£6**
SCHUBERT   Symphony No.3, Symphony No.4
Vienna Philharmonic Orchestra   Kubelik
Stereo Issue : ASD 418

ALP1845   Gold/Red : **£10**
SCHUBERT   Lieder Recital 6   Fischer-Dieskau   Engel
No Stereo

ALP1846   Gold/Red : **£3**
ROSSINI / BERLIOZ   Favourite Overtures etc
Royal Philharmonic Orchestra   Beecham
Stereo Issue : ASD 420

ALP1847   Gold/Red : **£3**
STRAUSS   Ein Heldenleben (Sir Thomas Beecham Memorial LP)
Royal Philharmonic Orchestra   Beecham
Stereo Issue : ASD 421

ALP1848   Gold/Red : **£6**
BORODIN   Symphony No.2, Dances
Vienna Philharmonic Orchestra   Kubelik
Stereo Issue : ASD 422

ALP1849   Gold/Red : **£5**
MOZART / RAVEL   Piano Trio K542, Piano Trio   Menuhin
Stereo Issue : ASD 423

ALP1850   Gold/Red : **£10**
SCHUBERT   Lieder Recital 5   Fischer-Dieskau   Engel
No Stereo

ALP1851   Gold/Red : **£1**
GILBERT & SULLIVAN   Trial by Jury   Pro Arte   Sargent
Stereo Issue : ASD 419

ALP1852-3   Gold/Red : **£3**
WOLF   Goethe Leider   Fischer-Dieskau
Stereo Issue : ASD 424-5

ALP1854   Gold/Red : **£16**
BEETHOVEN   Symphony No.3
Berlin Philharmonic Orchestra   Kempe
Stereo Issue : ASD 426

ALP1855   Gold/Red : **£12**
TAGORE   Shyama Parts 1 - 12
No Stereo

ALP1856   Gold/Red : **£400**
BACH / MOZART   Violin Concerto   De Vito
London Symphony Orchestra   Kubelik
Stereo Issue : ASD 429

ALP1857   Gold/Red : **£15**
Various   Songs and Ballads   Bjorling   Grevillius
No Stereo

ALP1858   Gold/Red : **£9**
MOZART   Violin Concerto No.4, Violin Concerto No.5
Ferras   Paris Conservatoire Orchestra   Vandernoot
Stereo Issue : ASD 427

ALP1859   Gold/Red : **£5**
TCHAIKOVSKY   Symphony No.5
Vienna Philharmonic Orchestra   Kubelik
Stereo Issue : ASD 428

ALP1860   Gold/Red : **£3**
BERLIOZ   Damnation of Faust (highlights - No full set)
Gedda   Paris Opera Orchestra   Cluytens
Stereo Issue : ASD 430

ALP1861   Gold/Red : **£9**
Various   Vienese Bonbons
Vienna Philharmonic Orchestra   Kempe
Stereo Issue : ASD 431

ALP1862   Gold/Red : **£3**
Various   More Beecham Lollipops
Royal Philharmonic Orchestra   Beecham
Stereo Issue : ASD 432

ALP1863   Gold/Red : **£6**
BEETHOVEN   Symphony No.6
Berlin Philharmonic Orchestra   Cluytens
Stereo Issue : ASD 433

ALP1864   Gold/Red : **£3**
BUSONI/LISZT   Recital   Ogdon
Stereo Issue : ASD 434

433

ALP1865   Gold/Red : **£3**
ROSSINI   Overtures Vienna Philharmonic Orchestra   Sargent
Stereo Issue : ASD 435

ALP1866-8   Gold/Red : **£9**
VERDI   Rigoletto   Scotto
Maggio Musici Florence   Gavazzeni
Stereo Issue : ASD 436-8

ALP1869   Gold/Red : **£3**
DELIBES   Sylvia & Coppelia   Menuhin
Philharmonia Orchestra   Irving
Stereo Issue : ASD 439

ALP1870   Gold/Red : **£10**
Various   Beecham Anthology 1915 - 1939   Beecham
No Stereo

ALP1871   Gold/Red : **£10**
Various   Beecham Anthology 1946 - 1958   Beecham
No Stereo

ALP1872   Gold/Red : **£5**
PAGANINI   Violin Concerto No.1, Violin Concerto No.2
Menuhin   Royal Philharmonic Orchestra
Stereo Issue : ASD 440

ALP1873   Gold/Red : **£3**
HOLST / WALTON / BRITTEN   Perfect Fool, Facade
Royal Philharmonic Orchestra   Sargent
Stereo Issue : ASD 443

ALP1874   Gold/Red : **£6**
HAYDN   Symphony No.100, Symphony No.101, Beecham in Rehearsal
Royal Philharmonic Orchestra   Beecham
No Stereo

ALP1875   Gold/Red : **£3**
STRAUSS   Zigeunerbaron, Die Fledermaus
Vienna Philharmonic Orchestra   Hollreiser
Stereo Issue : ASD 444

ALP1876-9   Gold/Red : **£9**
WAGNER   Tannhauser   Grummer
Berlin Opera   Konwitschny
Stereo Issue : ASD 445-8

ALP1880   Gold/Red : **£6**
DVORAK / WEINBERGER Music from Bohemia
Royal Philharmonic Orchestra   Kempe
Stereo Issue : ASD 449

ALP1881   Gold/Red : **£3**
BEETHOVEN / SCHUMANN   Piano Sonata No.17, Fantasia   Richter
Stereo Issue : ASD 450

ALP1882   Gold/Red : **£12**
MOZART   Symphony No.36, Symphony No.38
Vienna Philharmonic Orchestra   Kubelik
Stereo Issue : ASD 451

ALP1883   Gold/Red : **£3**
Various   Spanish songs of the Renaissance   De Los Angeles
Stereo Issue : ASD 452

ALP1884   Gold/Red : **£5**
Various   Harpsichord Recital   Tureck
Stereo Issue : ASD 453

ALP1885   Gold/Red : **£1**
STAINER   Crucifixion   Leeds Philharmonic Choir   Berdgett
Stereo Issue : ASD 454

ALP1886   Gold/Red : **£5**
SHOSTAKOVITCH   Symphony No.5
Vienna Philharmonic Orchestra   Silvestri
Stereo Issue : ASD 455

ALP1887   Gold/Red : **£5**
Various   Operatic Recital   Gorr
Philharmonia Orchestra   Cluytens
Stereo Issue : ASD 456

ALP1888   Gold/Red : **£3**
BACH   Cantata No.211, Cantata No.212   Fischer-Dieskau
Berlin Philharmonic Orchestra   Forster
Stereo Issue : ASD 457

ALP1889-90   Gold/Red : **£12**
DELIUS   Dance Rhapsody 1, Summer Evening etc
Royal Philharmonic Orchestra   Beecham
No Stereo

ALP1891   Gold/Red : **£3**
Various   Duets   De Los Angeles
Stereo Issue : ASD 459

ALP1892   Gold/Red : **£6**
MENDELSSOHN / HUMPERDINCK Midsummernights Dream, Hansel &
Gretel   Royal Philharmonic Orchestra   Kempe
Stereo Issue : ASD 460

ALP1893   Gold/Red : **£4**
Various   Music of India   Ravi Shankar
Stereo Issue : ASD 463

ALP1894   Gold/Red : **£6**
BRAHMS   Symphony No.4
Royal Philharmonic Orchestra   Kempe
Stereo Issue : ASD 461

ALP1895   Gold/Red : **£5**
TCHAIKOVSKY   Symphony No.6
Vienna Philharmonic Orchestra   Kubelik
Stereo Issue : ASD 462

ALP1896   Gold/Red : **£4**
Various   Favourites-piano recital   Cziffra
Stereo Issue : ASD 464

ALP1897   Gold/Red : **£3**
GLUCK   Iphigenie en Tauride (Highlights)
Paris Conservatoire Orchestra   Pretre
Stereo Issue : ASD 465

ALP1898   Gold/Red : **£9**
Various   Overtures from Italian Operas
Philharmonia Orchestra   Serafin
Stereo Issue : ASD 466

ALP1899   Gold/Red : **£3**
COLERIDGE TAYLOR   Hiawatha's Wedding Feast
Philharmonia Orchestra   Sargent
Stereo Issue : ASD 467

ALP1900   Gold/Red : **£10**
BEETHOVEN   Piano Sonata No.13, Piano Sonata No.31
Solomon
No Stereo

ALP1901   Gold/Red : **£10**
SCHUBERT   Piano Sonata No.13 in A, Piano Concerto in Amin
Solomon
No Stereo

ALP1902   Gold/Red : **£3**
Various   Song Recital   Di Stefano
Stereo Issue : ASD 469

ALP1903   Gold/Red : **£4**
Various   Pearls of Viennese Operetta Rysanek
Vienna Philharmonic Orchestra   Loibner
Stereo Issue : ASD 471

ALP1904   Gold/Red : **£1**
GILBERT & SULLIVAN   HMS Pinafore (Highlights)
Pro Arte   Sargent
Stereo Issue : ASD 472

ALP1905   Gold/Red : **£4**
MOZART   Violin Concerto No.3, Violin Concerto No.5
Menuhin   Bath Festival Chamber Orchestra
Stereo Issue : ASD 473

ALP1906   Gold/Red : **£4**
BRAHMS   Violin Concerto No.1, Violin Concerto No.2
Menuhin
Stereo Issue : ASD 474

ALP1907   Gold/Red : **£3**
SCHUBERT   Sonata No.3, Fantasy in Cmaj.   Menuhin
Stereo Issue : ASD 475

ALP1908   Gold/Red : **£3**
Various   Neopolitan Songs   Di Stefano
Stereo Issue : ASD 476

ALP1909   Gold/Red : **£5**
BACH   Recital   Tureck
Stereo Issue : ASD 477

ALP1910   Gold/Red : **£14**
SCHUBERT / GLUCK   Rosamunde, Ballet Suite
Vienna Philharmonic Orchestra   Kempe
Stereo Issue : ASD 478

ALP1911   Gold/Red : **£2**
Various   20th Century Spanish Songs   De Los Angeles
Stereo Issue : ASD 479

ALP1912   Gold/Red : **£2**
HANDEL / MOZART   Gods go a Begging, Sheba etc
Royal Philharmonic Orchestra   Beecham
Stereo Issue : ASD 480

ALP1913   Gold/Red : **£3**
SCHUBERT   Die Schone Mullerin   Fischer-Dieskau
Stereo Issue : ASD 481

ALP1914-5   (==== Not Issued ====)

ALP1916   Gold/Red : **£10**
LISZT   Transcendental Studies No.10-12, Hungarian Rhapsody
No.9,10 & 13   Cziffra
No Stereo

ALP1917   Gold/Red : **£9**
MAHLER   Symphony No.1
Vienna Philharmonic Orchestra   Kletzki
Stereo Issue : ASD 483

ALP1918-9   Gold/Red : **£2**
GILBERT & SULLIVAN   Patience   Pro Arte   Sargent
Stereo Issue : ASD 484-5

ALP1920   (==== Not Issued ====)

ALP1921   Gold/Red : **£3**
PUCCINI   La Boheme (Highlights)
RCA Victrola Orchestra   Beecham
No Stereo

ALP1922   Gold/Red : **£1**
GILBERT & SULLIVAN   Gilbert & Sullivan Excerpts
Pro Arte   Sargent
Stereo Issue : ASD 487

ALP1923   Gold/Red : **£4**
Various   Neopolitan Songs   Corelli
Stereo Issue : ASD 488

ALP1924   Gold/Red : **£5**
BACH   Violin & Harpsichord Sonatas No.1,4 & 6
Menuhin, Malcolm
Stereo Issue : ASD 489

ALP1925   Gold/Red : **£5**
BACH   Violin & Harpsichord Sonatas No.2, 3 & 5
Menuhin, Malcolm
Stereo Issue : ASD 490

ALP1926   Gold/Red : **£2**
DOHNANYI   Suite for Orchestra
Royal Philharmonic Orchestra   Sargent
Stereo Issue : ASD 497

ALP1927   Gold/Red : **£3**
HANDEL   Concerti Grossi No.7, 8, 9 & 11   Menuhin
Bath Festival Chamber Orchestra
Stereo Issue : ASD 491

ALP1928   Gold/Red : **£3**
RACHMANINOV Piano Concerto No.2   Ogdon
Philharmonia Orchestra   Pritchard
Stereo Issue : ASD 492

ALP1929   Gold/Red : **£14**
BRUCKNER   Symphony No.9
Vienna Philharmonic Orchestra   Schuricht
Stereo Issue : ASD 493

ALP1930   Gold/Red : **£12**
KODALY / TCHAIKOVSKY   Hari Janos, Gotovac
Vienna Philharmonic Orchestra   Kempe
Stereo Issue : ASD 494

ALP1931   (==== Not Issued ====)

ALP1932   Gold/Red : **£1**
GILBERT & SULLIVAN   Operatic Highlights   Pro Arte   Sargent
Stereo Issue : ASD 495

ALP1933-44   Gold/Red : **£3**   each
Spoken Word   The Living Bible   Sir Laurence Olivier
No Stereo

ALP1945   Gold/Red : **£3**
POULENC   Les Biches Paris Conservatoire Orchestra   Pretre
Stereo Issue : ASD 496

ALP1946   Gold/Red : **£4**
Various   Music of India   Imrat Khan
Stereo Issue : ASD 498

ALP1947   Gold/Red : **£10**
SIBELIUS   Symphony No.2
Royal Philharmonic Orchestra   Beecham
No Stereo

ALP1948   Gold/Red : **£3**
BLISS   Concerto for Piano and Orchestra
Philharmonia Orchestra   Sargent
Stereo Issue : ASD 499

ALP1949   Gold/Red : **£3**
BACH / HANDEL / VIVALDI   Concerto in D   Goossens
Bath Festival Chamber Orchestra   Menhuin
Stereo Issue : ASD 500

ALP1950   Gold/Red : **£2**
BACH   Christmas Oratorio   Fischer-Dieskau
Leipzig Gewandhaus Orchestra   Thomas
Stereo Issue : ASD 501

ALP1951-3   Gold/Red : **£4**
BACH   Oratorios 1-6   Fischer-Dieskau
Leipzig Gewandhaus Orchestra   Thomas
Stereo Issue : ASD 502-4

ALP1954   Gold/Red : **£3**
Various   Cantos de Espana   De Los Angeles
Paris Conservatoire Orchestra   De Burgos
Stereo Issue : ASD 505

ALP1955   Gold/Red : **£5**
HAYDN / MOZART   Symphony No.45, Eine Kleine,Notturn
Bath Festival Chamber Orchestra   Menhuin
Stereo Issue : ASD 506

ALP1956   Gold/Red : **£9**
STRAVINSKY   Pulcinella   Philharmonia Orchestra   Vandernoot
Stereo Issue : ASD 507

ALP1957   Gold/Red : **£6**
VAUGHAN-WILLIAMS   Symphony No.5
Philharmonia Orchestra   Barbirolli
Stereo Issue : ASD 508

ALP1958   Gold/Red : **£6**
Various   Russian Orchestral Masterpieces
Royal Philharmonic Orchestra   Pretre
Stereo Issue : ASD 509

ALP1959   Gold/Red : **£6**
BEETHOVEN   Violin Sonata No.7, Violin Sonata No.10
Yehudi & Hepzi Menuhin
Stereo Issue : ASD 510

441

ALP1960   Gold/Red : £ 3
STRAVINSKY   Oedipus Rex   Royal Philharmonic Orchestra   Davis
Stereo Issue : ASD 511

ALP1961   Gold/Red : £ 4
PROKOFIEV / TIPPETT   Concerto for Double String Orchestra, Etc
Moscow Chamber Orchestra   Barshai
Stereo Issue : ASD 512

ALP1962   Gold/Red : £ 9
GLINKA   Life for the Tzar   Philharmonia Orchestra   Kurtz
Stereo Issue : ASD 513

ALP1963   Gold/Red : £ 6
SCHUBERT / MOZART   Symphony No.8, Eine Kleine Nacht Music
Vienna Philharmonic Orchestra   Kubelik
Stereo Issue : ASD 514

ALP1964   Gold/Red : £ 3
BRUCKNER   Mass No.3   Berlin Symphony Orchestra   Forster
Stereo Issue : ASD 515

ALP1965   Gold/Red : £ 5
Various   Neopolitan Songs   Corelli
Stereo Issue : ASD 516

ALP1966   Gold/Red : £ 6
DVORAK   Slavonic Dances 1 & 2
Paris Conservatoire Orchestra   Silvestri
Stereo Issue : ASD 519

ALP1967   Gold/Red : £ 6
POULENC   Concerto For Two Pianos   Pretre,Poulenc
Paris Conservatoire Orchestra   Fevrier
Stereo Issue : ASD 517

ALP1968   Gold/Red : £ 2
Various   The Inimitable Sir Thomas
Royal Philharmonic Orchestra   Beecham
Stereo Issue : ASD 518

ALP1969   Gold/Red : **£2**
SCHUMANN   Piano Sonata No.2, Papillons Etc   Richter
Stereo Issue : ASD 520

ALP1970   Gold/Red : **£3**
ELGAR / VAUGHAN WILLIAMS   English String Music
Symphonia of London   Barbirolli
Stereo Issue : ASD 521

ALP1971-3   Gold/Red : **£18**
SMETANA   Bartered Bride
Bamburg Symphony Orchestra   Kempe
Stereo Issue : ASD 522-4

ALP1974   Gold/Red : **£10**
Various   Vienna Philharmonic on Holiday
Vienna Philharmonic Orchestra   Kempe
Stereo Issue : ASD 525

ALP1975-7   Gold/Red : **£6**
BACH   St. Johns Passion
Berlin Philharmonic Orchestra   Forster
Stereo Issue : ASD 526-8

ALP1978   Gold/Red : **£2**
Various   Operatic Recital   Corelli
Stereo Issue : ASD 529

ALP1979   Gold/Red : **£5**
Various   A French Recital   De Los Angeles
Stereo Issue : ASD 530

ALP1980   Gold/Red : **£5**
ENESCU / DEBUSSY / RAVEL   Violin Sonata No.3, Violin Sonata
Ferras
Stereo Issue : ASD 531

ALP1981   Gold/Red : **£5**
RIMSKY-KORSAKOV / KABALEVSKY   Le Coq D'or, Comedians
Philharmonia Orchestra   Kurtz
Stereo Issue : ASD 532

ALP1982   Gold/Red : **£3**
MOZART   Violin Concerto No.4, Violin Concerto No.6
Menuhin   Bath Festival Chamber Orchestra
Stereo Issue : ASD 533

ALP1983   Gold/Red : **£5**
DELIUS   Songs of Sunset
Royal Philharmonic Orchestra   Beecham
No Stereo

ALP1984   Gold/Red : **£5**
WAGNER   Das Rheingold (Highlights - No full Set)
State Opera Berlin   Kempe
Stereo Issue : ASD 535

ALP1985   Gold/Red : **£3**
BACH / TELEMAN   Hunting Cantata, Canary Cantata
Fischer-Dieskau   Berlin Symphony Orchestra   Forster
Stereo Issue : ASD 534

ALP1986   Gold/Red : **£2**
BERLIOZ   Harold in Italy   Menuhin
Philharmonia Orchestra   Davis
Stereo Issue : ASD 537

ALP1987   Gold/Red : **£3**
LISZT   Piano Recital: Annees de Pelerina   Kentner
Stereo Issue : ASD 538

ALP1988   Gold/Red : **£5**
Various   Music of India   Vilayat Khan
Stereo Issue : ASD 539

ALP1989   Gold/Red : **£3**
ELGAR   Symphony No.1   Halle Orchestra   Barbirolli
Stereo Issue : ASD 540

ALP1990   Gold/Red : **£3**
SIBELIUS   En Saga, Finlandia etc
Vienna Philharmonic Orchestra   Sargent
Stereo Issue : ASD 541

ALP1991 Gold/Red : **£3**
TCHAIKOVSKY / FRANCK Piano Concerto No.1, Symphonic
Variations Ogdon Philharmonia Orchestra Barbirolli
Stereo Issue : ASD 542

ALP1992 Gold/Red : **£6**
VERDI La Traviata
Orchestra of Rome Opera House Serafin
Stereo Issue : ASD 543

ALP1993 Gold/Red : **£3**
SCHUBERT Schwanengesang Fischer-Dieskau
Stereo Issue : ASD 544

ALP1994 Gold/Red : **£6**
FALLA Gardens of Spain
Paris Conservatoire Orchestra Soriano
Stereo Issue : ASD 545

ALP1995 Gold/Red : **£3**
Various Piano Recital Ogdon
Stereo Issue : ASD 546

ALP1996 Gold/Red : **£4**
GLINKA Songs of Glinka Christoff
Stereo Issue : ASD 547

ALP1997 Gold/Red : **£3**
GLUCK Orfeo & Euridice (Highlights)
Berlin Symphony Orchestra Stein
Stereo Issue : ASD 550

ALP1998 Gold/Red : **£3**
ELGAR Enigma Variations
Philharmonia Orchestra Barbirolli
Stereo Issue : ASD 548

ALP1999 Gold/Red : **£9**
BRAHMS / BEETHOVEN Double Concerto, Sonata No.1
Ferras, Tortelier
Stereo Issue : ASD 549

ALP2000   Gold/Red : **£6**
WAGNER   Wesendonck Lieder etc   Crespin
French National Radio Orchestra   Pretre
Stereo Issue : ASD 553

ALP2001-2   Gold/Red : **£4**
SCHUBERT   Winterreise   Fischer-Dieskau
Stereo Issue : ASD 551-2

ALP2003   Gold/Red : **£8**
DVORAK / WAGNER   Symphony No.8, Meistersinger Prelude
Royal Philharmonic Orchestra   Beecham
No Stereo

ALP2004   Gold/Red : **£3**
CORELLI   Concerto Grossi   Virtuosi di Roma   Fasano
Stereo Issue : ASD 554

ALP2005   Gold/Red : **£2**
WAGNER   Tannhauser (Highlights)   Grummer
Berlin Opera   Konwitschny
Stereo Issue : ASD 555

ALP2006   Gold/Red : **£2**
WAGNER   Flying Dutchman (Highlights)   Fischer-Dieskau
Berlin Opera   Konwitschny
Stereo Issue : ASD 556

ALP2007   Gold/Red : **£5**
Various   A Castle Bruhl Concert
Cologne Soloists Ensemble   Bruhl
Stereo Issue : ASD 557

ALP2008   Gold/Red : **£3**
Various   Great Sopranos   Callas, De Los Angeles
Stereo Issue : ASD 558

ALP2009   Gold/Red : **£4**
SHOSTAKOVITCH   Symphony No.12
Philharmonia Orchestra   Pretre
Stereo Issue : ASD 559

ALP2010 Gold/Red : **£3**
Various Operatic Recital Traxel Klobucar
Stereo Issue : ASD 560

ALP2011 Gold/Red : **£3**
SCHUBERT Wanderer fantasie, Sonata in A maj. Op.120 Richter
Stereo Issue : ASD 561

ALP2012 Gold/Red : **£2**
WEBER Der Freischutz (Highlights) Grummer
Berlin Philharmonic Orchestra Keilberth
Stereo Issue : ASD 562

ALP2013-4 Gold/Red : **£2**
GILBERT & SULLIVAN Ruddigore Pro Arte Sargent
Stereo Issue : ASD 563-4

ALP2015 Gold/Red : **£3**
Various Leider Recital Koth
Stereo Issue : ASD 565

ALP2016 Gold/Red : **£2**
TCHAIKOVSKY Eugen Onegin (Highlights) Prey
Bavarian Symphony Orchestra Zalinger
Stereo Issue : ASD 566

ALP2017 Gold/Red : **£4**
MOZART / HAYDN Sinfonia Concertante, Violin Concerto
Menuhin Bath Festival Chamber Orchestra Barshai
Stereo Issue : ASD 567

ALP2018 Gold/Red : **£3**
Various More Carols Royal Choral Society Sargent
Stereo Issue : ASD 568

ALP2019 Gold/Red : **£3**
MOZART / PALESTRINA Missa Brevis St. Hedwigs Choir Forster
Stereo Issue : ASD 569

ALP2020 Gold/Red : **£5**
Various Music of Spain
Paris Conservatoire Orchestra De Burgos
Stereo Issue : ASD 570

ALP2021   Gold/Red : **£3**
MASSENET   Herodiade (Highlights)   Crespin Pretre
Stereo Issue : ASD 571

ALP2022   Gold/Red : **£4**
BERG   Violin Concerto   Ferras
Stereo Issue : ASD 572

ALP2023   Gold/Red : **£6**
BRAHMS   Variations On a theme By Haydn Etc.
Philharmonia Orchestra   Krips
Stereo Issue : ASD 573

ALP2024   (=== Not Issued ===)

ALP2025   Gold/Red : **£4**
Various   Tzars & Kings   Christoff Cluytens
Stereo Issue : ASD 574

ALP2026   Gold/Red : **£5**
MOZART / TELEMAN   Concerto for Flute, Concerto for Harp
Bath Festival Chamber Orchestra   Menhuin
Stereo Issue : ASD 575

ALP2027   Gold/Red : **£3**
GLUCK   Alceste (Highlights) Paris Opera Orchestra   Pretre
Stereo Issue : ASD 576

ALP2028   Gold/Red : **£4**
HANDEL   Water Music
Bath Festival Chamber Orchestra   Menhuin
Stereo Issue : ASD 577

ALP2029   Gold/Red : **£10**
PROKOFIEV   Symphony No.5   Philharmonia Orchestra   Kletzki
Stereo Issue : ASD 578

ALP2030   Gold/Red : **£5**
VIVALDI   Concertos   Virtuosi di Roma Fasano
Stereo Issue : ASD 579

ALP2031-2   Gold/Red : **£7**
NICOLAI   Merry Wives of Windsor
Bavarian Symphony Orchestra   Heger
Stereo Issue : ASD 580-1

ALP2033   Gold/Red : **£10**
RIMSKY-KORSAKOV   Tzar Saltan, Snow Maiden
Philharmonia Orchestra   Kurtz
Stereo Issue : ASD 582

ALP2034   Gold/Red : **£6**
POULENC   Stabat Mater, 4 Motets   Crespin
Paris Conservatoire Orchestra   Pretre
Stereo Issue : ASD 583

ALP2035   Gold/Red : **£15**
BLOCH   Violin Concerto   Menuhin
Philharmonia Orchestra   Kletzki
Stereo Issue : ASD 584

ALP2036   Gold/Red : **£6**
SAINT-SAENS   Symphony No.3
Paris Conservatoire Orchestra   Pretre
Stereo Issue : ASD 585

ALP2037   (==== Not Issued ====)

ALP2038   Gold/Red : **£5**
BRAHMS   Sextet No.1   Menuhin
Stereo Issue : ASD 587

ALP2039   Gold/Red : **£3**
ROSSINI   Stabat Mater   Berlin Symphony Orchestra   Forster
Stereo Issue : ASD 588

ALP2040   Gold/Red : **£2**
GOUNOD   Messe Solenelle
Paris Conservatoire Orchestra   Hartemann
Stereo Issue : ASD 589

ALP2041   Gold/Red : **£1**
BIZET   Carmen (Highlights)   Callas
French National Radio Orchestra   Beecham
Stereo Issue : ASD 590

ALP2042   Gold/Red : **£5**
MOZART   Violin Concerto No.1, Violin Concerto No.2
Menuhin   Bath Festival Chamber Orchestra
Stereo Issue : ASD 591

ALP2043   Gold/Red : **£5**
MOZART   Violin Concerto No.7, Concertone in C K.190
Menuhin   Bath Festival Chamber Orchestra
Stereo Issue : ASD 592

ALP2044   Gold/Red : **£3**
SCHUMANN / STRAUSS   Leider Recital   Della Casa
Stereo Issue : ASD 593

ALP2045   Gold/Red : **£1**
STRAUSS   Ariadne auf Naxos (Highlights)
Berlin Philharmonic Orchestra   Erede
Stereo Issue : ASD 594

ALP2046   Gold/Red : **£2**
MOZART / HAYDN   Symphony No.29, Symphony No.49
Menuhin   Bath Festival Chamber Orchestra
Stereo Issue : ASD 595

ALP2047-8   Gold/Red : **£20**
MAHLER   Symphony No.9
Berlin Philharmonic Orchestra   Barbirolli
Stereo Issue : ASD 596-7

ALP2049   Gold/Red : **£4**
HANDEL   Concerti Grossi No.3, 6, 10 & 12   Menuhin
Bath Festival Chamber Orchestra
Stereo Issue : ASD 598

ALP2050   Gold/Red : **£4**
Various   Franco Corelli Sings Great Religious Arias   Corelli
Stereo Issue : ASD 599

ALP2051   Gold/Red : **£4**
LISZT   Sonata in Bmin. Hungarian Fantasia, Rapsodie Espagnole
Ogdon   Philharmonia Orchestra   Pritchard
Stereo Issue : ASD 600

ALP2052   Gold/Red : **£4**
CARTER   Piano Sonata, Double Concerto   Rosen
Stereo Issue : ASD 601

ALP2053-4   Gold/Red : **£12**
BRUCKNER   Symphony No.8
Vienna Philharmonic Orchestra   Schuricht
Stereo Issue : ASD 602-3

ALP2055   Gold/Red : **£4**
HANDEL   Concerti Grossi
Bath Festival Chamber Orchestra   Menhuin
Stereo Issue : ASD 604

ALP2056   Gold/Red : **£3**
MOZART   Trio In E Flat,Quintet In A Major   Melos Ensemble
Stereo Issue : ASD 605

ALP2057-8   Gold/Red : **£4**
Various   Song and Operatic Recital   Gobbi
Stereo Issue : ASD 606-7

ALP2059   Gold/Red : **£10**
FALLA   The Three Cornered Hat   De Los Angeles
Philharmonia Orchestra   De Burgos
Stereo Issue : ASD 608

ALP2060   Gold/Red : **£2**
PUCCINI   Madama Butterfly (Highlights)
Orchestra of Rome Opera House   Santini
Stereo Issue : ASD 609

ALP2061-2   Gold/Red : **£2**
ELGAR   Symphony No.2, Falstaff   Halle Orchestra   Barbirolli
Stereo Issue : ASD 610-11

ALP2063   Gold/Red : **£6**
GERHARD   Symphony No.1, Dances from Don Quixote
BBC Symphony Orchestra   Dorati
Stereo Issue : ASD 613

ALP2064   Gold/Red : **£5**
SCHONBERG   Symphony for Strings
Royal Philharmonic Orchestra   Del Mar
Stereo Issue : ASD 612

ALP2065   Gold/Red : **£5**
Various   Works for Two Pianos   Vronsky , Babin
Stereo Issue : ASD 614

ALP2066   Gold/Red : **£3**
Various   Religious Works   Fischer-Dieskau
Stereo Issue : ASD 615

ALP2067   Gold/Red : **£5**
VERDI   Simone Boccanegra (Highlights)   De Los Angeles
Rome Opera Orchestra   Santini
No Stereo

ALP2068   Gold/Red : **£2**
Various   Recital On Wings of Song   Hammond
Stereo Issue : ASD 616

ALP2069   Gold/Red : **£8**
MOZART   Symphony No.35, Symphony No.41
Vienna Philharmonic Orchestra   Kubelik
Stereo Issue : ASD 617

ALP2070   Gold/Red : **£5**
BEETHOVEN / CHAUSSON / WIENIEAWSKI   Romances
Menuhin Philharmonia Orchestra   Pritchard
Stereo Issue : ASD 618

ALP2071   Gold/Red : **£2**
THOMAS   Mignon (Highlights)
Paris Opera Orchestra   Hartemann
Stereo Issue : ASD 619

ALP2072 Gold/Red : **£3**
BRAHMS / REGER Quintet In B For Clarinet & Strings, Quintet In A
De Peyer Melos Ensemble
Stereo Issue : ASD 620

ALP2073 Gold/Red : **£4**
TIPPETT Piano Concerto, Sonata No.2 Ogdon
Philharmonia Orchestra Davis
Stereo Issue : ASD 621

ALP2074 Gold/Red : **£4**
Various Operatic Recital Freni
Orchestra of Rome Opera House Ferraris
Stereo Issue : ASD 622

ALP2075 Gold/Red : **£2**
BACH / FRESCOBALDI Organ Works Germani
Stereo Issue : ASD 623

ALP2076 Gold/Red : **£3**
BACH Easter Oratorio Fischer-Dieskau
South West Germany Chamber Orchestra Gonnenwein
Stereo Issue : ASD 624

ALP2077 Gold/Red : **£2**
MENDELSSOHN Elijah (Highlights)
Royal Philharmonic Orchestra Sargent
Stereo Issue : ASD 625

ALP2078 (==== Not Issued ====)

ALP2079 Gold/Red : **£4**
MOZART Serenade K.250 "Haffner"
Bath Festival Chamber Orchestra Menhuin
Stereo Issue : ASD 627

ALP2080 Gold/Red : **£4**
COUPERIN Apotheose de Lully, Corelli, etc.
Toulouse Chamber Orchestra Auriacombe
Stereo Issue : ASD 628

ALP2081 Gold/Red : **£8**
Spoken Word State Funeral of Sir Winston Churchill

ALP2082   Gold/Red : **£4**
LISZT   Piano Concerto No.1,Todtentanz, Hungarian Fantasy
Cziffra   Philharmonia Orchestra   Vandernoot
Stereo Issue : ASD 629

ALP2083   Gold/Red : **£3**
BRAHMS   Leider Recital   Fischer-Dieskau
Stereo Issue : ASD 630

ALP2084   Gold/Red : **£5**
TELEMANN   Orchestral Music   Moscow Chamber Orchestra Barshai
Stereo Issue : ASD 631

ALP2085   Gold/Red : **£15**
SCHUBERT   Symphony No.9   Halle Orchestra   Barbirolli
No Stereo

ALP2086   Gold/Red : **£5**
BACH   Flute Sonatas Vol.1   Shaffer
Stereo Issue : ASD 633

ALP2087   (===== Not Issued =====)

ALP2088   Gold/Red : **£5**
PURCELL   An Anthology Vol.1   Menuhin
Stereo Issue : ASD 635

ALP2089   Gold/Red : **£4**
TCHAIKOVSKY Symphony No.5   New Philharmonia Orchestra   Pretre
Stereo Issue : ASD 636

ALP2090   Gold/Red : **£2**
BRITTEN / CORRELLI / TIPPETT   Concerto Grosso, Fantasia
Concertante   Bath Festival Chamber Orchestra   Menuhin
Stereo Issue : ASD 637

ALP2091   (===== Not Issued =====)

ALP2092   Gold/Red : **£3**
BOULEZ   Soleil des Eaux, Messiaen
BBC Symphony Orchestra   Dorati
Stereo Issue : ASD 639

ALP2093   Gold/Red : **£2**
Various   Choral Music   Melos Ensemble
Stereo Issue : ASD 640

ALP2094   Gold/Red : **£2**
BYRD   Byrd and his contemporaries   Kings College Choir
Stereo Issue : ASD 641

ALP2095   Gold/Red : **£8**
Various   20th Century Spanish Piano Music   Soriano
Stereo Issue : ASD 642

ALP2096   Gold/Red : **£4**
BRAHMS / SCHUBERT   Sextet No.2, Trio In B Flat   Menuhin
Stereo Issue : ASD 643

ALP2097   Gold/Red : **£8**
DELIUS   Cello Concerto, Songs Farewell   Du Pre
Royal Philharmonic Orchestra   Sargent
Stereo Issue : ASD 644

ALP2098   Gold/Red : **£3**
HODDINOTT / HALL / GOEHR   Piano Music: 20th Century Composers
Ogdon
Stereo Issue : ASD 645

ALP2099   Gold/Red : **£1**
TCHAIKOVSKY   Serenade For Strings Arensky
London Symphony Orchestra   Barbirolli
Stereo Issue : ASD 646

ALP2100   (==== Not Issued ====)

ALP2101-2   Gold/Red : **£1**
ELGAR   The Dream Of Gerontius
Halle Orchestra   Barbirolli
Stereo Issue : ASD 648-9

ALP2103   Gold/Red : **£3**
SCHUMANN   Lieder   Fischer-Dieskau
Stereo Issue : ASD 650

ALP2104   Gold/Red : **£3**
Various   Victoria De Los Angeles A World Of Song
De Los Angeles   Symphonia of London   De Burgos
Stereo Issue : ASD 651

ALP2105   Gold/Red : **£5**
MASSENET   Manon (Highlights)   De Los Angeles
Paris Conservatoire Orchestra   Monteux
No Stereo

ALP2106   Gold/Red : **£4**
ELGAR   Cello Concerto, Sea Pictures   Du Pre
London Symphony Orchestra   Barbirolli
Stereo Issue : ASD 655

ALP2107-10   (==== Not Issued ====)

ALP2111   Gold/Red : **£3**
Various   From Christmas to Candlemass
Kings College Choir   Willcocks
Stereo Issue : ASD 653

ALP2112   Gold/Red : **£4**
STRAUSS / STRAVINSKY Der Rosankavalier Suite, etc.
Philharmonia Orchestra   Krips
Stereo Issue : ASD 654

ALP2113   Gold/Red : **£8**
Various   Mahatma Gandhi Centenary Commemoration Record
Choir of St. Pauls Cathedrel
No Stereo

ALP2114   Gold/Red : **£40**
WOLF   A Hugo Wolf Recital   Schwarzkopf
(Furtwangler on Piano)
No Stereo

ALP2115   Gold/Red : **£10**
Various   French Song Recital   Croiza
No Stereo

HMV ASD 3-digit series Stereophonic LP's

The First ASD label is Gold and cream and is used on all early ASD records until ASD 575. This label is referred to **G/c** (Gold/cream) throughout the guide.

From ASD 576, the first ASD label is red and has the words 'His Masters Voice' printed in bold white letters around a semi-circular 'Nipper' logo covering much of the top half of the label. The lettering on the label is printed in Black. These are referred to as **S/c** (Semicircle) in this section of the guide.

Re-pressed records from the ASD 3-digit series may have any one of a variety of similar labels. A full description appears before the ASD 4-digit section, but for simplicity, these labels have been collectively referred to as **P.Stamp** (postage stamp) throughout this section.

There are a small number of cases where re-pressed 3-digit ASD's were still being manufactured during the 1980's . These records may have a very late label referred to as the 'Large Dog' (or 2nd Semi in this guide). These records are generally of no interest to collectors and are not considered in this section. A full description of this label can be found before the ASD 4-digit section of this book.

It is important to note that although prices have been printed for all subsequent pressings of each record, in some cases these re-pressed records may not exist. A typical example would be ASD429, which almost certainly only exists as a Gold/Cream label.

ASD 251   G/c : **£35**   S/c : £10   P.Stamp : £4
RIMSKY-KORSAKOV   Scheherezade
Royal Philharmonic Orchestra   Beecham
Mono Issue : ALP1564

ASD 252   G/c : **£40**   S/c : £12   P.Stamp : £5
BIZET   L'Arlesienne   Royal Philharmonic Orchestra   Beecham
Mono Issue : ALP1497

ASD 253   G/c : **£50**   S/c : £15   P.Stamp : £5
TCHAIKOVSKY   Symphony No.4   Philharmonia Orchestra   Silvestri
Mono Issue : ALP1511

ASD 254   G/c : **£400**   S/c : £150   P.Stamp : £50
BEETHOVEN   Symphony No.7   Philharmonia Orchestra   Cantelli
Mono Issue : ALP1472

ASD 255   G/c : **£150**   S/c : £50   P.Stamp : £20
RAVEL / RACHMANINOV Piano Concerto in G, Piano Concerto No.4
Michelangeli   Philharmonia Orchestra   Gracis
Mono Issue : ALP1538

ASD 256-7   G/c : **£20**   S/c : £5   P.Stamp : £4
GILBERT & SULLIVAN   The Mikado   Glyndebourne   Sargent
Mono Issue : ALP1485-6

ASD 258   G/c : **£30**   S/c : £8   P.Stamp : £4
GRIEG   Peer Gynt   Royal Philharmonic Orchestra   Beecham
Mono Issue : ALP1530

ASD 259   G/c : **£20**   S/c : £7   P.Stamp : £2
Various   Beecham Lollipops
Royal Philharmonic Orchestra   Beecham
Mono Issue : ALP1533

ASD 260   G/c : **£40**   S/c : £20   P.Stamp : £4
SIBELIUS   Symphony No.1   BBC Symphony Orchestra   Sargent
Mono Issue : ALP1542

ASD 261   G/c : **£100**   S/c : £25   P.Stamp : £10
TCHAIKOVSKY   Symphony No.5   Philharmonia Orchestra   Silvestri
Mono Issue : ALP1491

ASD 262 G/c : **£100** S/c : £40 P.Stamp : £10
Various Russian Easter Festival
Philharmonia Orchestra Goossens
Mono Issue : ALP1490

ASD 263 G/c : **£60** S/c : £30 P.Stamp : £6
PROKOFIEV / SHOSTAKOVITCH Classical Symphony, Symphony No.1
Philharmonia Orchestra Kurtz
Mono Issue : ALP1554

ASD 264 G/c : **£50** S/c : £15 P.Stamp : £7
BRAHMS Violin Concerto Menuhin
Berlin Philharmonic Orchestra Kempe
Mono Issue : ALP1568

ASD 265-6 G/c : **£20** S/c : £5 P.Stamp : £2
GILBERT & SULLIVAN The Gondoliers
Glyndebourne Pro Arte Sargent
Mono Issue : ALP1504-5

ASD 267 G/c : **£100** S/c : £15 P.Stamp : £10
BEETHOVEN Symphony No.5, Leonora 3 Ov
Berlin Philharmonic Orchestra Cluytens
Mono Issue : ALP1657

ASD 268 G/c : **£75** S/c : £18 P.Stamp : £7
BRAHMS Piano Concerto No.2 Kentner Boult
Mono Issue : ALP1704

ASD 269 G/c : **£15** S/c : £8 P.Stamp : £2
HOLST The Planets BBC Symphony Orchestra Sargent
Mono Issue : ALP1600

ASD 270 G/c : **£120** S/c : £30 P.Stamp : £12
STRAUSS Tod und Verk, Dance of the 7 Veils
Philharmonia Orchestra Rodzinsky
Mono Issue : ALP1605

ASD 271 G/c : **£30** S/c : £12 P.Stamp : £4
TCHAIKOVSKY Swan Lake Menuhin
Philharmonia Orchestra Kurtz
Mono Issue : ALP1644

ASD 272   G/c : **£20**   S/c : £8   P.Stamp : £4
GRIEG / SCHUMANN   Piano Concertos   Solomon
Philharmonia Orchestra   Menges
Mono Issue : ALP1643

ASD 273   G/c : **£120**   S/c : £25   P.Stamp : £12
TCHAIKOVSKY   Symphony No.6   Philharmonia Orchestra   Silvestri
Mono Issue : ALP1495

ASD 274-7   G/c : **£400**   S/c : £90   P.Stamp : £25
MOZART   Marriage of Figaro   Glyndebourne Orchestra   Gui
Mono Issue : ALP1312-15

ASD 278   G/c : **£60**   S/c : £15   P.Stamp : £6
MENDELSSOHN / TCHAIKOVSKY   Violin Concertos   Ferras
Philharmonia Orchestra   Silvestri
Mono Issue : ALP1543

ASD 279   G/c : **£150**   S/c : £30   P.Stamp : £12
LEHAR / STRAUSS / SUPPE   Nights in Vienna
Vienna Philharmonic Orchestra   Kempe
Mono Issue : ALP1637

ASD 280   G/c : **£40**   S/c : £10   P.Stamp : £4
BEETHOVEN   Mass in C   Royal Philharmonic Orchestra   Beecham
Mono Issue : ALP1674

ASD 281   G/c : **£50**   S/c : £15   P.Stamp : £6
FALLA   Three cornered hat
Royal Philharmonic Orchestra   Rodzinsky
Mono Issue : ALP1688

ASD 282-4   G/c : **£120**   S/c : £40   P.Stamp : £12
HAYDN   The Seasons   Royal Philharmonic Orchestra   Beecham
Mono Issue : ALP1606-8

ASD 285   (==== Not Issued ====)

ASD 286   G/c : **£25**   S/c : £7   P.Stamp : £3
HANDEL   Water Music, Fireworks Music
Royal Philharmonic Orchestra   Sargent
Mono Issue : ALP1710

ASD 287   G/c : **£30**   S/c : £8   P.Stamp : £3
BEETHOVEN   Symphony No.2
Royal Philharmonic Orchestra   Beecham
Mono Issue : ALP1596

ASD 288   G/c : **£70**   S/c : £15   P.Stamp : £6
TCHAIKOVSKY   Romeo & Juliet
Royal Philharmonic Orchestra   Rodzinsky
Mono Issue : ALP1711

ASD 289   G/c : **£30**   S/c : £8   P.Stamp : £3
TCHAIKOVSKY   Nutcracker extracts   Philharmonia Orchestra   Kurtz
Mono Issue : ALP1609

ASD 290   G/c : **£50**   S/c : £20   P.Stamp : £6
LALO / SAINT-SAINS   Symphony Espagnole, Intro & Rondo Capricio
Menuhin   Philharmonia Orchestra   Goossens
Mono Issue : ALP1571

ASD 291   G/c : **£25**   S/c : £6   P.Stamp : £3
HANDEL   Airs   Lewis   London Symphony Orchestra   Sargent
Mono Issue : ALP1575

ASD 292-3   (═══ Not Issued ═══)

ASD 294   G/c : **£35**   S/c : £8   P.Stamp : £4
BEETHOVEN   Piano Concerto 1   Solomon
Philharmonia Orchestra   Menges
Mono Issue : ALP1583

ASD 295   G/c : **£40**   S/c : £10   P.Stamp : £6
PUCCINI   Gianni Schicchi   Gobbi
Orchestra of Rome Opera House   Santini
Mono Issue : ALP1726

ASD 296   G/c : **£60**   S/c : £20   P.Stamp : £7
SCHUBERT   Symphony No.8 (Unfinished), Rosamunde
Royal Philharmonic Orchestra   Kletzki
Mono Issue : ALP1725

ASD 297   G/c : **£85**   S/c : £20   P.Stamp : £8
FALLA   El Amor Brujo   Philharmonia Orchestra   Vandernoot
Mono Issue : ALP1727

ASD 298   G/c : **£ 28**   S/c : £6   P.Stamp : £3
HANDEL - BEECHAM   Love In Bath
Royal Philharmonic Orchestra   Beecham
Mono Issue : ALP1729

ASD 299   G/c : **£ 75**   S/c : £14   P.Stamp : £7
SAINT-SAENS   Carnival of the Animals, Peter & Wolf
Philharmonia Orchestra   Kurtz
Mono Issue : ALP1728

ASD 300   (==== Not Issued ====)

ASD 301   G/c : **£ 30**   S/c : £10   P.Stamp : £4
GRIEG / LISZT   Piano Concerto, Piano Concerto No.2 Cziffra
Philharmonia Orchestra   Vandernoot
Mono Issue : ALP1678

ASD 302   G/c : **£ 25**   S/c : £8   P.Stamp : £3
Various   Operatic Arias   Hammond
Philharmonia Orchestra   Susskind
Mono Issue : ALP1680

ASD 303   G/c : **£ 40**   S/c : £8   P.Stamp : £4
SIBELIUS   Symphony No.5 In E Flat
BBC Symphony Orchestra   Sargent
Mono Issue : ALP1732

ASD 304   G/c : **£ 100**   S/c : £18   P.Stamp : £8
Various   Popular Movements from the Symphonies
Vienna Philharmonic Orchestra   Cluytens
Mono Issue : ALP1736

ASD 305-6   (==== Not Issued ====)

ASD 307-10   G/c : **£ 70**   S/c : £20   P.Stamp : £10
GOUNOD   Faust
Orchestra of the Theatre National de L'Opera   Cluytens
Mono Issue : ALP1721-4

ASD 311   G/c : **£ 30**   S/c : £8   P.Stamp : £3
BEETHOVEN   Symphony No.7
Royal Philharmonic Orchestra   Beecham
Mono Issue : ALP1748

ASD 312   G/c : **£50**   S/c : £10   P.Stamp : £5
BARTOK   Concerto for Orchestra
Royal Philharmonic Orchestra   Kubelik
Mono Issue : ALP1744

ASD 313   G/c : **£150**   S/c : £30   P.Stamp : £15
STRAVINSKY   Rite of Spring   Philharmonia Orchestra   Markevitch
Mono Issue : ALP1745

ASD 314   G/c : **£100**   S/c : £20   P.Stamp : £10
BRUCH   Violin Concerto   Ferras
Philharmonia Orchestra   Susskind
Mono Issue : ALP1746

ASD 315   G/c : **£30**   S/c : £8   P.Stamp : £4
TCHAIKOVSKY   Piano Concerto No.1   Cziffra
Philharmonia Orchestra   Vandernoot
Mono Issue : ALP1718

ASD 316   (==== Not Issued ====)

ASD 317-8   G/c : **£40**   S/c : £10   P.Stamp : £6
LISZT   Faust Symphony, Orpheus
Royal Philharmonic Orchestra   Beecham
Mono Issue : ALP1737-8

ASD 319-21   G/c : **£85**   S/c : £20   P.Stamp : £12
WEBER   Der freischutz   Grummer
Berlin Philharmonic Orchestra   Keilberth
Mono Issue : ALP1752-4

ASD 322   G/c : **£50**   S/c : £15   P.Stamp : £5
SCHUBERT   Trout Quintet   H. Menuhin   Amadeus String Quartet
Mono Issue : ALP1733

ASD 323-4   G/c : **£12**   S/c : £5   P.Stamp : £3
GILBERT & SULLIVAN   Iolanthe   Glyndebourne   Sargent
Mono Issue : ALP1757-8

ASD 325   G/c : **£100**   S/c : £20   P.Stamp : £10
SCHUBERT   Symphony No.9
Royal Philharmonic Orchestra   Kubelik
Mono Issue : ALP1751

ASD 326   G/c : **£80**   S/c : £20   P.Stamp : £8
STRAUSS   Don Quixote, Till Eulenspiegel   Tortelier
Berlin Philharmonic Orchestra   Kempe
Mono Issue : ALP1759

ASD 327-8   G/c : **£50**   S/c : £12   P.Stamp : £4
BACH   Brandenburg Concertos
Bath Festival Chamber Orchestra   Menhuin
Mono Issue : ALP1755-6

ASD 329   G/c : **£30**   S/c : £6   P.Stamp : £4
DELIUS   Florida Suite, Over the Hills
Royal Philharmonic Orchestra   Beecham
Mono Issue : ALP1697

ASD 330   G/c : **£100**   S/c : £20   P.Stamp : £8
Various   Overtures Bartered Bride, Oberon, Hebrides
Vienna Philharmonic Orchestra   Kempe
Mono Issue : ALP1765

ASD 331-3   G/c : **£40**   S/c : £15   P.Stamp : £5
BIZET   Carmen   Callas
French National Radio Orchestra   Beecham
Mono Issue : ALP1762-4

ASD 334   G/c : **£25**   S/c : £14   P.Stamp : £5
MENDELSSOHN / BRUCH Violin Concertos In E & G Minor   Menuhin
Philharmonia Orchestra   Susskind
Mono Issue : ALP1669

ASD 335   G/c : **£40**   S/c : £12   P.Stamp : £5
Various   Recitals   Ambrosian Singers   Goldsbrough
Mono Issue : ALP1766

ASD 336   G/c : **£75**   S/c : £14   P.Stamp : £7
BEETHOVEN   Overtures   Berlin Philharmonic Orchestra   Kempe
Mono Issue : ALP1663

ASD 337   G/c : **£40**   S/c : £10   P.Stamp : £4
SCHUBERT   Leider Recital   Fischer Dieskau
Mono Issue : ALP1767

ASD 338   G/c : **£100**   S/c : £20   P.Stamp : £8
Various   Overtures Hansel Gretal, Midsummer Nights Dream etc
Philharmonia Orchestra   Silvestri
Mono Issue : ALP1749

ASD 339   G/c : **£25**   S/c : £8   P.Stamp : £3
HAYDN   Symphony No.99, Symphony No.100
Royal Philharmonic Orchestra   Beecham
Mono Issue : ALP1693

ASD 340   G/c : **£25**   S/c : £8   P.Stamp : £3
HAYDN   Symphony No.101, Symphony No.102
Royal Philharmonic Orchestra   Beecham
Mono Issue : ALP1694

ASD 341   G/c : **£25**   S/c : £8   P.Stamp : £3
HAYDN   Symphony No.103, Symphony No.104
Royal Philharmonic Orchestra   Beecham
Mono Issue : ALP1695

ASD 342   G/c : **£35**   S/c : £8   P.Stamp : £4
BACH   Cantata Arias   Fischer Dieskau
Berlin Philharmonic Orchestra   Forster
Mono Issue : ALP1703

ASD 343   G/c : **£75**   S/c : £12   P.Stamp : £7
TCHAIKOVSKY Capriccio Italiano   Philharmonia Orchestra   Kletzki
Mono Issue : ALP1679

ASD 344   G/c : **£30**   S/c : £8   P.Stamp : £3
MOZART   Clarinet concerto
Royal Philharmonic Orchestra   Beecham
Mono Issue : ALP1768

ASD 345   G/c : **£30**   S/c : £5   P.Stamp : £3
SCHUBERT   Symphony No.3, Symphony No.5
Royal Philharmonic Orchestra   Beecham
Mono Issue : ALP1743

ASD 346   G/c : **£40**   S/c : £10   P.Stamp : £4
BACH   Violin Concerto, Double Concerto   Ferras Menuhin
Bath Festival Chamber Orchestra
Mono Issue : ALP1760

ASD 347 G/c : **£ 150** S/c : £25 P.Stamp : £12
BRAHMS / DVORAK Hungarian Dances, Scherzo Caprico
Royal Philharmonic Orchestra Kubelik
Mono Issue : ALP1769

ASD 348 G/c : **£ 25** S/c : £8 P.Stamp : £3
BRAHMS Symphony No.2
Royal Philharmonic Orchestra Beecham
Mono Issue : ALP1770

ASD 349 G/c : **£ 125** S/c : £25 P.Stamp : £12
BEETHOVEN Symphony No.6 Philharmonia Orchestra Kubelik
Mono Issue : ALP1771

ASD 350 G/c : **£ 85** S/c : £12 P.Stamp : £8
BRAHMS Symphony No.1
Berlin Philharmonic Orchestra Kempe
Mono Issue : ALP1772

ASD 351-2 G/c : **£ 120** S/c : £20 P.Stamp : £12
MAHLER Das lied von der erde Philharmonia Orchestra Kletzki
Mono Issue : ALP1773-4

ASD 353-4 G/c : **£ 120** S/c : £20 P.Stamp : £12
VERDI Requiem Royal Philharmonic Orchestra Serafin
Mono Issue : ALP1775-6

ASD 355 (==== Not Issued ====)

ASD 356 G/c : **£ 60** S/c : £12 P.Stamp : £6
WOLF Lieder Recital Fischer-Dieskau
Mono Issue : ALP1778

ASD 357 G/c : **£ 28** S/c : £8 P.Stamp : £4
DELIUS Brigg Fair Etc Royal Philharmonic Orchestra Beecham
Mono Issue : ALP1586

ASD 358 G/c : **£ 45** S/c : £15 P.Stamp : £6
DVORAK Cello Concerto Rostropovitch
Royal Philharmonic Orchestra Boult
Mono Issue : ALP1595

ASD 359-61   G/c : **£100**   S/c : £30   P.Stamp : £14
VERDI   La Traviata   De Los Angeles
Orchestra of Rome Opera House   Serafin
Mono Issue : ALP1780-2

ASD 362   G/c : **£45**   S/c : £10   P.Stamp : £4
WOLF   Leider Recital   Fischer Dieskau
Mono Issue : ALP1783

ASD 363   G/c : **£40**   S/c : £8   P.Stamp : £4
WAGNER   Tannhauser, Gotterdammerung (Highlights) Grummer
Mono Issue : ALP1784

ASD 364-5   G/c : **£12**   S/c : £6   P.Stamp : £4
GILBERT & SULLIVAN   Yeomen of the Guard
Glyndebourne Pro Arte   Sargent
Mono Issue : ALP1601-2

ASD 366   G/c : **£70**   S/c : £12   P.Stamp : £6
RESPIGHI   Fountains Of Rome
Philharmonia Orchestra   Goossens
Mono Issue : ALP1785

ASD 367-9   G/c : **£85**   S/c : £15   P.Stamp : £8
VIVALDI   Concertos 1 - 12   Ferro, Mozzato
Virtuosi di Roma   Fasano
Mono Issue : ALP1786-8

ASD 370   G/c : **£30**   S/c : £8   P.Stamp : £4
CHOPIN   Piano Concerto No.1   Pollini
Philharmonia Orchestra   Kletzki
Mono Issue : ALP1794

ASD 371   G/c : **£38**   S/c : £6   P.Stamp : £4
TCHAIKOVSKY Sleeping Beauty   Philharmonia Orchestra   Kurtz
Mono Issue : ALP1790

ASD 372   G/c : **£85**   S/c : £15   P.Stamp : £8
BACH   Overtures in a French Style, Italian Conerto   Tureck
Mono Issue : ALP1791

ASD 373-5   G/c : **£80**   S/c : £20   P.Stamp : £10
PUCCINI   Madama Butterfly
Orchestra of Rome Opera House   Santini
Mono Issue : ALP1795-7

ASD 376   G/c : **£80**   S/c : £20   P.Stamp : £8
Various   Orchestral Marches   Philharmonia Orchestra   Kurtz
Mono Issue : ALP1798

ASD 377   G/c : **£50**   S/c : £15   P.Stamp : £6
BEETHOVEN   Violin Concerto   Menuhin
Vienna Philharmonic Orchestra   Silvestri
Mono Issue : ALP1799

ASD 378   G/c : **£50**   S/c : £10   P.Stamp : £4
WOLF   Lieder Recital of Spanish Songs   Moore Dieskau
Mono Issue : ALP1750

ASD 379   G/c : **£130**   S/c : £25   P.Stamp : £12
TCHAIKOVSKY   Symphony No.5
Berlin Philharmonic Orchestra   Kempe
Mono Issue : ALP1800

ASD 380   G/c : **£120**   S/c : £30   P.Stamp : £15
DVORAK   Symphony No.5 (New World)
Berlin Philharmonic Orchestra   Kempe
Mono Issue : ALP1623

ASD 381-2   G/c : **£10**   S/c : £6   P.Stamp : £4
GILBERT & SULLIVAN   Pirates of Penzance   Sargent
Mono Issue : ALP1801-2

ASD 383   G/c : **£30**   S/c : £8   P.Stamp : £6
Various   Christmas Carols   Royal Choral Society   Sargent
Mono Issue : ALP1792

ASD 384   G/c : **£30**   S/c : £4   P.Stamp : £2
Various   Love Duets   Hammond
Mono Issue : ALP1805

ASD 385-7   G/c : **£ 180**   S/c : £40   P.Stamp : £15
WAGNER   Flying Dutchman   Fischer Dieskau
German State Opera, Berlin   Konwitschny
Mono Issue : ALP1806-8

ASD 388   G/c : **£ 30**   S/c : £ 8   P.Stamp : £ 3
BIZET / LALO   Symphonies In C
Orchestre National de la Radiodiffusion Francaise   Beecham
Mono Issue : ALP1761

ASD 389   G/c : **£ 50**   S/c : £15   P.Stamp : £ 4
BEETHOVEN   Spring & Kreutzer Sonatas   Yehudi & Hepzi Menuhin
Mono Issue : ALP1739

ASD 390   G/c : **£ 60**   S/c : £15   P.Stamp : £ 6
TCHAIKOVSKY   Songs   Christoff
Mono Issue : ALP1793

ASD 391-3   G/c : **£ 120**   S/c : £25   P.Stamp : £15
VIVALDI   L'Estro Armonico   Collegium Musicum Italicum   Fasano
Mono Issue : ALP1809-11

ASD 394-5   G/c : **£ 80**   S/c : £15   P.Stamp : £ 8
STRAUSS   Gypsy Barron
Vienna Philharmonic Orchestra   Hollreiser
Mono Issue : ALP1812-3

ASD 396   G/c : **£ 100**   S/c : £20   P.Stamp : £ 8
DVORAK   Symphony No.2
Vienna Philharmonic Orchestra   Silvestri
Mono Issue : ALP1814
ASD 397   G/c : **£ 30**   S/c : £ 6   P.Stamp : £ 4
BACH / HANDEL Cantata No.203, Arias   Fischer Dieskau
Mono Issue : ALP1804

ASD 398   G/c : **£ 100**   S/c : £20   P.Stamp : £10
TCHAIKOVSKY   Symphony No.4
Vienna Philharmonic Orchestra   Kubelik
Mono Issue : ALP1815

ASD 399   G/c : **£ 25**   S/c : £8   P.Stamp : £4
BERLIOZ   Symphonie Fantastique
French National Radio Orchestra   Beecham
Mono Issue : ALP1633

ASD 400   G/c : **£ 90**   S/c : £15   P.Stamp : £8
Various   Russian Music, Capriccio Espagnol Op.34 Etc
Vienna Philharmonic Orchestra   Silvestri
Mono Issue : ALP1818

ASD 401   G/c : **£ 125**   S/c : £20   P.Stamp : £10
STRAVINSKY   Symphony in 3 movements
Philharmonia Orchestra   Silvestri
Mono Issue : ALP1819

ASD 402-3   G/c : **£ 150**   S/c : £45   P.Stamp : £15
DVORAK   Slavonic Dances   BBC Symphony Orchestra   Schwartz
Mono Issue : ALP1820-1

ASD 404-5   G/c : **£ 30**   S/c : £10   P.Stamp : £5
BACH   Suites   Bath Festival Chamber Orchestra   Menhuin
Mono Issue : ALP1822-3

ASD 406   G/c : **£ 110**   S/c : £20   P.Stamp : £10
BRAHMS   Symphony No.3
Berlin Philharmonic Orchestra   Kempe
Mono Issue : ALP1824

ASD 407   G/c : **£ 30**   S/c : £6   P.Stamp : £3
VERDI   Operatic Arias   Fischer Dieskau
Berlin Philharmonic Orchestra   Erede
Mono Issue : ALP1825

ASD 408   G/c : **£ 85**   S/c : £15   P.Stamp : £8
FRANCK   Symphony No.   Philharmonia Orchestra   Silvestri
Mono Issue : ALP1831

ASD 409-11   G/c : **£ 85**   S/c : £20   P.Stamp : £10
HAYDN   Die Schopfung (The Creation)   Grummer
Berlin Symphony Orchestra   Forster
Mono Issue : ALP1834-6

ASD 412 G/c : **£15** S/c : £6 P.Stamp : £4
GOUNOD Faust (Highlights)
Orchestra of the Theatre National de L'Opera Cluytens
Mono Issue : ALP1837

ASD 413 G/c : **£50** S/c : £10 P.Stamp : £5
Various The Fabulous De Los Angeles De Los Angeles
Mono Issue : ALP1838

ASD 414 G/c : **£28** S/c : £8 P.Stamp : £5
BACH The Musical Offering Shaffer
Bath Festival Chamber Orchestra Menuhin
Mono Issue : ALP1839

ASD 415-6 G/c : **£10** S/c : £6 P.Stamp : £4
GILBERT & SULLIVAN HMS Pinafore
Glyndebourne Pro Arte Sargent
Mono Issue : ALP1650-1

ASD 417 G/c : **£80** S/c : £15 P.Stamp : £8
LISZT / RAVEL Rhapsodies Vienna Philharmonic Orchestra Silvestri
Mono Issue : ALP1842

ASD 418 G/c : **£100** S/c : £20 P.Stamp : £8
SCHUBERT Symphony No.3, Symphony No.4
Vienna Philharmonic Orchestra Kubelik
Mono Issue : ALP1844

ASD 419 G/c : **£12** S/c : £4 P.Stamp : £2
GILBERT & SULLIVAN Trial by Jury Pro Arte Sargent
Mono Issue : ALP1851

ASD 420 G/c : **£25** S/c : £8 P.Stamp : £4
ROSSINI / BERLIOZ Favourite Overtures etc
Royal Philharmonic Orchestra Beecham
Mono Issue : ALP1846

ASD 421 G/c : **£25** S/c : £8 P.Stamp : £4
STRAUSS Ein Heldenleben (Sir Thomas Beecham Memorial LP)
Royal Philharmonic Orchestra Beecham
Mono Issue : ALP1847

ASD 422 G/c : **£100** S/c : £25 P.Stamp : £10
BORODIN Symphony No.2, Dances
Vienna Philharmonic Orchestra Kubelik
Mono Issue : ALP1848

ASD 423 G/c : **£60** S/c : £18 P.Stamp : £8
MOZART / RAVEL Piano Trio K542, Piano Trio Menuhin
Mono Issue : ALP1849

ASD 424-5 G/c : **£40** S/c : £10 P.Stamp : £4
WOLF Goethe Leider Fischer Dieskau
Mono Issue : ALP1852-3

ASD 426 G/c : **£250** S/c : £75 P.Stamp : £25
BEETHOVEN Symphony No.3 Berlin Philharmonic Orchestra Kempe
Mono Issue : ALP1854

ASD 427 G/c : **£120** S/c : £25 P.Stamp : £12
MOZART Violin Concerto No.4, Violin Concerto No.5 Ferras
Paris Conservatoire Orchestra Vandernoot
Mono Issue : ALP1858

ASD 428 G/c : **£90** S/c : £18 P.Stamp : £8
TCHAIKOVSKY Symphony No.5
Vienna Philharmonic Orchestra Kubelik
Mono Issue : ALP1859

ASD 429 G/c : **£1,500** S/c : £1,200 P.Stamp : £800
BACH / MOZART Violin Concerto DeVito
London Symphony Orchestra Kubelik
Mono Issue : ALP1856

ASD 430 G/c : **£25** S/c : £8 P.Stamp : £4
BERLIOZ Damnation of Faust (highlights - No full set) Gedda
Paris Opera Cluytens
Mono Issue : ALP1860

ASD 431 G/c : **£130** S/c : £25 P.Stamp : £12
Various Vienese Bonbons
Vienna Philharmonic Orchestra Kempe
Mono Issue : ALP1861

ASD 432   G/c : **£30**   S/c : £8   P.Stamp : £4
Various   More Beecham Lollipops
Royal Philharmonic Orchestra   Beecham
Mono Issue : ALP1862

ASD 433   G/c : **£120**   S/c : £20   P.Stamp : £10
BEETHOVEN   Symphony No.6
Berlin Philharmonic Orchestra   Cluytens
Mono Issue : ALP1863

ASD 434   G/c : **£30**   S/c : £8   P.Stamp : £4
BUSONI/LISZT   Recital   Ogdon
Mono Issue : ALP1864

ASD 435   G/c : **£35**   S/c : £10   P.Stamp : £4
ROSSINI   Overtures   Vienna Philharmonic Orchestra   Sargent
Mono Issue : ALP1865

ASD 436-8   G/c : **£85**   S/c : £20   P.Stamp : £12
VERDI   Rigoletto Scotto   Maggio Musici Florence   Gavazzeni
Mono Issue : ALP1866-8

ASD 439   G/c : **£35**   S/c : £12   P.Stamp : £5
DELIBES   Sylvia & Coppelia   Menuhin
Philharmonia Orchestra   Irving
Mono Issue : ALP1869

ASD 440   G/c : **£60**   S/c : £18   P.Stamp : £8
PAGANINI   Violin Concerto No.1, Violin Concerto No.2   Menuhin
Mono Issue : ALP1872

ASD 441-2   (═══ Not Issued ═══)

ASD 443   G/c : **£30**   S/c : £8   P.Stamp : £4
HOLST / WALTON / BRITTEN   Perfect Fool, Facade
Royal Philharmonic Orchestra   Sargent
Mono Issue : ALP1873

ASD 444   G/c : **£35**   S/c : £8   P.Stamp : £5
STRAUSS   Zigeunerbaron, Die Fledermaus
Vienna Philharmonic Orchestra   Hollreiser
Mono Issue : ALP1875

ASD 445-8   G/c : **£100**   S/c : £25   P.Stamp : £12
WAGNER   Tannhauser   Grummer Berlin Opera Konwitschny
Mono Issue : ALP1876-9

ASD 449   G/c : **£80**   S/c : £15   P.Stamp : £8
DVORAK / WEINBERGER   Music from Bohemia
Royal Philharmonic Orchestra   Kempe
Mono Issue : ALP1880

ASD 450   G/c : **£40**   S/c : £10   P.Stamp : £5
BEETHOVEN / SCHUMANN   Piano Sonata No.17, Fantasia Richter
Mono Issue : ALP1881

ASD 451   G/c : **£250**   S/c : £60   P.Stamp : £20
MOZART   Symphony No.36, Symphony No.38
Vienna Philharmonic Orchestra   Kubelik
Mono Issue : ALP1882

ASD 452   G/c : **£45**   S/c : £12   P.Stamp : £5
Various   Spanish songs of the Renaissance   De Los Angeles
Mono Issue : ALP1883

ASD 453   G/c : **£75**   S/c : £15   P.Stamp : £8
Various   Harpsichord Recital   Tureck
Mono Issue : ALP1884

ASD 454   G/c : **£15**   S/c : £6   P.Stamp : £2
STAINER   Crucifixion   Leeds Philharmonic Choir Berdgett
Mono Issue : ALP1885

ASD 455   G/c : **£75**   S/c : £15   P.Stamp : £7
SHOSTAKOVITCH   Symphony No.5
Vienna Philharmonic Orchestra   Silvestri
Mono Issue : ALP1886

ASD 456   G/c : **£80**   S/c : £20   P.Stamp : £8
Various   Operatic Recital   Gorr
Philharmonia Orchestra   Cluytens
Mono Issue : ALP1887

ASD 457   G/c : **£40**   S/c : £10   P.Stamp : £4
BACH   Cantatas Nos.211& 212   Fischer-Dieskau
Berlin Philharmonic Orchestra   Forster
Mono Issue : ALP1888

ASD 458   G/c : **£30**   S/c : £8   P.Stamp : £4
FRANCK   Symphony in Dmin.
French National Radio Orchestra   Beecham
Mono Issue : ALP1686

ASD 459   G/c : **£45**   S/c : £12   P.Stamp : £5
Various   Duets   De Los Angeles
Mono Issue : ALP1891

ASD 460   G/c : **£120**   S/c : £25   P.Stamp : £10
MENDELSSOHN / HUMPERDINCK Midsummernights Dream, Hansel &
Gretel   Royal Philharmonic Orchestra   Kempe
Mono Issue : ALP1892

ASD 461   G/c : **£100**   S/c : £20   P.Stamp : £10
BRAHMS   Symphony No.4
Royal Philharmonic Orchestra   Kempe
Mono Issue : ALP1894

ASD 462   G/c : **£85**   S/c : £15   P.Stamp : £8
TCHAIKOVSKY   Symphony No.6
Vienna Philharmonic Orchestra   Kubelik
Mono Issue : ALP1895

ASD 463   G/c : **£15**   S/c : £10   P.Stamp : £6
Various   Music of India   Ravi Shankar
Mono Issue : ALP1893

ASD 464   G/c : **£60**   S/c : £15   P.Stamp : £6
Various   Favourites-piano recital   Cziffra
Mono Issue : ALP1896

ASD 465   G/c : **£24**   S/c : £8   P.Stamp : £4
GUILLARD / GLUCK   Iphigenie en Tauride (Highlights)
Paris Conservatoire Orchestra   Pretre
Mono Issue : ALP1897

ASD 466   G/c : **£120**   S/c : £30   P.Stamp : £12
Various   Overtures from Italian Operas
Philharmonia Orchestra   Serafin
Mono Issue : ALP1898

ASD 467   G/c : **£16**   S/c : £8   P.Stamp : £5
COLERIDGE TAYLOR   Hiawatha's Wedding Feast
Philharmonia Orchestra   Sargent
Mono Issue : ALP1899

ASD 468   G/c : **£35**   S/c : £8   P.Stamp : £6
SIBELIUS   Symphony No.7, Pelleas Melisande etc
Royal Philharmonic Orchestra   Beecham
Mono Issue : ALP1480

ASD 469   G/c : **£40**   S/c : £12   P.Stamp : £5
Various   Song Recital   Di Stefano
Mono Issue : ALP1902

ASD 470   G/c : **£75**   S/c : £15   P.Stamp : £7
DVORAK   Symphony No.8, Carnival Overture
London Philharmonic Orchestra   Silvestri
Mono Issue : ALP1537

ASD 471   G/c : **£45**   S/c : £12   P.Stamp : £6
Various   Pearls of Viennese Operetta   Rysanek
Vienna Philharmonic Orchestra   Loibner
Mono Issue : ALP1903

ASD 472   G/c : **£6**   S/c : £4   P.Stamp : £2
GILBERT & SULLIVAN   HMS Pinafore (Highlights)   Pro Arte   Sargent
Mono Issue : ALP1904

ASD 473   G/c : **£50**   S/c : £15   P.Stamp : £6
MOZART   Violin Concerto No.3, Violin Concerto No.5
Menuhin   Bath Festival Chamber Orchestra
Mono Issue : ALP1905

ASD 474   G/c : **£50**   S/c : £15   P.Stamp : £6
BRAHMS   Violin Concerto No.1, Violin Concerto No.2   Menuhin
Mono Issue : ALP1906

ASD 475   G/c : **£ 40**   S/c : £10   P.Stamp : £5
SCHUBERT   Sonata No.3, Fantasy in Cmaj.   Menuhin
Mono Issue : ALP1907

ASD 476   G/c : **£ 45**   S/c : £12   P.Stamp : £5
Various   Neopolitan Songs   Di Stefano
Mono Issue : ALP1908

ASD 477   G/c : **£ 85**   S/c : £15   P.Stamp : £8
BACH   Recital   Tureck
Mono Issue : ALP1909

ASD 478   G/c : **£ 250**   S/c : £60   P.Stamp : £22
SCHUBERT / GLUCK   Rosamunde, Ballet Suite
Vienna Philharmonic Orchestra   Kempe
Mono Issue : ALP1910

ASD 479   G/c : **£ 40**   S/c : £10   P.Stamp : £4
Various   20th Century Spanish Songs   De Los Angeles
Mono Issue : ALP1911

ASD 480   G/c : **£ 30**   S/c : £8   P.Stamp : £4
HANDEL / MOZART   Gods go a Begging, Sheba etc
Royal Philharmonic Orchestra   Beecham
Mono Issue : ALP1912

ASD 481   G/c : **£ 40**   S/c : £10   P.Stamp : £5
SCHUBERT   Die Schone Mullerin   Fischer-Dieskau
Mono Issue : ALP1913

ASD 482   (==== Not Issued ====)

ASD 483   G/c : **£ 120**   S/c : £30   P.Stamp : £12
MAHLER   Symphony No.1
Vienna Philharmonic Orchestra   Kletzki
Mono Issue : ALP1917

ASD 484-5   G/c : **£ 12**   S/c : £6   P.Stamp : £3
GILBERT & SULLIVAN   Patience Pro Arte   Sargent
Mono Issue : ALP1918-9

ASD 486   (==== Not Issued ====)

ASD 487   G/c : **£6**   S/c : £3   P.Stamp : £2
GILBERT & SULLIVAN   Gilbert & Sullivan excerpts Pro Arte Sargent
Mono Issue : ALP1922

ASD 488   G/c : **£80**   S/c : £20   P.Stamp : £7
Various   Neopolitan Songs   Corelli
Mono Issue : ALP1923

ASD 489   G/c : **£48**   S/c : £15   P.Stamp : £8
BACH   Violin & Harpsichord Sonatas No.1,4 & 6
Menuhin, Malcolm
Mono Issue : ALP1924

ASD 490   G/c : **£48**   S/c : £15   P.Stamp : £8
BACH   Violin & Harpsichord Sonatas No.2, 3 & 5
Menuhin, Malcolm
Mono Issue : ALP1925

ASD 491   G/c : **£35**   S/c : £8   P.Stamp : £4
HANDEL   Concerti Grossi No.7, 8, 9 & 11   Menuhin
Bath Festival Chamber Orchestra
Mono Issue : ALP1927

ASD 492   G/c : **£20**   S/c : £8   P.Stamp : £5
RACHMANINOV   Piano Concerto No.2   Ogdon
Philharmonia Orchestra   Pritchard
Mono Issue : ALP1928

ASD 493   G/c : **£250**   S/c : £85   P.Stamp : £25
BRUCKNER   Symphony No.9
Vienna Philharmonic Orchestra   Schuricht
Mono Issue : ALP1929

ASD 494   G/c : **£150**   S/c : £45   P.Stamp : £20
KODALY / TCHAIKOVSKY   Hari Janos, Gotovac
Vienna Philharmonic Orchestra   Kempe
Mono Issue : ALP1930

ASD 495   G/c : **£6**   S/c : £4   P.Stamp : £2
GILBERT & SULLIVAN   Operatic Highlights
Pro Arte Sargent
Mono Issue : ALP1932

ASD 496   G/c : **£ 40**   S/c : £10   P.Stamp : £4
POULENC   Les Biches   Paris Conservatoire Orchestra   Pretre
Mono Issue : ALP1945

ASD 497   G/c : **£ 30**   S/c : £8   P.Stamp : £3
DOHNANYI   Suite for Orchestra
Royal Philharmonic Orchestra   Sargent
Mono Issue : ALP1926

ASD 498   G/c : **£ 18**   S/c : £10   P.Stamp : £6
Various   Music of India   Imrat Khan
Mono Issue : ALP1946

ASD 499   G/c : **£ 20**   S/c : £6   P.Stamp : £4
BLISS   Concerto For Piano And Orchestra
Philharmonia Orchestra   Sargent
Mono Issue : ALP1948

ASD 500   G/c : **£ 25**   S/c : £10   P.Stamp : £4
BACH / HANDEL / VIVALDI   Concerto in D   Goossens
Bath Festival Chamber Orchestra   Menhuin
Mono Issue : ALP1949

ASD 501   G/c : **£ 25**   S/c : £6   P.Stamp : £3
BACH   Christmas Oratorio Fischer-Dieskau
Leipzig Gewandhaus Orchestra   Thomas
Mono Issue : ALP1950

ASD 502-4   G/c : **£ 60**   S/c : £12   P.Stamp : £6
BACH   Oratorios 1-6   Fischer-Dieskau
Leipzig Gewandhaus Orchestra   Thomas
Mono Issue : ALP1951-3

ASD 505   G/c : **£ 45**   S/c : £12   P.Stamp : £5
Various   Cantos de Espana   De Los Angeles
Paris Conservatoire Orchestra   De Burgos
Mono Issue : ALP1954

ASD 506   G/c : **£ 40**   S/c : £12   P.Stamp : £8
HAYDN / MOZART   Symphony No.45, Eine Kleine,Notturn
Bath Festival Chamber Orchestra   Menhuin
Mono Issue : ALP1955

ASD 507   G/c : **£125**   S/c : £25   P.Stamp : £12
STRAVINSKY   Pulcinella   Philharmonia Orchestra   Vandernoot
Mono Issue : ALP1956

ASD 508   G/c : **£28**   S/c : £16   P.Stamp : £8
VAUGHAN WILLIAMS   Symphony No.5
Philharmonia Orchestra   Barbirolli
Mono Issue : ALP1957

ASD 509   G/c : **£70**   S/c : £15   P.Stamp : £8
Various   Russian Orchestral Masterpieces
Royal Philharmonic Orchestra   Pretre
Mono Issue : ALP1958

ASD 510   G/c : **£60**   S/c : £15   P.Stamp : £8
BEETHOVEN   Violin Sonata No.7, Violin Sonata No.10   Menuhin
Mono Issue : ALP1959

ASD 511   G/c : **£30**   S/c : £8   P.Stamp : £4
STRAVINSKY   Oedipus Rex   Royal Philharmonic Orchestra   Davis
Mono Issue : ALP1960

ASD 512   G/c : **£30**   S/c : £8   P.Stamp : £6
PROKOFIEV / TIPPETT   Concerto for Double String Orchestra, Etc
Moscow Chamber Orchestra   Barshai
Mono Issue : ALP1961

ASD 513   G/c : **£120**   S/c : £25   P.Stamp : £12
GLINKA   Life for the Tzar   Philharmonia Orchestra   Kurtz
Mono Issue : ALP1962

ASD 514   G/c : **£100**   S/c : £15   P.Stamp : £8
SCHUBERT / MOZART   Symphony No.8, Eine Kleine Nacht Music
Vienna Philharmonic Orchestra   Kubelik
Mono Issue : ALP1963

ASD 515   G/c : **£30**   S/c : £8   P.Stamp : £4
BRUCKNER   Mass No.3   Berlin Symphony Orchestra   Forster
Mono Issue : ALP1964

ASD 516   G/c : **£80**   S/c : £20   P.Stamp : £7
Various   Neopolitan Songs   Corelli
Mono Issue : ALP1965

ASD 517 G/c : **£50** S/c : £15 P.Stamp : £10
POULENC Concerto For Two Pianos Poulenc,Fevrier
Paris Conservatoire Orchestra Pretre
Mono Issue : ALP1967

ASD 518 G/c : **£30** S/c : £8 P.Stamp : £4
Various The Inimitable Sir Thomas
Royal Philharmonic Orchestra Beecham
Mono Issue : ALP1968

ASD 519 G/c : **£100** S/c : £25 P.Stamp : £10
DVORAK Slavonic Dances 1 & 2
Paris Conservatoire Orchestra Silvestri
Mono Issue : ALP1966

ASD 520 G/c : **£38** S/c : £10 P.Stamp : £4
SCHUMANN Piano Sonata No.2, Papillons Etc Richter
Mono Issue : ALP1969

ASD 521 G/c : **£35** S/c : £10 P.Stamp : £5
ELGAR / VAUGHAN WILLIAMS English String Music
Symphonia of London Barbirolli
Mono Issue : ALP1970

ASD 522-4 G/c : **£250** S/c : £70 P.Stamp : £30
SMETANA Bartered Bride Bamburg Symphony Orchestra Kempe
Mono Issue : ALP1971-3

ASD 525 G/c : **£150** S/c : £30 P.Stamp : £15
Various Vienna Philharmonic on Holiday
Vienna Philharmonic Orchestra Kempe
Mono Issue : ALP1974

ASD 526-8 G/c : **£80** S/c : £20 P.Stamp : £10
BACH St. Johns Passion
Berlin Philharmonic Orchestra Forster
Mono Issue : ALP1975-7

ASD 529 G/c : **£45** S/c : £12 P.Stamp : £4
Various Operatic Recital Corelli
Mono Issue : ALP1978

ASD 530   G/c : **£75**   S/c : £20   P.Stamp : £8
Various   A French Recital   De Los Angeles
Mono Issue : ALP1979

ASD 531   G/c : **£85**   S/c : £15   P.Stamp : £8
ENESCU / DEBUSSY / RAVEL   Violin Sonata No.3, Violin Sonata
Ferras
Mono Issue : ALP1980

ASD 532   G/c : **£85**   S/c : £15   P.Stamp : £8
RIMSKY-KORSAKOV / KABALEVSKY   Le Coq D'or, Comedians
Philharmonia Orchestra   Kurtz
Mono Issue : ALP1981

ASD 533   G/c : **£50**   S/c : £15   P.Stamp : £5
MOZART   Violin concerto No.4, Violin concerto No.6   Menuhin
Bath Festival Chamber Orchestra
Mono Issue : ALP1982

ASD 534   G/c : **£40**   S/c : £10   P.Stamp : £5
BACH / TELEMAN   Hunting Cantata, Canary Cantata   Fischer-Dieskau
Berlin Symphony Orchestra   Forster
Mono Issue : ALP1985

ASD 535   G/c : **£80**   S/c : £15   P.Stamp : £8
WAGNER   Das Rheingold (Highlights - No full Set)
State Opera Berlin   Kempe
Mono Issue : ALP1984

ASD 536   G/c : **£30**   S/c : £8   P.Stamp : £4
Various   An evening at the Proms
BBC Symphony Orchestra   Sargent
Mono Issue : ALP1658

ASD 537   G/c : **£30**   S/c : £8   P.Stamp : £4
BERLIOZ   Harold in Italy   Menuhin
Philharmonia Orchestra   Davis
Mono Issue : ALP1986

ASD 538   G/c : **£50**   S/c : £10   P.Stamp : £5
LISZT   Piano Recital: Annees de Pelerina   Kentner
Mono Issue : ALP1987

ASD 539   G/c : **£15**   S/c : £10   P.Stamp : £6
Various   Music of India   Vilayat Khan
Mono Issue : ALP1988

ASD 540   G/c : **£25**   S/c : £8   P.Stamp : £4
ELGAR   Symphony No.1   Halle Orchestra   Barbirolli
Mono Issue : ALP1989

ASD 541   G/c : **£40**   S/c : £15   P.Stamp : £4
SIBELIUS   En Saga, Finlandia etc
Vienna Philharmonic Orchestra   Sargent
Mono Issue : ALP1990

ASD 542   G/c : **£20**   S/c : £8   P.Stamp : £4
TCHAIKOVSKY / FRANCK   Piano Concerto No.1, Symphonic
Variations   Ogdon   Philharmonia Orchestra   Barbirolli
Mono Issue : ALP1991

ASD 543   G/c : **£30**   S/c : £18   P.Stamp : £8
VERDI   La Traviata   Orchestra of Rome Opera House   Serafin
Mono Issue : ALP1992

ASD 544   G/c : **£50**   S/c : £12   P.Stamp : £5
SCHUBERT   Schwanengesang   Fischer-Dieskau
Mono Issue : ALP1993

ASD 545   G/c : **£85**   S/c : £18   P.Stamp : £8
FALLA   Night in the Gardens of Spain
Paris Conservatoire Orchestra   Soriano
Mono Issue : ALP1994

ASD 546   G/c : **£20**   S/c : £8   P.Stamp : £4
Various   Piano Recital   Ogdon
Mono Issue : ALP1995

ASD 547   G/c : **£60**   S/c : £15   P.Stamp : £6
GLINKA   Songs of Glinka   Christoff
Mono Issue : ALP1996

ASD 548   G/c : **£40**   S/c : £16   P.Stamp : £4
ELGAR   Enigma Variations   Philharmonia Orchestra   Barbirolli
Mono Issue : ALP1998

ASD 549   G/c : **£120**   S/c : £25   P.Stamp : £12
BRAHMS / BEETHOVEN   Double Concerto, Sonata No.1 Ferras, Tortelier
Mono Issue : ALP1999

ASD 550   G/c : **£25**   S/c : £8   P.Stamp : £4
GLUCK   Orfeo & Euridice (Highlights)
Berlin Symphony Orchestra   Stein
Mono Issue : ALP1997

ASD 551-2   G/c : **£65**   S/c : £15   P.Stamp : £6
SCHUBERT   Winterreise   Fischer-Dieskau
Mono Issue : ALP2001-2

ASD 553   G/c : **£80**   S/c : £15   P.Stamp : £8
WAGNER   Wesendonck Lieder etc   Crespin
French National Radio Orchestra   Pretre
Mono Issue : ALP2000

ASD 554   G/c : **£50**   S/c : £10   P.Stamp : £5
CORELLI   Concerto Grossi   Virtuosi di Roma Fasano
Mono Issue : ALP2004

ASD 555   G/c : **£25**   S/c : £6   P.Stamp : £3
WAGNER   Tannhauser (Highlights)   Grummer
Berlin Opera   Konwitschny
Mono Issue : ALP2005

ASD 556   G/c : **£25**   S/c : £5   P.Stamp : £3
WAGNER   Flying Dutchman (Highlights)   Fischer Dieskau
Berlin Opera   Konwitschny
Mono Issue : ALP2006

ASD 557   G/c : **£75**   S/c : £15   P.Stamp : £8
Various   A Castle Bruhl Concert
Cologne Soloists Ensemble   Bruhl
Mono Issue : ALP2007

ASD 558   G/c : **£30**   S/c : £10   P.Stamp : £4
Various   Great Sopranos   Callas, De Los Angeles
Mono Issue : ALP2008

ASD 559   G/c : **£60**   S/c : £12   P.Stamp : £6
SHOSTAKOVITCH   Symphony No.12
Philharmonia Orchestra   Pretre
Mono Issue : ALP2009

ASD 560   G/c : **£35**   S/c : £10   P.Stamp : £4
Various   Operatic Recital   Traxel   Klobucar
Mono Issue : ALP2010

ASD 561   G/c : **£45**   S/c : £15   P.Stamp : £5
SCHUBERT   Wanderer fantasie, Sonata in A maj. Op.120   Richter
Mono Issue : ALP2011

ASD 562   G/c : **£25**   S/c : £6   P.Stamp : £3
WEBER   Der Freischutz (Highlights)   Grummer
Berlin Philharmonic Orchestra   Keilberth
Mono Issue : ALP2012

ASD 563-4   G/c : **£12**   S/c : £6   P.Stamp : £3
GILBERT & SULLIVAN   Ruddigore   Pro Arte   Sargent
Mono Issue : ALP2013-4

ASD 565   G/c : **£30**   S/c : £10   P.Stamp : £4
Various   Leider Recital   Koth
Mono Issue : ALP2015

ASD 566   G/c : **£25**   S/c : £8   P.Stamp : £3
TCHAIKOVSKY   Eugen Onegin (Highlights)   Prey
Bavarian Symphony Orchestra   Zalinger
Mono Issue : ALP2016

ASD 567   G/c : **£48**   S/c : £10   P.Stamp : £6
MOZART / HAYDN   Sinfonia Concertante, Violin Concerto
Menuhin   Bath Festival Chamber Orchestra   Barshai
Mono Issue : ALP2017

ASD 568   G/c : **£20**   S/c : £6   P.Stamp : £4
Various   More Carols   Royal Choral Society   Sargent
Mono Issue : ALP2018

ASD 569   G/c : **£35**   S/c : £8   P.Stamp : £4
MOZART / PALESTRINA   Missa Brevis   St. Hedwigs Choir   Forster
Mono Issue : ALP2019

ASD 570   G/c : **£85**   S/c : £15   P.Stamp : £8
Various   Music of Spain
Paris Conservatoire OrchestraDe Burgos
Mono Issue : ALP2020

ASD 571   G/c : **£28**   S/c : £10   P.Stamp : £4
MASSENET   Herodiade (Highlights)   Crespin   Pretre
Mono Issue : ALP2021

ASD 572   G/c : **£60**   S/c : £15   P.Stamp : £6
BERG   Violin Concerto   Ferras
Mono Issue : ALP2022

ASD 573   G/c : **£85**   S/c : £20   P.Stamp : £10
BRAHMS   Variations On a theme By Haydn Etc.
Philharmonia Orchestra   Krips
Mono Issue : ALP2023

ASD 574   G/c : **£75**   S/c : £18   P.Stamp : £7
Various   Tzars & Kings   Christoff   Cluytens
Mono Issue : ALP2025

ASD 575   G/c : **£40**   S/c : £10   P.Stamp : £8
MOZART / TELEMAN   Concerto for Flute, Concerto for Harp
Bath Festival Chamber Orchestra   Menhuin
Mono Issue : ALP2026

ASD 576   S/c : **£12**   P.Stamp : £4
GLUCK   Alceste (Highlights)   Paris Opera   Pretre
Mono Issue : ALP2027

ASD 577   S/c : **£30**   P.Stamp : £6
HANDEL   Water Music
Bath Festival Chamber Orchestra   Menhuin
Mono Issue : ALP2028

ASD 578   S/c : **£150**   P.Stamp : £25
PROKOFIEV   Symphony No.5   Philharmonia Orchestra   Kletzki
Mono Issue : ALP2029

ASD 579   S/c : **£25**   P.Stamp : £5
VIVALDI   Concertos   Virtuosi di Roma   Fasano
Mono Issue : ALP2030

ASD 580-1   S/c : **£30**   P.Stamp : £10
NICOLAI   Merry Wives of Windsor
Bavarian Symphony Orchestra   Heger
Mono Issue : ALP2031-2

ASD 582   S/c : **£70**   P.Stamp : £15
RIMSKY-KORSAKOV   Tzar Saltan, Snow Maiden
Philharmonia Orchestra   Kurtz
Mono Issue : ALP2033

ASD 583   S/c : **£35**   P.Stamp : £8
POULENC   Stabat Mater, 4 Motets   Crespin
Paris Conservatoire Orchestra   Pretre
Mono Issue : ALP2034

ASD 584   S/c : **£80**   P.Stamp : £25
BLOCH   Violin Concerto   Menuhin
Philharmonia Orchestra   Kletzki
Mono Issue : ALP2035

ASD 585   S/c : **£45**   P.Stamp : £10
SAINT-SAENS   Symphony No.3   Paris Conservatoire Orchestra Pretre
Mono Issue : ALP2036

ASD 586   (==== Not Issued ====)

ASD 587   S/c : **£35**   P.Stamp : £8
BRAHMS   Sextet No.1   Menuhin
Mono Issue : ALP2038

ASD 588   S/c : **£10**   P.Stamp : £4
ROSSINI   Stabat Mater   Berlin Symphony Orchestra   Forster
Mono Issue : ALP2039

ASD 589   S/c : **£8**   P.Stamp : £3
GOUNOD   Messe Solenelle
Paris Conservatoire Orchestra   Hartemann
Mono Issue : ALP2040

ASD 590   S/c : **£6**   P.Stamp : £2
BIZET   Carmen (Highlights)
French National Radio Orchestra   Beecham
Mono Issue : ALP2041

ASD 591 S/c : **£35** P.Stamp : £8
MOZART Violin Concerto No.1, Violin Concerto No.2
Menuhin Bath Festival Chamber Orchestra
Mono Issue : ALP2042

ASD 592 S/c : **£35** P.Stamp : £8
MOZART Violin Concerto No.7, Concertone in C K.190
Menuhin Bath Festival Chamber Orchestra
Mono Issue : ALP2043

ASD 593 S/c : **£30** P.Stamp : £5
SCHUMANN / STRAUSS Leider Recital Della Casa
Mono Issue : ALP2044

ASD 594 S/c : **£10** P.Stamp : £2
STRAUSS Ariadne auf Naxos (Highlights)
Berlin Philharmonic Orchestra Erede
Mono Issue : ALP2045

ASD 595 S/c : **£20** P.Stamp : £5
MOZART / HAYDN Symphony No.29, Symphony No.49
Menuhin Bath Festival Chamber Orchestra
Mono Issue : ALP2046

ASD 596-7 S/c : **£160** P.Stamp : £30
MAHLER Symphony No.9
Berlin Philharmonic Orchestra Barbirolli
Mono Issue : ALP2047-8

ASD 598 S/c : **£30** P.Stamp : £7
HANDEL Concerti Grossi No.3, 6, 10 & 12 Menuhin
Bath Festival Chamber Orchestra
Mono Issue : ALP2049

ASD 599 S/c : **£24** P.Stamp : £7
Various Franco Corelli Sings Great Religious Arias Corelli
Mono Issue : ALP2050

ASD 600 S/c : **£18** P.Stamp : £6
LISZT Sonata in Bmin. Hungarian Fantasia, Rapsodie Espagnole
Ogdon Philharmonia Orchestra Pritchard
Mono Issue : ALP2051

ASD 601 S/c : **£ 25** P.Stamp : £ 7
CARTER Piano Sonata, Double Concerto Rosen
Mono Issue : ALP2052

ASD 602-3 S/c : **£ 400** P.Stamp : £50
BRUCKNER Symphony No.8
Vienna Philharmonic Orchestra Schuricht
Mono Issue : ALP2053-4

ASD 604 S/c : **£ 28** P.Stamp : £6
HANDEL Concerti Grossi
Bath Festival Chamber Orchestra Menhuin
Mono Issue : ALP2055

ASD 605 S/c : **£ 16** P.Stamp : £5
MOZART Trio In E Flat,Quintet In A Major Melos Ensemble
Mono Issue : ALP2056

ASD 606-7 S/c : **£ 40** P.Stamp : £7
Various Song and Operatic Recital Gobbi
Mono Issue : ALP2057-8

ASD 608 S/c : **£ 60** P.Stamp : £18
FALLA The Three Cornered Hat De Los Angeles
Philharmonia Orchestra De Burgos
Mono Issue : ALP2059

ASD 609 S/c : **£ 12** P.Stamp : £3
PUCCINI Madama Butterfly (Highlights)
Orchestra of Rome Opera House Santini
Mono Issue : ALP2060

ASD 610-11 S/c : **£ 20** P.Stamp : £3
ELGAR Symphony No.2, Falstaff Halle Orchestra Barbirolli
Mono Issue : ALP2061-2

ASD 612 S/c : **£ 35** P.Stamp : £8
SCHONBERG Symphony for Strings
Royal Philharmonic Orchestra Del Mar
Mono Issue : ALP2064

ASD 613   S/c : **£40**   P.Stamp : £10
GERHARD   Symphony No.1, Dances from Don Quixote
BBC Symphony Orchestra   Dorati
Mono Issue : ALP2063

ASD 614   S/c : **£30**   P.Stamp : £8
Various   Works for Two Pianos   Vronsky , Babin
Mono Issue : ALP2065

ASD 615   S/c : **£15**   P.Stamp : £5
Various   Religious Works   Fischer-Dieskau
Mono Issue : ALP2066

ASD 616   S/c : **£8**   P.Stamp : £3
Various   Recital On Wings of Song   Hammond
Mono Issue : ALP2068

ASD 617   S/c : **£65**   P.Stamp : £12
MOZART   Symphony No.35, Symphony No.41
Vienna Philharmonic Orchestra   Kubelik
Mono Issue : ALP2069

ASD 618   S/c : **£30**   P.Stamp : £7
BEETHOVEN / CHAUSSON / WIENIEAWSKI   Romances
Menuhin   Philharmonia Orchestra   Pritchard
Mono Issue : ALP2070

ASD 619   S/c : **£8**   P.Stamp : £3
THOMAS   Mignon (Highlights)   Paris Opera   Hartemann
Mono Issue : ALP2071

ASD 620   S/c : **£24**   P.Stamp : £5
BRAHMS / REGER   Quintet In B For Clarinet & Strings, Quintet In A
De Peyer   Melos Ensemble
Mono Issue : ALP2072

ASD 621   S/c : **£20**   P.Stamp : £6
TIPPETT   Piano Concerto, Sonata No.2   Ogdon
Philharmonia Orchestra   Davis
Mono Issue : ALP2073

ASD 622   S/c : **£30**   P.Stamp : £6
Various   Operatic Recital   Freni
Orchestra of Rome Opera House   Ferraris
Mono Issue : ALP2074

ASD 623   S/c : **£10**   P.Stamp : £3
BACH / FRESCOBALDI   Organ Works   Germani
Mono Issue : ALP2075

ASD 624   S/c : **£15**   P.Stamp : £5
BACH   Easter Oratorio   Fischer-Dieskau
South West Germany Chamber Orchestra   Gonnenwein
Mono Issue : ALP2076

ASD 625   S/c : **£6**   P.Stamp : £4
MENDELSSOHN   Elijah (Highlights)
Royal Philharmonic Orchestra   Sargent
Mono Issue : ALP2077

ASD 626   (==== Not Issued ====)

ASD 627   S/c : **£30**   P.Stamp : £6
MOZART   Serenade K.250 "Haffner"
Bath Festival Chamber Orchestra   Menhuin
Mono Issue : ALP2079

ASD 628   S/c : **£20**   P.Stamp : £6
COUPERIN   Apotheose de Lully, Corelli, etc.
Toulouse Chamber Orchestra   Auriacombe
Mono Issue : ALP2080

ASD 629   S/c : **£30**   P.Stamp : £6
LISZT   Piano Concerto No.1,Todtentanz, Hungarian Fantasy
Czyffra   Philharmonia Orchestra   Vandernoot
Mono Issue : ALP2082

ASD 630   S/c : **£15**   P.Stamp : £5
BRAHMS   Leider Recital   Fischer-Dieskau
Mono Issue : ALP2083

ASD 631   S/c : **£20**   P.Stamp : £8
TELEMANN   Orchestral Music   Moscow Chamber Orchestra Barshai
Mono Issue : ALP2084

ASD 632   (=== Not Issued ===)

ASD 633   S/c : **£30**   P.Stamp : £8
BACH   Flute Sonatas Vol.1   Shaffer
Mono Issue : ALP2086

ASD 634   (=== Not Issued ===)

ASD 635   S/c : **£35**   P.Stamp : £8
PURCELL   An Anthology Vol.1   Menuhin
Mono Issue : ALP2088

ASD 636   S/c : **£28**   P.Stamp : £7
TCHAIKOVSKY   Symphony No.5   New Philharmonia Orchestra   Pretre
Mono Issue : ALP2089

ASD 637   S/c : **£8**   P.Stamp : £3
BRITTEN / CORRELLI / TIPPETT   Concerto Grosso, Fantasia
Concertante   Bath Festival Chamber Orchestra   Menuhin
Mono Issue : ALP2090

ASD 638   (=== Not Issued ===)

ASD 639   S/c : **£12**   P.Stamp : £5
BOULEZ / MESSIAEN   Soleil des Eaux, Chronochromie
BBC Symphony Orchestra   Dorati
Mono Issue : ALP2092

ASD 640   S/c : **£10**   P.Stamp : £4
Various   Choral Music   Melos Ensemble
Mono Issue : ALP2093

ASD 641   S/c : **£8**   P.Stamp : £3
BYRD   Byrd and his contemporaries   Kings College Choir
Mono Issue : ALP2094

ASD 642   S/c : **£30**   P.Stamp : £12
Various   20th Century Spanish Piano Music   Soriano
Mono Issue : ALP2095

ASD 643   S/c : **£30**   P.Stamp : £6
BRAHMS / SCHUBERT   Sextet No.2, Trio In B Flat   Menuhin
Mono Issue : ALP2096

ASD 644　　　S/c : **£50**　　　P.Stamp : £12
DELIUS　　　　Cello Concerto, Songs Farewell　　　Du Pre
Royal Philharmonic Orchestra　　　　Sargent
Mono Issue : ALP2097

ASD 645　　　S/c : **£12**　　　P.Stamp : £4
HODDINOTT / HALL / GOEHR Etc.　Piano Music: 20th Century
Composers　　　　Ogdon
Mono Issue : ALP2098

ASD 646　　　S/c : **£10**　　　P.Stamp : £2
TCHAIKOVSKY　Serenade For Strings　　　Arensky
London Symphony Orchestra　　　　Barbirolli
Mono Issue : ALP2099

ASD 647　　　(==== Not Issued ====)

ASD 648-9　　S/c : **£10**　　　P.Stamp : £2
ELGAR　　　　The Dream Of Gerontius
Halle Orchestra　　Barbirolli
Mono Issue : ALP2101-2

ASD 650　　　S/c : **£15**　　　P.Stamp : £5
SCHUMANN　　Lieder　　　　Fischer-Dieskau
Mono Issue : ALP2103

ASD 651　　　S/c : **£28**　　　P.Stamp : £5
Various　　　　Victoria De Los Angeles A World Of Song
De Los Angeles　Symphonia of London　　De Burgos
Mono Issue : ALP2104

ASD 652　　　(==== Not Issued ====)

ASD 653　　　S/c : **£20**　　　P.Stamp : £5
Various　　　　From Christmas to Candlemass
Kings College Choir　　　Willcocks
Mono Issue : ALP2111

ASD 654　　　S/c : **£22**　　　P.Stamp : £6
STRAUSS / STRAVINSKY Der Rosankavalier Suite, etc.
Philharmonia Orchestra　　Krips
Mono Issue : ALP2112

ASD 655   S/c : **£35**   P.Stamp : £10
ELGAR   Cello Concerto, Sea Pictures   Du Pre
London Symphony Orchestra   Barbirolli
Mono Issue : ALP2106

HMV ASD 4-digit series Stereophonic LP's

The labels used for the ASD 4-digit series are somewhat complicated by the fact that HMV used the totally different 'Melodya' label for all Russian recordings, which accounts for many records throughout the entire 4-digit series. The label first appears on ASD2269 and is red with a white outline Melodya logo on the top left hand side of the label and a white outline of nipper on the top right hand side, with a small white EMI logo at the bottom of the label. This is the only label used for the Melodya recordings and the relevant records are referred to as **Melodya** throughout this section of the guide.

The first ASD 4-digit label is the same as the 2nd label in the 3-digit series; IE. Red and has the words 'His Masters Voice' printed in bold white letters around a semi-circular 'Nipper' logo covering much of the top half of the label. The lettering on the label is printed in Black. These are referred to as **1st Semi** (Semicircle) in this section of the guide and is the first label for all English recordings from ASD2251 through to ASD2456, after which 1st Semi labels can only be found on ASD2458, 2459, 2462, 2465, 2466, 2468, 2470, 2477, 2478 & 2483.

The second label, used on all UK recordings from ASD2484 through to ASD2800, has a small, coloured rectangular 'nipper' printed within a white frame at the top of the label (measuring about 25mm x 35mm). Directly beneath this 'postage stamp' picture are the words *'Sold in the UK subject to resale price conditions, see price lists'* printed in black. This is also the first label for ASD2457, 2460, 2467, 2469, 2473 & 2476. This label is referred to as **col.stamp** throughout this section of the guide

The third label, used on all UK recordings from ASD2801 through to ASD3798, sees the removal of the *'Sold in the UK....'* text, the coloured rectangular 'nipper' becomes black and white and a solid white line now runs around the circumference of the label. This label is referred to as **B/w Band** throughout this section of the guide.

The fourth label, used on all UK recordings from ASD3801 through to ASD3998, sees the black and white 'nipper' revert to colour, but this time, the solid white line remains around the circumference of the label. This label is referred to as **Col. Band** throughout this section of the guide.

The fifth label is similar in appearance to 1st Semi, but the 'Nipper' now covers the entire top half of the label without the words 'His Masters voice'. This label is referred to as **2nd Semi** in this section of the guide.

ASD 2251   1st Semi : £**10**   Col.Stamp : £3
SCHUBERT   Symphony No.9   Halle Orchestra   Barbirolli

ASD 2252   1st Semi : £**4**   Col.Stamp : £1
LEHAR   Merry Widow (Highlights)   Schwarzkopf
Philharmonia Orchestra   Matacic

ASD 2254   1st Semi : £**12**   Col.Stamp : £4
MOZART   Piano Concerto No.14   Menuhin
Bath Festival Chamber Orchestra   Menuhin

ASD 2255   1st Semi : £**8**   Col.Stamp : £3
STRAVINSKY / HINDEMITH / BARTOK   Twentieth Century Classics
Bath Festival Chamber Orchestra   Menuhin

ASD 2256   1st Semi : £**10**   Col.Stamp : £3
MOZART / BEETHOVEN   Quintet K452, Quintet Op.16
Melios Ensemble

ASD 2257   1st Semi : £**6**   Col.Stamp : £2
MUSSORGSKY   Boris Godounov (Highlights)
Paris Conservatory Orchestra   Cluytens

ASD 2258   1st Semi : £**10**   Col.Stamp : £3
BEETHOVEN   Two Piano Trios   Menuhin, Gendron   Menuhin

ASD 2259   1st Semi : £**8**   Col.Stamp : £3
ELGAR   `Violin Concerto in Bmin op 61   Menuhin
New Philharmonia Orchestra   Boult

ASD 2260   1st Semi : £**25**   Col.Stamp : £8
RAVEL   Sheherazade   De Los Angeles
Paris Conservatory Orchestra   Pretre

ASD 2261   1st Semi : £**12**   Col.Stamp : £4
PURCELL   An Anthology Vol.2   Carlyle
Bath Festival Chamber Orchestra   Menuhin

ASD 2262   1st Semi : £**8**   Col.Stamp : £3
HANDEL   Dixit Dominus
English Chamber Orchestra   Willcocks

ASD 2263   1st Semi : **£15**   Col.Stamp : £5
SCHUBERT   Songs   Fischer-Dieskau

ASD 2264   1st Semi : **£14**   Col.Stamp : £5
Various   Westminster Abbey 900th Aniversary Service

ASD 2265   1st Semi : **£4**   Col.Stamp : £1
MOZART   Cosi fan Tutte (Highlights)
Philharmonia Orchestra   Bohm

ASD 2267   1st Semi : **£6**   Col.Stamp : £2
BACH   Concerto in Dmin., Concerto in Amin. Malcolm
Bath Festival Chamber Orchestra   Menuhin

ASD 2268   1st Semi : **£6**   Col.Stamp : £2
BACH   Flute Sonatas Vol.2   Schaffer

ASD 2269   Melodya : **£18**
MOZART / SCHUBERT   Symphony No.40, Symphony No.5
Moscow Chamber Orchestra   Barshai

ASD 2270   1st Semi : **£6**   Col.Stamp : £2
Spoken Word   Marlowe Dr. Faustus   Burton

ASD 2271   1st Semi : **£6**   Col.Stamp : £2
PUCCINI   La Boheme (Highlights)   Gedda
Rome Opera   Schippers

ASD 2272   1st Semi : **£10**   Col.Stamp : £3
SIBELIUS   Karelia Suite, Valse Triste
Halle Orchestra   Barbirolli

ASD 2273   1st Semi : **£10**   Col.Stamp : £3
SCHUBERT   Recital   Fischer-Dieskau

ASD 2274   1st Semi : **£12**   Col.Stamp : £4
Various   Favorite Arias   De Los Angeles

ASD 2275   1st Semi : **£10**   Col.Stamp : £3
VERDI   Arias   Crespin   Paris Conservatory Orchestra   Pretre

ASD 2276-7   1st Semi : **£18**   Col.Stamp : £6
BERLIOZ   Sceanes fron The Trojans
Paris Conservatory Orchestra   Pretre

ASD 2279   1st Semi : **£15**   Col.Stamp : £5
ORR / MUSGRAVE / HAMILTON   Symphony in 1 Movement, Tryptich,
Symphonia   Scottish National Orchestra   Gibson

ASD 2280   1st Semi : **£6**   Col.Stamp : £2
MOZART   Concerto for 2 Pianos, Concerto for 3 Pianos
Menuhin, Ts'ong

ASD 2281   1st Semi : **£20**   Col.Stamp : £7
BARTOK   Violin Concerto No.2   Menuhin
Philharmonia Orchestra   Dorati

ASD 2282   1st Semi : **£6**   Col.Stamp : £2
BIZET   Carmen (Highlights)   Paris Opera Orchestra   Pretre

ASD 2283   1st Semi : **£8**   Col.Stamp : £3
LISZT   Operatic Fantasies, Piano Works   Ogdon

ASD 2284   1st Semi : **£30**   Col.Stamp : £10
BRUCKNER   Symphony No.3
Vienna Philharmonic Orchestra   Schuricht

ASD 2285   1st Semi : **£15**   Col.Stamp : £5
BEETHOVEN   Violin Concerto   Menuhin
Philharmonia Orchestra   Klemperer

ASD 2286   1st Semi : **£18**   Col.Stamp : £6
Various   Barbar the Elephant   Ustinov
Paris Conservatory Orchestra   Pretre

ASD 2287   1st Semi : **£25**   Col.Stamp : £8
Various   Melodies   De Los Angeles

ASD 2289   1st Semi : **£6**   Col.Stamp : £2
SKALKOTTAS   Octet, 8 Variations on Greek Folk Tunes   Masters

ASD 2290   1st Semi : **£12**   Col.Stamp : £4
Various   Sing Praises
Choir of Kings College Cambridge   Willcocks

ASD 2292   1st Semi : **£6**   Col.Stamp : £2
ELGAR   Pomp & Circumstance Marches, Elegy etc
Philharmonia Orchestra   Barbirolli

ASD 2294   1st Semi : **£15**   Col.Stamp : £7
Various   West Meets East   Shankar

ASD 2295   1st Semi : **£10**   Col.Stamp : £5
Various   Music of India   Vilyat Khan

ASD 2296   1st Semi : **£10**   Col.Stamp : £3
POULENC   Bal Masque, Rhapsodie Negre
Paris Conservatory Orchestra   Pretre

ASD 2297   1st Semi : **£6**   Col.Stamp : £2
HAYDN   Symphony No.26, Symphony No.44, Symphony No.48
Bath Festival Chamber Orchestra   Menuhin

ASD 2298   1st Semi : **£15**   Col.Stamp : £5
PANUFNIK   Sinfonia Sacra, Sinfonia Rustica
Monte Carlo Orchestra   Panufnik

ASD 2299   1st Semi : **£10**   Col.Stamp : £3
WALTON   Symphony No.1
New Philharmonia Orchestra   Sargent

ASD 2300   1st Semi : **£4**   Col.Stamp : £1
PUCCINI   Tosca (Highlights)   Callas   Pretre

ASD 2301   1st Semi : **£5**   Col.Stamp : £2
HOLST   The Planets   New Philharmonia Orchestra   Boult

ASD 2302   1st Semi : **£6**   Col.Stamp : £2
BACH   Cantata No.82   Baker

ASD 2303   1st Semi : **£8**   Col.Stamp : £3
HAYDN   Missa in Tempore Belli
English Chamber Orchestra   Willcocks

ASD 2304   1st Semi : **£20**   Col.Stamp : £8
Various   Duets : Ravi Shankar & Ali Akbar Khan   Shankar

ASD 2305   1st Semi : **£6**   Col.Stamp : £2
BAX / IRELAND   Tintagel, London Overture
London Symphony Orchestra   Barbirolli

ASD 2306   1st Semi : **£8**   Col.Stamp : £3
POULENC   Piano Concerto   Tacchino
Paris Conservatory Orchestra   Pretre

ASD 2307   1st Semi : **£4**   Col.Stamp : £1
ROSSINI   Barber of Seville (Highlights)De Los Angeles
Philharmonia Orchestra   Gui

ASD 2308   1st Semi : **£10**   Col.Stamp : £3
SIBELIUS   Symphony No.2   Halle Orchestra   Barbirolli

ASD 2309   1st Semi : **£6**   Col.Stamp : £2
MOZART   Music for the Archbishop
Bath Festival Chamber Orchestra   Menuhin

ASD 2311   1st Semi : **£5**   Col.Stamp : £2
ELGAR / PARY   Music Makers, Pair Of SirensBaker
London Philharmonic Orchestra   Boult

ASD 2312   1st Semi : **£20**   Col.Stamp : £8
Various   Music of India Vol.3   Shankar

ASD 2313   1st Semi : **£6**   Col.Stamp : £2
MOZART   2 Salzburg Divertimenti
Bath Festival Chamber Orchestra   Menuhin

ASD 2314   1st Semi : **£6**   Col.Stamp : £2
MOZART   Die Zauberflote (Highlights) Gedda
Philharmonia Orchestra   Klemperer

ASD 2315   1st Semi : **£25**   Col.Stamp : £8
STRAVINSKY / PROKOVIEV   Rite Of Spring, Classical Symphony
New Philharmonia Orchestra   De Burgos

ASD 2316   1st Semi : **£12**   Col.Stamp : £4
SAINT-SAENS / MILHAUD   Carnival of the Animals, Creation
Paris Conservatory Orchestra   Pretre

ASD 2317   1st Semi : **£18**   Col.Stamp : £6
Various   Recital   Bumbry

ASD 2318   1st Semi : **£12**   Col.Stamp : £4
MOZART   Piano Concerto No.20, Piano Concerto No.23
Barenboim   English Chamber Orchestra

ASD 2319   1st Semi : **£10**   Col.Stamp : £3
MOZART   Piano Quartet No.1, Piano Quartet No.2   Ts'ong

ASD 2320   1st Semi : **£10**   Col.Stamp : £3
STRAUSS   Oboe Concerto, Duet Concerto
Berlin Radio Orchestra   Rogner

ASD 2321-2   1st Semi : **£10**   Col.Stamp : £3
STEVENSON / TIPPETT / OGDON   Passacaglia, Sonata No.1, Theme &
Variation   Ogdon

ASD 2323   1st Semi : **£35**   Col.Stamp : £14
BARTOK   Violin Concerto, Viola Concerto   Menuhin
Philharmonia Orchestra   Dorati

ASD 2324   1st Semi : **£6**   Col.Stamp : £2
Various   Grand Opera Gala   Callas

ASD 2325   1st Semi : **£12**   Col.Stamp : £4
BRUCKNER   5 Motets   Philharmonia Orchestra   Pitz

ASD 2326   1st Semi : **£20**   Col.Stamp : £7
SIBELIUS   Symphony No.5, Symphony No.7
Halle Orchestra   Barbirolli

ASD 2327   1st Semi : **£10**   Col.Stamp : £3
MOZART   Symphony No.32, Symphony No.35, Symphony No.38
English Chamber Orchestra   Barenboim

ASD 2328   1st Semi : **£8**   Col.Stamp : £3
SCHUBERT   Trout Quintet, Concertante for Piano & Strings
Crowson   Melios Ensemble

ASD 2329   1st Semi : **£5**   Col.Stamp : £2
VAUGHAN-WILLIAMS   Symphony No.6
New Philharmonia Orchestra   Boult

ASD 2330   1st Semi : **£5**   Col.Stamp : £2
OFFENBACH   Tales of Hoffman (Highlights)   Schwarzkopf
Orchestra de Paris   Cluytens

ASD 2331   1st Semi : **£65**   Col.Stamp : £25
HAYDN / BOCCHERINI   Cello Concertos   Du Pre

ASD 2332   1st Semi : **£30**   Col.Stamp : £10
TCHAIKOVSKY   Symphony No.6
London Symphony Orchestra   Horenstein

ASD 2333   1st Semi : **£20**   Col.Stamp : £7
BIRTWISTLE / CROSS / WOOD   Concerto da Camera, 3 Piano Pieces
Parikian   Melios Ensemble

ASD 2334   1st Semi : **£15**   Col.Stamp : £5
HANDEL / MOZART   Arias   Popp   English Chamber Orchestra

ASD 2335   1st Semi : **£8**   Col.Stamp : £3
STRAUSS   Duets from Der Rosenkavalier   Della Casa
Dresden Staatskapelle

ASD 2336-7   1st Semi : **£20**   Col.Stamp : £7
BUSONI   Piano Concerto   Ogdon
Royal Philharmonic Orchestra   Revenaugh

ASD 2338   1st Semi : **£12**   Col.Stamp : £4
MAHLER   Kindertotenlieder   Baker
Halle Orchestra   Barbirolli

ASD 2339   1st Semi : **£8**   Col.Stamp : £3
PUCCINI   Recital of Puccini Arias   Freni

ASD 2340   1st Semi : **£8**   Col.Stamp : £3
CHARPENTIER   Midnight Mass for Christmas Eve
English Chamber Orchestra   Willcocks

ASD 2341   1st Semi : **£20**   Col.Stamp : £8
Various   Music of India Vol.4   Shankar

ASD 2342   1st Semi : **£12**   Col.Stamp : £4
BERLIOZ   Symphonie Fantastique   Orchestra de Paris   Munch

ASD 2343   1st Semi : **£6**   Col.Stamp : £2
SCHUBERT   Symphony No.2, Symphony No.6
Bath Festival Chamber Orchestra   Menuhin

ASD 2344   1st Semi : **£14**   Col.Stamp : £5
JANACEK   Concertino, In the Mist   Melios Ensemble

ASD 2345   1st Semi : **£6**   Col.Stamp : £2
BORODIN   Prince Igor (Highlights)   Christoff
Sofia National Opera

ASD 2346   1st Semi : **£10**   Col.Stamp : £3
SCHOENBERG / WAGNER   Verklarte Nacht, Siegfried Idyll
English Chamber Orchestra   Barenboim

ASD 2347   1st Semi : **£18**   Col.Stamp : £6
BARTOK   Piano Concerto No.3, Sonata for 2 Pianos   Ogdon
Philharmonia Orchestra   Sargent

ASD 2348   1st Semi : **£30**   Col.Stamp : £10
BEETHOVEN   Symphony No.3
BBC Symphony Orchestra   Barbirolli

ASD 2349   1st Semi : **£18**   Col.Stamp : £6
SCHOENBERG / WEBERN   Chamber Symphony, Cantata No.1
New Philharmonia Orchestra   Harper, Prausnitz

ASD 2350   1st Semi : **£25**   Col.Stamp : £8
DVORAK   String Quartet Op.96 'American', Piano Quintet
Smetana Quartet

ASD 2351   1st Semi : **£8**   Col.Stamp : £3
Various   English Music for Strings
Bournemouth Symphony Orchestra   Del Mar

ASD 2352   1st Semi : **£5**   Col.Stamp : £2
HANDEL   Organ concertos No.1, 15, 13 & 14   Preston
Bath Festival Chamber Orchestra   Menuhin

ASD 2353   1st Semi : **£6**   Col.Stamp : £3
BRAHMS   Piano Concerto No.1   Barenboim
Philharmonia Orchestra   Barbirolli

ASD 2354   1st Semi : **£20**   Col.Stamp : £7
BRAHMS   Horn Trio Op.40, Piano Trio Op.87
Civil, Gendron, Menuhin

ASD 2355   1st Semi : **£25**   Col.Stamp : £8
RAVEL   Daphnis & Chloe complete   Ambrosians
Philharmonia Orchestra   De Burgos

ASD 2356   1st Semi : **£6**   Col.Stamp : £3
ELGAR   Wand of Youth suites, etc
London Philharmonic Orchestra   Boult

ASD 2357   1st Semi : **£10**   Col.Stamp : £3
MOZART   Piano Concerto No.13, Piano Concerto No.17
Barenboim   English Chamber Orchestra

ASD 2358   1st Semi : **£8**   Col.Stamp : £3
FAURE   Requiem   New Philharmonia Orchestra   Willcocks

ASD 2359   1st Semi : **£4**   Col.Stamp : £1
GIORDANO   Andre Chenier (Highlights)   Rome Opera   Santini

ASD 2360   1st Semi : **£6**   Col.Stamp : £2
VAUGHAN-WILLIAMS   London Symphony
Halle Orchestra   Barbirolli

ASD 2361   1st Semi : **£8**   Col.Stamp : £3
RACHMANINOV   Rhapsody On A Theme Of Paganini
New Philharmonia Orchestra   Atzmon

ASD 2362   1st Semi : **£10**   Col.Stamp : £3
BRAHMS   Clarinet Sonatas   De Peyer

ASD 2363   1st Semi : **£10**   Col.Stamp : £4
RODRIGO   Concert de Aranjuez   Diaz
Spanish National Orchestra   De Burgos

ASD 2364   1st Semi : **£12**   Col.Stamp : £4
Various   German Opera Arias   Gedda
Bavarian State Opera

ASD 2365   1st Semi : £**140**   Col.Stamp : £60
GLAZUNOV / DVORAK   Violin Concerto   Milstein
Philharmonia Orchestra   De Burgos

ASD 2366   1st Semi : £**20**   Col.Stamp : £8
SIBELIUS   Symphony No.1   Halle Orchestra   Barbirolli

ASD 2367   1st Semi : £**20**   Col.Stamp : £8
Various   Music of India Vol.5   Ali Akbar Khan

ASD 2369   1st Semi : £**15**   Col.Stamp : £5
SATIE   Parade, Gymnopedies
Paris Conservatory Orchestra   Auriacombe

ASD 2370   1st Semi : £**10**   Col.Stamp : £3
VAUGHAN-WILLIAMS   Fantasia on a Theme of Thomas Tallis, Wasps
Bournemouth Symphony Orchestra   Silvestri

ASD 2371   1st Semi : £**12**   Col.Stamp : £4
CHOPIN   Music for Piano & Orchestra
Paris Conservatory Orchestra   Skrowaczewski

ASD 2373   1st Semi : £**6**   Col.Stamp : £2
SAINT-SAENS   Samson & Delilah (Highlights)   Vickers
Orchestra National de France   Pretre

ASD 2374   1st Semi : £**12**   Col.Stamp : £4
WEBER / SCHUMANN   Fantasy Pieces   De Peyer   Melios Ensemble

ASD 2375   1st Semi : £**8**   Col.Stamp : £3
VAUGHAN-WILLIAMS   Symphony No.4
New Philharmonia Orchestra   Boult

ASD 2376-7   1st Semi : £**10**   Col.Stamp : £3
MAHLER   Symphony No.6   Philharmonia Orchestra   Barbirolli

ASD 2378   1st Semi : £**4**   Col.Stamp : £1
GLUCK   Orfeo ed Euridice (Highlights)   Bumbry
Leipzig Gewandhaus Orchestra   Newman

ASD 2379   1st Semi : £**8**   Col.Stamp : £3
MOZART   Symphony No.31, Symphony No.41 Jupiter
English Chamber Orchestra   Barenboim

ASD 2381   1st Semi : **£8**   Col.Stamp : £4
BACH   Cantatas Baker
Consortium Musicum   Gonnenwein

ASD 2382   1st Semi : **£5**   Col.Stamp : £2
Various   Opera Duets   Various

ASD 2384   1st Semi : **£15**   Col.Stamp : £5
HANDEL   Sonatas for Violin, Harpsichord & Viola de Gamba
Malcolm

ASD 2386   1st Semi : **£30**   Col.Stamp : £10
SCHUMANN / TCHAIKOVSKY   Piano Quintet, String Quartet No.1
Smetana Quartet

ASD 2388   1st Semi : **£15**   Col.Stamp : £5
BUSONI   Berceuse Elegaique, Dallapicola
Philharmonia Orchestra   Prausnitz

ASD 2389   1st Semi : **£8**   Col.Stamp : £3
SATIE   Piano Music   Ciccolini

ASD 2390   1st Semi : **£20**   Col.Stamp : £6
WEILL   Symphony No.1, Symphony No.2
BBC Symphony Orchestra   Bertini

ASD 2391   1st Semi : **£10**   Col.Stamp : £3
BRAHMS   Alto Rhapsody   Ludwig
Philharmonia Orchestra   Klemperer

ASD 2393   1st Semi : **£8**   Col.Stamp : £3
VAUGHAN-WILLIAMS   A Pastoral Symphony
New Philharmonia Orchestra   Boult

ASD 2395   1st Semi : **£4**   Col.Stamp : £1
VERDI   Il Trovatore (Highlights)
Rome Opera   Schiooers

ASD 2396   1st Semi : **£10**   Col.Stamp : £3
BACH   Cantatas   Baker   Consortium Musicum

ASD 2397   1st Semi : **£8**   Col.Stamp : £3
DELIUS   Requiem   Royal Philharmonic Orchestra   Davies

ASD 2399   1st Semi : **£8**   Col.Stamp : £3
STRAUSS   Songs   Fischer-Dieskau

ASD 2400   1st Semi : **£15**   Col.Stamp : £6
SMYTH / HARTY   Music Of The 4 Countries
Scottish National Orchestra   Gibson

ASD 2401   1st Semi : **£40**   Col.Stamp : £12
BRAHMS   Symphony No.1
Vienna Philharmonic Orchestra   Barbirolli

ASD 2402   1st Semi : **£20**   Col.Stamp : £7
DVORAK / SCHUBERT   String Quartet, Quartettsatz   Smetana Quartet

ASD 2403   1st Semi : **£4**   Col.Stamp : £1
PUCCINI   Turandot (Highlights)   Nilsson

ASD 2404   1st Semi : **£20**   Col.Stamp : £6
Various   Song Book Vol.II (recital)   Schwarzkopf

ASD 2406   1st Semi : **£6**   Col.Stamp : £2
Various   Soviet Army Chorus & Band on Parade
Soviet Army Chorus

ASD 2407   Melodya : **£20**
SIBELIUS   Violin Concerto   Oistrakh

ASD 2408   Melodya : **£6**
Various   Singers of the Bolshoi Theatre
Chorus & Orchestra of the Bolshoi Theatre

ASD 2409   Melodya : **£8**
SHOSTAKOVICH   Execution of Stepan Razin, Symphony No.9
Moscow Philharmonic Orchestra   Kondrashin

ASD 2410   Melodya : **£8**
PROKOFIEV   Symphony No.1, Symphony No.7
Moscow Radio Symphony Orchestra   Rozhdestvensky

ASD 2411   Melodya : **£8**
PROKOFIEV / RACHMANINOV   Piano Concerto No.3, Piano Concerto
No.4   Petrov   Moscow Radio Symphony Orchestra   Rozhdestvensky

ASD 2413   1st Semi : **£15**   Col.Stamp : £6
BRAHMS   Piano Concerto No.2   Barenboim
New Philharmonia Orchestra   Barbirolli

ASD 2415   1st Semi : **£15**   Col.Stamp : £5
Various   Zarzuela Songs   De Los Angeles
Spanish National Orchestra   De Burgos

ASD 2416   1st Semi : **£5**   Col.Stamp : £3
LISZT   Popular Liszt recital   Ogdon

ASD 2417   1st Semi : **£5**   Col.Stamp : £3
SCHUBERT   Octet   Melios Ensemble

ASD 2418   1st Semi : **£18**   Col.Stamp : £7
Various   Music of India Vol.8   Shankar

ASD 2420   Melodya : **£6**
SHOSTAKOVICH   Symphony No.10
USSR Symphony Orchestra   Svetlanov

ASD 2421   1st Semi : **£45**   Col.Stamp : £12
BRAHMS   Symphony No.2, Tragic Overture
Vienna Philharmonic Orchestra   Barbirolli

ASD 2422   1st Semi : **£14**   Col.Stamp : £5
VAUGHAN-WILLIAMS   Sancta Civitas
London Symphony Orchestra   Willcocks

ASD 2423   1st Semi : **£15**   Col.Stamp : £5
LOEWE   Ballads   Fischer-Dieskau

ASD 2424   1st Semi : **£5**   Col.Stamp : £3
MOZART   Symphony No.39, Symphony No.40
English Chamber Orchestra   Barenboim

ASD 2425   1st Semi : **£10**   Col.Stamp : £5
Various   Music of India Vol.7   Vilyat Khan

ASD 2426   1st Semi : **£10**   Col.Stamp : £3
SCHUBERT   Symphony No.1, Symphony No.3
Menhuin Festival Orchestra   Menuhin

ASD 2427   1st Semi : **£25**   Col.Stamp : £8
GERHARD   Collages BBC Symphony Orchestra   Prausnitz

ASD 2429-30   Melodya : **£6**
PROKOFIEV   Cinderella
Moscow Radio Symphony Orchestra   Rozhdestvensky

ASD 2431   1st Semi : **£6**   Col.Stamp : £2
Various   Leider Recital   Baker

ASD 2432   1st Semi : **£40**   Col.Stamp : £12
BRAHMS   Symphony No.3
Vienna Philharmonic Orchestra   Barbirolli

ASD 2433   1st Semi : **£50**   Col.Stamp : £15
BRAHMS   Symphony No.4
Vienna Philharmonic Orchestra   Barbirolli

ASD 2434   1st Semi : **£9**   Col.Stamp : £3
MOZART   Piano Concerto No.14, Piano Concerto No.15
Barenboim   English Chamber Orchestra

ASD 2435   1st Semi : **£5**   Col.Stamp : £2
SULLIVAN   Irish Symphony
Royal Liverpool Philharmonic Orchestra   Groves

ASD 2436   1st Semi : **£140**   Col.Stamp : £30
BRAHMS   Cello Sonatas   Du Pre

ASD 2437   1st Semi : **£4**   Col.Stamp : £1
DELIUS   Songs Of Sunset
London Philharmonic Orchestra   Groves

ASD 2438   1st Semi : **£8**   Col.Stamp : £3
NIELSEN / BERWALD   Wind Quintet, Septet   Melios Ensemble

ASD 2439-40   1st Semi : **£20**   Col.Stamp : £6
VAUGHAN-WILLIAMS   Sea Symphony,Wasps Suite
London Philharmonic Orchestra   Boult

ASD 2441   1st Semi : **£8**   Col.Stamp : £3
Various   The Music of Iannis Xenakis   Pasquier

ASD 2442 1st Semi : **£10** Col.Stamp : £4
DEBUSSY La mer, Nocturnes Orchestra de Paris Barbirolli

ASD 2443 1st Semi : **£5** Col.Stamp : £2
HANDEL Organ Concerto Preston
Bath Festival Chamber Orchestra Menuhin

ASD 2444 1st Semi : **£15** Col.Stamp : £5
BERLIOZ / RAVEL Les Nuits d'Ete, Scheherzo
Philharmonia Orchestra Barbirolli

ASD 2445 1st Semi : **£15** Col.Stamp : £5
Various Popular Arias Gedda

ASD 2446 1st Semi : **£15** Col.Stamp : £5
Various Music of India Vol.9 Basmallah Khan

ASD 2447 Melodya : **£15**
SHOSTAKOVICH Violin Concerto No.2, Symphony No.6
Oistrakh Moscow Philharmonic Orchestra Kondrashin

ASD 2448 Melodya : **£8**
BIZET Carmen
Chorus & Orchestra of the Bolshoi Theatre Rozhdestvensky

ASD 2449 1st Semi : **£30** Col.Stamp : £8
BERG / BARTOK Violin Concerto Menuhin
BBC Symphony Orchestra Boulez

ASD 2450 1st Semi : **£15** Col.Stamp : £5
POULENC Sinfonietta, Suite Francaise Orchestra de Paris Pretre

ASD 2451 Melodya : **£14**
Various Russian Opera Arias Vishnevskaya
Chorus & Orchestra of the Bolshoi Theatre

ASD 2453 1st Semi : **£4** Col.Stamp : £1
PUCCINI Madame Butterfly (Highlights) Bergonzi
Rome Opera Scotto

ASD 2454 1st Semi : **£40** Col.Stamp : £12
SCHUMANN Symphony No.2 Philharmonia Orchestra Klemperer

ASD 2455   1st Semi : **£16**   Col.Stamp : £5
WEBER / ROSSINI   Concerto, Theme & Variations
Philharmonia Orchestra   De Burgos

ASD 2457   Col.Stamp : **£8**   B/w Band: £3
Various   French and Italian Opera Arias   Freni
La Scala   Votto

ASD 2458   1st Semi : **£6**   Col.Stamp : £2
VAUGHAN-WILLIAMS   Mystical Songs, Mass
Choir of Kings College Cambridge   Willcocks

ASD 2459   1st Semi : **£20**   Col.Stamp : £8
SCHOENBERG   Pelleas & Melisande
Philharmonia Orchestra   Barbirolli

ASD 2460   Col.Stamp : **£10**   B/w Band: £5
Various   Music of India Vol.11   Vilyat Khan

ASD 2462   1st Semi : **£10**   Col.Stamp : £3
MOZART / HAYDN   Sinfonia Concertante
English Chamber Orchestra   Barenboim

ASD 2463   Melodya : **£8**
PROKOFIEV   Symphony No.2
Moscow Radio Symphony Orchestra   Rozhdestvensky

ASD 2464   Melodya : **£16**
SHOSTAKOVICH / TCHAIKOVSKY   String Quartet No.1, String Septet
Rostropovich   Borodin Quartet

ASD 2465   1st Semi : **£10**   Col.Stamp : £4
MOZART   Piano Concerto No.21, Piano Concerto No.27
English Chamber Orchestra   Barenboim

ASD 2466   1st Semi : **£150**   Col.Stamp : £65
HAYDN   Cello Concertos   Du Pre
London Symphony Orchestra   Barbirolli

ASD 2467   Col.Stamp : **£10**   B/w Band: £3
HONEGGER / MESSIAEN   Symphony No.2, Exspecto   Baudo
Orchestra of the Theatre National de l'opera   Munch

ASD 2468   1st Semi : **£10**   Col.Stamp : £3
HANDEL   Italian Cantatas   Baker
English Chamber Orchestra   Leppard

ASD 2469   Col.Stamp : **£10**   B/w Band: £3
VAUGHAN-WILLIAMS   Symphony No.8, Concerto for 2 Pianos Babin
Philharmonia Orchestra   Boult

ASD 2470   1st Semi : **£15**   Col.Stamp : £5
MESSIAEN   Quartet for the End of Time   Pleeth

ASD 2471   Melodya : **£6**
RACHMANINOV   Symphony No.1
USSR Symphony Orchestra   Svetlanov

ASD 2472   Melodya : **£20**
KHACHATURIAN / PROKOFIEV   Violin Concerto, Violin Concerto
No.1   Oistrakh
Moscow Radio Symphony Orchestra   Khachaturian

ASD 2473   Col.Stamp : **£10**   B/w Band: £3
BELLINI / DONIZETTI   Arias and Duets   Gedda
Philharmonia Orchestra

ASD 2474   Melodya : **£8**
SHOSTAKOVICH   Symphony No.8
USSR Symphony Orchestra   Kondrashin

ASD 2475   Melodya : **£10**
Various   Russian Opera and Cantata Arias   Arkhipova
Chorus & Orchestra of the Bolshoi Theatre   Rozhdestvensky

ASD 2476   Col.Stamp : **£8**   B/w Band: £3
BARTOK   Piano Concerto No.1, Piano Concerto No.3
Barenboim   Philharmonia Orchestra   Boulez

ASD 2477   1st Semi : **£10**   Col.Stamp : £4
DELIUS   Music Of Delius   Halle Orchestra   Barbirolli

ASD 2478   1st Semi : **£8**   Col.Stamp : £3
SCHUBERT   Symphony No.4, Symphony No,5
Bath Festival Orchestra   Menuhin

ASD 2480 Melodya : £**8**
TCHAIKOVSKY Symphony No.1
USSR Symphony Orchestra Svetlanov

ASD 2481 Melodya : £**10**
KHACHATURIAN / SHOSTAKOVICH Piano Concerto, Piano
Concerto No.1 Moscow Philharmonic Orchestra Kondrashin

ASD 2482 Melodya : £**8**
RACHMANINOV Isle of the Dead
USSR Symphony Orchestra Svetlanov

ASD 2483 1st Semi : £**40** Col.Stamp : £10
SCHUBERT / SCHUMANN Moments Musiceaux, Nachtstucke Gilels

ASD 2484 Col.Stamp : £**7** B/w Band: £3
MOZART Piano Concerto No.5, Piano Concerto No.9
English Chamber Orchestra Barenboim

ASD 2485 Col.Stamp : £**4** B/w Band: £1
HANDEL Music for the Royal Fireworks
Bath Festival Chamber Orchestra Menuhin

ASD 2486 Col.Stamp : £**14** B/w Band: £4
SIBELIUS En Saga London Symphony Orchestra Dorati

ASD 2487 Col.Stamp : £**8** B/w Band: £3
VAUGHAN-WILLIAMS Flos Campi etc
Choir of Kings College Cambridge Willcocks

ASD 2488 Melodya : £**8**
RACHMANINOV Symphonic Dances, 3 Russian Songs
Moscow Philharmonic Orchestra Kondrashin

ASD 2489 Col.Stamp : £**4** B/w Band: £1
VAUGHAN-WILLIAMS Five Tudor Portraits
Philharmonia Orchestra Willcocks

ASD 2490 Melodya : £**8**
TCHAIKOVSKY Symphony No.2
USSR Symphony Orchestra Svetlanov

ASD 2491-2   Col.Stamp : **£35**   B/w Band: £12
MAHLER   Symphony No.7
Philharmonia Orchestra   Klemperer

ASD 2493   Col.Stamp : **£10**   B/w Band: £3
STRAUSS / MOZART   7 Songs, 4 Concert Arias   Schwarzkopf
London Symphony Orchestra   Brendel

ASD 2494   Col.Stamp : **£10**   B/w Band: £3
SIBELIUS   Symphony No.4   Halle Orchestra   Barbirolli

ASD 2495   Col.Stamp : **£5**   B/w Band: £2
SCHUBERT   Symphony No.8, Overtures
Bath Festival Chamber Orchestra   Menuhin

ASD 2496   Col.Stamp : **£8**   B/w Band: £3
Various   Many Happy Returns Sir John
BBC Symphony Orchestra   Barbirolli

ASD 2497   Col.Stamp : **£10**   B/w Band: £3
RAVEL   Bolero, Rhapsody Espagnol, Pavane etc.
Orchestra de Paris   Munch

ASD 2498   Col.Stamp : **£50**   B/w Band: £20
SCHUMANN / SAINT-SAENS   Cello Concertos   Du Pre
Philharmonia Orchestra   Barenboim

ASD 2499   Melodya : **£5**
TCHAIKOVSKY   Symphony No.3
USSR Symphony Orchestra   Svetlanov

ASD 2500   Col.Stamp : **£4**   B/w Band: £1
BEETHOVEN   Piano Concerto No.5   Barenboim
Philharmonia Orchestra   Klemperer

ASD 2501   Col.Stamp : **£10**   B/w Band: £3
ELGAR   Piano Quintet, Concert Allegro   Ogdon Allegri Quartet

ASD 2502   Col.Stamp : **£6**   B/w Band: £2
ELGAR   Nusery & Severn Suites Etc
Philharmonia Orchestra   Groves

ASD 2506   Col.Stamp : **£6**   B/w Band: £2
RAVEL   Introduction & Allegro   Melios Ensemble

ASD 2508   Col.Stamp : **£4**   B/w Band: £1
MOZART   Don Giovanni (Highlights)
Philharmonia Orchestra   Klemperer

ASD 2511-2   Melodya : **£25**
SHOSTAKOVICH / KABALEVSKY Symphony No.7, Cello Concerto No.2
Shafran   Leningrad Philharmonic Orchestra   Svetlanov

ASD 2513   Col.Stamp : **£10**   B/w Band: £3
Various   Great Sceans from French Opera   Sills
Royal Philharmonic Orchestra   Mackerras

ASD 2515   Col.Stamp : **£8**   B/w Band: £3
BEETHOVEN   Creatures Of Prometheus
Menhuin Festival Orchestra   Menuhin

ASD 2516   Col.Stamp : **£4**   B/w Band: £1
BERLIOZ   The Trojans (Highlights)   Baker
London Symphony Orchestra   Gibson

ASD 2517   Col.Stamp : **£15**   B/w Band: £5
Various   Songs of Catalonia   De Los Angeles

ASD 2518-9   Col.Stamp : **£20**   B/w Band: £7
MAHLER   Symphony No.5   Philharmonia Orchestra   Barbirolli

ASD 2520   Melodya : **£5**
RIMSKY-KORSAKOV   Sheherazade
USSR Symphony Orchestra   Svetlanov

ASD 2521   Melodya : **£6**
PROKOFIEV / RIMSKY-KORSAKOV   Alexandra Nevsky, Song of
Oleg the Wise   USSR Symphony Orchestra   Svetlanov, Khaikin

ASD 2522   Melodya : **£8**
GLAZUNOV   The Seasons
Moscow Radio Symphony Orchestra   Khaikin

ASD 2523   Melodya : £**5**
SCRIABIN   The Divine Poem
USSR Symphony Orchestra   Svetlanov

ASD 2524   Col.Stamp : £**20**   B/w Band: £7
SCHUBERT   Trio No.1 in Bflat   Gendron   Menuhin Trio

ASD 2525   Col.Stamp : £**12**   B/w Band: £4
BRAHMS   Violin Concerto   Oistrakh
Cleveland Orchestra   Szell

ASD 2531   Col.Stamp : £**6**   B/w Band: £2
BARTOK / KODALY   Concerto for Orchestra, Dances of Galanta
Chicago Symphony Orchestra   Ozawa

ASD 2533   Col.Stamp : £**6**   B/w Band: £2
BACH / BRUCKNER   Magnificat, Te Deum
Philharmonia Orchestra   Barenboim

ASD 2534   Col.Stamp : £**5**   B/w Band: £2
HANDEL   Organ Concertos   Preston
Bath Festival Chamber Orchestra   Menuhin

ASD 2535   Col.Stamp : £**5**   B/w Band: £2
BEETHOVEN   Symphony No.6, Egmont Overture
Philharmonia Orchestra   Giulini

ASD 2536   Col.Stamp : £**14**   B/w Band: £5
SCHUBERT   Trio No.2, Nocturne D897   Gendron Menuhin Trio

ASD 2537   Col.Stamp : £**10**   B/w Band: £3
BEETHOVEN / KLEMPERER   Symphony No.7, Rameau Variations
Philharmonia Orchestra   Klemperer

ASD 2538   Col.Stamp : £**5**   B/w Band: £2
VAUGHAN-WILLIAMS   Symphony No.5
London Philharmonic Orchestra   Boult

ASD 2539   Melodya : £**8**
RACHMANINOV   The Bells
Moscow Philharmonic Orchestra   Kondrashin

ASD 2540 Melodya : £**8**
RIMSKY-KORSAKOV / GLAZUNOV Symphony No.1, Symphony No.5
Moscow Radio Symphony Orchestra Khaikin

ASD 2541 Melodya : £**4**
MUSSORGSKY Boris Godunov (Highlights)
Chorus & Orchestra of the Bolshoi Theatre Melik-Pashaev

ASD 2542 Col.Stamp : £**10** B/w Band: £3
WALTON Violin Concerto, Viola Concerto Menuhin
London Symphony Orchestra Walton

ASD 2543 Col.Stamp : £**8** B/w Band: £3
VERDI Aida - Scenes & Arias
Orchestra of the Opera House Rome Mehta

ASD 2544 Col.Stamp : £**12** B/w Band: £4
Various Piano Recital at Carnegie Hall Gilels

ASD 2545 Melodya : £**6**
RACHMANINOV Symphony No.2
Chorus & Orchestra of the Bolshoi Theatre Svetlanov

ASD 2546 Col.Stamp : £**8** B/w Band: £3
MENDELSSOHN Piano Concerto No.1, Piano Concerto No.2 Ogdon
London Symphony Orchestra Ceccato

ASD 2547 Col.Stamp : £**30** B/w Band: £8
SCHUMANN Symphony No.3
Philharmonia Orchestra Klemperer

ASD 2548 Col.Stamp : £**4** B/w Band: £1
SCHUBERT Symphony No.9
Menuhin Festival Orchestra Menuhin

ASD 2549 Col.Stamp : £**10** B/w Band: £3
Various Portrait of the Artist Fischer-Dieskau

ASD 2550 Col.Stamp : £**5** B/w Band: £2
BEETHOVEN Piano Concerto No.4 Barenboim
New Philharmonia Orchestra Klemperer

ASD 2551 Col.Stamp : £**12**   B/w Band: £4
Various Modern British Piano Works Ogdon

ASD 2552 Col.Stamp : £**5**   B/w Band: £2
FRANCK Symphony in Dmin. Orchestra de Paris Karajan

ASD 2553 Col.Stamp : £**6**   B/w Band: £2
Various Duets at the Queen Elizabeth Hall Fischer-Dieskau

ASD 2554 Col.Stamp : £**15**   B/w Band: £5
BRAHMS Piano Concerto No.2 Richter
Orchestra de Paris Maazel

ASD 2555 Col.Stamp : £**10**   B/w Band: £3
BRAHMS 16 Songs Ludwig

ASD 2557 Melodya : £**6**
PROKOFIEV / SCHEDRIN Symphony No.4, Concerto for Orchestra
Moscow Radio Symphony Orchestra Rozhdestvensky

ASD 2558 Melodya : £**6**
TCHAIKOVSKY Manfred, Symphonic Poem
USSR Symphony Orchestra Svetlanov

ASD 2559 Col.Stamp : £**8**   B/w Band: £3
Various Portrait of the Artist Christoff

ASD 2560 Col.Stamp : £**6**   B/w Band: £2
BEETHOVEN Symphony No.1, Symphony No.8
Philharmonia Orchestra Klemperer

ASD 2561 Col.Stamp : £**6**   B/w Band: £2
BEETHOVEN Symphony No.2, Leonora 2, Prometheus
Philharmonia Orchestra Klemperer

ASD 2562 Col.Stamp : £**6**   B/w Band: £2
BEETHOVEN Symphony No.3, Fidelio Overture
Philharmonia Orchestra Klemperer

ASD 2563 Col.Stamp : £**6**   B/w Band: £2
BEETHOVEN Symphony No.4, Egmont
Philharmonia Orchestra Klemperer

ASD 2564   Col.Stamp : £**6**   B/w Band: £2
BEETHOVEN   Symphony No.5, Corolian Overture
Philharmonia Orchestra   Klemperer

ASD 2565   Col.Stamp : £**6**   B/w Band: £2
BEETHOVEN   Symphony No.6, Leonara Overture
Philharmonia Orchestra   Klemperer

ASD 2566   Col.Stamp : £**6**   B/w Band: £2
BEETHOVEN   Symphony No.7, Cons of the house Overture
Philharmonia Orchestra   Klemperer

ASD 2567-8   Col.Stamp : £**6**   B/w Band: £2
BEETHOVEN   Symphony No.9
Philharmonia Orchestra   Klemperer

ASD 2571   Col.Stamp : £**40**   B/w Band: £15
BEETHOVEN   Piano Trio No.4, Piano Trio No.5   Du Pre

ASD 2572   Col.Stamp : £**50**   B/w Band: £20
BEETHOVEN   Archduke Trio, Trio no 7   Du Pre

ASD 2574   Col.Stamp : £**8**   B/w Band: £3
Various   Portrait of the Artist   Gedda

ASD 2575   Col.Stamp : £**8**   B/w Band: £3
KLEMPERER   Symphony No.2, String Quartet No.7
Philharmonia Orchestra   Klemperer

ASD 2576   Col.Stamp : £**8**   B/w Band: £3
TCHAIKOVSKY   Piano Concerto No.1   Weissenberg
Orchestra de Paris   Karajan

ASD 2577   Col.Stamp : £**8**   B/w Band: £3
CHOPIN   2 Polonaises, 4 Nocturnes, Ballade   Pollini

ASD 2578   Col.Stamp : £**15**   B/w Band: £4
BELLINI / DONIZETTI   Heroines (recital) Sills

ASD 2579   Col.Stamp : £**4**   B/w Band: £1
BEETHOVEN   Piano Concerto No.3   Barenboim
Philharmonia Orchestra   Klemperer

ASD 2580   Col.Stamp : **£4**   B/w Band: £1
FAURE   Pelleas, Masques et Bergamasques
Orchestra of the Theatre National de l'opera   Baudo

ASD 2581   Col.Stamp : **£6**   B/w Band: £2
VAUGHAN-WILLIAMS   Symphony No.9, Fantasy on old 104th
Katin   London Philharmonic Orchestra   Boult

ASD 2582   Col.Stamp : **£8**   B/w Band: £3
BEETHOVEN   Triple Concerto   Oistrakh, Rostropovitch
Berlin Philharmonic Orchestra   Karajan

ASD 2583   Col.Stamp : **£8**   B/w Band: £3
MOZART   Symphony No.33, Symphony No.36
English Chamber Orchestra   Barenboim

ASD 2584   Col.Stamp : **£10**   B/w Band: £3
HANDEL   Coronation Anthems
Menhuin Festival Orchestra   Menuhin

ASD 2585   Melodya : **£15**
SHOSTAKOVICH   Violin Concerto No.1, Cello Concerto No.1
Kogan, Khomitser   Moscow Radio Symphony Orchestra   Kondrashin

ASD 2586   Col.Stamp : **£20**   B/w Band: £7
ROUSSEL   Cello Concertino, Suite in F, Piano Concerto
Orchestra de Paris   Jacquillat

ASD 2587   Col.Stamp : **£20**   B/w Band: £7
RACHMANINOV / CHOPIN   Cello Sonatas   Tortelier
Ciccolini on Piano

ASD 2589   Col.Stamp : **£20**   B/w Band: £7
BRAHMS   Haydn Variations, Academic, Tragic Overture
Vienna Philharmonic Orchestra   Barbirolli

ASD 2590   Col.Stamp : **£5**   B/w Band: £2
Various   French Songs   Baker

ASD 2592   Melodya : **£6**
TCHAIKOVSKY / GLINKA   Symphony No.4, Jota Aragonesa
USSR Symphony Orchestra   Svetlanov

ASD 2593   Melodya : **£8**
PROKOFIEV   Cantata for the 30th Aniversary of the October Revolution
Petrov   Moscow Philharmonic Orchestra   Kondrashin

ASD 2594   Col.Stamp : **£8**   B/w Band: £3
TCHAIKOVSKY   Piano Trio in Amin. Op.50   Menuhin

ASD 2596-7   Col.Stamp : **£8**   B/w Band: £3
SHAPORIN / PETROV   The Story of the Battle for the Russian Land
Svetlanov

ASD 2598   Melodya : **£10**
SHOSTAKOVICH   Symphony No.12
Leningrad Philharmonic Orchestra   Mravinsky

ASD 2599   Melodya : **£8**
TCHAIKOVSKY   Symphony No.5
USSR Symphony Orchestra   Svetlanov

ASD 2600   Col.Stamp : **£15**   B/w Band: £5
HOWELLS   Hymnus Paradisi   Philharmonia Orchestra   Willcocks

ASD 2601   Col.Stamp : **£8**   B/w Band: £3
BEETHOVEN   Songs   Gedda

ASD 2602   Col.Stamp : **£15**   B/w Band: £7
Various   West Meets East : Indian Music   Shankar

ASD 2603   Col.Stamp : **£8**   B/w Band: £3
SATIE   Piano Works Vol.2 Ciccolini

ASD 2606   Col.Stamp : **£5**   B/w Band: £2
BERLIOZ   Romeo and Juliet
Chicago Symphony Orchestra   Giulini

ASD 2607   Melodya : **£14**
ARENSKY / SCRIABIN   Piano Concerto   Khaikin
Moscow Radio Symphony Orchestra

ASD 2608   Col.Stamp : **£7**   B/w Band: £2
BEETHOVEN   Piano Concerto No.2   Barenboim
London Philharmonic Orchestra   Klemperer

ASD 2610   Col.Stamp : **£4**   B/w Band: £1
MOZART   Serenade No.13, Divertimento No.7, Etc.
English Chamber Orchestra   Barenboim

ASD 2611   Col.Stamp : **£8**   B/w Band: £3
Various Portrait of the Artist   Rothenberger

ASD 2612   Col.Stamp : **£8**   B/w Band: £3
ARNOLD / BLISS / JACOB   Concerto for Two Pianos
City of Birmingham Symphony Orchestra   Arnold

ASD 2613   Col.Stamp : **£6**   B/w Band: £2
STRAUSS   Ein Heldenleben
London Symphony Orchestra Barbirolli

ASD 2614   Col.Stamp : **£14**   B/w Band: £5
STRAVINSKY   Petrouchka & Firebird Suites
Chicago Symphony Orchestra   Giulini

ASD 2615   Col.Stamp : **£6**   B/w Band: £2
MONTEVERDI / SCARLATTI   Monteverdi and Scarltti   Baker

ASD 2616   Col.Stamp : **£5**   B/w Band: £2
BEETHOVEN   Piano Concerto No.1   Barenboim
Philharmonia Orchestra   Klemperer

ASD 2617   Melodya : **£8**
TCHAIKOVSKY / GLINKA   Symphony No.6, Kamarinskaya
USSR Symphony Orchestra   Svetlanov

ASD 2618   Col.Stamp : **£20**   B/w Band: £7
FRANCK / BRAHMS   Violin Sonata, Violin Sonata No.3   Oistrakh

ASD 2619-21   Melodya : **£6**
TCHAIKOVSKY   Swan Lake
Moscow Philharmonic Orchestra   Rozhdestvensky

ASD 2630   Col.Stamp : **£25**   B/w Band: £8
RHEINBERGER   Star of Bethlehem   Streich

ASD 2631   Col.Stamp : **£5**   B/w Band: £2
VAUGHAN-WILLIAMS   Sinfonia Antartica
London Philharmonic Orchestra   Boult

ASD 2632   Col.Stamp : £6   B/w Band: £2
PUCCINI   Arias   Caballe
London Symphony Orchestra   Mackarres

ASD 2633   Melodya : £6
SHOSTAKOVICH   Symphony No.14
Moscow Chamber Orchestra   Barshai

ASD 2634   Col.Stamp : £12   B/w Band: £4
Various   Elisabeth Schwarzkopf Songbook Vol.3   Schwarzkopf

ASD 2635   Col.Stamp : £6   B/w Band: £2
DELIUS   Appalachia, Brigg Fair   Halle Orchestra   Barbirolli

ASD 2636   Melodya : £5
PROKOFIEV   Symphony No.3
Moscow Radio Symphony Orchestra   Rozhdestvensky

ASD 2637   Col.Stamp : £5   B/w Band: £2
BRITTEN   St. Nicholas
Acadamy of St.Martins in the Fields   Willcocks

ASD 2638   Col.Stamp : £6   B/w Band: £2
ELGAR   The Lighter Elgar
Northern Sinfonia Orchestra   Marriner

ASD 2639   Melodya : £6
PROKOFIEV   Symphony No.6
Moscow Radio Symphony Orchestra   Rozhdestvensky

ASD 2640   Melodya : £8
IPPOLITOV-IVANOV   Caucasian Sketches
Moscow Philharmonic Orchestra   Rozhdestvensky

ASD 2641   Col.Stamp : £10   B/w Band: £3
Various   Glorious John   Barbirolli

ASD 2644   Col.Stamp : £25   B/w Band: £8
HAYDN / SCHUBERT   String Quartet No.67, String Quartet No.10
Smetana Quartet

ASD 2645　　Melodya : £**4**
TCHAIKOVSKY　Piano Concerto No.2　　Zhukov
Moscow Radio Symphony Orchestra　　Rozhdestvensky

ASD 2646　　Melodya : £**4**
RACHMANINOV / MUSSORGSKY　Symphony No.3, Khovantschina
Moscow Radio Symphony Orchestra　　Svetlanov

ASD 2647　　Col.Stamp : £**4**　　B/w Band: £1
BACH　　　　Concerto for Two Harpsichords　　Malcolm
Bath Festival Chamber Orchestra　　Menuhin

ASD 2648　　Col.Stamp : £**8**　　B/w Band: £3
SIBELIUS　　Symphony No.3, Symphony No.6
Halle Orchestra　　Barbirolli

ASD 2649　　Col.Stamp : £**15**　　B/w Band: £5
Various　　Spanish & Sephardic Songs　　De Los Angeles

ASD 2650　　Col.Stamp : £**8**　　B/w Band: £3
BRAHMS　　Symphony No.4
Chicago Symphony Orchestra　　Giulini

ASD 2651　　Col.Stamp : £**10**　　B/w Band: £3
STRAUSS　　Sonatina No.1 in F, Suite in Bb　　De Peyer
London Symphony Orchestra

ASD 2652　　Col.Stamp : £**6**　　B/w Band: £2
JANACEK / LUTOSLAWSKI　　Sinfionetta, Concerto for Orchestra
Chicago Symphony Orchestra　　Ozawa

ASD 2653　　Col.Stamp : £**10**　　B/w Band: £3
DVORAK　　Symphony No.8　Cleveland Orchestra　　Szell

ASD 2654　　Melodya : £**6**
KALINNIKOV / LIADOV　Symphony No.2, Enchanted Lake
USSR Symphony Orchestra　　Svetlanov

ASD 2655　　Col.Stamp : £**6**　　B/w Band: £2
Various　　Opera Choruses　Various

ASD 2656　　Col.Stamp : £**8**　　B/w Band: £3
POULENC　St Franc, Novelts, Nocturnes etc　　Tacchino

ASD 2660   Col.Stamp : £6   B/w Band: £2
BRAHMS   Symphony No.3, Tragic Overture
London Symphony Orchestra   Boult

ASD 2661   Col.Stamp : £5   B/w Band: £2
BEETHOVEN   Mass In C   New Philharmonia Orchestra   Guilini

ASD 2662   Col.Stamp : £5   B/w Band: £2
HANDEL   Organ Concerto No.7, 11 & 12   Preston
Menuhin Festival Orchestra   Menuhin

ASD 2664   Melodya : £6
Various   Russian Orchestral Works
USSR Symphony Orchestra   Svetlanov

ASD 2667   Col.Stamp : £8   B/w Band: £3
BEETHOVEN   Violin Concerto   Suk
New Philharmonia Orchestra   Boult

ASD 2668   Melodya : £6
SHOSTAKOVICH   Symphony No.5
USSR Symphony Orchestra   Shostakovich

ASD 2669   Melodya : £8
PROKOFIEV   Love of 3 Oranges
Moscow Radio Symphony Orchestra   Rozhdestvensky

ASD 2670   Col.Stamp : £4   B/w Band: £1
BARTOK   Music for Strings, Percussion & Celeste, Divertimenti for
Strings   English Chamber Orchestra   Barenboim

ASD 2671   Col.Stamp : £6   B/w Band: £2
BEETHOVEN   Chamber Works   Melios Ensemble

ASD 2672   Col.Stamp : £4   B/w Band: £1
ELGAR   Crown of India Suite
Royal Liverpool Philharmonic Orchestra   Groves

ASD 2673   Col.Stamp : £10   B/w Band: £3
VAUGHAN-WILLIAMS   Job, Masque for Dancing
London Symphony Orchestra   Boult

ASD 2688 Melodya : £**6**
Various Stars of the Bolshoi
Chorus & Orchestra of the Bolshoi Theatre

ASD 2689 Melodya : £**4**
BORODIN / LIADOV Symphony No.1, From Days of Old
USSR Symphony Orchestra Svetlanov

ASD 2690 Col.Stamp : £**4** B/w Band: £1
VERDI Othello (Highlights) Fischer-Dieskau
Philharmonia Orchestra Barbirolli

ASD 2691-2 Col.Stamp : £**20** B/w Band: £7
MAHLER Symphony No.2
Philharmonia Orchestra Klemperer

ASD 2693-4 Col.Stamp : £**10** B/w Band: £3
SIBELIUS Kullervo Symphony
Bournemouth Symphony Orchestra Berglund

ASD 2695 Col.Stamp : £**6** B/w Band: £2
WAGNER Klemperer Conducts Wagner Vol.1 Klemperer

ASD 2696 Col.Stamp : £**6** B/w Band: £2
WAGNER Klemperer Conducts Wagner Vol.2 Klemperer

ASD 2697 Col.Stamp : £**6** B/w Band: £2
WAGNER Walkure,Rheingold,Siegfried Etc
Philharmonia Orchestra Klemperer

ASD 2698 Col.Stamp : £**6** B/w Band: £2
VAUGHAN-WILLIAMS Symphony No.5, Tallis Fantasia
Philharmonia Orchestra Barbirolli

ASD 2699 Col.Stamp : £**6** B/w Band: £2
VAUGHAN-WILLIAMS Riders to Sea, Magnificat
London Philharmonic Orchestra Davies

ASD 2700 Melodya : £**6**
BORODIN / LIADOV Symphony No.2, Eight Russian Folksongs
USSR Symphony Orchestra Svetlanov

ASD 2701   Col.Stamp : **£8**   B/w Band: £3
RAVEL / PROKOFIEV   Piano Concerto, Piano Concerto No.3
Weissenberg   Orchestra de Paris   Ozawa

ASD 2705   Col.Stamp : **£10**   B/w Band: £3
BRAHMS   Symphony No.1   Philharmonia Orchestra   Klemperer

ASD 2706   Col.Stamp : **£12**   B/w Band: £4
BRAHMS   Symphony No.2, Tragic Overture
Philharmonia Orchestra   Klemperer

ASD 2707   Col.Stamp : **£8**   B/w Band: £3
BRAHMS   Symphony No.3, Academic Festival Overture
Philharmonia Orchestra   Klemperer

ASD 2708   Col.Stamp : **£8**   B/w Band: £3
BRAHMS   Symphony No.4   Philharmonia Orchestra   Klemperer

ASD 2709   Col.Stamp : **£8**   B/w Band: £3
SHOSTAKOVICH / OGDON   Piano Concerto No.2, Piano Concerto No.1
Ogdon   Royal Philharmonic Orchestra   Foster

ASD 2710   Col.Stamp : **£6**   B/w Band: £2
Various   Duets at the Royal Festival Hall   Fischer-Dieskau

ASD 2712   Col.Stamp : **£5**   B/w Band: £2
MASSENET   Werther (Highlights)   De Los Angeles
Orchestra de Paris   Pretre

ASD 2713   Col.Stamp : **£5**   B/w Band: £2
BACH   Harpsichord Concerto   Malcolm
Bath Festival Chamber Orchestra   Menuhin

ASD 2717   Melodya : **£6**
GLAZUNOV   Symphony No.8
Moscow Radio Symphony Orchestra   Svetlanov

ASD 2718   Col.Stamp : **£35**   B/w Band: £10
SHOSTAKOVICH   Violin Sonata Op.134, Piano Trio   Oistrakh

ASD 2719   Col.Stamp : **£25**   B/w Band: £8
BRUCKNER   Symphony No.9   Philharmonia Orchestra   Klemperer

528

ASD 2720   Melodya : **£8**
KALINIKOV / LIAPOUNOV   Symphony No.1, Piano Concerto No.2
Moscow Radio Symphony Orchestra   Khaikin

ASD 2721   Col.Stamp : **£6**   B/w Band: £2
ELGAR   Sea Pictures   Baker
London Symphony Orchestra   Barbirolli

ASD 2722   Col.Stamp : **£8**   B/w Band: £3
MAHLER   Symphony No.1
Chicago Symphony Orchestra   Giulini

ASD 2723   Col.Stamp : **£6**   B/w Band: £2
Various   Great Operatic Duos   Caballe
London Symphony Orchestra   Mackerras

ASD 2724   Col.Stamp : **£4**   B/w Band: £1
WAGNER   Flying Dutchman (Highlights)
Philharmonia Orchestra   Klemperer

ASD 2725   Col.Stamp : **£10**   B/w Band: £3
BEETHOVEN   2 Romances for Violin and Orchestra   Suk
Acadamy of St.Martins in the Fields   Marriner

ASD 2726-9   Col.Stamp : **£10**   B/w Band: £3
STRAUSS   Der Rosenkavalier   Philharmonia Orchestra   Karajan

ASD 2732   Col.Stamp : **£5**   B/w Band: £2
MOZART   Symphony No.40, Symphony No.41
Berlin Philharmonic Orchestra   Karajan

ASD 2737   Col.Stamp : **£8**   B/w Band: £3
BEETHOVEN   Symphony No.7
Chicago Symphony Orchestra   Giulini

ASD 2738   Col.Stamp : **£8**   B/w Band: £3
TCHAIKOVSKY   Francesca da Rimini, Serenade
Philharmonia Orchestra   Barbirolli

ASD 2739   Col.Stamp : **£14**   B/w Band: £2
GRACE WILLIAMS   Penillion,English Concert
Royal Philharmonic Orchestra   Groves

ASD 2740 Col.Stamp : £6 B/w Band: £2
VAUGHAN-WILLIAMS A London Symphony
London Philharmonic Orchestra Boult

ASD 2741 Melodya : £8
SHOSTAKOVICH Symphony No.4
Moscow Philharmonic Orchestra Kondrashin

ASD 2743 Col.Stamp : £6 B/w Band: £2
SCHUBERT Symphony No.8 ("completed"), Rosamonde
Royal Liverpool Philharmonic Orchestra Groves

ASD 2744 Col.Stamp : £10 B/w Band: £3
BARTOK / PROKOFIEV Piano Concerto, Piano Concerto No.5 Richter
Orchestra de Paris Maazel

ASD 2746 Col.Stamp : £5 B/w Band: £2
BRAHMS Symphony No.2, Alto Rhapsody Baker
London Philharmonic Orchestra Boult

ASD 2747 Melodya : £6
SHOSTAKOVICH Symphony No.2
Leningrad Philharmonic Orchestra Blazhkov

ASD 2748 Col.Stamp : £6 B/w Band: £2
ELGAR Symphony No.1 Philharmonia Orchestra Barbirolli

ASD 2749 Col.Stamp : £6 B/w Band: £2
ELGAR Symphony No.2 Halle Orchestra Barbirolli

ASD 2750 Col.Stamp : £4 B/w Band: £1
ELGAR / VAUGHAN-WILLIAMS Enigma,Fantasia On Greensleeves
London Symphony Orchestra Boult

ASD 2751 Col.Stamp : £75 B/w Band: £25
DVORAK Cello Concerto, Silent Woods Du Pre
Chicago Symphony Orchestra Barenboim

ASD 2752 Col.Stamp : £20 B/w Band: £8
SHANKAR Concerto for Sitar & Orchestra Shankar
London Symphony Orchestra Previn

ASD 2753   Col.Stamp : **£10**   B/w Band: £3
SAINT-SAENS   Carnival of the Animals   Ogdon
City of Birmingham Symphony Orchestra   Fremaux

ASD 2754   Col.Stamp : **£6**   B/w Band: £2
GERSHWIN   Previn Plays Gershwin
London Symphony Orchestra   Previn

ASD 2755   Melodya : **£40**
VAINBERG   Violin Concerto, Symphony No.4   Kogan
Moscow Philharmonic Orchestra   Kondrashin

ASD 2756   Col.Stamp : **£5**   B/w Band: £2
RIMSKY-KORSAKOV / BORODIN   Sheherazade, Polovtsian Dances
Chicago Symphony Orchestra   Ozawa

ASD 2757   Melodya : **£15**
TCHAIKOVSKY   Swan Lake
Moscow Symphony Orchestra   Rozhdestvensky

ASD 2758   Melodya : **£10**
PROKOFIEV   Symphony No.5
Moscow Symphony Orchestra   Rozhdestvensky

ASD 2759   Col.Stamp : **£10**   B/w Band: £3
WILLIAMSON / BERKELEY   Violin Concerto   Menuhin
London Philharmonic Orchestra   Boult

ASD 2760   Col.Stamp : **£25**   B/w Band: £8
SCHUBERT   Symphony No.9   Cleveland Orchestra   Szell

ASD 2761   Melodya : **£5**
SCRIABIN   Symphony No.1
USSR Symphony Orchestra   Svetlanov

ASD 2762   Col.Stamp : **£4**   B/w Band: £1
VERDI   Falstaff, Froissart, Introduction & Allegro
Halle Orchestra   Barbirolli

ASD 2763   Melodya : **£6**
PROKOFIEV / SHOSTAKOVICH   Chout, Age of Gold
Moscow Radio Symphony Orchestra   Rozhdestvensky

ASD 2764   Col.Stamp : £**25**   B/w Band: £8
ELGAR / DELIUS   Cello Concertos   Du Pre
London Symphony Orchestra   Barbirolli

ASD 2765   Melodya : £**10**
PROKOFIEV / SHOSTAKOVICH   Sinfionetta, Symphony No1
Moscow Radio Symphony Orchestra   Aranovich

ASD 2766   Col.Stamp : £**6**   B/w Band: £2
RAVEL   Tombeau, Rhapsony Espagnol
Orchestra de Paris   Karajan

ASD 2770   Col.Stamp : £**8**   B/w Band: £3
STRAVINSKY   Music for Piano & Orchestra Beroff
Orchestra de Paris   Ozawa

ASD 2771   Melodya : £**4**
TCHAIKOVSKY   Eugene Onegin
Chorus & Orchestra of the Bolshoi Theatre   Rostropovich

ASD 2772   Col.Stamp : £**8**   B/w Band: £3
Various   Piano Recital   Postnikova

ASD 2773   Col.Stamp : £**8**   B/w Band: £3
GRIEG   Lyric Suite, Homage March, Peer Gynt
Halle Orchestra   Barbirolli

ASD 2774   Col.Stamp : £**4**   B/w Band: £1
BIZET   Carmen (Highlights)   Bumbry
Paris Opera Orchestra   De Burgos

ASD 2775   Melodya : £**4**
TCHAIKOVSKY   Hamlet, The Tempest
USSR Symphony Orchestra   Svetlanov

ASD 2776   Col.Stamp : £**18**   B/w Band: £6
GOUNOD   Faust   Gedda
Orchestra of the Theatre National de L'Opera   Cluytens

ASD 2780   Col.Stamp : £**4**   B/w Band: £1
MOZART   Four Horn Concertos   Tuckwell
Acadamy of St.Martins in the Fields   Marriner

ASD 2781   Melodya : **£10**
SHOSTAKOVICH   Ballet Suites, Overture on Russian Songs
Chorus & Orchestra of the Bolshoi Theatre   Shostakovich

ASD 2782   Col.Stamp : **£12**   B/w Band: £4
PAGANINI   Violin Concerto No.1   Perlman
Royal Philharmonic Orchestra

ASD 2783   Col.Stamp : **£5**   B/w Band: £2
BACH   Violin Concerto, Double Concerto   Perlman
English Chamber Orchestra

ASD 2784   Col.Stamp : **£5**   B/w Band: £2
Various   LSO Gala Concert   Previn
London Symphony Orchestra   Heath

ASD 2786   Col.Stamp : **£5**   B/w Band: £2
WALTON   Façade
Acadamy of St.Martins in the Fields   Marriner

ASD 2787   Col.Stamp : **£7**   B/w Band: £2
VERDI   Arias   Caballe
Royal Philharmonic Orchestra

ASD 2788   Col.Stamp : **£8**   B/w Band: £3
MOZART   Requiem   English Chamber Orchestra   Barenboim

ASD 2789   Col.Stamp : **£15**   B/w Band: £5
BRAHMS   German Requiem   Philharmonia Orchestra   Klemperer

ASD 2791   Col.Stamp : **£8**   B/w Band: £3
Various   Arias from Aida, Attila, El Pirata etc   Callas

ASD 2793-6   Col.Stamp : **£12**   B/w Band: £4
BACH   St. Matthew Passion
Philharmonia Orchestra   Klemperer

ASD 2797-8   Col.Stamp : **£14**   B/w Band: £5
PUCCINI   Tosca   La Scala   Sabata

ASD 2799   Col.Stamp : **£8**   B/w Band: £3
MAHLER   Symphony No.4   Schwarzkopf
Philharmonia Orchestra   Klemperer

ASD 2800   Col.Stamp : **£10**   B/w Band: £3
PROKOFIEV   Alexander Nevsky   London Symphony Orchestra   Previn

ASD 2801   Melodya : **£5**
LIADOV   Enchanted Lake, Baba Yaga, Etc.
USSR Symphony Orchestra   Svetlanov

ASD 2802   B/w Band: **£6**   Col. Band: £2
GRIEG / SCHUMANN   Piano Concertos   Ogdon
New Philharmonia Orchestra   Berglund

ASD 2803   Melodya : **£14**
SAUGUET / TISHCHENKO   Cello Concerto   Rostropovich
Moscow Radio Symphony Orchestra

ASD 2804   B/w Band: **£6**   Col. Band: £2
DELIUS   Paris
Royal Liverpool Philharmonic Orchestra   Groves

ASD 2805   Melodya : **£10**
SHOSTAKOVICH / SIBELIUS   Symphony No.6, Symphony No.7
Leningrad Philharmonic Orchestra   Mravinsky

ASD 2806   B/w Band: **£8**   Col. Band: £3
MOZART   Symphony No.29, Symphony No.30, Symphony No.34
English Chamber Orchestra   Barenboim

ASD 2807   B/w Band: **£6**   Col. Band: £2
Various   Elisabeth Schwartzkopf Sings Operetta
Philharmonia Orchestra   Ackermann

ASD 2808   B/w Band: **£16**   Col. Band: £5
BRUCKNER   Symphony in F
London Symphony Orchestra   Shapirra

ASD 2809   B/w Band: **£6**   Col. Band: £2
MENDELSSOHN / BRUCH   Violin Concerto   Menuhin
London Symphony Orchestra   De Burgos

ASD 2810   B/w Band: **£15**   Col. Band: £5
GOEHR / HAMILTON   Violin Concerto   Parikian
Royal Philharmonic Orchestra   Del Mar

ASD 2811   B/w Band: **£4**   Col. Band: £1
VERDI   La Forza del Destino (Highlights)   Bergonzi
Royal Philharmonic Orchestra   Gardelli

ASD 2812   B/w Band: **£5**   Col. Band: £2
WAGNER   Lohengrin, Meistersinger, Tristan
New Philharmonia Orchestra   Boult

ASD 2813   Melodya : **£8**
TCHAIKOVSKY Violin Concerto   Igor Oistrakh
Moscow Philharmonic Orchestra   Rozhdestvensky

ASD 2814   B/w Band: **£5**   Col. Band: £2
TCHAIKOVSKY   Symphony No.4
Berlin Philharmonic Orchestra   Karajan

ASD 2815   B/w Band: **£5**   Col. Band: £2
TCHAIKOVSKY   Symphony No.5
Berlin Philharmonic Orchestra   Karajan

ASD 2816   B/w Band: **£5**   Col. Band: £2
TCHAIKOVSKY   Symphony No.6
Berlin Philharmonic Orchestra   Karajan

ASD 2817   B/w Band: **£6**   Col. Band: £2
HAYDN   Symphony No.83, Symphony No.101
Berlin Philharmonic Orchestra   Karajan

ASD 2818   B/w Band: **£15**   Col. Band: £5
HAYDN   Symphonu No.92 'Oxford', Symphony No.95
Philharmonia Orchestra   Klemperer

ASD 2822   B/w Band: **£5**   Col. Band: £2
ELGAR   Overtures   London Philharmonic Orchestra   Boult

ASD 2823   B/w Band: **£4**   Col. Band: £1
VERDI   Don Carlos (Highlights)   Caballe
Royal Opera House Covent Garden   Giulini

ASD 2824   B/w Band: **£8**   Col. Band: £3
MOZART   Lieder Recital   Fischer-Dieskau

ASD 2825   B/w Band: £**8**   Col. Band: £3
TCHAIKOVSKY   Piano Concerto No.2   Kersenbaum
ORTF   Martinon

ASD 2826   B/w Band: £**6**   Col. Band: £2
Various   Songs of Auvergne Canteloube, Chausson etc
De Los Angeles   Lamoureux Orchestra

ASD 2827   B/w Band: £**12**   Col. Band: £4
TCHAIKOVSKY   Nutcracker Suite
London Symphony Orchestra   Previn

ASD 2830   B/w Band: £**6**   Col. Band: £2
ELGAR   Serenade for Strings   Arensky
Philharmonia Orchestra   Barbirolli

ASD 2831   B/w Band: £**6**   Col. Band: £2
HOLST / PURCELL   English String Music
Acadamy of St.Martins in the Fields   Marriner

ASD 2834   B/w Band: £**4**   Col. Band: £1
MOZART   Overtures:Il Re Pastore Etc
Acadamy of St.Martins in the Fields   Marriner

ASD 2835   B/w Band: £**6**   Col. Band: £2
POULENC   Gloria, Organ Concerto   Durufle
French National Radio Orchestra   Pretre

ASD 2836   B/w Band: £**6**   Col. Band: £2
BRUCKNER   Mass No.3 in Fmin.
Philharmonia Orchestra   Barenboim

ASD 2837   B/w Band: £**6**   Col. Band: £2
WAGNER   Rare Orchestral Pieces
London Symphony Orchestra   Janowski

ASD 2838   B/w Band: £**8**   Col. Band: £3
MOZART   Piano Concerto No.22   Barenboim
English Chamber Orchestra

ASD 2844   B/w Band: £**15**   Col. Band: £5
Various   Elisabeth Schwartzkopf Songbook Vol.4   Schwarzkopf

ASD 2845 B/w Band: £**6** Col. Band: £2
STRAVINSKY Firebird Orchestra de Paris Ozawa

ASD 2846 Melodya : £**8**
RIMSKY-KORSAKOV Symphony No.3, Piano Concerto
Moscow Radio Symphony Orchestra Rozhdestvensky

ASD 2847 B/w Band: £**6** Col. Band: £2
VAUGHAN-WILLIAMS Seranade to Music, Lark Ascending
London Philharmonic Orchestra Boult

ASD 2851 B/w Band: £**80** Col. Band: £30
CHOPIN / FRANCK Cello Sonatas Du Pre

ASD 2852 B/w Band: £**6** Col. Band: £2
BRUCH Violin Concerto No.1, Violin Concerto No.2
Menuhin London Symphony Orchestra Boult

ASD 2855 B/w Band: £**15** Col. Band: £5
JONES Symphony No.4, Symphony No.7
Royal Philharmonic Orchestra Groves

ASD 2856 B/w Band: £**6** Col. Band: £2
SCHUBERT Great C Symphony
London Philharmonic Orchestra Boult

ASD 2857 Melodya : £**8**
SHOSTAKOVICH Symphony No.15
Borodin Quartet Shostakovich

ASD 2858 Melodya : £**8**
GLAZUNOV / RACHMANINOV Symphony No.2, The Crag
Moscow Radio Symphony Orchestra Rozhdestvensky

ASD 2863 B/w Band: £**8** Col. Band: £3
DVORAK / SMETANA New World Symphony, Vltava
Berlin Philharmonic Orchestra Karajan

ASD 2868-9 B/w Band: £**12** Col. Band: £4
BEETHOVEN Symphony No.8, Symphony No.9
London Symphony Orchestra Giulini

ASD 2870   B/w Band: **£12**   Col. Band: £4
WIENIAWSKI   Two Violin Concertos   Perlman
London Philharmonic Orchestra

ASD 2871   B/w Band: **£6**   Col. Band: £2
BRAHMS   Symphony No.1
London Philharmonic Orchestra   Boult

ASD 2872   B/w Band: **£8**   Col. Band: £3
RACHMANINOV / FRANCK   Piano Concerto No.1, Symphonic Variations
Wiessenberg   Berlin Philharmonic Orchestra   Karajan

ASD 2873   B/w Band: **£10**   Col. Band: £3
BRAHMS   Piano Quintet   Yale Quartet   Previn

ASD 2874   B/w Band: **£10**   Col. Band: £3
SIBELIUS   Symphony No.7, Tapiola
Bournemouth Symphony Orchestra   Berglund

ASD 2875   Melodya : **£12**
SHOSTAKOVICH   The Song of the Forests
Moscow Philharmonic Orchestra   Kondrashin

ASD 2876   B/w Band: **£8**   Col. Band: £3
BACH   Cantatas
Acadamy of St.Martins in the Fields   Marriner

ASD 2877   B/w Band: **£4**   Col. Band: £1
MASSENET   Manon (Highlights)   Gedda
Philharmonia Orchestra   Rudel

ASD 2878   B/w Band: **£10**   Col. Band: £3
ARNOLD   Symphony No.5
City of Birmingham Symphony Orchestra   Arnold

ASD 2879-81   Melodya : **£14**
TCHAIKOVSKY   The Maid of Orleans
Moscow Philharmonic Orchestra   Rozdestvensky

ASD 2883   B/w Band: **£6**   Col. Band: £2
ELGAR   Violin Concerto in Bmin op 61   Bean
London Philharmonic Orchestra   Groves

ASD 2884 B/w Band: **£10** Col. Band: £3
MOZART Serenade No.7 Zukerman
English Chamber Orchestra Haffner

ASD 2887 B/w Band: **£8** Col. Band: £3
MOZART Piano Concerto No.18, Piano Concerto No.24
Barenboim English Chamber Orchestra

ASD 2888 B/w Band: **£4** Col. Band: £1
STRAUSS 4 Last Songs Schwarzkopf
Bavarian Radio Symphony Orchestra Szell

ASD 2889 B/w Band: **£10** Col. Band: £3
RACHMANINOV Symphony No.2
London Symphony Orchestra Previn

ASD 2890 Melodya : **£6**
RACHMANINOV The Covetous Knight
Moscow Radio Symphony Orchestra Rozhdestvensky

ASD 2891 B/w Band: **£4** Col. Band: £1
STRAUSS Die Fledermaus (Highlights) Fischer-Dieskau
Boskovsky

ASD 2892 B/w Band: **£8** Col. Band: £3
SCHMITT Psalm 47, La Tradegie de Salome
ORTF Martinon

ASD 2893 Melodya : **£10**
SHOSTAKOVICH Symphony No.13
Moscow Philharmonic Orchestra Kondrashin

ASD 2894 B/w Band: **£8** Col. Band: £3
TCHAIKOVSKY Ov 1812, Romeo & Juliet
London Symphony Orchestra Previn

ASD 2898-9 B/w Band: **£12** Col. Band: £4
Various Operatic Duets Callas, Stefano

ASD 2900 Melodya : **£8**
GLAZUNOV Symphony No.3
Moscow Radio Symphony Orchestra Khaikin

ASD 2901 B/w Band: **£6** Col. Band: £2
BRAHMS Symphony No.4
London Philharmonic Orchestra Boult

ASD 2902 B/w Band: **£10** Col. Band: £3
Various Concert by Elly Ameling Ameling

ASD 2903 B/w Band: **£6** Col. Band: £2
Various Music from the Golden Age Fischer-Dieskau

ASD 2904 B/w Band: **£8** Col. Band: £3
McCABE Symphony No.2
City of Birmingham Symphony Orchestra Fremaux

ASD 2905 B/w Band: **£10** Col. Band: £3
Various Concert Sills

ASD 2906 B/w Band: **£6** Col. Band: £2
ELGAR Cello Concerto Tortelier
London Philharmonic Orchestra Boult

ASD 2911 B/w Band: **£4** Col. Band: £1
BEETHOVEN Fidelio (Highlights)
Berlin Philharmonic Orchestra Karajan

ASD 2912 Melodya : **£10**
HINDEMITH Harmonie der Welt Symphony
Leningrad Philharmonic Orchestra Mravinsky

ASD 2913 B/w Band: **£10** Col. Band: £3
MOERAN Symphony in Gmin.
English Sinfionetta Dykes

ASD 2914 B/w Band: **£4** Col. Band: £1
VAUGHAN-WILLIAMS The Wasps, Concerto for 2 Pianos
Vronsky, Babin London Philharmonic Orchestra Boult

ASD 2915 B/w Band: **£8** Col. Band: £3
BIZET Carmen Suite, L'Arleienne Suite, Etc.
Orchestra de Paris Barenboim

ASD 2916   B/w Band: £**6**   Col. Band: £2
MOZART   Clarinet Concerto, Bassoon Concerto
Berlin Philharmonic Orchestra   Karajan

ASD 2917   B/w Band: £**12**   Col. Band: £4
SHOSTAKOVICH   Symphony No.8
London Symphony Orchestra   Previn

ASD 2918   B/w Band: £**6**   Col. Band: £2
MOZART   Symphony No.36, Symphony No.38
Berlin Philharmonic Orchestra   Karajan

ASD 2919-21   B/w Band: £**14**   Col. Band: £5
OFFENBACH   Tales of Hoffmann London Symphony Orchestra Rudel

ASD 2924   B/w Band: £**25**   Col. Band: £8
SHOSTAKOVICH / WALTON   Cello Concerto   Tortelier
Bournemouth Symphony Orchestra   Berglund

ASD 2925   Melodya : £**10**
GLAZUNOV   Chopiniana
Chorus & Orchestra of the Bolshoi Theatre   Zuraitis

ASD 2926   B/w Band: £**10**   Col. Band: £3
MENDELSSOHN / BRUCH   Violin Concerto   Perlman
London Symphony Orchestra   Previn

ASD 2927   Melodya : £**8**
MIASKOVSKY / SCHEDRIN   Symphony No.23, Symphony No.1
Moscow Radio Symphony Orchestra   Kovalyov

ASD 2928   B/w Band: £**10**   Col. Band: £3
RACHMANINOV   Songs   Gedda

ASD 2929   B/w Band: £**5**   Col. Band: £2
Various   Janet Baker Favorites   Baker

ASD 2934   B/w Band: £**6**   Col. Band: £2
WAGNER   Concert: Valkyries, Murmers etc
London Philharmonic Orchestra   Boult

ASD 2935   B/w Band: **£12**   Col. Band: £4
PROKOFIEV / BRITTEN   Peter and the Wolf, Young persons guide
London Symphony Orchestra   Previn

ASD 2936   B/w Band: **£20**   Col. Band: £7
SHOSTAKOVICH   Violin Concerto No.1   Oistrakh
Philharmonia Orchestra   Shostakovich

ASD 2938   B/w Band: **£6**   Col. Band: £2
HAYDN / TELEMANN   Trumpet Concerto Wilbraham
Acadamy of St.Martins in the Fields   Marriner

ASD 2939-40   B/w Band: **£12**   Col. Band: £4
PROKOFIEV   Romeo and Juliet London Symphony Orchestra   Previn

ASD 2942   B/w Band: **£4**   Col. Band: £1
SCHUBERT   Symphony No.5, Symphony No.8   Fischer-Dieskau
Philharmonia Orchestra

ASD 2945   B/w Band: **£8**   Col. Band: £3
BERLIOZ   Symphonie Fantastique   ORTF   Martinon

ASD 2946   B/w Band: **£4**   Col. Band: £1
SAINT-SAENS   Symphony No.1, Symphony No.2
ORTF   Martinon

ASD 2947   Melodya : **£8**
PROKOFIEV   Ballad of the Boy who Remained Unknown
Moscow Philharmonic Orchestra   Rozhdestvensky

ASD 2948-50   B/w Band: **£12**   Col. Band: £4
VERDI   Il Trovatore   Callas   La Scala   Karajan

ASD 2951   B/w Band: **£10**   Col. Band: £3
MOZART   Piano Concerto No.17, Piano Concerto No.24   Previn
London Symphony Orchestra   Boult

ASD 2952   B/w Band: **£5**   Col. Band: £2
GRIEG   Peer Gynt Suites
Bournemouth Symphony Orchestra   Berglund

ASD 2953   B/w Band: £**6**   Col. Band: £2
DUKAS   Symphony in C
Orchestra National Radio France   Martinon

ASD 2954   B/w Band: £**8**   Col. Band: £3
TCHAIKOVSKY / GRIEG   Variations on Rococo, Holburg Suite   Tortelier
Northern Sinfonia Orchestra

ASD 2955   B/w Band: £**6**   Col. Band: £2
STRAUSS   Sinfonia Domestica
Berlin Philharmonic Orchestra   Karajan

ASD 2956   B/w Band: £**7**   Col. Band: £2
MOZART   Piano Concerto No.12, Piano Concerto No.19
Barenboim   English Chamber Orchestra

ASD 2958   B/w Band: £**6**   Col. Band: £2
DELIUS   Sea Drift, Song Of The High Hills
Royal Liverpool Philharmonic Orchestra   Groves

ASD 2959   B/w Band: £**4**   Col. Band: £1
MOZART   Mass in Cmin.   Philharmonia Orchestra   Leppard

ASD 2960   B/w Band: £**8**   Col. Band: £3
BEETHOVEN   Symphony No.5   London Symphony Orchestra   Previn

ASD 2961   B/w Band: £**16**   Col. Band: £5
SIBELIUS   The Tempest
Royal Liverpool Philharmonic Orchestra   Groves

ASD 2962   B/w Band: £**6**   Col. Band: £2
VAUGHAN-WILLIAMS   Toward Unknown Region
London Philharmonic Orchestra   Boult

ASD 2963   B/w Band: £**5**   Col. Band: £2
CHOPIN   Fantasie, Berceuse, Etc.   Barenboim

ASD 2964   Melodya : £**10**
BARTOK / HONEGGER   Music for Strings, Percussion & Celeste,
Symphony No.3   Leningrad Philharmonic Orchestra   Mravinsky

ASD 2970   B/w Band: £**10**   Col. Band: £3
BACH / ELGAR   Fantasia & Fugue in C Min.
London Philharmonic Orchestra   Boult

ASD 2971   B/w Band: £**8**   Col. Band: £3
BACH   Piano Transcriptions   Weissenberg

ASD 2973   Melodya : £**12**
RACHMANINOV   Vespers
USSR Symphony Orchestra & Chorus   Sveshnikov

ASD 2974   Melodya : £**5**
RIMSKY-KORSAKOV / GLAZUNOV Antartic Symphony, Sceans de
Ballet   Moscow Radio Symphony Orchestra   Rozhdestvensky

ASD 2975-6   B/w Band: £**16**   Col. Band: £5
ROSSINI   The Barber of Seville   Callas
Philharmonia Orchestra   Galliera

ASD 2985   B/w Band: £**4**   Col. Band: £1
Various   Horn Concertos   Tuckwell
Acadamy of St.Martins in the Fields   Marriner

ASD 2988   B/w Band: £**10**   Col. Band: £3
MOZART   Violin Concerto No.3 & 5 K216,219   Oistrakh
Berlin Philharmonic Orchestra

ASD 2989   B/w Band: £**8**   Col. Band: £3
IBERT / HONEGGER / SATIE   Pacific 231, Gymnopedies, Biches
City of Birmingham Symphony Orchestra   Fremaux

ASD 2990   B/w Band: £**6**   Col. Band: £2
WALTON   Symphony No.2, Portsmouth Point Overture
London Symphony Orchestra   Previn

ASD 2992   B/w Band: £**8**   Col. Band: £3
BRAHMS   Piano Concerto No.1   Weissenberg
London Symphony Orchestra   Giulini

ASD 2993   B/w Band: £**6**   Col. Band: £2
MOZART   Flute Concert No.1, Flute & Harp Concerto   Galway
Berlin Philharmonic Orchestra   Karajan

ASD 2994   B/w Band: **£5**   Col. Band: £2
VILLA-LOBOS   Bachianas Brasileiras No.2, 5, 6 & 9
Orchestra de Paris   Capolongo

ASD 2999   B/w Band: **£5**   Col. Band: £2
MOZART   Piano Concerto No.11, Piano Concerto No.16
Barenboim   English Chamber Orchestra

ASD 3000   B/w Band: **£6**   Col. Band: £2
WAGNER   Siegfried Idyll, Parsifal   Philharmonia Orchestra   Boult

ASD 3001   B/w Band: **£25**   Col. Band: £8
PAGANINI / KREISLER / SARASATE   Encores   Perlman

ASD 3002   B/w Band: **£10**   Col. Band: £3
HOLST   The Planets   London Symphony Orchestra   Previn

ASD 3006   B/w Band: **£40**   Col. Band: £10
GRACE WILLIAMS   Fantasia on Welsh Nursery Tunes
London Symphony Orchestra   Groves

ASD 3007   B/w Band: **£5**   Col. Band: £2
BACH   Harpsichord Concertos Vol.3   Malcolm
Menuhin Festival Orchestra

ASD 3008   B/w Band: **£10**   Col. Band: £3
RAVEL / CHABRIER / SAINT-SEANS   Bolero, Espana, Danse Macabre
City of Birmingham Symphony Orchestra   Fremaux

ASD 3009   B/w Band: **£6**   Col. Band: £2
MENDELSSOHN   The First Walpurgis Night   Buchner
Leipzig Gewandhaus Orchestra   Masur

ASD 3010   Melodya : **£8**
SHOSTAKOVICH   Symphony No.11
Moscow Philharmonic Orchestra   Kondrashin

ASD 3013   B/w Band: **£50**   Col. Band: £12
RACHMANINOV-RESPIGHI   5 Etudes Tableaux   Krasnapolsky

ASD 3014   B/w Band: **£15**   Col. Band: £5
BARTOK   Violin Concerto No.2   Perlman
London Symphony Orchestra   Previn

ASD 3015 B/w Band: **£14** Col. Band: £5
Various Cello Concerto etc Tortelier

ASD 3016 B/w Band: **£6** Col. Band: £2
MOZART Symphony No.35, Symphony No.39
Berlin Philharmonic Orchestra Karajan

ASD 3017 B/w Band: **£10** Col. Band: £3
ALBINONI / BACH / HANDEL Academy in Concert
Acadamy of St.Martins in the Fields Marriner

ASD 3018 B/w Band: **£20** Col. Band: £7
TCHAIKOVSKY Manfred London Symphony Orchestra Previn

ASD 3019 Melodya : **£6**
RACHMANINOV Prince Rostislav, Schertzo
USSR Symphony Orchestra Sveshnikov

ASD 3020 B/w Band: **£6** Col. Band: £2
BLISS / HOWELLS Music for Strings, Concerto for String Orchestra
London Philharmonic Orchestra Boult

ASD 3028 B/w Band: **£6** Col. Band: £2
TELEMANN / HANDEL Concert Munrow
Acadamy of St.Martins in the Fields Marriner

ASD 3029 B/w Band: **£10** Col. Band: £3
SHOSTAKOVICH / PROKOFIEV Symphony No.6, Lt Kije
London Symphony Orchestra Previn

ASD 3032 B/w Band: **£5** Col. Band: £2
MOZART Piano Concerto No.6, Piano Concerto No.26
Barenboim English Chamber Orchestra

ASD 3033 B/w Band: **£5** Col. Band: £2
MOZART Piano Concerto No.8, Piano Concerto No.25
Barenboim English Chamber Orchestra

ASD 3034 B/w Band: **£8** Col. Band: £3
RODRIGO Concerto de Aranjuez
Spanish National Orchestra De Burgos

ASD 3035   B/w Band: £**6**   Col. Band: £2
BERNSTEIN / BRITTEN   Chichester Psalms, Etc.   Ellis
Choir of Kings College Cambridge   Ledger

ASD 3036   B/w Band: £**5**   Col. Band: £2
DVORAK / TCHAIKOVSKY   Serenade for Strings
English Chamber Orchestra   Barenboim

ASD 3038   B/w Band: £**8**   Col. Band: £3
SIBELIUS   Symphony No.5, En Saga
Bournemouth Symphony Orchestra   Berglund

ASD 3039   B/w Band: £**8**   Col. Band: £3
BIZET   Symphony in C, Etc.
City of Birmingham Symphony Orchestra   Fremaux

ASD 3040-2   B/w Band: £**12**   Col. Band: £4
TCHAIKOVSKY   Sleeping Beauty   London Symphony Orchestra   Previn

ASD 3043   B/w Band: £**8**   Col. Band: £3
BEETHOVEN   Piano Concerto No.5   Weissenberg
Berlin Philharmonic Orchestra   Karajan

ASD 3044   B/w Band: £**5**   Col. Band: £2
HUMMEL / VIVALDI / TELEMANN   Trumpet Concertos   Andre
Berlin Philharmonic Orchestra   Karajan

ASD 3045   Melodya : £**10**
SHOSTAKOVICH   Symphony No.1, Symphony No.3
Moscow Philharmonic Orchestra   Kondrashin

ASD 3046   B/w Band: £**8**   Col. Band: £3
BARTOK   Concerto for Orchestra
Berlin Philharmonic Orchestra   Karajan

ASD 3047   B/w Band: £**4**   Col. Band: £1
RIMSKY-KORSAKOV   Sheherazade
Orchestra de Paris   Rostropovich

ASD 3050   B/w Band: £**4**   Col. Band: £1
ELGAR   Triumphal March, Dream Children, Elegy, Etc.
London Philharmonic Orchestra   Boult

ASD 3051 B/w Band: **£4** Col. Band: £1
TCHAIKOVSKY Nutcracker (Highlights)
London Symphony Orchestra Previn

ASD 3053 B/w Band: **£5** Col. Band: £2
SCHUMANN Piano Concerto Barenboim

ASD 3054 B/w Band: **£5** Col. Band: £2
PROKOFIEV Romeo & Juliet scenes & dances
London Symphony Orchestra Previn

ASD 3058 B/w Band: **£12** Col. Band: £4
SAINT-SAENS Cello Concerto etc Tortelier
City of Birmingham Symphony Orchestra Fremaux

ASD 3060 Melodya : **£8**
PROKOFIEV / SHOSTAKOVICH Scythian Suite, Symphony No.2
Moscow Philharmonic Orchestra Kondrashin

ASD 3061 B/w Band: **£50** Col. Band: £18
RACHMANINOV Trio Elegiaque in Dmin. Kogan

ASD 3063 B/w Band: **£5** Col. Band: £2
NIELSEN Symphony No.5
Bournemouth Symphony Orchestra Berglund

ASD 3064 B/w Band: **£5** Col. Band: £2
CHOPIN Piano Sonata No.2, Piano Sonata No.3 Barenboim

ASD 3065 B/w Band: **£8** Col. Band: £3
FAURE Requiem Orchestra de Paris Barenboim

ASD 3066 B/w Band: **£30** Col. Band: £10
STRAUSS / BEETHOVEN Cello Sonata, Variations Rostropovich

ASD 3067 B/w Band: **£6** Col. Band: £2
TCHAIKOVSKY Piano Concerto No.1, Piano Concerto No.3 Gilels
New Philharmonia Orchestra Maazel

ASD 3068-70 B/w Band: **£20** Col. Band: £7
BEETHOVEN Fidelio Philharmonia Orchestra Klemperer

ASD 3071   B/w Band: **£6**   Col. Band: £2
WAGNER   Boult Conducts. Vol.4
London Philharmonic Orchestra   Boult

ASD 3072   Melodya : **£12**
SHOSTAKOVICH / STRAVINSKY   Piano Quintet, 3 Pieces for String
Quartet   Borodin Quartet

ASD 3073   B/w Band: **£6**   Col. Band: £2
CHERUBINI   Requiem   Philharmonia Orchestra   Muti

ASD 3074   B/w Band: **£12**   Col. Band: £4
STRAUSS   Don Quixote, Rosenkavalier   Tortelier
Dresden Staatskapelle   Kempe

ASD 3075   B/w Band: **£8**   Col. Band: £3
JOPLIN   The Easy Winners   Perlman   Previn

ASD 3076   B/w Band: **£10**   Col. Band: £3
BACH   Violin Concertos in Amin & Dmin   Perlman

ASD 3077   B/w Band: **£10**   Col. Band: £3
STRAVINSKY   Dumbarton Oaks, Concerto in D
Los Angeles Chamber Orchestra   Marriner

ASD 3078   Melodya : **£6**
KABELEVSKY   Piano Concerto No.3, Violin Concerto
Moscow Philharmonic Orchestra   Kabelevsky

ASD 3079   B/w Band: **£8**   Col. Band: £3
BRUCKNER   Mass No.2
English Chamber Orchestra   Barenboim

ASD 3080   B/w Band: **£8**   Col. Band: £3
BERLIOZ   Royal Hunt Storm Overture, Carnival Romain
City of Birmingham Symphony Orchestra   Fremaux

ASD 3081   B/w Band: **£8**   Col. Band: £3
SHOSTAKOVICH   Piano Concerto No.2, Concerto for Piano and
Trumpet   Ortiz   Bournemouth Symphony Orchestra   Berglund

ASD 3082   B/w Band: £**8**   Col. Band: £3
STRAUSS   4 Last Songs   Rothenberger
London Symphony Orchestra   Previn

ASD 3083   B/w Band: £**8**   Col. Band: £3
GOUNOD   Melodies   Souzay

ASD 3084   B/w Band: £**4**   Col. Band: £1
RAMEAU   Ballet Music for Les Fetes d'Hebe
English Chamber Orchestra   Leppard

ASD 3090   Melodya : £**8**
SHOSTAKOVICH   Symphony No.14
Moscow Philharmonic Orchestra   Rostropovich

ASD 3091   B/w Band: £**6**   Col. Band: £2
SCHUMANN / BRAHMS   Choral Music
Choir of Kings College Cambridge   Ledger

ASD 3092   B/w Band: £**50**   Col. Band: £18
SIBELIUS   4 Legends   Royal Philharmonic Orchestra   Groves

ASD 3093   B/w Band: £**4**   Col. Band: £1
TCHAIKOVSKY RIMSKY-KORSAKOV   Capriccio Italiano,
Capriccio Espagnole   London Philharmonic Orchestra   Boult

ASD 3096   B/w Band: £**6**   Col. Band: £2
McCABE   The Chagelle Windows, Etc.
Halle Orchestra   Loughran

ASD 3097   B/w Band: £**6**   Col. Band: £2
HOLST   Wandering Scholar, Perfect Fool
London Symphony Orchestra   Previn

ASD 3101   Melodya : £**6**
MUSSORGSKY   Night on Bare Mountain, Boris Godunov, Etc.
USSR Symphony Orchestra   Svetlanov

ASD 3102   Melodya : £**8**
Various   Russian Choral Music of th 17th & 18th Century
USSR Symphony Orchestra & Chorus   Yurlov

ASD 3103   B/w Band: £**10**   Col. Band: £3
MUSSORGSKY   Songs & Dances of Death   Arkhipova

ASD 3104   Melodya : £**8**
STRAVINSKY   Mavra   Moscow Radio Symphony Orchestra   Jarvi

ASD 3105   B/w Band: £**40**   Col. Band: £12
PROKOFIEV / BARTOK   Violin Sonata No.1   Oistrakh

ASD 3106   Melodya : £**8**
TANEIEV   Symphony in Cmin.
Moscow Radio Symphony Orchestra   Rozhdestvensky

ASD 3107   Melodya : £**5**
RIMSKY-KORSAKOV   Showpieces for Symphonic Band
USSR Symphony Orchestra

ASD 3108   Melodya : £**12**
KHACHATURIAN   Symphony No.3, Rhapsody for Cello
Rostropovich   USSR Symphony Orchestra   Svetlanov

ASD 3115   B/w Band: £**10**   Col. Band: £3
PROKOFIEV   Symphony No.5   London Symphony Orchestra   Previn

ASD 3117   B/w Band: £**10**   Col. Band: £3
ORFF   Carmina Burana   London Symphony Orchestra   Previn

ASD 3118   B/w Band: £**12**   Col. Band: £4
STRAUSS   Don Quixote   Rostropovich
Berlin Philharmonic Orchestra   Karajan

ASD 3119   B/w Band: £**6**   Col. Band: £2
BEETHOVEN   Symphony No.7   London Symphony Orchestra   Previn

ASD 3120   B/w Band: £**12**   Col. Band: £4
DVORAK   Violin Concerto, Romance   Perlman
London Philharmonic Orchestra   Barenboim

ASD 3124   B/w Band: £**8**   Col. Band: £3
Various   Songs I Love   Schwarzkopf

ASD 3125   B/w Band: £**15**   Col. Band: £5
SAINT-SAENS   Havanaise, Chausson Poeme   Perlman   Martinon

ASD 3126   B/w Band: £**6**   Col. Band: £2
STRAUSS   Ein Heldenleben
Berlin Philharmonic Orchestra   Karajan

ASD 3127   B/w Band: £**12**   Col. Band: £4
VAUGHAN-WILLIAMS   Symphony No.6, Oboe Concerto
Bournemouth Symphony Orchestra   Berglund

ASD 3128   B/w Band: £**10**   Col. Band: £3
HAYDN   Piano Concerto in D, Piano Concerto in G
Michelangeli   Zurich Chamber Orchestra   De Stoutz

ASD 3129   B/w Band: £**14**   Col. Band: £5
SCHUMANN   Carnival, Etc.   Michelangeli

ASD 3130   B/w Band: £**8**   Col. Band: £3
WAGNER   Tannhauser, Lohengrin
Berlin Philharmonic Orchestra   Karajan

ASD 3131   B/w Band: £**10**   Col. Band: £3
Various   Andre Previn's Music Night
London Symphony Orchestra   Previn

ASD 3132   B/w Band: £**4**   Col. Band: £1
STRAUSS   Strauss
Berlin Philharmonic Orchestra   Karajan

ASD 3133   B/w Band: £**12**   Col. Band: £4
GRIEG / SCHUMANN   Piano Concertos   Richter   Matacic

ASD 3134   B/w Band: £**8**   Col. Band: £3
CANTELOUBE   More Sons of the Auvergne   De Los Angeles
Paris Opera Orchestra

ASD 3135   B/w Band: £**6**   Col. Band: £2
TCHAIKOVSKY   Suite No.3   London Philharmonic Orchestra   Boult

ASD 3136   B/w Band: £**6**   Col. Band: £2
HAYDN   Symphony No.82, Symphony No.84
Menuhin Festival Orchestra   Menuhin

ASD 3137   B/w Band: **£8**   Col. Band: £3
RACHMANINOV   Symphony No.1
London Symphony Orchestra   Previn

ASD 3138   B/w Band: **£10**   Col. Band: £3
SAINT-SAENS   Symphony In A, Symphony in F   ORTF   Martinon

ASD 3139   B/w Band: **£12**   Col. Band: £4
DELIUS   North Country Sketches
Royal Liverpool Philharmonic Orchestra   Groves

ASD 3140   B/w Band: **£6**   Col. Band: £2
SILLS   Music of Victor Herbert Sills   Sills
London Symphony Orchestra

ASD 3141   B/w Band: **£10**   Col. Band: £3
RIMSKY-KORSAKOV / PROKOFIEV   Golden cockerel Suite,
Summer night   Bournemouth Symphony Orchestra   Berglund

ASD 3145   B/w Band: **£14**   Col. Band: £5
DUTILLEUX / LUTOSLAWSKI   Cello Concerto   Rostropovich
Orchestra de Paris

ASD 3146   B/w Band: **£10**   Col. Band: £3
BRUCKNER   Symphony No.2
Vienna Symphony Orchestra   Giulini

ASD 3147   B/w Band: **£8**   Col. Band: £3
IBERT   Escales, Overtures de Fete etc
French National Radio Orchestra   Martinon

ASD 3148   B/w Band: **£8**   Col. Band: £3
HANDEL   The Choice of Hercules
Acadamy of St.Martins in the Fields   Marriner

ASD 3153   B/w Band: **£30**   Col. Band: £10
FAURE   Cello Sonata No.1 & 2, Elegie, Etc.   Tortelier

ASD 3154   B/w Band: **£14**   Col. Band: £5
BRITTEN   4 Sea Interludes, Sinfonia da Requiem
London Symphony Orchestra   Previn

ASD 3155 B/w Band: £**8** Col. Band: £3
SIBELIUS Symphony No.6
Bournemouth Symphony Orchestra Berglund

ASD 3156-7 B/w Band: £**12** Col. Band: £4
LISZT Transcendental Studies Berman

ASD 3158 B/w Band: £**10** Col. Band: £3
MOZART Symphony No.35, Symphony No.41
London Philharmonic Orchestra Boult

ASD 3159 B/w Band: £**10** Col. Band: £3
LISZT Piano Concerto No.1, Piano Concerto No.2 Ohlsson
Philharmonia Orchestra Atzmon

ASD 3160 B/w Band: £**10** Col. Band: £3
WAGNER Meistersinger, Flying Dutchman
Berlin Philharmonic Orchestra Karajan

ASD 3164 B/w Band: £**10** Col. Band: £3
FRANCK Psyche Liege Symphony Orchestra Strauss

ASD 3165 Melodya : £**6**
TCHAIKOVSKY Choral Music
USSR Symphony Orchestra Sveshnikov

ASD 3166 B/w Band: £**8** Col. Band: £3
PURCELL Come ye Sons of Art
Early Music Consort of London Munrow

ASD 3167 B/w Band: £**5** Col. Band: £2
HAYDN / BEETHOVEN Scottish Folk Songs Baker

ASD 3169 B/w Band: £**6** Col. Band: £2
DVORAK Symphony No.6
Royal Philharmonic Orchestra Groves

ASD 3173 B/w Band: £**10** Col. Band: £3
STRAUSS Alpine Symphony Dresden Staatskapelle Kempe

ASD 3176 B/w Band: £**10** Col. Band: £3
IBERT Bacchanale, Louisville Concert
City of Birmingham Symphony Orchestra Fremaux

ASD 3177-9   B/w Band: £**45**   Col. Band: £15
BACH   The Unaccompanied Sonatas & Partitas   Menuhin

ASD 3182   B/w Band: £**6**   Col. Band: £2
HANDEL   Two Double Concertos
Acadamy of St.Martins in the Fields   Marriner

ASD 3184   B/w Band: £**6**   Col. Band: £2
MENDELSSOHN Symphony No.3, Calm Sea and Prosperous Voyage
Philharmonia Orchestra   Muti

ASD 3185   B/w Band: £**12**   Col. Band: £4
MARTIN   Polyptique, Ballade, Etc.
Menhuin Festival Orchestra   Menuhin

ASD 3186   B/w Band: £**6**   Col. Band: £2
HAYDN   Symphony No.85, Symphony No.87
Menhuin Festival Orchestra   Menuhin

ASD 3188   B/w Band: £**6**   Col. Band: £2
RESPIGHI   Ancient Dances and Airs
Acadamy of St.Martins in the Fields   Marriner

ASD 3190   B/w Band: £**8**   Col. Band: £3
BRIDGE   The Sea, Summer, Cherry Ripe et
Royal Liverpool Philharmonic Orchestra   Groves

ASD 3191   B/w Band: £**5**   Col. Band: £2
MOZART   Oboe Concerto K314, Etc.
Berlin Philharmonic Orchestra   Karajan

ASD 3193   B/w Band: £**7**   Col. Band: £2
BORODIN / BALAKIREV / RIMSKY-K   Symphony No.2, Russia,
Skazka   Bournemouth Symphony Orchestra   Brusilow

ASD 3194-6   B/w Band: £**12**   Col. Band: £4
PUCCINI   Madame Butterfly   La Scala   Karajan

ASD 3197   B/w Band: £**4**   Col. Band: £1
RACHMANINOV / DOHNANYI   Rhapsody on a Theme of Paganini,
Nursery Variations   Koizumi   New Philharmonia Orchestra   Ortiz

ASD 3198 B/w Band: **£10** Col. Band: £3
MOZART Violin Concerto K271, Adelaide Concerto
Menuhin Menhuin Festival Orchestra

ASD 3199 B/w Band: **£30** Col. Band: £10
SIBELIUS Violin Concerto Haendel
Bournemouth Symphony Orchestra Berglund

ASD 3200 B/w Band: **£6** Col. Band: £2
Various Calvary Song Soviet Army Ensemble

ASD 3202 B/w Band: **£6** Col. Band: £2
SCHUMANN Album for the Young Wiessenberg

ASD 3203 B/w Band: **£10** Col. Band: £3
SCHUBERT / HAYDN Symphony No.8, Symphony No.104
Berlin Philharmonic Orchestra Karajan

ASD 3208 B/w Band: **£10** Col. Band: £3
MENDELSSOHN / SAINT-SAENS Piano Concerto No.1, Piano Concerto
No.2 Adni Royal Liverpool Philharmonic Orchestra Groves

ASD 3209 B/w Band: **£12** Col. Band: £4
LALO Symphony Espagnole, Cello Concerto Tortelier
City of Birmingham Symphony Orchestra Fremaux

ASD 3212 B/w Band: **£10** Col. Band: £3
BERLIOZ Overtures London Symphony Orchestra Previn

ASD 3213 B/w Band: **£6** Col. Band: £2
TCHAIKOVSKY Symphony No.1 Philharmonia Orchestra Muti

ASD 3214 B/w Band: **£6** Col. Band: £2
HAYDN Symphony No.83, Symphony No.86
Menhuin Festival Orchestra Menuhin

ASD 3215 B/w Band: **£15** Col. Band: £5
RAVEL Bolero, Rhapsody Espagnole, La Valse, Etc.
Orchestra de Paris Martinon

ASD 3216 B/w Band: **£8** Col. Band: £3
SIBELIUS Symphony No.1, Scenes Historique
Bournemouth Symphony Orchestra Berglund

ASD 3217   B/w Band: **£5**   Col. Band: £2
SCHUMANN   Frauenliebe und Leben   Baker

ASD 3218   B/w Band: **£8**   Col. Band: £3
MOZART   Piano Concerto No.1 - 4   Barenboim
English Chamber Orchestra

ASD 3219   B/w Band: **£20**   Col. Band: £7
STRAVINSKY   Duo Concertant, Etc.   Perlman

ASD 3226   Melodya : **£4**
TCHAIKOVSKY   Symphony No.6
Moscow Radio Symphony Orchestra   Rozhdestvensky

ASD 3227   Melodya : **£4**
KHRENNIKOV   Piano Concerto No.1, Piano Concerto No.2
Moscow Philharmonic Orchestra   Kondrashin

ASD 3228   B/w Band: **£5**   Col. Band: £2
LISZT   Sonata in B, Mephisto Waltz   Berman

ASD 3236   Melodya : **£8**
Various   Three Trumpet Concertos By Soviet Composers
Moscow Radio Symphony Orchestra   Rozhdestvensky

ASD 3237   Melodya : **£35**
MIASKOVSKY / YSAYE   Violin Concerto, Ecstasy   Feigin
Moscow Radio Symphony Orchestra   Dmitriev

ASD 3238   Melodya : **£6**
GLAZUNOV   Symphony No.4
Moscow Radio Symphony Orchestra   Rozhdestvensky

ASD 3254   B/w Band: **£4**   Col. Band: £1
CHOPIN   Preludes   Barenboim

ASD 3255   B/w Band: **£15**   Col. Band: £5
HAYDN   Cello Concertos in D & C   Rostropovich
Acadamy of St.Martins in the Fields

ASD 3258   B/w Band: **£15**   Col. Band: £5
KREISLER   Recital Vol.1   Perlman

ASD 3259   B/w Band: **£12**   Col. Band: £4
RACHMANINOV   Isle of Dead, Symphonic Dances
London Symphony Orchestra   Previn

ASD 3260   B/w Band: **£8**   Col. Band: £3
WAGNER / BRAHMS   Wesendonk Leider, Alto Rhapsody   Baker
London Philharmonic Orchestra   Boult

ASD 3261   B/w Band: **£12**   Col. Band: £4
BRAHMS   Violin Concerto   Kremer
Berlin Philharmonic Orchestra   Karajan

ASD 3262   B/w Band: **£4**   Col. Band: £1
TCHAIKOVSKY / LISZT   Piano Concerto No.1   Gutuirrez
London Symphony Orchestra   Previn

ASD 3263   B/w Band: **£8**   Col. Band: £3
BERLIOZ   Symphonie Fantastique   ORTF   Martinon

ASD 3264   B/w Band: **£6**   Col. Band: £2
Various   Music for Double Bass   Slatford
Acadamy of St.Martins in the Fields   Marriner

ASD 3265   B/w Band: **£4**   Col. Band: £1
BACH   Arias from Cantatas and Oratorios   Baker
Acadamy of St.Martins in the Fields   Marriner

ASD 3266   B/w Band: **£8**   Col. Band: £3
ELGAR   Symphony No.2
London Philharmonic Orchestra   Boult

ASD 3277   B/w Band: **£5**   Col. Band: £2
BIZET   Symphony in C, Maid of Perth
Orchestra de Paris   Barenboim

ASD 3283   B/w Band: **£8**   Col. Band: £3
Various   Soiree Musicale   Tortelier

ASD 3284   B/w Band: **£20**   Col. Band: £7
RACHMANINOV   The Bells   London Symphony Orchestra   Previn

ASD 3285   B/w Band: **£6**   Col. Band: £2
DVORAK   Symphony No.9   Philharmonia Orchestra   Muti

ASD 3286   B/w Band: £8   Col. Band: £3
VAUGHAN-WILLIAMS   Thomas Tallis Fantasia, Concerto Grosso
London Philharmonic Orchestra   Boult

ASD 3287   B/w Band: £8   Col. Band: £3
SIBELIUS   Spring Song
Royal Liverpool Philharmonic Orchestra   Groves

ASD 3292   B/w Band: £6   Col. Band: £2
VERDI   Aida (Highlights)   New Philharmonia Orchestra   Muti

ASD 3293   B/w Band: £10   Col. Band: £3
VIVALDI   4 Seasons   London Philharmonic Orchestra   Perlman

ASD 3294   B/w Band: £16   Col. Band: £5
THOMPSON   Plough that broke the Plains
Los Angeles Chamber Orchestra   Marriner

ASD 3295   B/w Band: £50   Col. Band: £20
BEETHOVEN   Violin Sonata No.4, Spring Sonata   Kogan
Los Angeles Chamber Orchestra

ASD 3299   B/w Band: £8   Col. Band: £3
POULENC   Gloria, Piano Concerto   Ortiz
City of Birmingham Symphony Orchestra   Fremaux

ASD 3300   B/w Band: £4   Col. Band: £1
SCHUBERT   The Twin Brothers   Fischer-Dieskau
Bavarian Radio Symphony Orchestra   Sawallish

ASD 3301   B/w Band: £8   Col. Band: £3
MATHIAS   This Worlds Joy
Philharmonia Orchestra   Willcocks

ASD 3302   B/w Band: £6   Col. Band: £2
Various   Great Tenors of Today   Various

ASD 3307   B/w Band: £8   Col. Band: £3
Various   6 Cossack Folk Songs   Don Cossacks of Rostov

ASD 3308   B/w Band: £8   Col. Band: £3
FRANCK   Symphony No.in Dmn, Symph Variations
Bournemouth Symphony Orchestra   Berglund

ASD 3309   Melodya : £**8**
SHOSTAKOVICH   Music from The Gadfly
USSR Symphony Orchestra   Khachaturian

ASD 3310   B/w Band: £**10**   Col. Band: £3
BRUCH   Violin Concerto No.2, Scottish Fantasy   Perlman
Philharmonia Orchestra   Lopez-Cobos

ASD 3311   B/w Band: £**5**   Col. Band: £2
OFFENBACH   Ballet Music   Rosenthal

ASD 3312   B/w Band: £**16**   Col. Band: £5
BRAHMS / DVORAK   Double Concerto, Slavonic Dances
Oistrakh, Rostropovitch   Cleveland Orchestra   Szell

ASD 3315   Melodya : £**5**
BALAKIREV / RACHMANINOV   Symphony No.1, Caprice Bohemien
USSR Symphony Orchestra   Svetlanov

ASD 3316   B/w Band: £**6**   Col. Band: £2
PURCELL   Queen Mary Funeral Music
Academy of St.Martin in the Fields   Ledger

ASD 3317   B/w Band: £**8**   Col. Band: £3
WALTON   Facade, Wise Virgins Ballet St
City of Birmingham Symphony Orchestra   Fremaux

ASD 3318   B/w Band: £**4**   Col. Band: £1
Various   Music for Trumpet and Organ   Andre

ASD 3319   B/w Band: £**8**   Col. Band: £3
STRAUSS   Aus Italien   Dresden Staatskapelle   Kempe

ASD 3320   B/w Band: £**4**   Col. Band: £1
MOZART   Flute Concerto, Oboe Concerto   Debost, Burge

ASD 3321   B/w Band: £**12**   Col. Band: £4
BACH   Suite No.3 in D   Tortelier   SCO

ASD 3322   B/w Band: £**10**   Col. Band: £3
SCHUMANN   Piano Sonata No.1, Piano Sonata No.2 Berman

ASD 3325 B/w Band: **£10** Col. Band: £3
DVORAK Symphony No.7
London Philharmonic Orchestra Giulini

ASD 3326 B/w Band: **£6** Col. Band: £2
MOZART Symphony No.25, Symphony No.29
Philharmonia Orchestra Muti

ASD 3327 B/w Band: **£7** Col. Band: £2
RESPIGHI The Birds, Three Botticelli Pictures
Acadamy of St.Martins in the Fields Marriner

ASD 3328 B/w Band: **£8** Col. Band: £3
HAYDN Symphony No.88, Symphony No.96
London Symphony Orchestra Previn

ASD 3329 B/w Band: **£8** Col. Band: £3
MOZART Oboe Quartet, Flute Quartet, Piano Quartet
Menuhin, Gendron

ASD 3330 B/w Band: **£5** Col. Band: £2
ELGAR Symphony No.1
London Philharmonic Orchestra Boult

ASD 3334 B/w Band: **£20** Col. Band: £6
BLOCH Schelemo, Hebrew Rhapsody Rostropovich
Orchestra National de France Bernstein

ASD 3337 B/w Band: **£12** Col. Band: £4
MOZART Piano Concerto K466, Double Concerto Lupu
London Symphony Orchestra Previn

ASD 3338 B/w Band: **£10** Col. Band: £3
Various Andre Previn's Music Night 2
London Symphony Orchestra Previn

ASD 3339 Melodya : **£6**
BALAKIREV / MEDTNER Piano Concerto Op.1, Piano Concerto No.1
Moscow Radio Symphony Orchestra Dmitriev

ASD 3340 B/w Band: **£8** Col. Band: £3
SIBELIUS Symphony No.4, The Bard
Bournemouth Symphony Orchestra Berglund

ASD 3341   B/w Band: **£8**   Col. Band: £3
Various   Rule Britannia! (concert)
Royal Liverpool Philharmonic Orchestra   Groves

ASD 3342   B/w Band: **£8**   Col. Band: £3
BLISS   Cello Concerto, Suite from Miracle in the Gorbals
Bournemouth Symphony Orchestra   Berglund

ASD 3343   B/w Band: **£10**   Col. Band: £3
DELIUS   Violin Concerto, Double Concerto   Menuhin,
Tortelier   Royal Philharmonic Orchestra

ASD 3345   B/w Band: **£10**   Col. Band: £3
ELGAR   Coronation Ode   Philharmonia Orchestra   Ledger

ASD 3346   B/w Band: **£20**   Col. Band: £7
KREISLER   Violin Recital Vol.2   Perlman

ASD 3347   B/w Band: **£5**   Col. Band: £2
KHACHATURIAN   Spartacus & Gayaneh Ballt
London Symphony Orchestra   Khachaturian

ASD 3348   B/w Band: **£8**   Col. Band: £3
WALTON   Gloria, Te Deum, Crown Imperial
City of Birmingham Symphony Orchestra   Fremaux

ASD 3352   B/w Band: **£80**   Col. Band: £35
TARTINI / CORELLI   Violin Sonatas   Haendel

ASD 3353   B/w Band: **£8**   Col. Band: £3
ARNOLD   Symphony No.2, Symphony No.8, English Dances
Bournemouth Symphony Orchestra   Groves

ASD 3354   B/w Band: **£8**   Col. Band: £3
WAGNER   Tristan and Isolde Sceanes   Ludwig
Berlin Philharmonic Orchestra   Karajan

ASD 3357   B/w Band: **£10**   Col. Band: £5
Various   Improvisations   Shankar, Menuhin

ASD 3358   B/w Band: **£8**   Col. Band: £3
NIELSEN   Hymnus Amoris
Danish Radio Symphony Orchestra   Woldyke

ASD 3361-2   B/w Band: £**15**   Col. Band: £5
LISZT   Hungarian Rhapsodies   Cziffra

ASD 3363   Melodya : £**6**
GLAZUNOV / TANEIEV   Symphony No.2, Symphony No.5
Moscow Radio Symphony Orchestra   Fedoseyev

ASD 3364   B/w Band: £**10**   Col. Band: £3
BEETHOVEN   Piano Sonata No.1, Piano Sonata No.7   Richter

ASD 3365   B/w Band: £**6**   Col. Band: £2
MENDELSOHNN / SCHUMANN   Symphony No.4
Philharmonia Orchestra   Muti

ASD 3366   B/w Band: £**5**   Col. Band: £2
VERDI   Force of Destiny Overture, Etc.
Philharmonia Orchestra   Muti

ASD 3367   B/w Band: £**6**   Col. Band: £2
GLAZUNOV / YARDUMIAN   Piano Concerto No.1, Passacaglia Etc.
Ogdon   Bournemouth Symphony Orchestra   Berglund

ASD 3368   B/w Band: £**12**   Col. Band: £4
BARTOK / BLOCH   Violin Sonata, 2 Suites   Menuhin

ASD 3369   B/w Band: £**10**   Col. Band: £3
RACHMANINOV   Symphony No.3
London Symphony Orchestra   Previn

ASD 3370   B/w Band: £**5**   Col. Band: £2
TCHAIKOVSKY   Sleeping Beauty (Excerpts)
London Symphony Orchestra   Previn

ASD 3371   B/w Band: £**12**   Col. Band: £4
DVORAK   Piano Concerto In G   Richter
Bavarian Symphony Orchestra   Kleiber

ASD 3372   B/w Band: £**5**   Col. Band: £2
RESPIGHI   Pines of Rome, Fountains of Rome
London Symphony Orchestra   Gardelli

ASD 3373   B/w Band: **£8**   Col. Band: £3
MOZART   Coronation Mass   Fischer-Dieskau
Bavarian Radio Symphony Orchestra   Jochum

ASD 3374   B/w Band: **£8**   Col. Band: £3
SIBELIUS   Finlandia, En Saga, Tapiola Etc
Berlin Philharmonic Orchestra   Karajan

ASD 3375   B/w Band: **£12**   Col. Band: £4
MOZART / HAYDN / GLUCK   Eine Kleine Nachtmusik
Acadamy of St.Martins in the Fields   Marriner

ASD 3376   B/w Band: **£8**   Col. Band: £3
BEETHOVEN   Symphony No.3
London Symphony Orchestra   Jochum

ASD 3377   B/w Band: **£20**   Col. Band: £7
MENDELSSOHN   Midsummer Night's Dream
London Symphony Orchestra   Previn

ASD 3381   Melodya : **£8**
SHOSTAKOVICH   New Babylon, Hamlet Suite
Moscow Philharmonic Orchestra   Rozhdestvensky

ASD 3382   B/w Band: **£8**   Col. Band: £3
BRUCKNER   Symphony No.9
Chicago Symphony Orchestra   Giulini

ASD 3383   Melodya : **£8**
GLAZUNOV   Symphony No.6, Saxophone Concerto
Moscow Radio Symphony Orchestra   Fedoseyev

ASD 3384   B/w Band: **£20**   Col. Band: £7
PAGANINI   24 Caprices   Perlman

ASD 3385   B/w Band: **£12**   Col. Band: £4
BRAHMS   Violin Concerto   Perlman
Chicago Symphony Orchestra   Giulini

ASD 3386-7   B/w Band: **£10**   Col. Band: £3
DELIBES   Coppellia   Paris Opera Orchestra   Mari

ASD 3388   B/w Band: £**4**   Col. Band: £1
ELGAR   Pomp & Circumstance Marches
London Philharmonic Orchestra   Boult

ASD 3389   B/w Band: £**5**   Col. Band: £2
BERLIOZ   Harold in Italy   McInnes
French National Radio Orchestra   Bernstein

ASD 3393   B/w Band: £**6**   Col. Band: £2
MONTEVERDI   Monteverdi's Contemporaries
Early Music Consort of London   Munrow

ASD 3394   B/w Band: £**5**   Col. Band: £2
Various   Trumpet Concertos   Andre
English Chamber Orchestra   Mackerras

ASD 3395   B/w Band: £**5**   Col. Band: £2
HANDEL   Music For The Royal Fireworks
London Symphony Orchestra   Mackerras

ASD 3396   B/w Band: £**10**   Col. Band: £3
SCRIABIN   Piano Sonata No.1, Piano Sonata No.3   Berman

ASD 3397   B/w Band: £**8**   Col. Band: £3
BERLIOZ   Symphonie Fantastique
French National Radio Orchestra   Bernstein

ASD 3399   B/w Band: £**8**   Col. Band: £3
STRAUSS   Violin Concerto, Burleske   Hoelscher
Dresden Staatskapelle   Kempe

ASD 3407   B/w Band: £**10**   Col. Band: £3
DVORAK   New World Symphony, Ma Vlast
Berlin Philharmonic Orchestra   Karajan

ASD 3408   B/w Band: £**14**   Col. Band: £5
GOLDMARK   Violin Concerto, Sarasate   Perlman
London Symphony Orchestra   Previn

ASD 3409   B/w Band: £**10**   Col. Band: £3
SIBELIUS   Symphony No.5, En Saga
Berlin Philharmonic Orchestra   Karajan

ASD 3414 B/w Band: £**10** Col. Band: £3
SIBELIUS Symphony No.2
Pittsburgh Symphony Orchestra Previn

ASD 3415 B/w Band: £**8** Col. Band: £3
RODRIGO Guitar Concerto Romero
London Symphony Orchestra Previn

ASD 3416 B/w Band: £**15** Col. Band: £5
BLISS Colour Symphony, Things to Come
Royal Philharmonic Orchestra Groves

ASD 3417 B/w Band: £**6** Col. Band: £2
ELGAR Enigma Variations
Royal Liverpool Philharmonic Orchestra Groves

ASD 3418 B/w Band: £**6** Col. Band: £2
VIVALDI Magnificat, Gloria Bergonzi
New Philharmonia Orchestra Muti

ASD 3421 B/w Band: £**10** Col. Band: £3
Various Russian Music Orchestra de Paris Rostropovich

ASD 3425 B/w Band: £**12** Col. Band: £4
BRAHMS Violin Sonata No.1, Violin Sonata No.2 Oistrakh

ASD 3426 B/w Band: £**6** Col. Band: £2
MOZART Serenade For 13 Wind Instruments
English Chamber Orchestra Barenboim

ASD 3429 B/w Band: £**8** Col. Band: £3
VILLA-LOSBOS Bachianas Brasileiras Ashkenazy
New Philharmonia Orchestra Ortiz

ASD 3430 B/w Band: £**10** Col. Band: £3
Various Duets for Two Violins Perlman, Zukerman

ASD 3431 B/w Band: £**8** Col. Band: £3
RAVEL / DEBUSSY Bolero, La Mer
Berlin Philharmonic Orchestra Karajan

ASD 3435   B/w Band: **£6**   Col. Band: £2
HOLST   Hymn of Jesus, Choral Hymns etc
London Symphony Orchestra   Groves

ASD 3436   B/w Band: **£8**   Col. Band: £3
Various   Songs and Marches of Death   Rostropovich

ASD 3440   B/w Band: **£20**   Col. Band: £7
SHOSTAKOVICH   Symphony No.4
Chicago Symphony orchestra   Previn

ASD 3441-2   Melodya : **£20**
SHOSTAKOVICH   Symphony No.7
Moscow Philharmonic Orchestra   Kondrashin

ASD 3443   B/w Band: **£10**   Col. Band: £3
SHOSTAKOVICH   Symphony No.5
Chicago Symphony orchestra   Previn

ASD 3444   B/w Band: **£8**   Col. Band: £3
MILHAUD   Creation du Monde, Boeuf Toit
Orchestre National de Francaise   Bernstein

ASD 3447   Melodya : **£8**
SCHEDRIN / PETROV   Not Love Alone, Creation of the World
Moscow Philharmonic Orchestra   Kondrashin

ASD 3448   B/w Band: **£10**   Col. Band: £3
SAINT-SAENS   Carnival of the Animals   Ensemble Beroff Collard

ASD 3449   B/w Band: **£4**   Col. Band: £1
TCHAIKOVSKY   Symphony No.3   Philharmonia Orchestra   Muti

ASD 3450   B/w Band: **£8**   Col. Band: £3
Various   Music For Holy Week
Choir of Kings College Cambridge   Ledger

ASD 3451   B/w Band: **£6**   Col. Band: £2
HAYDN   7 Last Words
Acadamy of St.Martins in the Fields   Marriner

ASD 3452 B/w Band: **£12** Col. Band: £4
DVORAK / SAINT-SAENS Cello Concerto Rostropovich
London Philharmonic Orchestra Giulini

ASD 3453 B/w Band: **£4** Col. Band: £1
Various Music for Trumpet and Organ Andre

ASD 3454 B/w Band: **£8** Col. Band: £3
Various Guillaume de Machaut and his Age
Early Music Consort of London Munrow

ASD 3455 B/w Band: **£10** Col. Band: £3
CHAUSSON Poeme de L'Amour et de La Mer Baker
London Symphony Orchestra Previn

ASD 3456 B/w Band: **£6** Col. Band: £2
BEETHOVEN Symphony No.6
London Philharmonic Orchestra Boult

ASD 3457 B/w Band: **£6** Col. Band: £2
RACHMANINOV Piano Concerto No.2, Piano Concerto No.3
Alexeev Royal Philharmonic Orchestra Fedoseyev

ASD 3458 B/w Band: **£14** Col. Band: £5
KODALY / TORTELIER Sonata for Cello, Suite in Dmin. Tortelier

ASD 3460 Melodya : **£6**
GLAZUNOV From The Middle Ages Suite
Moscow Radio Symphony Orchestra Fedoseyev

ASD 3464 B/w Band: **£8** Col. Band: £3
ROSSINI String Sonatas
Polish Chamber Orchestra Maksymiuk

ASD 3465 B/w Band: **£10** Col. Band: £3
MOZART Divertimentifor Strings K137,138
Polish Chamber Orchestra Maksymiuk

ASD 3468-70 B/w Band: **£12** Col. Band: £4
BELLINI Norma Callas La Scala Serafin

ASD 3478-9   B/w Band: £**15**   Col. Band: £5
DE FALLA / HALFFTER   Atlantida
Scottish National Orchestra   De Burgos

ASD 3480   B/w Band: £**8**   Col. Band: £3
SAINT-SAENS   Piano Concerto No.5   Ciccolini
Orchestra de Paris   Baudo

ASD 3481   Melodya : £**8**
SHOSTAKOVICH   Symphony No.14
Leningrad Concert Orchestra   Gozman

ASD 3482   B/w Band: £**5**   Col. Band: £2
CHARPENTIER   Te Deum, Magnificat
Choir of Kings College Cambridge   Ledger

ASD 3483   B/w Band: £**45**   Col. Band: £20
BRITTEN / WALTON   Violin Concerto   Haendel
Bournemouth Symphony Orchestra   Berglund

ASD 3484   B/w Band: £**10**   Col. Band: £3
BEETHOVEN   Symphony No.5, Fidelio Overture
London Symphony Orchestra   Jochum

ASD 3485   B/w Band: £**6**   Col. Band: £2
SIBELIUS   Symphony No.2, Tapiola
Berlin Philharmonic Orchestra   Karajan

ASD 3486   B/w Band: £**18**   Col. Band: £6
BRIAN   Symphony No.8, Symphony No.9
Royal Liverpool Philharmonic Orchestra   Groves

ASD 3487   B/w Band: £**8**   Col. Band: £3
ARNOLD   Concerto for Flute and Strings   Solum
Philharmonia Orchestra   Dilkes

ASD 3488   B/w Band: £**8**   Col. Band: £3
TCHAIKOVSKY   Symphony No.2, Romeo And Juliet
Philharmonia Orchestra   Muti

ASD 3489   B/w Band: £**8**   Col. Band: £3
POULENC   Concerto for Organ, Strings and Timpani   Preston
London Symphony Orchestra   Previn

ASD 3490   Melodya : **£8**
RACHMANINOV   Francesca da Rimini
Chorus & Orchestra of the Bolshoi Theatre   Ermler

ASD 3492   B/w Band: **£8**   Col. Band: £3
VIOTTI   Violin Concerto No.16, Violin Concerto No.22
Menuhin   Menuhin Festival Orchestra

ASD 3496   B/w Band: **£15**   Col. Band: £5
BERLIOZ   Symphonie Fantastique
London Symphony Orchestra   Previn

ASD 3497   B/w Band: **£10**   Col. Band: £3
SIBELIUS   Symphony No.2
Bournemouth Symphony Orchestra   Berglund

ASD 3498   B/w Band: **£8**   Col. Band: £3
SCHUBERT   Rosamunde   Dresden Staatskapelle   Boskovsky

ASD 3499   B/w Band: **£8**   Col. Band: £3
WAGNER   Die Walkure, Parsifal, Flying Dutchman
Fischer-Dieskau   Bavarian Radio Symphony Orchestra   Kubelik

ASD 3501   B/w Band: **£10**   Col. Band: £3
FAURE   Requiem   Cook
City of Birmingham Symphony Orchestra   Fremaux

ASD 3502   Melodya : **£6**
KALINNIKOV / TCHAIKOVSKY   Symphony No.1, Overture in C
USSR Symphony Orchestra   Svetlanov

ASD 3503   Melodya : **£5**
BALAKIREV   Symphony No.2
Moscow Radio Symphony Orchestra   Rozhdestvensky

ASD 3504   Melodya : **£8**
GLAZUNOV   Symphony No.7
Moscow Radio Symphony Orchestra   Fedoseyev

ASD 3505   Melodya : **£8**
GLAZUNOV   Piano Concerto No.1, Piano Concerto No.2   Arensky
Moscow Radio Symphony Orchestra   Nikolaevsky

ASD 3506   Melodya : £**8**
TCHAIKOVSKY / RIMSKY-KORSAKOV   Concert Fantasy, Piano
Concerto   Kitayenko   USSR Symphony Orchestra   Rozhdestvensky

ASD 3513   B/w Band: £**8**   Col. Band: £3
Various   Slavonic Orthodox Liturgy   Christoff

ASD 3514   B/w Band: £**8**   Col. Band: £3
RIMSKY-KORSAKOV   Entry Of The Boyars, My Night Ov
Bournemouth Symphony Orchestra   Berglund

ASD 3515   B/w Band: £**8**   Col. Band: £3
TCHAIKOVSKY   Symphony No.6
London Philharmonic Orchestra   Rostropovich

ASD 3518-9   Melodya : £**18**
MAHLER   Symphony No.5, Fidelio Overture
Moscow Radio Symphony Orchestra   Rozhdestvensky

ASD 3520   Melodya : £**10**
SHOSTAKOVICH   Symphony No.12, 5 Fragments
Moscow Philharmonic Orchestra   Kondrashin

ASD 3521   B/w Band: £**8**   Col. Band: £3
GRIEG / SCHUMANN   Piano Conceros   Gutierrez
London Philharmonic Orchestra   Tennstedt

ASD 3525-6   B/w Band: £**12**   Col. Band: £4
DELIBES   Sylvia   Paris Opera Orchestra   Mari

ASD 3535   B/w Band: £**12**   Col. Band: £4
VERDI / BELLINI   Maria Callas - The Ledgend Callas

ASD 3536-7   B/w Band: £**12**   Col. Band: £4
RACHMANINOV   Liturgy of St.John   Milkoov

ASD 3541   B/w Band: £**6**   Col. Band: £2
MAHLER   Symphony No.1
London Philharmonic Orchestra   Tennstedt

ASD 3542   B/w Band: £**8**   Col. Band: £3
KETELBEY   In a Monastary Garden
Philharmonia Orchestra   Lanchberry

ASD 3543 B/w Band: £10 Col. Band: £3
BEETHOVEN Piano Concerto No.3, Andante Favori in F Richter
Philharmonia Orchestra Muti

ASD 3544 B/w Band: £6 Col. Band: £2
BACH Sinfonias
Bournemouth Symphony Orchestra Montgomery

ASD 3545 B/w Band: £8 Col. Band: £3
Various Sea Fever Lloyd

ASD 3546 B/w Band: £8 Col. Band: £3
FRANCK Piano Quintet Ortiz
Medici String Quartet

ASD 3548 Melodya : £5
GOUNOD / MASSENET / HEROLD Faust Ballet Music, Le Cid, Zampa
Chorus & Orchestra of the Bolshoi Theatre Rozhdestvensky

ASD 3549 Melodya : £8
RIMSKY-KORSAKOV Tale of Tsar Sultan Suite, Nobles, Etc.
Moscow Radio Symphony Orchestra Ivanov

ASD 3551 B/w Band: £8 Col. Band: £3
BRAHMS Piano Sonatas Ohlsson

ASD 3552 B/w Band: £9 Col. Band: £3
CHOPIN Ballades, Polonaises, Etc. Ortiz

ASD 3553 B/w Band: £8 Col. Band: £3
MOZART Oboe Concertos De Vries
Prague Chamber Orchestra Kersjes

ASD 3554 B/w Band: £6 Col. Band: £2
VIVALDI Flute & Recorder Concertos Prague Chamber Orchestra

ASD 3555 B/w Band: £12 Col. Band: £4
VIEUXTEMPS Violin Concerto No.4, Violin Concerto No.5 Perlman
Orchestra de Paris Barenboim

ASD 3556 B/w Band: £10 Col. Band: £3
PROKOFIEV Symphony No.1, Symphony No.7
London Symphony Orchestra Previn

572

ASD 3559 B/w Band: **£6** Col. Band: £2
PALESTRINA Missa Hodie Christus Natus, Etc.
Choir of Kings College Cambridge Ledger

ASD 3566 B/w Band: **£20** Col. Band: £7
SCHUBERT / SCHUMANN / CHOPIN Arpeggione sonatas,
Fantasiestuke, etc. Shafran

ASD 3567 B/w Band: **£6** Col. Band: £2
TCHAIKOVSKY Francesca da Rimini Fantasy, Etc.
London Philharmonic Orchestra Rostropovich

ASD 3568-9 B/w Band: **£12** Col. Band: £4
BELLINI La Sonnambula Callas La Scala Votto

ASD 3571 B/w Band: **£8** Col. Band: £3
PROKOFIEV / RAVEL Piano Concerto No.1, Concerto for Left Hand
Gavrilov London Symphony Orchestra Rattle

ASD 3583 B/w Band: **£10** Col. Band: £3
BEETHOVEN Symphony No.6
London Symphony Orchestra Jochum

ASD 3584 B/w Band: **£8** Col. Band: £3
TCHAIKOVSKY Ballet Extracts:Swan Lake etc Haendel
London Symphony Orchestra Previn

ASD 3588-9 B/w Band: **£12** Col. Band: £4
BELLINI I Puritani Callas La Scala Serafin

ASD 3593-4 B/w Band: **£12** Col. Band: £4
SCHUBERT Piano Duets Eschenbach, Frantz

ASD 3595 B/w Band: **£5** Col. Band: £2
Various Trumpet Concertos Andre
Franz List Chamber Orchestra Mackerras

ASD 3596 B/w Band: **£8** Col. Band: £3
MOZART Piano Concerto No.21, Piano Concerto No.23
Eschenbach London Philharmonic Orchestra

ASD 3597 B/w Band: **£5** Col. Band: £2
HANDEL Water Music Prague Chamber Orchestra Mackerras

ASD 3598   B/w Band: **£45**   Col. Band: £20
ELGAR   Violin Concerto Bmin op 61   Haendel
London Philharmonic Orchestra   Boult

ASD 3599   B/w Band: **£10**   Col. Band: £3
FIELD   Nocturnes   Adni

ASD 3600   B/w Band: **£10**   Col. Band: £3
RAVEL / BALAKIREV   Gaspard de la Nuit, Islamey Gavrilov

ASD 3601   B/w Band: **£5**   Col. Band: £2
GLAZUNOV   The Seasons   Philharmonia Orchestra Svetlanov

ASD 3604   B/w Band: **£5**   Col. Band: £2
STRAVINSKY   Pulcinella Suites No.1 & 2
Northern Sinfonia Orchestra   Rattle

ASD 3605   B/w Band: **£5**   Col. Band: £2
BRAHMS   4 Serious Songs   Baker

ASD 3606   B/w Band: **£8**   Col. Band: £3
RACHMANINOV   Symphony No.2
Royal Philharmonic Orchestra   Temirkanov

ASD 3608   B/w Band: **£8**   Col. Band: £3
BRITTEN   The Little Sweep
Medici String Quartet   Ledger

ASD 3612   B/w Band: **£15**   Col. Band: £5
BRAHMS   2 Sonatas for Cello   Tortelier

ASD 3613-14   B/w Band: **£14**   Col. Band: £5
Various   Treasures of the Baroque Era
National Iranian Radio & Television Chamber Orchestra   Tchakarov

ASD 3620   B/w Band: **£10**   Col. Band: £3
SCHUBERT   Piano Sonata in G   Zacharias

ASD 3621   B/w Band: **£8**   Col. Band: £3
Various   The Art of Courtley Love
Early Music Consort of London   Munrow

ASD 3622 B/w Band: **£10**   Col. Band: £3
SCHUBERT Piano Sonata D960   Berman

ASD 3623-4 B/w Band: **£20**   Col. Band: £7
BRUCKNER Symphony No.8   Dresden Staatskapelle   Jochum

ASD 3627 B/w Band: **£10**   Col. Band: £3
BEETHOVEN Symphony No.4
London Symphony Orchestra   Jochum

ASD 3628 B/w Band: **£12**   Col. Band: £4
MENDELSSOHN Concerto for Violin, Piano & Strings, String Symphony12
Menuhin Menhuin Festival Orchestra

ASD 3629 B/w Band: **£8**   Col. Band: £3
SIBELIUS Symphony No.3, Pelleas
Bournemouth Symphony Orchestra   Berglund

ASD 3630 B/w Band: **£6**   Col. Band: £2
Various Baroque Concertos
Bournemouth Symphony Orchestra   Wangenheim

ASD 3631 B/w Band: **£6**   Col. Band: £2
TELEMANN Water Music   Prague Chamber Orchestra   Bjorlin

ASD 3633 Melodya : **£5**
JANACEK / WEBERN Cunning Little Vixen, 5 Orchestral Pieces
USSR Symphony Orchestra   Rozhdestvensky

ASD 3634-5 B/w Band: **£15**   Col. Band: £5
SMETANA Ma Vlast   Dresden Staatskapelle   Berglund

ASD 3639 B/w Band: **£8**   Col. Band: £3
MOZART Violin Concerto   Spivakov
English Chamber Orchestra

ASD 3640 B/w Band: **£10**   Col. Band: £3
GRIEG Peer Gynt
Dresden Staatskapelle   Blomstedt

ASD 3641 B/w Band: **£8**   Col. Band: £3
TCHAIKOVSKY Symphony No.5
London Philharmonic Orchestra   Rostropovich

ASD 3642   Melodya : £5
ARENSKY   Symphony No.1, Suite No.1
Moscow Radio Symphony Orchestra   Serov

ASD 3644   B/w Band: £8   Col. Band: £3
SIBELIUS   4 Ledgends
Philadelphia Orchestra   Ormandy

ASD 3645   B/w Band: £5   Col. Band: £2
MUSSORSKY   Pictures at an Exhibition
Philharmonia Orchestra   Muti

ASD 3646   B/w Band: £6   Col. Band: £2
BEETHOVEN   Symphony No.7   Philharmonia Orchestra   Muti

ASD 3647   B/w Band: £8   Col. Band: £3
TCHAIKOVSKY   Symphony No.4
London Philharmonic Orchestra   Rostropovich

ASD 3648   B/w Band: £5   Col. Band: £2
SCHUMANN   Symphony No.2   Philharmonia Orchestra   Muti

ASD 3649   B/w Band: £4   Col. Band: £1
HOLST   The Planets
London Philharmonic Orchestra   Boult

ASD 3650   B/w Band: £6   Col. Band: £2
BRITTEN   Spring Symphony   London Symphony Orchestra   Previn

ASD 3651   B/w Band: £8   Col. Band: £3
GRAINGER   Grainger on the Shore   English Sinfionetta   Dilkes

ASD 3652   B/w Band: £12   Col. Band: £4
DVORAK   Cello Concerto   Tortelier
London Symphony Orchestra   Previn

ASD 3655   B/w Band: £8   Col. Band: £3
BARTOK   Music for Strings, Percussion & Celeste
Philadelphia Orchestra   Ormandy

ASD 3656   B/w Band: £8   Col. Band: £3
Various   Victoria De Los Angeles in Concert   De Los Angeles

ASD 3658-9   B/w Band: **£15**   Col. Band: £5
BACH   Brandenburg Concertos
Polish Chamber Orchestra   Maksymiuk

ASD 3660   Melodya : **£4**
BALAKIREV / GLAZUNOV   Tamar, Stenka Razin
USSR Symphony Orchestra   Svetlanov

ASD 3670   B/w Band: **£10**   Col. Band: £3
BRAHMS   Symphony No.1
London Philharmonic Orchestra   Jochum

ASD 3671   Melodya : **£8**
SIBELIUS   Symphony No.3, Symphony No.7
Moscow Radio Symphony Orchestra   Rozhdestvensky

ASD 3672   Melodya : **£8**
SIBELIUS   Symphony No.1
Moscow Radio Symphony Orchestra   Rozhdestvensky

ASD 3674   B/w Band: **£10**   Col. Band: £3
SAINT-SAENS   Symphony No.3
French National Radio Orchestra   Martinon

ASD 3675   B/w Band: **£6**   Col. Band: £2
BEETHOVEN   Violin Sonatas Op 30/3 Op 47   Zukerman
Barenboim

ASD 3676   B/w Band: **£15**   Col. Band: £5
SCHUBERT   String Quintet in C   Smetana Quartet

ASD 3687   B/w Band: **£12**   Col. Band: £4
BLISS   Adam Zero, Checkmate
Royal Liverpool Philharmonic Orchestra   Handley

ASD 3688   B/w Band: **£8**   Col. Band: £3
DELIUS   La Calinda, 5 Little Pieces, Etc.
Bournemouth Symphony Orchestra   Fenby

ASD 3690   B/w Band: **£4**   Col. Band: £1
VIVALDI   Violin Concertos   Grobholz
Prague Chamber Orchestra   Vajnar

ASD 3694   B/w Band: £**10**   Col. Band: £3
DVORAK / SMETANA   String Quartet No.12, Quartet No.1
Medici String Quartet

ASD 3695   B/w Band: £**10**   Col. Band: £3
BEETHOVEN   Piano Sonatas (Moonlight, Pathetic, Etc.)   Eschenbach

ASD 3696   B/w Band: £**5**   Col. Band: £2
SHUMANN   Symphony No.3   Philharmonia Orchestra   Muti

ASD 3698   B/w Band: £**14**   Col. Band: £5
TELEMANN   Paris Quartets No.7, 8 & 9   Linde

ASD 3699   Melodya : £**8**
SIBELIUS   Symphony No.4, Belshazzars Feast
Moscow Radio Symphony Orchestra   Rozhdestvensky

ASD 3705   Melodya : £**8**
STRAVINSKY / RAVEL   Petrouchka, Daphnis Et Chloe
Leningrad Symphony Orchestra   Temirkanov

ASD 3706   Melodya : £**8**
SHOSTAKOVICH   Symphony No.6, Symphony No.9
USSR Symphony Orchestra   Svetlanov

ASD 3709   Melodya : £**6**
BALAKIREV / GLINKA   Islamey, Ivan Susanin Overture, Etc.
USSR Symphony Orchestra   Svetlanov

ASD 3710   Melodya : £**6**
RIMSKY-KORSAKOV   Golden Cockerel, Etc.
USSR Symphony Orchestra   Svetlanov

ASD 3711   Melodya : £**6**
TCHAIKOVSKY / ARENSKY   Suite No.4, Suite No.2
Moscow Radio Symphony Orchestra   Shostakovich

ASD 3712   Melodya : £**10**
GRETCHANINOV / GLINKA / HUMMEL   Symphony No.4
Moscow Radio Symphony Orchestra   Zuraitis

ASD 3713   Melodya : £**10**
SHOSTAKOVICH / PROKOFIEV   Concerto for Piano, Piano Concerto
No.3   Krainev   Moscow Radio Symphony Orchestra   Shostakovich

ASD 3714   Melodya : £**5**
LISZT / WEBER / BERLIOZ   Tasso, Turnadot, etc.
Moscow Radio Symphony Orchestra   Rozhdestvensky

ASD 3716   B/w Band: £**9**   Col. Band: £3
Various   Spanish Soul   Ortiz

ASD 3717   B/w Band: £**5**   Col. Band: £2
TCHAIKOVSKY   Symphony No.5   Philharmonia Orchestra   Muti

ASD 3723   B/w Band: £**10**   Col. Band: £3
MOZART   Requiem   Philharmonia Orchestra   Giulini

ASD 3724   B/w Band: £**6**   Col. Band: £2
SCHUMANN   Symphony No.3
Berlin Philharmonic Orchestra   Tennstedt

ASD 3725   B/w Band: £**6**   Col. Band: £2
PARRY   Symphony No.5, Symphonic Variations, Elegy
London Philharmonic Orchestra   Boult

ASD 3726   B/w Band: £**15**   Col. Band: £5
TCHAIKOVSKY   Violin Concerto, Serenade Melancolique   Perlman
Philharmonia Orchestra   Ormandy

ASD 3728   B/w Band: £**25**   Col. Band: £8
SCHUMANN / BRUCH   Cello Concerto, Kol Nidrei   Tortelier
Royal Philharmonic Orchestra

ASD 3729   B/w Band: £**12**   Col. Band: £4
RAVEL / SAINT-SAENS   Piano trio in Amin., Piano Trio Op.18   Tortelier

ASD 3730   B/w Band: £**6**   Col. Band: £2
TCHAIKOVSKY   Manfred Symphony
London Philharmonic Orchestra   Rostropovich

ASD 3732   B/w Band: £**6**   Col. Band: £2
BLOCH / MARTIN   Concerto Grosso, Etc.
Academy of St.Martins in the Fields   Marriner

ASD 3735-6 B/w Band: **£12** Col. Band: £4
MAHLER Symphony No.5, Adagio from Sumphony No.10
London Philharmonic Orchestra Tennstedt

ASD 3743 B/w Band: **£8** Col. Band: £3
HINDEMITH Concert Music for String and Brass, Etc.
Philadelphia Orchestra Ormandy

ASD 3744 B/w Band: **£5** Col. Band: £2
Various Romantic Music For Flute And Orchestra Solum
Philharmonia Orchestra Dilkes

ASD 3750 B/w Band: **£8** Col. Band: £3
SAINT-SAENS Piano Concerto No.2, Piano Concerto No.4 Baudo
Orchestra de Paris Ciccolini

ASD 3760 B/w Band: **£5** Col. Band: £2
Various Trumpet Concertos by Haydn, Telemann, Etc. Andre
London Philharmonic Orchestra Lopez-Cobos

ASD 3761 B/w Band: **£8** Col. Band: £3
Various L'Arlesienne, Espana, Faust, Etc.
Berlin Philharmonic Orchestra Karajan

ASD 3762 B/w Band: **£5** Col. Band: £2
BRAHMS Piano Concerto No.1 Ohlsson
London Symphony Orchestra Tennstedt

ASD 3763 B/w Band: **£8** Col. Band: £3
MENDELSSOHN Symphony No.4, Hebrides Ov etc
London Symphony Orchestra Previn

ASD 3764 B/w Band: **£6** Col. Band: £2
Various Choral Music for Ascension Day
Choir of Kings College Cambridge Ledger

ASD 3772-3 B/w Band: **£8** Col. Band: £3
SHOSTAKOVICH Symphony No.11
Bournemouth Symphony Orchestra Berglund

ASD 3774 B/w Band: **£6** Col. Band: £2
HAYDN Horn Concertos Tuckwell

ASD 3775   B/w Band: **£5**   Col. Band: £2
DVORAK   Symphony No.8
Berlin Philharmonic Orchestra   Karajan

ASD 3776   B/w Band: **£6**   Col. Band: £2
MOZART   Piano concerto No.9, Piano Concerto No.27
Eschenbach

ASD 3777   B/w Band: **£6**   Col. Band: £2
DELIUS   Incidental Music to Hassan
Bournemouth Symphony Orchestra   Handley

ASD 3778   B/w Band: **£6**   Col. Band: £2
Various   A Festival of Carols from Kings
Choir of Kings College Cambridge   Ledger

ASD 3779   B/w Band: **£8**   Col. Band: £3
RIMSKY-KORSAKOV   Sheherazade
London Symphony Orchestra   Svetlanov

ASD 3780   Melodya : **£8**
SIBELIUS   Symphony No.5, Symphony No.6
Moscow Radio Symphony Orchestra   Rozhdestvensky

ASD 3781   B/w Band: **£5**   Col. Band: £2
SCHUMANN / MENDELSSOHN   Symphony No.1, Symphony No.5
Philharmonia Orchestra   Muti

ASD 3783   B/w Band: **£8**   Col. Band: £3
MAHLER   Symphony No.4   Ameling
Pittsburgh Symphony Orchestra   Previn

ASD 3785   B/w Band: **£80**   Col. Band: £35
Various   Bravissima   Haendel

ASD 3786   B/w Band: **£6**   Col. Band: £2
DVORAK   Symphony No.9
London Philharmonic Orchestra   Rostropovich

ASD 3797   B/w Band: **£10**   Col. Band: £3
Various   British Music for Film & TV
City of Birmingham Symphony Orchestra   Dodds

ASD 3798 B/w Band: **£12** Col. Band: £3
Various The Schwarzkopf Christmas Album Schwarzkopf
Mackerras

ASD 3801 Col. Band: **£8** 2nd Semi : £3
Various Mad Sceans Callas
Philharmonia Orchestra Rescigno

ASD 3802 Col. Band: **£12** 2nd Semi : £3
PROKOFIEV Piano Sonata No.8 Gavrilov

ASD 3804 Col. Band: **£5** 2nd Semi : £2
DEBUSSY Images, Prelude de L'Apres Midi d'un Faun
London Symphony Orchestra Previn

ASD 3807 Col. Band: **£8** 2nd Semi : £3
STRAVINSKY Rite of Spring Philadelphia Orchestra Muti

ASD 3810 Col. Band: **£15** 2nd Semi : £4
Various Encores Vol 2 Perlman

ASD 3811 Col. Band: **£4** 2nd Semi : £1
VERDI Opera Choruses
Welsh National Orchestra Armstrong

ASD 3816 Col. Band: **£5** 2nd Semi : £2
TCHAIKOVSKY Symphony No.4 Philharmonia Orchestra Muti

ASD 3817 Col. Band: **£10** 2nd Semi : £3
VERDI Callas Portrays Verdi Heroines Callas
Philharmonia Orchestra Rescigno

ASD 3818 Col. Band: **£8** 2nd Semi : £3
TCHAIKOVSKY Piano Concerto No.1 Gavrilov
Philharmonia Orchestra Muti

ASD 3820 Col. Band: **£14** 2nd Semi : £3
ELGAR / VAUGHAN-WILLIAMS Violin Sonatas Y & H Menuhin

ASD 3823 Col. Band: **£10** 2nd Semi : £3
ARNOLD Symphony No.1, Scottish Dances
Bournemouth Symphony Orchestra Arnold

ASD 3825   Col. Band: **£10**   2nd Semi : £3
BRUCKNER   Symphony No.1
Dresden Staatskapelle   Jochum

ASD 3827   Col. Band: **£6**   2nd Semi : £2
STRAVINSKY   Sacre du Printemps
Philadelphia Orchestra   Muti

ASD 3839   Col. Band: **£14**   2nd Semi : £5
HAYDN   Symphony No.94, Symphony No.104
Pittsburgh Symphony Orchestra   Previn

ASD 3842   Col. Band: **£6**   2nd Semi : £2
AVISON   6 Concertos
Bournemouth Symphony Orchestra   Thomas

ASD 3844   Col. Band: **£8**   2nd Semi : £3
KERN   A Sure Thing - Music of Jerome Kern   Tuckwell

ASD 3845   Col. Band: **£10**   2nd Semi : £3
RAVEL   Piano Concerto in Gmaj., Piano Concerto in Dmaj.
Collard   Orchestra National de France   Maazel

ASD 3854   Col. Band: **£6**   2nd Semi : £2
BEETHOVEN   Symphony No.6   Philharmonia Orchestra   Muti

ASD 3855   Melodya : **£10**
SHOSTAKOVICH   Symphony No.5, Festival Overture
USSR Symphony Orchestra   Svetlanov

ASD 3857   Col. Band: **£12**   2nd Semi : £3
ELGAR   Enigma Variations London Symphony Orchestra   Previn

ASD 3858   Col. Band: **£8**   2nd Semi : £3
MOZART   Song Recital   Schwarzkopf   Gieseking (Piano)

ASD 3859   Col. Band: **£8**   2nd Semi : £3
MOZART   Sinfonia Concertanti, Violin Concerto 3
Spivakov   English Chamber Orchestra

ASD 3861   Col. Band: **£16**   2nd Semi : £4
MOSZKOWSKI / SHOSTAKOVITCH / PROKOVIEV   Suite for Two
Violins   Perlman, Zukerman

ASD 3862   Col. Band: **£10**   2nd Semi : £3
Various   Music from the Movies   Adni
Bournemouth Symphony Orchestra   Alwyn

ASD 3864   Col. Band: **£10**   2nd Semi : £3
DELIUS   The 3 Violin Sonatas   Menuhin

ASD 3865   Col. Band: **£10**   2nd Semi : £3
Various   Victorian Collection   King Singers

ASD 3868   Col. Band: **£6**   2nd Semi : £2
ARNOLD   Concerto for Flute and Strings   Adeney
Bournemouth Symphony Orchestra   Thomas

ASD 3869   Col. Band: **£6**   2nd Semi : £2
DVORAK   Symphony No.7
London Philharmonic Orchestra   Rostropovich

ASD 3871   Col. Band: **£6**   2nd Semi : £2
PROKOFIEV   Piano Concerto No.2 in Gmin., Piano Concerto No.3 in C
Alexeev   Royal Philharmonic Orchestra   Temirkanov

ASD 3872   Melodya : **£8**
RACHMANINOV / PROKOFIEV   Piano Concerto No.2, Classical
Symphony   Petrov   USSR Symphony Orchestra   Svetlanov

ASD 3875   Col. Band: **£5**   2nd Semi : £2
BLISS   Meditations on a theme of John Blow
City of Birmingham Symphony Orchestra   Handley

ASD 3878   Col. Band: **£5**   2nd Semi : £2
BLISS   John Blow, Discourse, Edibburgh Overture
City of Birmingham Symphony Orchestra   Handley

ASD 3879   Melodya : **£6**
MIASKOVSKY   Symphony No.11, 2 Pieces for Strings
Moscow Radio Symphony Orchestra   Dudarova

ASD 3880   Melodya : **£10**
SHOSTAKOVICH   The Gamblers
Leningrad Philharmonic Orchestra   Rozhdestvensky

ASD 3882   Col. Band: **£12**   2nd Semi : £3
SCHUBERT   String Quartet D887   Alban Berg Quartet

ASD 3888   Col. Band: **£6**   2nd Semi : £2
MARTINU   Symphony No.4, Sinfonietta La Jolla
Royal Liverpool Philharmonic Orchestra   Weller

ASD 3891   Col. Band: **£6**   2nd Semi : £2
GOLDMARK   Rustic Wedding Symphony
Pittsburgh Symphony Orchestra   Previn

ASD 3894   Col. Band: **£10**   2nd Semi : £3
MENDELSSOHN / SCHUMANN   Piano Trios   Chung, Tortelier,
Previn

ASD 3896   Col. Band: **£6**   2nd Semi : £2
VAUGHAN-WILLIAMS / ELGAR   On Wenlock Edge, Etc
City of Birmingham Symphony Orchestra   Handley

ASD 3899   Col. Band: **£8**   2nd Semi : £3
Various   Violin Concertos by Vivaldi, Couperin & Bach
Zukerman   English Chamber Orchestra   Harrell

ASD 3900   Col. Band: **£10**   2nd Semi : £3
ORFF   Carmina Burana   Philharmonia Orchestra   Muti

ASD 3901   Col. Band: **£6**   2nd Semi : £2
TCHAIKOVSKY   Symphony No.6   Philharmonia Orchestra   Muti

ASD 3903   Col. Band: **£6**   2nd Semi : £2
ROSSINI   Overtures   Philharmonia Orchestra   Muti

ASD 3904   Col. Band: **£8**   2nd Semi : £3
VAUGHAN-WILLIAMS   Symphony No.4, The Lark Ascending
Royal Philharmonic Orchestra   Berglund

ASD 3905   Col. Band: **£15**   2nd Semi : £4
BRAHMS   Double Concerto   Perlman, Rostropovich
Amsterdam Concertgebouw Orchestra   Haitink

ASD 3906   Col. Band: **£6**   2nd Semi : £2
LISZT   Songs   Baker

ASD 3908 Col. Band: £5 2nd Semi : £2
Various Favorite Opera Duets Callas, Ludwig, Pavarotti

ASD 3910 Col. Band: £**18** 2nd Semi : £4
Various The Spanish Album Perlman

ASD 3911 Col. Band: £**75** 2nd Semi : £10
SHOSTAKOVICH Symphony No.13
London Symphony Orchestra Previn

ASD 3912 Col. Band: £8 2nd Semi : £3
RAVEL Bolero, Daphnis et Chloe, Pavanne
London Symphony Orchestra Previn

ASD 3914 Col. Band: £**16** 2nd Semi : £4
VIVALDI Cello Concerto, Violin & Cello Concerto
Tortelier London Mozart Players

ASD 3915 Col. Band: £8 2nd Semi : £3
Various Great Sopranos of our time Callas

ASD 3933 Col. Band: £**12** 2nd Semi : £3
SIBELIUS Violin Concerto Perlman
London Symphony Orchestra Previn

ASD 3943 Col. Band: £5 2nd Semi : £2
Various The Academy in Concert
Acadamy of St.Martins in the Fields Marriner

ASD 3952 Col. Band: £7 2nd Semi : £2
ELGAR The Light Of Life
Royal Liverpool Philharmonic Orchestra Groves

ASD 3953 Col. Band: £8 2nd Semi : £3
HOLST / VAUGHAN-WILLIAMS A Somerset Rhapsody, The Wasps
Bournemouth Sinfonietta Del Mar

ASD 3960 Col. Band: £8 2nd Semi : £3
GRIEG / FRANCK Piano Concerto, Les Djinns Ashkenazy
Philharmonia Orchestra Ortiz

ASD 3964 Col. Band: £6 2nd Semi : £2
VIVALDI The Four Seasons Menuhin Camerata

ASD 3979
VERDI
Col. Band: £**6**   2nd Semi :
Verdi Choruses   Philharmo.... Orchestra   Muti

ASD 3980
Various
Col. Band: £**15**   2nd Semi : £**4**
Kreisler Recital Vol.3   Perlman

ASD 3981
Various
Col. Band: £**5**   2nd Semi : £**2**
Songs for Sunday   Baker

ASD 3993
GLAZUNOV
Melodya : £**6**
Symphony No.3
Moscow Radio Symphony Orchestra   Fedoseyev

ASD 4006
MUSSORGSKY
Melodya : £**6**
Great Sceans from Boris Godunov   Nesterenko
Chorus & Orchestra of the Bolshoi Theatre   Simonov

ASD 4008
PUNTO
2nd Semi : £**6**
Four Horn Concertos   Tuckwell
Acadamy of St.Martins in the Fields   Marriner

ASD 4009
BRUCKNER
2nd Semi : £**10**
Symphony No.3   Dresden Staatskapelle   Jochum

ASD 4011
BARTOK
2nd Semi : £**20**
Duo for TwoViolins   Perlman, Zuckerman

ASD 4015
VERDI
2nd Semi : £**6**
Ballets from Verdi Operas
Philharmonia Orchestra   Muti

ASD 4031
Various
2nd Semi : £**4**
A Portrait of Placido Domingo   Domingo

ASD 4032
SCHUBERT
2nd Semi : £**4**
Trout Quintet   Richter   Borodin Quartet

ASD 4036
TCHAIKOVSKY
2nd Semi : £**10**
Piano Trio   Ashkenazy, Perlman

ASD 4039
BRAHMS
2nd Semi : £**12**
Violin Sonata Op.120/1, Op.120/2   Menuhin

ASD 4046   2nd Semi : **£15**
SHOSTAKOVICH   Violin Concerto No.1, Cello Concerto No.1
Oistrakh, Tortelier   Bournemouth Symphony Orchestra   Berglund

ASD 4054   2nd Semi : **£5**
SCHUBERT   Songs   Baker

ASD 4056   2nd Semi : **£8**
MOZART   Flute Concerto K313, K314, Andante K315
Hanoverian Orchestra   Solum

ASD 4058   2nd Semi : **£6**
DVORAK   Symphony No.8
London Philharmonic Orchestra   Rostropovich

ASD 4059   2nd Semi : **£5**
BEETHOVEN   Violin Concerto   Perlman Giulini

ASD 4061   2nd Semi : **£8**
ELGAR / VAUGHAN-WILLIAMS   From the Bavarian Highlands
Bournemouth Symphony Orchestra   Del Mar

ASD 4075   2nd Semi : **£10**
SCHUBERT / BEETHOVEN   Arpeggione Sonata, Cello Sonata Op.69
Tortelier

ASD 4080   2nd Semi : **£10**
BRUCKNER   Symphony No.6   Dresden Staatskapelle   Jochum

ASD 4081   2nd Semi : **£10**
BRUCKNER   Symphony No.2   Dresden Staatskapelle   Jochum

ASD 4086   2nd Semi : **£8**
DURUFLE   Requiem, Two Motets   Baker
Choir of Kings College Cambridge   Ledger

ASD 4099   2nd Semi : **£10**
RAVEL   Daphnis et Chloe
London Symphony Orchestra   Previn

ASD 4100   2nd Semi : **£12**
BORODIN   String Quartet No.1, String Quartet No.2
Borodin Quartet

HMV Angel SAN series Stereophonic LP's

The first labels were Gold with a white 'Nipper within a white oval above the centre hole and a white 'Angel' flanked with the words *'angel series'* printed in white at the bottom of the label. All other label text is printed in black and the words 'His Masters Voice' dominate the top circumference of the label. This label is referred to as **White** (White Angel) in this section of the guide.

The second label retains the Gold background, but now has a coloured 'Nipper' picture within a white rectangular frame above the centre hole flanked with the words *'angel series'* printed in black. There is also a small black 'Angel' logo above the postage stamp nipper and a small boxed EMI logo at the bottom of the label. All label text is printed in black. This label is referred to as **P/s Blk** (Postage stamp, Black Angel) in this section of the guide.

A third label was used which is identical to the second label, but printed on a yellow background, rather than gold. These were the first labels an all records from SAN 291 onwards and of subsequent pressings of the earlier records. This label is referred to as **Yellow** in this section of the guide.

Finally, a special label was used for the Deluxe edition SDAN 143-5. This label is identical to the first label, but has a red angel replacing the white angel. The set comes in a 'Deluxe' padded red box and should have the original cardboard 'mailer' sleeve around the box. (Deduct £25 where this sleeve is missing). The label has been referred to as **red** in this section of the guide.

SAN 101-2   White : **£75**   P/s Blk : £22
LEHAR   Merry Widow   Schwarztkopf
Philharmonia Orchestra   Matacic

SAN 103-6   White : **£60**   P/s Blk : £20
MOZART   Cosi Fan Tutte   Schwarztkopf
Philharmonia Orchestra   Bohm

SAN 107   White : **£40**   P/s Blk : £14
FAURE   Requiem   De Los Angles
Paris Conservatoire Orchestra   Cluytens

SAN 108-9   White : **£80**   P/s Blk : £25
MASCAGNI   Cavalleria Rusticana   De Los Angles
Rome Opera Orchestra   Santini

SAN 110-3   White : **£60**   P/s Blk : £20
MUSSORGSKY   Boris Godunov
Paris Conservatoire Orchestra   Cluytens

SAN 114-6   White : **£120**   P/s Blk : £35
ROSSINI   Barber of Seville
Glyndebourne Festival Orchestra   Gui

SAN 117-9   White : **£45**   P/s Blk : £15
SAINT-SAENS   Samson et Delilah   Vickers
Orchestra National de France   Pretre

SAN 120   White : **£38**   P/s Blk : £12
VERDI   Four Sacred Pieces
Philharmonia Orchestra   Giulini

SAN 121-5   White : **£120**   P/s Blk : £35
WAGNER   Lohenegrin   Grummer
Vienna Philharmonic Orchestra   Kempe

SAN 126-7   White : **£20**   P/s Blk : £8
MONTEVERDI   L'incoronazione Di Poppea
Royal Philharmonic Orchestra   Pritchard

SAN 128-30   White : **£30**   P/s Blk : £10
GIORDANO   Andrea Chenier
Rome Opera Orchestra   Santini

SAN 131-2   White : **£40**   P/s Blk : £12
PUCCINI   La Boheme
Rome Opera Orchestra   Schippers

SAN 133-4   White : **£25**   P/s Blk : £10
VERDI   Requiem Schwarztkopf
Philharmonia Orchestra   Giulini

SAN 135-6   (═══ Not Issued ═══)

SAN 137-9   White : **£100**   P/s Blk : £25
MOZART   Die Zauberflote
Philharmonia Orchestra   Klemperer

SAN 140-2   White : **£60**   P/s Blk : £15
BIZET   Carmen   Callas
Paris Opera   Pretre

SAN 143-5   See SDAN143-5

SAN 146-8   White : **£120**   P/s Blk : £40
HANDEL   Messiah
Philharmonia Orchestra   Klemperer

SAN 149-0   White : **£60**   P/s Blk : £18
PUCCINI   Tosca   Callas
Orchestra de Paris Pretre

SAN 151-3   White : **£40**   P/s Blk : £12
VERDI   Il Travatore
Rome Opera Orchestra   Schippers

SAN 154-6   White : **£70**   P/s Blk : £20
OFFENBACH   Tales Of Hoffmann   De Los Angeles, Schwartzkopf
Orchestra de Paris Cluytens

SAN 157-8   White : **£60**   P/s Blk : £18
FALLA   La Vida Breve   De Los Angeles
Spanish National Orchestra   De Burgos

SAN 159-61   White : **£45**   P/s Blk : £15
PUCCINI   Turandot
Rome Opera Orchestra   Pradelli

SAN 162   White : **£16**   P/s Blk : £4
ORFF   Carmina Burana
New Philharmonia Orchestra   De Burgos

SAN 163-4   White : **£44**   P/s Blk : £12
BRAHMS   Deutche Volksleider   Fischer-Dieskau

SAN 165-6   White : **£35**   P/s Blk : £10
BEETHOVEN   Missa Solemnis
New Philharmonia Orchestra   Klemperer

SAN 167-8   (==== Not Issued ====)

SAN 169   White : **£20**   P/s Blk : £5
PURCELL   Dido & Aeneas
English Chamber Orchestra Barbirolli

SAN 170-1   White : **£75**   P/s Blk : £15
BERLIOZ   L'Enfance du Christ   De Los Angeles
Paris Conservatoire Orchestra   Cluytens

SAN 172-5   White : **£100**   P/s Blk : £30
MOZART   Don Giovani
Philharmonia Orchestra   Klemperer

SAN 179   White : **£35**   P/s Blk : £8
MAHLER   Das Lied Von Der Erde
New Philharmonia Orchestra   Klemperer

SAN 180-1   White : **£40**   P/s Blk : £10
DONIZETTI   L'Elisir D'Amour Gedda
Rome Opera Orchestra   Pradelli

SAN 182-3   White : **£24**   P/s Blk : £8
Various   Homage To Gerald Moore   De Los Angeles,Etc.

SAN 184-6   White : **£38**   P/s Blk : £10
PUCCINI   Madama Butterfly
Rome Opera Orchestra   Barbirolli

SAN 187-8   (==== Not Issued ====)

SAN 189-91 White : **£40**   P/s Blk : £12
VERDI   Aida   Rome Opera Orchestra   Mehta

SAN 192 White : **£8**   P/s Blk : £4
WALTON   The Bear   English Chamber Orchestra   Lockhart

SAN 193 White : **£25**   P/s Blk : £7
MOZART   Requiem   New Philharmonia Orchestra   De Burgos

SAN 194 White : **£30**   P/s Blk : £10
Various   Andalusian Songs   De Los Angles

SAN 195-7 White : **£50**   P/s Blk : £18
BACH   Mass In B Minor
New Philharmonia Orchestra   Klemperer

SAN 198-00   (==== Not Issued ====)

SAN 201-3 White : **£35**   P/s Blk : £12
MOZART   Abduction From The Seraglio
Bath Festival Chamber Orchestra   Menuhin

SAN 204-6 P/s Blk : **£30**   Yellow : £10
VERDI   Rigoletto   Rome Opera Orchestra   Molinari-Pradelli

SAN 207-9 P/s Blk : **£50**   Yellow : £15
WAGNER   Flying Dutchman
Philharmonia Orchestra   Klemperer

SAN 210-1 P/s Blk : **£25**   Yellow : £12
WOLF   The Italian Song Book   Fischer-Dieskau

SAN 212-4 P/s Blk : **£22**   Yellow : £10
MENDELSSOHN   Elijah   Philharmonia Orchestra   De Burgos

SAN 215-7 P/s Blk : **£60**   Yellow : £18
STRAUSS R   Ariadne Auf Naxos   Janowitz
Dresden Symphony Orchestra   Kempe

SAN 218 P/s Blk : **£30**   Yellow : £8
MAHLER   Des Knaben Wunderhorn   Schwarztkopf
London Symphony Orchestra   Szell

SAN 219-27 (==== Not Issued ====)

SAN 228-31 P/s Blk : **£ 30** Yellow : £12
BACH St.Mathews Passion Gedda
Vienna Consortium Musicum Gonnenwein

SAN 232-4 (==== Not Issued ====)

SAN 235-7 P/s Blk : **£ 25** Yellow : £9
GOUNOD Romeo And Juliet Paris Opera Lombard

SAN 238-41 P/s Blk : **£ 25** Yellow : £12
BEETHOVEN The 5 Piano Concertos Barenboim
Philharmonia Orchestra Klemperer

SAN 242-3 P/s Blk : **£ 20** Yellow : £10
MASCAGNI L'Amico Fritz Pavarotti
Royal Opera House Covent Garden Gavazzeni

SAN 244-5 P/s Blk : **£ 20** Yellow : £8
ELGAR The Kingdom
London Philharmonic Orchestra Boult

SAN 246-8 P/s Blk : **£ 35** Yellow : £12
FLOTOW Martha Gedda
Bavarian State Opera Orchestra Prey

SAN 249-51 P/s Blk : **£ 30** Yellow : £12
MASSENET Werther De Los Angeles
Orchestra de Paris Pretre

SAN 252-4 P/s Blk : **£ 40** Yellow : £15
VERDI Otello Fischer-Dieskau
Philharmonia Orchestra Barbrolli

SAN 255 P/s Blk : **£ 25** Yellow : £8
Various Tribute To Gerald Moore Gerald Moore

SAN 256-7 P/s Blk : **£ 25** Yellow : £12
JANACEK Jenufa Prague National Orchestra Gregor

SAN 258-9   P/s Blk : **£28**   Yellow : £12
BERLIOZ   Damnation Of Faust   Gedda
Orchestra de Paris Pretre

SAN 260-3   P/s Blk : **£20**   Yellow : £12
VERDI   La Forza Del Destino
Royal Philharmonic Orchestra   Gardelli

SAN 264-6   P/s Blk : **£15**   Yellow : £8
BACH   St. Johns Passion
Vienna Consortium Musicum   Gonnenwein

SAN 267-8   P/s Blk : **£10**   Yellow : £6
VERDI   Requiem   Vickers
Philharmonia Orchestra   Barbrolli

SAN 269-72   (==== Not Issued ====)

SAN 273-5   P/s Blk : **£25**   Yellow : £15
BIZET   Carmen   Vickers
Paris Opera   De Burgos

SAN 276-8   P/s Blk : **£15**   Yellow : £6
BELLINI   Il Pirata Caballe
Philharmonia Orchestra   Gavazzeni

SAN 279   (==== Not Issued ====)

SAN 280-2   P/s Blk : **£30**   Yellow : £10
BEETHOVEN   Fidelio   Vickers
Berlin Philharmonic Orchestra   Karajan

SAN 283-6   P/s Blk : **£50**   Yellow : £15
MOZART   Marriage Of Figaro
Philharmonia Orchestra   Klemperer

SAN 287-90   P/s Blk : **£30**   Yellow : £12
VERDI   Don Carlo   Caballe
Rome Opera Orchestra   Giulini

SAN 291   Yellow : **£15**
BRAHMS   Die Schone Magelone   Fischer-Dieskau

SAN 292-7   Yellow : **£24**
WAGNER   Die Meistersinger Von Nurnberg
Dresden Symphony Orchestra   Karajan

SAN 298-323   (==== Not Issued ====)

SAN 316-9   Yellow : **£20**
DELIUS   A Village Romeo and Juliet
Royal Philharmonic Orchestra   Davis

SAN 320-323   (==== Not Issued ====)

SAN 324   Yellow : **£12**
WALTON   Belshazzars Feast
London Symphony Orchestra   Previn

SAN 325-30   (==== Not Issued ====)

SAN 331-3   Yellow : **£15**
VERDI   Giovanna d'arco   Caballe
London Symphony Orchestra   Levine

SAN 334-44   (==== Not Issued ====)

SAN 345-7   Yellow : **£18**
BOITO   Mefistofele   Caballe
London Symphony Orchestra   Rudel

SAN 348-50   (==== Not Issued ====)

SAN 351-3   Yellow : **£25**
VERDI   Otello   Freni
Berlin Philharmonic Orchestra   Karajan

SAN 354   Yellow : **£12**
HOLST   Choral Symphony
London Philharmonic Orchestra   Boult

SAN 355-57   Yellow : **£16**
ELGAR   The Apostles   Armstrong
London Philharmonic Orchestra   Boult

SAN 358-64   (==== Not Issued ====)

SAN 365   Yellow : **£10**
BLISS   Morning Heroes
Royal Liverpool Philharmonic Orchestra   Groves

SAN 366-7   Yellow : **£14**
BEETHOVEN   Missa Solemnis   Janowitz
Berlin Philharmonic Orchestra   Karajan

SAN 368-73   (==== Not Issued ====)

SAN 374-5   Yellow : **£16**
BERLIOZ   Requiem
City of Birmingham Symphony Orchestra   Fremaux

SAN 376-92   (==== Not Issued ====)

SAN 393   Yellow : **£12**
HADLEY   The Hills   London Philharmonic Orchestra   Ledger

SAN 394-5   Yellow : **£20**
BEETHOVEN   Missa Solemnis   Baker
London Philharmonic Orchestra   Giulini

SAN 396-419   (==== Not Issued ====)

SAN 420-23   Yellow : **£18**
MOZART   Marriage Of Figaro
English Chamber Orchestra   Barenboim

SDAN 143-5   Red : **£225**
BIZET   The Callas Carmen (in Deluxe Box with 3 Books)   Callas